THE PORTABLE

Melville

The Viking Portable Library

Each Portable Library volume is made up of
representative works of a favorite modern or
classic author, or is a comprehensive anthology
on a special subject. The format is designed
for compactness and for pleasurable reading.
The books average about 700 pages in length.
Each is intended to fill a need not hitherto
met by any single book. Each is edited by
an authority distinguished in his field, who
adds a thoroughgoing introductory essay and
other helpful material. Most "Portables" are
available both in durable cloth and
in stiff paper covers.

THE PORTABLE

Melville

Edited, and with an Introduction, by

JAY LEYDA

New York

THE VIKING PRESS

COPYRIGHT 1952 BY JAY LEYDA

PUBLISHED BY THE VIKING PRESS IN JANUARY 1952

PUBLISHED ON THE SAME DAY IN THE DOMINION OF CANADA
BY THE MACMILLAN COMPANY OF CANADA LIMITED

SECOND PRINTING FEBRUARY 1959
THIRD PRINTING MARCH 1961
FOURTH PRINTING JULY 1962

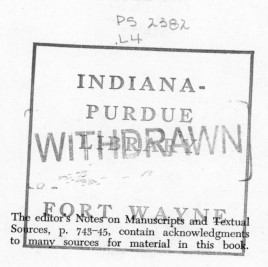
The editor's Notes on Manuscripts and Textual
Sources, p. 743–45, contain acknowledgments
to many sources for material in this book.

PRINTED IN U.S.A. BY THE COLONIAL PRESS INC.

This collection of
Melville's writing
is dedicated to
Leon Howard

Contents

CONTENTS

Introduction

THERE is a link between Melville's experiences and his works, which are all a transmutation, to some degree, of a reality he had observed or lived. A sense of actuality was the constant spur of his imagination, but this could be the psychological actuality of a defeat as much as the physically mutilating actuality of a whale's jaw. A determining factor in Melville's whole development was that success, ease, comfort evaded him when his circumstances needed them most. If he had merely written of his exotic experiences without probing their implications, it is likely that Melville's romantically exciting "narratives" would have had success in the nineteenth century—and would be buried in the twentieth. Fortunately for posterity Melville knew the taste of failure before his full-grown mind had used up the waiting frames of real experience. He was almost twenty-seven when he experienced the sensation of sudden success which, coming earlier, might have bound him for life. In little more than two years, however, he had taken his first deliberate step away from the guarantees of continued approval and sales: *Mardi* alerted his contemporaries' suspicions, so that when his sixth book again broke away from what was expected (demanded!) of him, he had moved too far out of line ever to return again to the sure thing. Before he was conscious that *Moby Dick* was to be his next work, he had told his father-in-law, with no equivocation, ". . . it is my earnest desire to write those sort of books which are said to 'fail.' " The "whaling story" was confirmation that the agreeable author of *Typee*, *Omoo*, etc., etc., was wrong-headed, stubbornly blind to his own pleasant talents. Those who worried about *Mardi* and *Moby Dick* fled the very sight of *Pierre,* and later attempts to put his writing back on a paying basis were ineffectual. The magazines paid, but he couldn't turn out anonymous "magazinish" pieces fast enough to make this a steady income; an avoidance of his dangerous "humors" was noticed in *Israel Potter,* but the point of the whole was "unhealthy"; the *Battle-Pieces* were aimed at attention but brushed past it. Then the Revenue Service took over the problem of supporting Melville and his family.

At this point the legend of the "great refusal" would gloss over his last twenty-five years, but there is too much evidence that, except for brief halts, customs inspector Melville seized every stray hour for his old, non-paying profession. If there was a refusal it was merely a refusal to face the rejections of publishers and publics —he submitted no more of his work to their caprices. Poetry, adopted to kill the taste of lecturing, sustained Melville through these years. When he began his major work in verse, *Clarel,* after three years on his government job, its chances for acceptance played no slightest part in its making, for it was not intended for publication. Several years after its completion a generous uncle heard of its existence, gave Melville enough money to have it printed, and Melville gratefully and nervously supervised its appearance—only to relearn the other half of his old lesson: that critics and readers were as impatient with him as he was with them. Most preferred to ignore the fact that the author of *White-Jacket* was still functioning. Thereafter, Melville had only two slim volumes of poems printed—privately, and in editions of twenty-five copies. There is no knowing what launching he planned for his last, perhaps unfinished, novel.

This was the latter direction of the "unsuccessful"

Melville—not towards less work, but towards less exposure of his work to what he called, in 1870, the "consummate flower of civilization." Though his writing failed to make a living for his family, it never ceased to be employed as a deepening ravine for his probing honesty. "Woe to him who seeks to please rather than to appall!" Like Captain Vere's, his "honesty prescribes . . . directness, sometimes far-reaching like that of a migratory fowl that in its flight never heeds when it crosses a frontier." In 1851 Melville promised Hawthorne a figurative champagne with the warning that its grapes required a dry heat; this heat was neither popular success nor the expectation of it—it was failure.

When Melville offered a story-subject to Hawthorne, he also turned over several suggestions for treatment, all based on some "tributary items, collected by me, by chance, during my strolls thro the island; & which—as you will perceive—seem legitimately to belong to the story." This "collection" reinforces a belief, stirred by all of Melville's work, that he was an artist who depended for coherence and connection on actual experience rather than on forms, the designs offered by art. It suggests that he needed the concreteness of the low ceiling and wall-lamp of his tiny cabin on the homeward-bound *Independence* to support even such a work of the spirit as Father Mapple's sermon.

Partly because of his incomplete training, but far more because of the stored attitudes and images that waited to pour through any channel offered them, Melville was less conscious of the divisions between the forms he employed than were other writers of his century. Whether he was writing novels or narratives, lyrics or letters, it was the *whole* development of his mind and *all* his capacities that moved rhythmically onto the page, and the development was limited or enlarged by financial or psychological urgencies rather than by the "proprieties" of a particular category of literature.

For that reason this collection has by-passed the departments and strung the work selected along the thread of the life that produced it. Connecting comment is employed only when Melville's own explanation is missing. Thus ordered, even the portion of his work included here shows unity of purpose and consistency of imagery, though these did not govern the selection.

One main line of purpose thrusts itself through the center of all his work wherever you sample it—search. His desertion from the *Acushnet* may have been motivated by simple dissatisfaction (though the stakes of risk and humiliation were considerable), yet his *telling* of this adventure embodies a search for a social state more consonant with the ideals of his schooling and reading than was offered by the world and the ships of the nineteenth century. This search was communicated from Melville through Loti to Gauguin, through Stoddard to Stevenson and Jack London—all with their own good reasons to prefer a "sojourn among cannibals" to the "world of care and anxiety." Melville was not the literary Columbus of the Pacific, but he seems to have been the first artist to say with the authority of an eye-witness that "it would seem perhaps better for what we call the barbarous part of the world to remain unchanged." His tale of a luxurious captivity among gentle cannibals, told against a blessedly but only temporarily distant background of civilized barbarism, dramatized a basic conflict as successfully as he could have dreamed. I know that this effect of *Typee* can be appallingly clear, for I first read it amid the ethical contradictions of an army hospital.

There is a casual but inevitable phrase in *Typee*— the natives treat Tommo "with a degree of deference which could hardly have been surpassed had I been some celestial visitant"—that produced all the timber Melville needed for his broadest voyaging, in the world of the mind and through the social universe. The narrator of *Mardi* is recognized by islanders as Taji, a visiting demigod, an emissary from Oro, the supreme god, and they aid his allegorical search through the island-world of Mardi. When the shores of Mardi's follies and virtues have been explored, the searching canoes probe the rocky political world of 1848, touching at Dominora (Britain), Porpheero (Europe)—Franko's (France's) volcano is again erupting—and finally the United States, thinly masked as Vivenza, where Taji finds and hears many cogent things. They sail on—"Hug the shore, naught new is seen"—visit King Abrazza, in whose groves occurs a harsh dialogue that is Melville's apologia for the mazes of *Mardi,* tearing open his brain to show what makes it write. His account of the making of Lombardo's *Koztanza* tells us almost more than we are willing to learn about the making of *Mardi.* One shrinks back from Babbalanja's words, "Oh! there is a fierce, a cannibal delight, in the grief that shrieks to multiply itself." *Mardi* became the fullest articulation of Melville's search, as *Moby Dick* was his deepest dive.

Bartleby, the Wall Street scrivener, and Hunilla, widowed by the waters of the Encantadas, are both stubborn, dignified searchers for firm ground in a bog of doubt. The fable of Israel Potter shows as little confidence in the victory of right as *The Confidence-Man* shows in the rightness of faith, and the searcher's voice has grown more hopeless—he already saw all as "an oblique, tedious, barren game hardly worth that poor candle burnt out in playing it." His bitter questions became more piercing and unanswerable in the pilgrimage of *Clarel* and the trials of *Billy Budd* and Captain Vere. The search continued to the end, but the struggling had been replaced by a steady stride across a battleground where the battle had paused. Or, to quote a favorite image (in the letter to Sophia Hawthorne):

Life is a long Dardenelles, My Dear Madam, the shores whereof are bright with flowers, which we want to pluck, but the bank is too high; & so we float on & on, hoping to come to a landing-place at last—but swoop! we launch into the great sea! Yet the geographers say, even then we must not despair, because across the great sea, however desolate & vacant it may look, lie all Persia & the delicious lands round-about Damascus.

"What unlike things must meet and mate" in Melville's search through the nature of his art, to find his place in it. The letters to his friends gruffly grope for answer to this ("blubber is blubber, you know; tho' you may get oil out of it, the poetry runs as hard as sap from a frozen maple tree") as they grope for friendship. Books are bought for the hints and advice of his predecessors on the path; Browning must have guided him to much, including the marriage of meter and material in "Christmas-Eve and Easter-Day" that Melville sought for *Clarel*. An essay on the art of Hawthorne turns into a challenging definition of the American author's—his own—aims; his letter to Hawthorne of 13 August 1852 shows him almost involuntarily carried into the stream of creation; the symbolic Mississippi of *The Confidence-Man* carries along an essay on craftsmanship with its other freight. His description of Hawthorne can be applied to himself—"a seeker, not a finder yet."

It is in these lines of search (and the opposite, shunning side of the coin), with their images of failure and glimpses of resolution, that the modern reader can be caught and held by Melville, who offers his findings to all of us. Not that we all hear the same counsel—by no means! Melville is today cited in as many mutually canceling causes as is Scripture. For Melville was not a neat, systematic searcher (or shunner)—through the years his line of thought detoured, backtracked, flung itself to the right and to the left; any advances and retreats in society and politics, especially those of the United States, would shake him with hope or revulsion. Back and forth, across his mind, pushed the unended wrestling of fate and free will. No decision in this contest was ever final, not even "A Sketch" in *Clarel*, giving fabulous treatment to "the miserable pertinaciousness of misfortune" which pursued Captain Pollard of the *Essex*. This was for him the storm "formed behind the storm we feel."

To assemble Melville's work, regardless of form, is to see some elements in his writing left submerged by his critics. I never before had such a sense of Melville's humor, growing from such comic effects as bawling *"Ach, du lieber Augustin"* in the Eden landscape of the Typee Valley, through the office staff at No. — Wall Street and his sly joshing of Ben Franklin, to the subtle, tragic irony of Billy Budd's fate.

Any continuity of any selections would show a fundamental stylistic trait in the work—Melville's pictorial quality, so boldly announced in *Typee*, with the highly colored boarding of the *Dolly* by the shoal of whinhenies, with the black and white slashings of the Marquesan cataracts and chasms, with the swirling romantic compositions of the Feast of the Calabashes, the "delightful little party on the lake" and the nocturnal fishing excursion. All his work is hung with such vivid portraits as those of Kory-Kory, of Captain Graveling and John Claggart, and even of the privately recorded fellow passengers on the *Southampton*. And there is the painful miniature framed in thicket, watched helplessly by Hunilla that strikes the pictorial key to that masterpiece in stern monotone.

A certain vocabulary of imagery comes to light here to lure the reader who enjoys psychological detection (though I warn him that Melville is a labyrinth easier to enter than to leave). Over the work of a writer identified with tropical luxuriance and equatorial seas glistens the arctic imagery of the "Dreams" in *Mardi*, which finds a deepened reflection decades later in the dream of "The Berg" and even sparkles through the icy comedy of the interview with Moxon. And what is Moby Dick but the implacable ambassador sent abroad from that impenetrable whiteness? Some images—like the Pyramids—were used for years before Melville saw the actuality; the eye of faith (with which Tommo looked upon the funeral canoe) had sped ahead of the material eye. A picture of a place could rouse his imagination as fully as a word about that place or the place itself. A woodcut in *The Penny Magazine* would supply the polar bears that Melville could not have seen on real icebergs in Antarctic waters.

Juxtaposition also reveals some of Melville's more lasting admirations and models. Take the jolly tones of Dibdin's "Poor Jack," resounding through his memory of the Typee Valley as well as across the deck of the *Indomitable*. When someone undertakes to examine the British poets who attracted Melville, the modest songs

of Charles Dibdin will get their due, with their tars—
those Tom Tackles, Bill Bobstays, and Jack Ratlins—
who find mess-mates in the Tom Deadlight, Captain
Turret, Jack Genteel, of Melville's *John Marr* verses.
Dibdin's "poor Tom Bowling, the darling of our crew,"
may have waked the old memory that produced Melville's last book:

> His form was of the manliest beauty,
> His heart was kind and soft,
> Faithful below he did his duty,
> And now he's gone aloft. . . .

The continuity traces another, more spurring relation-
ship, from that first overwhelming revelation of a kindred spirit in Hawthorne's *Mosses from an Old Manse,*
to its last echo in illustration of Billy's stammer.

One task, kept in mind, but hopelessly unaccom-
plished, in making this collection was to convey the impression made on his contemporaries by Melville the
talker. In any congenial company, the smaller the better,
Melville's conversational and yarn-spinning faculty blos-
somed memorably. N. P. Willis tells us that Melville
talked as he wrote; Dana considered him "incomparable
in dramatic story telling"; and various Hawthornes were
deeply impressed by the conviction of his voice. Its
sound is perhaps more reliably recorded in some of his
letters than elsewhere—chiefly in his impulsive letters
to Hawthorne, most of which are included here. The
stenographic record of his lecture cannot, however, give
us much idea of Melville the talker—the lecture was
written, perhaps laboriously, and for him a lecture audience was anything but congenial company. Yet what an
evangelist one drop of something else might have made
him! There is nothing in Ethan Allen's records as fiery

as the rhetorical flames that the author of *Israel Potter* lit in his mouth. And who can read Father Mapple's sermon without hearing its rush, its pauses, its volumes?

These private, undisguised thoughts that surge out on the many-paged letters to Hawthorne are as close to the interior monologue of reality as we can find in the nineteenth century. "I know little about you, but something about myself. So I write about myself,—at least, to you." These letters seem scarcely one side of a two-sided correspondence; they race on, apparently little dependent on Hawthorne's responses—his importance to Melville was deeper than that. "The divine magnet is on you, and my magnet responds." When Hawthorne's magnet lost its power, Melville turned frankly to his journals, finding an outlet there for thoughts as unconcealed as written thoughts can be: "Bitter is it to be poor & bitter, to be reviled. . . ." The stones of Judea reminded him of a stony world—"stony homes & stony tombs; stony eyes & stony hearts." Meditations on Ray's fate end his attempt at an 1860 journal. A more dangerous macabre humor invades his letters of the '60s. The last comments he thought private occur in the marginalia of his later reading. Long before this he had joined the company of his own reflected isolatoes —Ahab, Bartleby, Rolfe, John Marr.

His work too became more and more employed for privacy. Often a personal poem would have to slip on a robe of objectivity before it could be considered for appearance outside his room; the "Camoens" titles on those two poems were added long after their franker composition. The Shelleyesque "Lake" tried to answer the eternal anxiety:

> The poet's forms of beauty pass,
> And noblest deeds they are undone

> Even truth itself decays, and lo,
> From truth's sad ashes fraud and falsehood grow.

In a period between the death of his son Malcom, just past, and his own death, coming, the minor key is modulated to a positive major:

> But through such strange illusions have they passed
> Who in life's pilgrimage have baffled striven—
> Even death may prove unreal at the last,
> And stoics be astounded into heaven.

and then—all in brasses:

> Emerge thou mayst from the last whelming sea,
> And prove that death but routs life into victory.

In any campaign to beckon readers to go beyond *Moby Dick* the very great temptation is to dangle tasty samples of every work by Melville. For a collection that pretends to indicate the scope of his career, some corner of the world of *Mardi* must be included—there would have been no *Moby Dick* without *Mardi*. Undeserved neglect is my excuse for excerpting *Israel Potter* and *Clarel*. *The Confidence-Man* no longer lacks readers, but they make a circle that widens too slowly. If the mind displayed here attracts, the reader will need no urging to look into *Omoo* and *Redburn* and *White-Jacket*, and even into the labyrinthine *Pierre*, and to weigh the missing stories and poems for himself. As for Melville's greatest book, it is represented here by the merest splinter.

"A Melville anthology without *Moby Dick!*" Happily, Melville's masterpiece is not unavailable because this volume slights it, for there are a dozen inexpensive editions in print; I trust that every shelf on which this *Portable* stands will also attempt to hold a breaching white whale. In apology for this shift of responsibility to the reader I have tried to include here all that Melville himself said of his most-written-about book.

That "all," in this and other connections, should always be read as "all that survives," for the destruction of Melville papers, especially in his family, was intensive. It is almost certainly he, however, who is responsible for the lack of all his major manuscripts with the single exception of his last novel, left behind at death. Proofreading and speculation continue to play a large part in the editing of his work.

There is another obstacle less tangible than destruction: you will encounter it by inquiring about Herman Melville in any community where he lived. You will not find him listed among the writers who have lived in Albany; no resident today in Lansingburgh can tell you in which house he lived; nor can anyone in Greenbush point to the school where he taught, or its site; among the other honors Melville has bestowed upon Pittsfield, the stone seat of his favorite spot now furnishes the base for a golf tee; New Yorkers do not believe you when you tell them he was born and buried in that city. To those who attended schools where no syllabus was conscious of his name, mention of Melville is usually greeted with skepticism, as some hoax. It has become difficult to convince Americans that Melville was no legend, but a real person with ordinary weaknesses and troubles.

It is ourselves who are at fault, however, if we turn aside from Melville's immense art. There it will always wait for us, ready to show new depths and heights in our own reality.

THE PORTABLE

Melville

Biographical

To AN artist who worries that he is taking too long on too wandering a path to arrive at the practice of his art, Melville's life is a comfort. To get to that point Herman Melville had to be son of a business failure, academy student who did not graduate to college, engineering student who did not build, bank clerk and messenger, president of a debating society, farmhand, journalist, deckhand, country school teacher, sailor on a whaler, deserter, harpooneer, mutineer, pin boy in a bowling alley, store clerk and ordinary seaman in the navy. When he came home in this last job, there was a pause before Melville decided on his next occupation; he was not disposed to return to the sea; he had accumulated some trades and some entertaining stories to tell his family. It seems almost an accident that his next job grew out of those stories. And who can say that the bank, the farm, and the debating society had less to do with this choice than the deck and try-pots?

The boy born at 6 Pearl Street, New York City, near the midnight of August 1, 1819, was baptized Herman Melvill. His mother was the only daughter of the stolid Revolutionary defender of Fort Stanwix, General Peter Gansevoort. His father was Allan, second son of another Revolutionary fighter, Thomas Melvill, one of the "Mohawks" who emptied the tea ships into Boston Harbor. When, in Herman's last year, he was asked by Havelock Ellis for details of his racial background, he replied with no display of interest, "My great grandfather on the paternal side was a native of Scotland. On the maternal side, and in the same remove, my progenitor was a native of Holland; and, on that side, the wives were all of like ancestry. As to any strain of other

3

blood, I am ignorant, except that my paternal grandfather's wife was of Irish Protestant stock."

Allan and Maria Melvill had had a son and daughter before Herman's birth, and the family grew steadily to the number of four brothers and four sisters. Not long before the birth of this third child Allan had brought his family from Albany to establish an import and commission business in the seaport. As Allan's business and family increased the Melvills rented more commodious houses in more pleasant neighborhoods, but in 1830 Allan Melvill's credit, propped up with loans and hopes, fell apart and the family retreated to Albany, where Allan found employment that kept all fed and enabled eleven-year-old Herman and his fourteen-year-old brother Gansevoort to enter the Albany Academy.

Within little more than a year after this move, Allan died, leaving his family in a financial state whose uncertainty was revealed when his many loans became collectible. The two older boys were withdrawn from the Academy before a new term began, and work was found for both: Gansevoort was put in charge of the hat and fur manufactory of his father, and his uncle found a junior clerking job for Herman at the New York State Bank. After two years at this job Herman spent some months helping his uncle Thomas Melvill on his Pittsfield farm and, on returning to Albany, went to work as clerk at his brother's store. Their mother had encouraged Gansevoort to take over the responsibilities of head of the large family, now completely dependent on his store. Among other changes he effected in the family life, Gansevoort may have been responsible for the revision of the family name to "Melville," while other branches of the family maintained the Scottish "Melvill."

In 1835, with the aim of seeking a teaching post, Herman resumed his education by attending a few classes at the Albany Classical School and by taking a more active part in the Young Men's Association for Mutual Improvement and its offshoot, the Philo Logos Debating Society. His first teaching job, in a remote district school outside Pittsfield, where he improved the rare leisure that his thirty pupils allowed him by "occasional writting & reading," terminated abruptly (and possibly violently) three months after it had commenced. Melville returned to civilized Albany, where he bossed an upheaval in the debating society and defended his actions in a prolonged and heated polemic, his earliest work written for print.

Gansevoort's enterprise collapsed in the panic of 1837 and the Melvilles were compelled to move to the neighboring Hudson community of Lansingburgh—perhaps to Herman that "bleakest part of the civilized world" in which the "destitute widow, with an inordinate supply of young children" had been doomed, as mentioned in *Typee*. There Herman took courses in engineering and surveying at the Lansingburgh Academy with a view to finding employment in the construction division of the Erie Canal. When this hope was not realized, Gansevoort arranged for Herman to sign on a trading vessel, the *St. Lawrence*, for a summer's voyage to Liverpool in 1839.

His first experience at sea seems to have been neither too onerous nor too attractive. He and his family regarded it as a necessary interlude that was happily over when a more advanced school, in Greenbush, placed him on the faculty; this school neglected to pay his salary, and eventually closed without completing the term. As Thomas Melvill had taken his family from the hopelessness of the Pittsfield farm to the fresher hopes of the West, specifically in Galena, Illinois, this made a natural target for his unemployed nephew; so Melville, accompanied by an Albany friend, set out for Illinois via the Canal and the Lakes in the early summer of 1840. So little is known of this trip and what its destination finally offered the adventurers that we can only assume from their reappearance that fall in New York as temporary charges of the employed Gansevoort that Illinois did not have what Melville looked for.

New England's whaling fleet was at its industrial peak and the collection of crews for new whalers was too urgent a matter to require much sailing experience: green hands were in as much demand as seasoned ones. Possibly through a New York agency Melville was brought to New Bedford and signed aboard a new vessel, the *Acushnet*, where he was advanced eighty-four dollars on the strength of his "future services and earnings." With twenty-five other sailors, under Captain Valentine Pease, Jr., Melville and the *Acushnet* sailed on January 3, 1841, for the Pacific Ocean to kill whales.

In *Typee* Melville described this crew as, with a very few exceptions, "a parcel of dastardly and mean-spirited wretches"; yet one is forced to compare this with his gratification (relayed through Gansevoort soon after the *Acushnet* reached the Pacific) at finding his shipmates "so much superior in morale & early advantages to the ordinary run of whaling crews" and conclude that the letter's description was intended to soothe the anxious family at home, or that circumstances on the ship changed drastically between the two described periods, or that the book's description is part of a fine net of fictional emphasis spread over the "narrative" of *Typee*. If the last alternative be accepted, then the "unmitigated tyranny" of the *Dolly's* Captain Vangs may be thought less a characteristic of the *Acushnet's* Pease than it is a storyteller's motivation for his hero's desperate act. What we can know for sure is that the *Acushnet* arrived at the Marquesas Islands eighteen months after leaving New Bedford, in which time the whaling had been a little less than normal and the desertions and officer departures a little more than normal. Pease, as part owner, was logical in sending home part of his oil in a homeward-bound whaler he found anchored at Tumbes, but this meant a longer voyage. (There is in *Typee* a passionate paragraph[1] on the subject of Yankee captains' greater respect for profit than for time.) The consequent restlessness among the crew, especially after the unproductive months before arriving at the Marquesas, may be enough to explain the desertion there of Melville and his friend, Toby Greene.

The four months spent in the "Happy Valley" by Tommo can be brutally reduced by fact and ordinary calendar to a

[1] See page 35.

scant month that Melville spent in the Marquesas, between ships. Though he remained in the valley less than two weeks after Toby's escape on the *London Packet*, that period's artistic extension, spun as a yarn and fed though it was by various other narratives and authorities, had so much imaginative truth that contemporary readers were provided with the rich flavor of real experience. This alone should make us pause before measuring Melville's stay with the Typees by our clocks alone; for him it was an experience larger than twenty-seven mere days and nights. Nor did the experience end when he made his way from the valley to the Australian whaler *Lucy Ann;* in the retelling and remembering that Typeean paradise went on expanding until it was finally set down on paper—and perhaps beyond that, as well.

A similar comparison may be drawn between Melville's next move through the Pacific and the use made of it in *Omoo.* The poor luck of the *Lucy Ann* and her captain, Henry Ventom, brought good luck, reinforced with artist's license, to Melville. From the fortunes of a dry whaling season, a sick captain, a quashed mutiny, and his observation of an insecure consul and other residents of the Society Islands (plus the usual helpful sources at elbow), Melville later made his most picaresquely humorous book. When the mutineers, joined tardily by Melville (a ringleader, according to *Omoo*), were dumped into Papeite's *calabooza,* Melville was given his second opportunity to watch a Pacific people from the inside, and here the contrast with the civilization of his race was tragically emphasized by the visible infection it had conferred on the Tahitians. By the time he left Tahiti and Eimeo, Melville's allegiance was firmly with the infected as against the infecters.

The whole Tahitian experience can also be fitted into a literal month. This time it was a Nantucket whaler, the *Charles & Henry,* which employed Melville, now experienced enough to assume the responsibilities of boat steerer and harpooneer on that ship. He signed on her on November 3, 1842, and when, after a six months' cruise through southern waters, Captain Coleman discharged Melville at Lahaina in the Hawaiian Islands, before sailing for the coast of Japan, the rhapsode of the whaling industry had stepped ashore from his third and last whaler.

The fourteen weeks that Melville remained in Hawaii are, biographically, one of the most tantalizing episodes in his life. Though he witnessed a crisis in Hawaiian history and observed conditions that unsteadied even a man of his experience, he never risked a use of this "material" (as he used the Marquesan and Tahitian sojourns and his three whalers) beyond scattered bitter references. He was in no mood for another whaler, and the American consul's repeated offers of such a berth were ignored. He must have told his family that his stay in Honolulu was not to be brief, for mail for him arrived there long after his departure. It is not clear how he earned a living—the beachcombing he tasted in Tahiti may have furnished his chief occupation during the first weeks. A Lansingburgh neighbor heard that Melville worked in a Honolulu bowling alley. In June he signed a contract to work as clerk and bookkeeper for a British auctioneer when a new store was opened in July, yet by mid-August he left this apparently secure employment to ship on board the U.S. frigate United States as "ordinary seaman." This ship of the Pacific Squadron was not bound for a home port, so haste to get back to Lansingburgh could not have directly motivated the change of plan. About a year later, however, the United States, after giving him last glimpses of the scenes of his island adventures—the Marquesas and Societies, but not the Galápagos—was ordered home from her Peruvian station, and by October 1844 Melville, shortly after his twenty-fifth birthday, was paid off by the United States Navy in Boston and on his way home from "the pent-up wickedness of five hundred men."

He found Gansevoort a political figure of considerable oratorical weight in Democratic circles, stumping for Polk in the Presidential campaign, and the family glowing in the light of his fame. With Gansevoort about to justify his mother's hopes, the younger Allan was also trying the law; the boy Thomas was still as dependent as the four unmarried sisters. When James K. Polk was elected President, the Melvilles considered that their years of strain were near an end. Their home must have been warm that winter, with Gansevoort's prospects and the wandering brother back again. One of the most attractive yarns with which Melville "beguiled the long winter hours of his own home circle" was the escape from the frying pan of the *Acushnet* into the constant threat of fire among the Typees; someone suggested that he write out that adventure.

Melville wrote it, partly at his mother's house and during visits to his brothers in New York, and by spring of 1845 he had a book to peddle. Harpers rejected it on the ground that "it was impossible that it could be true and therefore was without real value." Gansevoort finally received his promised appointment—Secretary of the Legation in London —and took the manuscript of *Typee* with him, to offer it to British publishers. When John Murray displayed interest, Melville sent his brother more material for it (these last written chapters were xx, xxi, xxvii, with large additions to xxiv, xxvi, and xxx). With some qualms as to its authenticity Murray bought it for his Home and Colonial Library series, and G. P. Putnam contracted to follow with an American edition. Melville could now declare himself a writer by profession.

❖❖❖

Typee

A Peep at Polynesian Life

. . . Sailors are the only class of men who nowadays see anything like stirring adventure; and many things which to fireside people appear strange and romantic, to them seem as common-place as a jacket out at elbows. Yet, notwithstanding the familiarity of sailors with all sorts of curious adventure, the incidents recorded in the following pages have often served, when "spun as a yarn," not only to relieve the weariness of many a night-watch at sea, but to excite the warmest sympathies of the author's shipmates. He has been therefore led to think that his story could scarcely fail to interest those who are less familiar than the sailor with a life of adventure. . . .

There are some things related in the narrative which will be sure to appear strange, or perhaps entirely incomprehensible, to the reader; but they cannot appear more so to him than they did to the author at the time.

FROM the Preface

I

SIX MONTHS at sea! Yes, reader, as I live, six months out of sight of land; cruising after the sperm-whale beneath the scorching sun of the Line, and tossed on the billows of the wide-rolling Pacific—the sky above, the sea around, and nothing else! Weeks and weeks ago our fresh provisions were all exhausted. There is not a sweet potato left; not a single yam. Those glorious bunches of bananas which once decorated our stern and quarter-deck have, alas, disappeared! and the delicious oranges which hung suspended from our tops and stays—they, too, are gone! Yes, they are all departed, and there is nothing left us but salt-horse and sea-biscuit. Oh! ye state-room sailors, who make so much ado about a fourteen-days' passage across the Atlantic; who so pathetically relate the privations and hardships of the sea, where, after a day of breakfasting, lunching, dining off five courses, chatting, playing whist, and drinking champagne-punch, it was your hard lot to be shut up in little cabinets of mahogany and maple, and sleep for ten hours, with nothing to disturb you but "those good-for-nothing tars, shouting and tramping overhead,"—what would ye say to our six months out of sight of land?

Oh! for a refreshing glimpse of one blade of grass— for a snuff at the fragrance of a handful of the loamy earth! Is there nothing fresh around us? Is there no green thing to be seen? Yes, the inside of our bulwarks is painted green; but what a vile and sickly hue it is, as if nothing bearing even the semblance of verdure could flourish this weary way from land. Even the bark that once clung to the wood we use for fuel has been gnawed off and devoured by the captain's pig; and so long ago, too, that the pig himself has in turn been devoured.

There is but one solitary tenant in the chicken-coop, once a gay and dapper young cock, bearing him so bravely among the coy hens. But look at him now; there he stands, moping all the day long on that everlasting one leg of his. He turns with disgust from the mouldy corn before him and the brackish water in his little trough. He mourns no doubt his lost companions, literally snatched from him one by one, and never seen again. But his days of mourning will be few; for Mungo, our black cook, told me yesterday that the word had at last gone forth, and poor Pedro's fate was sealed. His attenuated body will be laid out upon the captain's table next Sunday, and long before night will be buried with all the usual ceremonies beneath that worthy individual's vest. Who would believe that there could be any one so cruel as to long for the decapitation of the luckless Pedro; yet the sailors pray every minute, selfish fellows, that the miserable fowl may be brought to his end. They say the captain will never point the ship for the land so long as he has in anticipation a mess of fresh meat. This unhappy bird can alone furnish it; and when he is once devoured, the captain will come to his senses. I wish thee no harm, Peter; but as thou art doomed, sooner or later, to meet the fate of all thy race; and if putting a period to thy existence is to be the signal for our deliverance, why—truth to speak—I wish thy throat cut this very moment; for, oh! how I wish to see the living earth again! The old ship herself longs to look out upon the land from her hawse-holes once more, and Jack Lewis said right the other day when the captain found fault with his steering.

"Why, d'ye see, Captain Vangs," says bold Jack, "I'm as good a helmsman as ever put hand to spoke; but none of us can steer the old lady now. We can't keep her full and bye, sir: watch her ever so close, she will fall off; and then, sir, when I put the helm down so gently, and try like to coax her to the work, she won't take it kindly, but will fall round off again; and it's all because she knows the land is under the lee, sir, and she won't go any more to windward." Aye, and why should she, Jack? Didn't every one of her stout timbers grow on shore, and hasn't she sensibilities as well as we?

Poor old ship! Her very looks denote her desires: how deplorably she appears! The paint on her sides, burnt up by the scorching sun, is puffed out and cracked. See the weeds she trails along with her, and what an unsightly bunch of those horrid barnacles has formed about her stern-piece; and every time she rises on a sea, she shows her copper torn away, or hanging in jagged strips.

Poor old ship! I say again: for six months she has been rolling and pitching about, never for one moment at rest. But courage, old lass, I hope to see thee soon within a biscuit's toss of the merry land, riding snugly at anchor in some green cove, and sheltered from the boisterous winds.

.   .   .   .   .   .

"Hurra, my lads! It's a settled thing; next week we shape our course to the Marquesas!" The Marquesas! What strange visions of outlandish things does the very name spirit up! Naked houris—cannibal banquets—groves of coco-nut—coral-reefs—tattooed chiefs—and bamboo temples; sunny valleys planted with breadfruit-trees—carved canoes dancing on the flashing blue waters—savage woodlands guarded by horrible idols—*heathenish rites and human sacrifices.*

Such were the strangely jumbled anticipations that haunted me during our passage from the cruising ground. I felt an irresistible curiosity to see those islands which the olden voyagers had so glowingly described.

The group for which we were now steering (although among the earliest of European discoveries in the South Seas, having been first visited in the year 1595) still continues to be tenanted by beings as strange and barbarous as ever. The missionaries, sent on a heavenly errand, had sailed by their lovely shores, and had abandoned them to their idols of wood and stone. How interesting the circumstances under which they were discovered! In the watery path of Mendana, cruising in quest of some region of gold, these isles had sprung up like a scene of enchantment, and for a moment the Spaniard believed his bright dream was realized. In honor of the Marquess de Mendoza, then viceroy of Peru—under whose auspices the navigator sailed—he bestowed upon them the name which denoted the rank of his patron, and gave to the world on his return a vague and magnificent account of their beauty. But these islands, undisturbed for years, relapsed into their previous obscurity; and it is only recently that anything has been known concerning them. Once in the course of a half century, to be sure, some adventurous rover would break in upon their peaceful repose, and, astonished at the unusual scene, would be almost tempted to claim the merit of a new discovery.

Of this interesting group, but little account has ever been given, if we except the slight mention made of them in the sketches of South-Sea voyages. Cook, in his repeated circumnavigations of the globe, barely touched at their shores; and all that we know about them is from a few general narratives. Among these, there are two that claim particular notice. Porter's *Journal of the Cruise of the U.S. Frigate Essex, in the Pacific, during the late War,* is said to contain some interesting particulars concerning the islanders. This is a work, however, which I have never happened to meet with; and Stewart, the chaplain of the American sloop-of-war *Vincennes,* has likewise devoted a portion of his book, entitled *A Visit to the South Seas,* to the same subject.

Within the last few years American and English vessels engaged in the extensive whale fisheries of the Pacific have occasionally, when short of provisions, put into the commodious harbor which there is in one of the islands; but a fear of the natives, founded on a recollection of the dreadful fate which many white men have received at their hands, has deterred their crews from intermixing with the population sufficiently to gain any insight into their peculiar customs and manners.

The Protestant Missions appear to have despaired of reclaiming these islands from heathenism. The usage they have in every case received from the natives has been such as to intimidate the boldest of their number. Ellis, in his *Polynesian Researches*, gives some interesting accounts of the abortive attempts made by the Tahiti Mission to establish a branch Mission upon certain islands of the group. A short time before my visit to the Marquesas, a somewhat amusing incident took place in connection with these efforts, which I cannot avoid relating.

An intrepid missionary, undaunted by the ill-success that had attended all previous endeavors to conciliate the savages, and believing much in the efficacy of female influence, introduced among them his young and beautiful wife, the first white woman who had ever visited their shores. The islanders at first gazed in mute admiration at so unusual a prodigy, and seemed inclined to regard it as some new divinity. But after a short time, becoming familiar with its charming aspect, and jealous of the folds which encircled its form, they sought to pierce the sacred veil of calico in which it was enshrined, and in the gratification of their curiosity so far overstepped the limits of good breeding as deeply to offend the lady's sense of decorum. Her sex once ascertained, their idolatry was changed into contempt; and there was no end to the contumely showered upon her by the savages, who were exasperated at the deception which they conceived had been practiced upon them. To the horror of her affectionate spouse, she was stripped of her garments, and given to understand that she could no longer carry on her deceits with impunity. The gentle dame was not sufficiently evangelized to endure this, and, fearful of further improprieties, she forced her husband to relinquish his undertaking, and together they returned to Tahiti.

Not thus shy of exhibiting her charms was the Island Queen, herself, the beauteous wife of Mowanna, the king of Nukuheva. Between two and three years after the adventures recorded in this volume, I chanced, while aboard of a man-of-war, to touch at these islands. The French had then held possession of the Marquesas some time, and already prided themselves upon the beneficial effects of their jurisdiction, as discernible in the deportment of the natives. To be sure, in one of their efforts at reform they had slaughtered about a hundred and fifty of them at Whitihoo—but let that pass. At the time I mention, the French squadron was rendezvousing in the bay of Nukuheva, and, during an interview between one of their captains and our worthy Commodore, it was suggested by the former that we, as the flag-ship of the American squadron, should receive, in state, a visit from the royal pair. The French officer likewise represented, with evident satisfaction, that under their tuition the king and queen had imbibed proper notions of their elevated station, and on all ceremonious occasions conducted themselves with suitable dignity. Accordingly, preparations were made to give their majesties a reception on board in a style corresponding with their rank.

One bright afternoon, a gig, gaily bedizened with streamers, was observed to shove off from the side of one of the French frigates, and pull directly for our gangway. In the stern sheets reclined Mowanna and his consort. As they approached, we paid them all the honors due to royalty—manning our yards, firing a salute, and making a prodigious hubbub.

They ascended the accommodation ladder, were

greeted by the Commodore, hat in hand, and passing along the quarter-deck, the marine guard presented arms, while the band struck up "The King of the Cannibal Islands." So far all went well. The French officers grimaced and smiled in exceedingly high spirits, wonderfully pleased with the discreet manner in which these distinguished personages behaved themselves.

Their appearance was certainly calculated to produce an effect. His majesty was arrayed in a magnificent military uniform, stiff with gold lace and embroidery, while his shaven crown was concealed by a huge *chapeau bras,* waving with ostrich plumes. There was one slight blemish, however, in his appearance. A broad patch of tattooing stretched completely across his face, in a line with his eyes, making him look as if he wore a huge pair of goggles; and royalty in goggles suggested some ludicrous ideas. But it was in the adornment of the fair person of his dark-complexioned spouse that the tailors of the fleet had evinced the gaiety of their national taste. She was habited in a gaudy tissue of scarlet cloth, trimmed with yellow silk, which, descending a little below the knees, exposed to view her bare legs, embellished with spiral tattooing, and somewhat resembling two miniature Trajan's columns. Upon her head was a fanciful turban of purple velvet, figured with silver sprigs, and surmounted by a tuft of variegated feathers.

The ship's company, crowding into the gangway to view the sight, soon arrested her majesty's attention. She singled out from their number an old salt, whose bare arms and feet and exposed breast were covered with as many inscriptions in India ink as the lid of an Egyptian sarcophagus. Notwithstanding all the sly hints and remonstrances of the French officers, she immediately approached the man, and pulling further open the bosom of his duck frock, and rolling up the leg of his wide trousers, she gazed with admiration at the bright blue and vermilion pricking, thus disclosed to view. She hung over the fellow, caressing him, and expressing her delight in a variety of wild exclamations and gestures. The embarrassment of the polite Gauls at such an unlooked-for occurrence may be easily imagined; but picture their consternation, when all at once the royal lady, eager to display the hieroglyphics on her own sweet form, bent forward for a moment, and turning sharply round, threw up the skirts of her mantle, and revealed a sight from which the aghast Frenchmen retreated precipitately, and, tumbling into their boat, fled the scene of so shocking a catastrophe.

II

I can never forget the eighteen or twenty days during which the light trade-winds were silently sweeping us towards the islands. In pursuit of the sperm-whale, we had been cruising on the Line some twenty degrees to the westward of the Galápagos; and all that we had to do, when our course was determined on, was to square in the yards and keep the vessel before the breeze, and then the good ship and the steady gale did the rest between them. The man at the wheel never vexed the old lady with any superfluous steering, but, comfortably adjusting his limbs at the tiller, would doze away by the hour. True to her work, the *Dolly* headed to her course, and, like one of those characters who always do best when let alone, she jogged on her way like a veteran old sea-pacer—as she was.

What a delightful, lazy, languid time we had whilst we were thus gliding along! There was nothing to be done; a circumstance that happily suited our disinclina.

tion to do anything. We abandoned the forepeak altogether, and spreading an awning over the forecastle, slept, ate, and lounged under it the livelong day. Every one seemed to be under the influence of some narcotic. Even the officers aft, whose duty required them never to be seated whilst keeping a deck watch, vainly endeavored to keep on their pins; and were obliged invariably to compromise the matter by leaning up against the bulwarks and gazing abstractedly over the side. Reading was out of the question; take a book in your hand, and you were asleep in an instant.

Although I could not avoid yielding in a great measure to the general languor, still at times I contrived to shake off the spell, and to appreciate the beauty of the scene around me. The sky presented a clear expanse of the most delicate blue, except along the skirts of the horizon, where you might see a thin drapery of pale clouds which never varied their form or color. The long, measured, dirge-like swell of the Pacific came rolling along, with its surface broken by little tiny waves, sparkling in the sunshine. Every now and then a shoal of flying-fish, scared from the water under the bows, would leap into the air, and fall the next moment like a shower of silver into the sea. Then you would see the superb albacore, with his glittering sides, sailing aloft, and, often describing an arc in his descent, disappear on the surface of the water. Far off, the lofty jet of the whale might be seen, and nearer at hand the prowling shark, that villainous footpad of the seas, would come skulking along and, at a wary distance, regard us with his evil eye. At times some shapeless monster of the deep, floating on the surface, would, as we approached, sink slowly into the blue waters, and fade away from the sight. But the most impressive feature of the scene was the almost unbroken silence that reigned over sky and water. Scarcely a sound could be heard but the occasional breathing of the grampus and the rippling at the cutwater.

As we drew nearer the land, I hailed with delight the appearance of innumerable sea-fowl. Screaming and whirling in spiral tracks, they would accompany the vessel, and at times alight on our yards and stays. That piratical-looking fellow, appropriately named the man-of-war's hawk, with his blood-red bill and raven plumage, would come sweeping round us in gradually diminishing circles, till you could distinctly mark the strange flashings of his eye; and then, as if satisfied with his observation, would sail up into the air and disappear from the view. Soon, other evidences of our vicinity to the land were apparent, and it was not long before the glad announcement of its being in sight was heard from aloft—given with that peculiar prolongation of sound that a sailor loves—"Land ho!"

The captain, darting on deck from the cabin, bawled lustily for his spy-glass; the mate in still louder accents hailed the masthead with a tremendous "Where-away?" The black cook thrust his woolly head from the galley, and Boatswain, the dog, leaped up between the knightheads, and barked most furiously. Land ho! Aye, there it was. A hardly perceptible blue irregular outline, indicating the bold contour of the lofty heights of Nukuheva.

This island, although generally called one of the Marquesas, is by some navigators considered as forming one of a distinct cluster, comprising the islands of Ruhooka, Ropo, and Nukuheva; upon which three the appellation of the Washington Group has been bestowed. They form a triangle, and lie within the parallels of 8° 38″ and 9° 32″ South latitude, and 139° 20′ and 140° 10′ West longitude from Greenwich. With how little propriety they are to be regarded as forming a separate group will be at once apparent, when it is considered that they lie in the immediate vicinity of the other islands, that is to say, less than a degree to the north-west of them, that their inhabitants speak the Marquesan dialect, and that their laws, religion, and general customs are identical. The only reason why they were ever thus arbitrarily distinguished may be attributed to the singular fact that their existence was altogether unknown to the world until the year 1791, when they were discovered by Captain Ingraham, of Boston, Massachusetts, nearly two centuries after the discovery of the adjacent islands by the agent of the Spanish Viceroy. Notwithstanding this, I shall follow the example of most voyagers, and treat of them as forming part and parcel of the Marquesas.

Nukuheva is the most important of these islands, being the only one at which ships are much in the habit of touching, and is celebrated as being the place where the adventurous Captain Porter refitted his ships during the late war between England and the United States, and whence he sallied out upon the large whaling fleet then sailing under the enemy's flag in the surrounding seas. This island is about twenty miles in length and nearly as many in breadth. It has three good harbors on its coast; the largest and best of which is called by the people living in its vicinity "Tyohee," and by Captain Porter was denominated Massachusetts Bay. Among the adverse tribes dwelling about the shores of the other bays, and by all voyagers, it is generally known by the name bestowed upon the island itself—Nukuheva. Its inhabitants have become somewhat corrupted owing to their recent commerce with Europeans; but so far as regards their peculiar customs and general mode of life, they retain their original primitive character, remaining very nearly in the same state of nature in which they were first beheld by white men. The hostile clans, residing in the more remote sections of the island, and very seldom holding any communication with foreigners, are in every respect unchanged from their earliest known condition.

In the bay of Nukuheva was the anchorage we desired to reach. We had perceived the loom of the mountains about sunset; so that after running all night with a very light breeze, we found ourselves close in with the island the next morning, but as the bay we sought lay on its farther side, we were obliged to sail some distance along the shore, catching, as we proceeded, short glimpses of blooming valleys, deep glens, waterfalls, and waving groves, hidden here and there by projecting and rocky headlands, every moment opening to the view some new and startling scene of beauty.

Those who for the first time visit the South Seas, generally are surprised at the appearance of the islands when beheld from the sea. From the vague accounts we sometimes have of their beauty, many people are apt to picture to themselves enameled and softly swelling plains, shaded over with delicious groves, and watered by purling brooks, and the entire country but little elevated above the surrounding ocean. The reality is very different; bold rock-bound coasts, with the surf beating high against the lofty cliffs, and broken here and there into deep inlets, which open to the view thickly wooded valleys, separated by the spurs of mountains clothed with tufted grass, and sweeping down towards the sea from an elevated and furrowed interior, form the principal features of these islands.

Towards noon we drew abreast the entrance to the harbor, and at last we slowly swept by the intervening promontory, and entered the bay of Nukuheva. No description can do justice to its beauty; but that beauty was lost to me then, and I saw nothing but the tri-colored flag of France trailing over the stern of six vessels, whose black hulls and bristling broadsides proclaimed their warlike character. There they were, floating in that lovely bay, the green eminences of the shore looking down so tranquilly upon them, as if rebuking the sternness of their aspect. To my eye nothing could be more out of keeping than the presence of these vessels; but we soon learnt what brought them there. The whole group of islands had just been taken possession of by Rear-Admiral Du Petit Thouars, in the name of the invincible French nation.

This item of information was imparted to us by a most extraordinary individual, a genuine South-Sea vagabond, who came alongside of us in a whale-boat as soon as we entered the bay, and, by the aid of some benevolent persons at the gangway, was assisted on board, for our visitor was in that interesting stage of intoxication when a man is amiable and helpless. Although he was utterly unable to stand erect or to navigate his body across the deck, he still magnanimously proffered his services to pilot the ship to a good and secure anchorage. Our captain, however, rather distrusted his ability in this respect, and refused to recognize his claim to the character he assumed; but our gentleman was determined to play his part, for by dint of much scrambling he succeeded in getting into the weather-quarter boat, where he steadied himself by holding on to a shroud, and then commenced issuing his commands with amazing volubility and very peculiar gestures. Of course no one obeyed his orders; but as it was impossible to quiet him, we swept by the ships of the squadron with this strange fellow performing his antics in full view of all the French officers.

We afterwards learned that our eccentric friend had been a lieutenant in the English navy; but, having disgraced his flag by some criminal conduct in one of the principal ports on the main, he had deserted his ship, and spent many years wandering among the islands of the Pacific, until accidentally being at Nuku-heva when the French took possession of the place, he had been appointed pilot of the harbor by the newly constituted authorities.

As we slowly advanced up the bay, numerous canoes pushed off from the surrounding shores, and we were soon in the midst of quite a flotilla of them, their savage occupants struggling to get aboard of us, and jostling one another in their ineffectual attempts. Occasionally the projecting outriggers of their slight shallops, running foul of one another, would become entangled beneath the water, threatening to capsize the canoes, when a scene of confusion would ensue that baffles description. Such strange outcries and passionate gesticulations I never certainly heard or saw before. You would have thought the islanders were on the point of flying at one another's throats, whereas they were only amicably engaged in disentangling their boats.

Scattered here and there among the canoes might be seen numbers of coco-nuts floating closely together in circular groups, and bobbing up and down with every wave. By some inexplicable means these coco-nuts were all steadily approaching towards the ship. As I leaned curiously over the side endeavoring to solve their mysterious movements, one mass far in advance of the rest attracted my attention. In its center was something I could take for nothing else than a coco-nut, but which I certainly considered one of the most extraordinary specimens of the fruit I had ever seen. It kept twirling and dancing about among the rest in the most singular

manner, and as it drew nearer I thought it bore a remarkable resemblance to the brown shaven skull of one
of the savages. Presently it betrayed a pair of eyes, and
soon I became aware that what I had supposed to have
been one of the fruit was nothing else than the head of
an islander, who had adopted this singular method of
bringing his produce to market. The coco-nuts were all
attached to one another by strips of the husk, partly torn
from the shell and rudely fastened together. Their proprietor, inserting his head into the midst of them, impelled his necklace of coco-nuts through the water
by striking out beneath the surface with his feet.

I was somewhat astonished to perceive that among
the number of natives that surrounded us not a single
female was to be seen. At that time I was ignorant of
the fact that by the operation of the "taboo" the use of
canoes in all parts of the island is rigorously prohibited
to the entire sex, for whom it is death even to be seen
entering one when hauled on shore; consequently,
whenever a Marquesan lady voyages by water, she puts
in requisition the paddles of her own fair body.

We had approached within a mile and a half perhaps
of the foot of the bay, when some of the islanders, who
by this time had managed to scramble aboard of us at
the risk of swamping their canoes, directed our attention
to a singular commotion in the water ahead of the
vessel. At first I imagined it to be produced by a shoal
of fish sporting on the surface, but our savage friends
assured us that it was caused by a shoal of "whinhenies"
(young girls), who in this manner were coming off from
the shore to welcome us. As they drew nearer, and I
watched the rising and sinking of their forms, and beheld the uplifted right arm bearing above the water the
girdle of tappa, and their long dark hair trailing beside
them as they swam, I almost fancied they could be

nothing else than so many mermaids—and very like mermaids they behaved too.

We were still some distance from the beach, and under slow headway, when we sailed right into the midst of these swimming nymphs, and they boarded us at every quarter; many seizing hold of the chainplates and springing into the chains; others, at the peril of being run over by the vessel in her course, catching at the bob-stays, and wreathing their slender forms about the ropes, hung suspended in the air. All of them at length succeeded in getting up the ship's side, where they clung dripping with the brine and glowing from the bath, their jet-black tresses streaming over their shoulders, and half enveloping their otherwise naked forms. There they hung, sparkling with savage vivacity, laughing gaily at one another, and chattering away with infinite glee. Nor were they idle the while, for each one performed the simple offices of the toilet for the other. Their luxuriant locks, wound up and twisted into the smallest possible compass, were freed from the briny element; the whole person carefully dried and, from a little round shell that passed from hand to hand, anointed with a fragrant oil: their adornments were completed by passing a few loose folds of white tappa, in a modest cincture, around the waist. Thus arrayed they no longer hesitated, but flung themselves lightly over the bulwarks, and were quickly frolicking about the decks. Many of them went forward, perching upon the head-rails or running out upon the bowsprit, while others seated themselves upon the taffrail, or reclined at full length upon the boats. What a sight for us bachelor sailors! how avoid so dire a temptation? For who could think of tumbling these artless creatures overboard, when they had swam miles to welcome us?

Their appearance perfectly amazed me; their extreme youth, the light clear brown of their complexions, their delicate features, and inexpressibly graceful figures, their softly moulded limbs, and free unstudied action, seemed as strange as beautiful.

The *Dolly* was fairly captured; and never I will say was vessel carried before by such a dashing and irresistible party of boarders! The ship taken, we could not do otherwise than yield ourselves prisoners, and, for the whole period that she remained in the bay, the *Dolly*, as well as her crew, were completely in the hands of the mermaids.

In the evening after we had come to an anchor the deck was illuminated with lanterns, and this picturesque band of sylphs, tricked out with flowers, and dressed in robes of variegated tappa, got up a ball in great style. These females are passionately fond of dancing, and in the wild grace and spirit of their style excel everything that I have ever seen. The varied dances of the Marquesan girls are beautiful in the extreme, but there is an abandoned voluptuousness in their character which I dare not attempt to describe.

Our ship was now wholly given up to every species of riot and debauchery. Not the feeblest barrier was interposed between the unholy passions of the crew and their unlimited gratification. The grossest licentiousness and the most shameful inebriety prevailed, with occasional and but short-lived interruptions, through the whole period of her stay. Alas for the poor savages when exposed to the influence of these polluting examples! Unsophisticated and confiding, they are easily led into every vice, and humanity weeps over the ruin thus remorselessly inflicted upon them by their European civilizers. Thrice happy are they who, inhabiting some yet undiscovered island in the midst of the ocean, have never been brought into contaminating contact with the white man.

III

It was in the summer of 1842 that we arrived at the islands; the French had then held possession of them for several weeks. During this time they had visited some of the principal places in the group, and had disembarked at various points about five hundred troops. These were employed in constructing works of defense, and otherwise providing against the attacks of the natives, who at any moment might be expected to break out in open hostility. The islanders looked upon the people who made this cavalier appropriation of their shores with mingled feelings of fear and detestation. They cordially hated them; but the impulses of their resentment were neutralized by their dread of the floating batteries, which lay with their fatal tubes ostentatiously pointed, not at fortifications and redoubts, but at a handful of bamboo sheds, sheltered in a grove of coco-nuts! A valiant warrior doubtless, but a prudent one too, was this same Rear-Admiral Du Petit Thouars. Four heavy, double-banked frigates and three corvettes to frighten a parcel of naked heathen into subjection! Sixty eight-pounders to demolish huts of coco-nut boughs, and Congreve rockets to set on fire a few canoe sheds!

At Nukuheva, there were about one hundred soldiers ashore. They were encamped in tents, constructed of the old sails and spare spars of the squadron, within the limits of a redoubt mounted with a few ninepounders, and surrounded with a fosse. Every other day, these troops were marched out in martial array, to a

level piece of ground in the vicinity, and there for hours
went through all sorts of military evolutions, surrounded
by flocks of the natives, who looked on with savage
admiration at the show, and as savage a hatred of the
actors. A regiment of the Old Guard, reviewed on a
summer's day in the Champs Élysées, could not have
made a more critically correct appearance. The officers'
regimentals, resplendent with gold lace and embroidery,
as if purposely calculated to dazzle the islanders, looked
as if just unpacked from their Parisian cases.

The sensation produced by the presence of the
strangers had not in the least subsided at the period of
our arrival at the islands. The natives still flocked in
numbers about the encampment, and watched with the
liveliest curiosity everything that was going forward.
A blacksmith's forge, which had been set up in the
shelter of a grove near the beach, attracted so great a
crowd that it required the utmost efforts of the sentries
posted around to keep the inquisitive multitude at a
sufficient distance to allow the workmen to ply their
vocation. But nothing gained so large a share of admiration as a horse, which had been brought from
Valparaiso by the *Achille,* one of the vessels of the
squadron. The animal, a remarkably fine one, had been
taken ashore and stabled in a hut of coco-nut boughs
within the fortified enclosure. Occasionally it was
brought out, and, being gaily caparisoned, was ridden
by one of the officers at full speed over the hard sand
beach. This performance was sure to be hailed with
loud plaudits, and the "puarkee nuee" (big hog) was
unanimously pronounced by the islanders to be the
most extraordinary specimen of zoology that had ever
come under their observation.

The expedition for the occupation of the Marquesas
had sailed from Brest in the spring of 1842, and the

secret of its destination was solely in the possession of its commander. No wonder that those who contemplated such a signal infraction of the rights of humanity should have sought to veil the enormity from the eyes of the world. And yet, notwithstanding their iniquitous conduct in this and in other matters, the French have ever plumed themselves upon being the most humane and polished of nations. A high degree of refinement, however, does not seem to subdue our wicked propensities so much after all; and were civilization itself to be estimated by some of its results, it would seem perhaps better for what we call the barbarous part of the world to remain unchanged.

One example of the shameless subterfuges under which the French stand prepared to defend whatever cruelties they may hereafter think fit to commit in bringing the Marquesan natives into subjection is well worthy of being recorded. On some flimsy pretext or other Mowanna, the king of Nukuheva, whom the invaders by extravagant presents have cajoled over to their interests, and move about like a mere puppet, has been set up as the rightful sovereign of the entire island —the alleged ruler by prescription of various clans who for ages perhaps have treated with each other as separate nations. To reinstate this much-injured prince in the assumed dignities of his ancestors, the disinterested strangers have come all the way from France: they are determined that his title shall be acknowledged. If any tribe shall refuse to recognize the authority of the French, by bowing down to the laced chapeau of Mowanna, let them abide the consequences of their obstinacy. Under cover of a similar pretense, have the outrages and massacres at Tahiti the beautiful, the queen of the South Seas, been perpetrated.

On this buccaneering expedition, Rear-Admiral Du

Petit Thouars, leaving the rest of his squadron at the Marquesas—which had then been occupied by his forces about five months—set sail for the doomed island in the *Reine Blanche* frigate. On his arrival, as an indemnity for alleged insults offered to the flag of his country, he demanded some twenty or thirty thousand dollars to be placed in his hands forthwith, and, in default of payment, threatened to land and take possession of the place.

The frigate, immediately upon coming to an anchor, got springs on her cables, and with her guns cast loose and her men at their quarters, lay in the circular basin of Papeete, with her broadside bearing upon the devoted town; while her numerous cutters, hauled in order alongside, were ready to effect a landing, under cover of her batteries. She maintained this belligerent attitude for several days, during which time a series of informal negotiations were pending, and wide alarm spread over the island. Many of the Tahitians were at first disposed to resort to arms, and drive the invaders from their shores; but more pacific and feebler councils ultimately prevailed. The unfortunate queen, Pomare, incapable of averting the impending calamity, terrified at the arrogance of the insolent Frenchman, and driven at last to despair, fled by night in a canoe to Eimeo.

During the continuance of the panic there occurred an instance of feminine heroism that I cannot omit to record.

In the grounds of the famous missionary consul, Pritchard, then absent in London, the consular flag of Britain waved as usual during the day, from a lofty staff planted within a few yards of the beach, and in full view of the frigate. One morning an officer, at the head of a party of men, presented himself at the verandah of Mr. Pritchard's house, and inquired in broken English for the lady his wife. The matron soon made her appearance; and the polite Frenchman, making one of his best bows, and playing gracefully with the aiguillettes that danced upon his breast, proceeded in courteous accents to deliver his mission. "The admiral desired the flag to be hauled down—hoped it would be perfectly agreeable —and his men stood ready to perform the duty." "Tell the pirate your master," replied the spirited Englishwoman, pointing to the staff, "that if he wishes to strike those colors, he must come and perform the act himself; I will suffer no one else to do it." The lady then bowed haughtily and withdrew into the house. As the discomfited officer slowly walked away, he looked up to the flag, and perceived that the cord by which it was elevated to its place, led from the top of the staff, across the lawn, to an open upper window of the mansion, where sat the lady, from whom he had just parted, tranquilly engaged in knitting. Was that flag hauled down? Mrs. Pritchard thinks not; and Rear-Admiral Du Petit Thouars is believed to be of the same opinion.

IV

Our ship had not been many days in the harbor of Nukuheva before I came to the determination of leaving her. That my reasons for resolving to take this step were numerous and weighty, may be inferred from the fact that I chose rather to risk my fortunes among the savages of the island than to endure another voyage on board the *Dolly*. To use the concise, point-blank phrase of the sailors, I had made up my mind to "run away." Now as a meaning is generally attached to these two words no way flattering to the individual to whom they are applied, it behooves me, for the sake of my own character, to offer some explanation of my conduct.

When I entered on board the *Dolly*, I signed as a
matter of course the ship's articles, thereby voluntarily
engaging and legally binding myself to serve in a certain
capacity for the period of the voyage; and, special considerations apart, I was of course bound to fulfill the
agreement. But in all contracts, if one party fail to
perform his share of the compact, is not the other
virtually absolved from his liability? Who is there who
will not answer in the affirmative?

Having settled the principle, then, let me apply it to
the particular case in question. In numberless instances
had not only the implied but the specified conditions of
the articles been violated on the part of the ship in
which I served. The usage on board of her was tyranni-
cal; the sick had been inhumanly neglected; the provisions had been doled out in scanty allowance; and her
cruises were unreasonably protracted. The captain was
the author of these abuses; it was in vain to think that
he would either remedy them, or alter his conduct,
which was arbitrary and violent in the extreme. His
prompt reply to all complaints and remonstrances was
—the butt end of a hand-spike, so convincingly administered as effectually to silence the aggrieved party.

To whom could we apply for redress? We had left
both law and equity on the other side of the Cape; and
unfortunately, with a very few exceptions, our crew was
composed of a parcel of dastardly and mean-spirited
wretches, divided among themselves, and only united
in enduring without resistance the unmitigated tyranny
of the captain. It would have been mere madness for
any two or three of the number, unassisted by the rest,
to attempt making a stand against his ill usage. They
would only have called down upon themselves the
particular vengeance of this "Lord of the Plank," and
subjected their shipmates to additional hardships.

But, after all, these things could have been endured awhile, had we entertained the hope of being speedily delivered from them by the due completion of the term of our servitude. But what a dismal prospect awaited us in this quarter! The longevity of Cape Horn whaling voyages is proverbial, frequently extending over a period of four or five years.

Some long-haired bare-necked youths who, forced by the united influences of Captain Marryat and hard times, embark at Nantucket for a pleasure excursion to the Pacific, and whose anxious mothers provide them with bottled milk for the occasion, oftentimes return very respectable middle-aged gentlemen.

The very preparations made for one of these expeditions are enough to frighten one. As the vessel carries out no cargo, her hold is filled with provisions for her own consumption. The owners, who officiate as caterers for the voyage, supply the larder with an abundance of dainties. Delicate morsels of beef and pork, cut on scientific principles from every part of the animal, and of all conceivable shapes and sizes, are carefully packed in salt, and stored away in barrels; affording a never-ending variety in their different degrees of toughness, and in the peculiarities of their saline properties. Choice old water, too, decanted into stout six-barrel-casks, and two pints of which are allowed every day to each soul on board; together with ample store of sea-bread, previously reduced to a state of petrifaction, with a view to preserve it either from decay or consumption in the ordinary mode, are likewise provided for the nourishment and gastronomic enjoyment of the crew.

But not to speak of the quality of these articles of sailors' fare, the abundance in which they are put on board a whaling vessel is almost incredible. Oftentimes, when we had occasion to break out in the hold, and I beheld the successive tiers of casks and barrels, whose contents were all destined to be consumed in due course by the ship's company, my heart has sunk within me.

Although, as a general case, a ship unlucky in falling in with whales continues to cruise after them until she has barely sufficient provisions remaining to take her home, turning round then quietly and making the best of her way to her friends; yet there are instances when even this natural obstacle to the further prosecution of the voyage is overcome by headstrong captains, who, bartering the fruits of their hard-earned toils for a new supply of provisions in some of the ports of Chile or Peru, began the voyage afresh with unabated zeal and perseverance. It is in vain that the owners write urgent letters to him to sail for home, and for their sake to bring back the ship, since it appears he can put nothing in her. Not he. He has registered a vow: he will fill his vessel with good sperm-oil, or, failing to do so, never again strike Yankee soundings.

I heard of one whaler, which after many years' absence was given up for lost. The last that had been heard of her was a shadowy report of her having touched at some of those unstable islands in the far Pacific, whose eccentric wanderings are carefully noted in each new edition of the South-Sea charts. After a long interval, however, the *Perseverance*—for that was her name—was spoken somewhere in the vicinity of the ends of the earth, cruising along as leisurely as ever, her sails all bepatched and bequilted with rope-yarns, her spars fished with old pipe staves, and her rigging knotted and spliced in every possible direction. Her crew was composed of some twenty venerable Greenwich-pensioner-looking old salts, who just managed to hobble about deck. The ends of all the running ropes, with the exception of the signal halyards and poop-down-haul, were rove through snatch-blocks, and led to the capstan or windlass, so that not a yard was braced or a sail set without the assistance of machinery.

Her hull was incrusted with barnacles, which completely encased her. Three pet sharks followed in her wake and every day came alongside to regale themselves from the contents of the cook's bucket, which were pitched over to them. A vast shoal of bonitos and albacores always kept her company.

Such was the account I heard of this vessel, and the remembrance of it always haunted me; what eventually became of her I never learned; at any rate she never reached home, and I suppose she is still regularly tacking twice in the twenty-four hours somewhere off Buggerry Island, or the Devil's-Tail Peak.

Having said thus much touching the usual length of these voyages, when I inform the reader that ours had as it were just commenced, we being only fifteen months out, and even at that time hailed as a late arrival, and boarded for news, he will readily perceive that there was little to encourage one in looking forward to the future, especially as I had always had a presentiment that we should make an unfortunate voyage, and our experience so far had justified the expectation.

I may here state, and on my faith as an honest man, that though more than three years have elapsed since I left this same identical vessel, she still continues in the Pacific, and but a few days since I saw her reported in the papers as having touched at the Sandwich Islands previous to going on the coast of Japan.

But to return to my narrative. Placed in these circumstances then, with no prospect of matters mending if I remained aboard the *Dolly*, I at once made up my mind to leave her: to be sure it was rather an inglorious thing to steal away privily from those at whose hands I had received wrongs and outrages that I could not resent; but how was such a course to be avoided when it was the only alternative left me? Having made up my mind, I proceeded to acquire all the information I could obtain relating to the island and its inhabitants, with a view of shaping my plans of escape accordingly. The result of these inquiries I will now state, in order that the ensuing narrative may be the better understood.

The bay of Nukuheva in which we were then lying is an expanse of water not unlike in figure the space included within the limits of a horse-shoe. It is, perhaps, nine miles in circumference. You approach it from the sea by a narrow entrance, flanked on either side by two small twin islets which soar conically to the height of some five hundred feet. From these the shore recedes on both hands, and describes a deep semicircle.

From the verge of the water the land rises uniformly on all sides, with green and sloping acclivities, until from gently rolling hill-sides and moderate elevations it insensibly swells into lofty and majestic heights, whose blue outlines, ranged all around, close in the view. The beautiful aspect of the shore is heightened by deep and romantic glens, which come down to it at almost equal distances, all apparently radiating from a common center, and the upper extremities of which are lost to the eye beneath the shadow of the mountains. Down each of these little valleys flows a clear stream, here and there assuming the form of a slender cascade, then stealing invisibly along until it bursts upon the sight again in larger and more noisy waterfalls, and at last demurely wanders along to the sea.

The houses of the natives, constructed of the yellow bamboo, tastefully twisted together in a kind of wicker-work, and thatched with the long tapering leaves of the palmetto, are scattered irregularly along these valleys beneath the shady branches of the coco-nut trees.

Nothing can exceed the imposing scenery of this bay. Viewed from our ship as she lay at anchor in the middle of the harbor, it presented the appearance of a vast natural amphitheater in decay, and overgrown with vines, the deep glens that furrowed its sides appearing like enormous fissures caused by the ravages of time. Very often when lost in admiration at its beauty, I have experienced a pang of regret that a scene so enchanting should be hidden from the world in these remote seas, and seldom meet the eyes of devoted lovers of nature.

Besides this bay the shores of the island are indented by several other extensive inlets, into which descend broad and verdant valleys. These are inhabited by as many distinct tribes of savages, who, although speaking kindred dialects of a common language, and having the same religion and laws, have from time immemorial waged hereditary warfare against each other. The intervening mountains, generally two or three thousand feet above the level of the sea, geographically define the territories of each of these hostile tribes, who never cross them, save on some expedition of war or plunder. Immediately adjacent to Nukuheva, and only separated from it by the mountains seen from the harbor, lies the lovely valley of Happar, whose inmates cherish the most friendly relations with the inhabitants of Nukuheva. On the other side of Happar, and closely adjoining it, is the magnificent valley of the dreaded Typees, the unappeasable enemies of both these tribes.

These celebrated warriors appear to inspire the other islanders with unspeakable terrors. Their very name is a frightful one; for the word "Typee" in the Marquesan dialect signifies a lover of human flesh. It is rather singular that the title should have been bestowed upon them exclusively, inasmuch as the natives of all this group are irreclaimable cannibals. The name may, perhaps, have been given to denote the peculiar ferocity of this clan, and to convey a special stigma along with it.

These same Typees enjoy a prodigious notoriety all over the islands. The natives of Nukuheva would frequently recount in pantomime to our ship's company their terrible feats, and would show the marks of wounds they had received in desperate encounters with them. When ashore they would try to frighten us by pointing to one of their own number, and calling him a Typee, manifesting no little surprise that we did not take to our heels at so terrible an announcement. It was quite amusing, too, to see with what earnestness they disclaimed all cannibal propensities on their own part while they denounced their enemies—the Typees—as inveterate gormandizers of human flesh; but this is a peculiarity to which I shall hereafter have occasion to allude.

Although I was convinced that the inhabitants of our bay were as arrant cannibals as any of the other tribes on the island, still I could not but feel a particular and most unqualified repugnance to the aforesaid Typees. Even before visiting the Marquesas, I had heard from men who had touched at the group on former voyages some revolting stories in connection with these savages; and fresh in my remembrance was the adventure of the master of the *Katherine,* who, only a few months previous, imprudently venturing into this bay in an armed boat for the purpose of barter, was seized by the natives, carried back a little distance into their valley, and was only saved from a cruel death by the intervention of a young girl, who facilitated his escape by night along the beach to Nukuheva.

I had heard too of an English vessel that many years

ago, after a weary cruise, sought to enter the bay of Nukuheva, and, arriving within two or three miles of the land, was met by a large canoe filled with natives, who offered to lead the way to the place of their destination. The captain, unacquainted with the localities of the island, joyfully acceded to the proposition—the canoe paddled on and the ship followed. She was soon conducted to a beautiful inlet, and dropped her anchor in its waters beneath the shadows of the lofty shore. That same night the perfidious Typees, who had thus inveigled her into their fatal bay, flocked aboard the doomed vessel by hundreds, and at a given signal murdered every soul on board.

I shall never forget the observation of one of our crew as we were passing slowly by the entrance of this bay in our way to Nukuheva. As we stood gazing over the side at the verdant headlands, Ned, pointing with his hand in the direction of the treacherous valley exclaimed, "There—there's Typee. Oh, the bloody cannibals, what a meal they'd make of us if we were to take it into our heads to land! but they say they don't like sailor's flesh, it's too salt. I say, matey, how should you like to be shoved ashore there, eh?" I little thought, as I shuddered at the question, that in the space of a few weeks I should actually be a captive in that self-same valley.

The French, although they had gone through the ceremony of hoisting their colors for a few hours at all the principal places of the group, had not as yet visited the bay of Typee, anticipating a fierce resistance on the part of the savages there, which for the present at least they wished to avoid. Perhaps they were not a little influenced in the adoption of this unusual policy from a recollection of the warlike reception given by the Typees to the forces of Captain Porter, about the year

1814, when that brave and accomplished officer endeavored to subjugate the clan merely to gratify the mortal hatred of his allies the Nukuhevas and Happars.

On that occasion I have been told that a considerable detachment of sailors and marines from the frigate *Essex*, accompanied by at least two thousand warriors of Happar and Nukuheva, landed in boats and canoes at the head of the bay, and, after penetrating a little distance into the valley, met with the stoutest resistance from its inmates. Valiantly, although with much loss, the Typees disputed every inch of ground, and after some hard fighting obliged their assailants to retreat and abandon their design of conquest.

The invaders, on their march back to the sea, consoled themselves for their repulse by setting fire to every house and temple in their route; and a long line of smoking ruins defaced the once-smiling bosom of the valley, and proclaimed to its pagan inhabitants the spirit that reigned in the breasts of Christian soldiers. Who can wonder at the deadly hatred of the Typees to all foreigners after such unprovoked atrocities?

Thus it is that they whom we denominate "savages" are made to deserve the title. When the inhabitants of some sequestered island first descry the "big canoe" of the European rolling through the blue waters towards their shores, they rush down to the beach in crowds, and with open arms stand ready to embrace the strangers. Fatal embrace! They fold to their bosoms the vipers whose sting is destined to poison all their joys; and the instinctive feeling of love within their breasts is soon converted into the bitterest hate.

The enormities perpetrated in the South Seas upon some of the inoffensive islanders well nigh pass belief. These things are seldom proclaimed at home; they happen at the very ends of the earth; they are done in a corner, and there is none to reveal them. But there is, nevertheless, many a petty trader that has navigated the Pacific whose course from island to island might be traced by a series of cold-blooded robberies, kidnapings, and murders, the iniquity of which might be considered almost sufficient to sink her guilty timbers to the bottom of the sea.

Sometimes vague accounts of such things reach our firesides, and we coolly censure them as wrong, impolitic, needlessly severe, and dangerous to the crews of other vessels. How different is our tone when we read the highly wrought description of the massacre of the crew of the *Hobomak* by the Feejees; how we sympathize for the unhappy victims, and with what horror do we regard the diabolical heathens, who, after all, have but avenged the unprovoked injuries which they have received. We breathe nothing but vengeance, and equip armed vessels to traverse thousands of miles of ocean in order to execute summary punishment upon the offenders. On arriving at their destination, they burn, slaughter, and destroy, according to the tenor of written instructions, and sailing away from the scene of devastation, call upon all Christendom to applaud their courage and their justice.

How often is the term "savages" incorrectly applied! None really deserving of it were ever yet discovered by voyagers or by travelers. They have discovered heathens and barbarians, whom by horrible cruelties they have exasperated into savages. It may be asserted without fear of contradiction, that in all the cases of outrages committed by Polynesians, Europeans have at some time or other been the aggressors, and that the cruel and bloodthirsty disposition of some of the islanders is mainly to be ascribed to the influence of such examples.

But to return. Owing to the mutual hostilities of

the different tribes I have mentioned, the mountainous tracts which separate their respective territories remain altogether uninhabited; the natives invariably dwelling in the depths of the valleys, with a view of securing themselves from the predatory incursions of their enemies, who often lurk along their borders, ready to cut off any imprudent straggler, or make a descent upon the inmates of some sequestered habitation. I several times met with very aged men, who from this cause had never passed the confines of their native vale, some of them having never even ascended midway up the mountains in the whole course of their lives, and who, accordingly, had little idea of the appearance of any other part of the island, the whole of which is not perhaps more than sixty miles in circuit. The little space in which some of these clans pass away their days would seem almost incredible.

The glen of Tior will furnish a curious illustration of this. The inhabited part is not more than four miles in length, and varies in breadth from half a mile to less than a quarter. The rocky vine-clad cliffs on one side tower almost perpendicularly from their base to the height of at least fifteen hundred feet; while across the vale—in striking contrast to the scenery opposite —grass-grown elevations rise one above another in blooming terraces. Hemmed in by these stupendous barriers, the valley would be altogether shut out from the rest of the world, were it not that it is accessible from the sea at one end, and by a narrow defile at the other.

The impression produced upon my mind, when I first visited this beautiful glen, will never be obliterated.

I had come from Nukuheva by water in the ship's boat, and when we entered the bay of Tior it was high noon. The heat had been intense, as we had been floating upon the long smooth swell of the ocean, for there

was but little wind. The sun's rays had expended all
their fury upon us; and to add to our discomfort, we
had omitted to supply ourselves with water previous to
starting. What with heat and thirst together, I became
so impatient to get ashore that, when at last we glided
towards it, I stood up in the bow of the boat ready for a
spring. As she shot two thirds of her length high upon
the beach, propelled by three or four strong strokes of
the oars, I leaped among a parcel of juvenile savages,
who stood prepared to give us a kind reception, and
with them at my heels, yelling like so many imps, I
rushed forward across the open ground in the vicinity
of the sea, and plunged, diver fashion, into the recesses
of the first grove that offered.

What a delightful sensation did I experience! I felt
as if floating in some new element, while all sorts of
gurgling, trickling, liquid sounds fell upon my ear.
People may say what they will about the refreshing
influences of a cold-water bath, but commend me when
in a perspiration to the shade baths of Tior, beneath the
coco-nut trees, and amidst the cool delightful atmosphere which surrounds them.

How shall I describe the scenery that met my eye, as
I looked out from this verdant recess! The narrow valley, with its steep and close-adjoining sides draperied
with vines, and arched overhead with a fretwork of interlacing boughs, nearly hidden from view by masses of
leafy verdure, seemed from where I stood like an immense arbor disclosing its vista to the eye, whilst as I
advanced it insensibly widened into the loveliest vale
eye ever beheld.

It so happened that the very day I was in Tior the
French admiral, attended by all the boats of his squadron, came down in state from Nukuheva to take formal
possession of the place. He remained in the valley about

two hours, during which time he had a ceremonious interview with the king.

The patriarch-sovereign of Tior was a man very far advanced in years; but though age had bowed his form and rendered him almost decrepit, his gigantic frame retained all its original magnitude and grandeur of appearance. He advanced, slowly and with evident pain, assisting his tottering steps with the heavy warspear he held in his hand, and attended by a group of gray-bearded chiefs, on one of whom he occasionally leaned for support. The admiral came forward with head uncovered and extended hand, while the old king saluted him by a stately flourish of his weapon. The next moment they stood side by side, these two extremes of the social scale—the polished, splendid Frenchman, and the poor tattooed savage. They were both tall and noble-looking men; but in other respects how strikingly contrasted! Du Petit Thouars exhibited upon his person all the paraphernalia of his naval rank. He wore a richly decorated admiral's frock-coat, a laced *chapeau bras,* and upon his breast were a variety of ribbons and orders; while the simple islander, with the exception of a slight cincture about his loins, appeared in all the nakedness of nature.

At what an immeasurable distance, thought I, are there two beings removed from each other. In the one is shown the result of long centuries of progressive civilization and refinement, which have gradually converted the mere creature into the semblance of all that is elevated and grand; while the other, after the lapse of the same period, has not advanced one step in the career of improvement. "Yet, after all," quoth I to myself, "insensible as he is to a thousand wants, and removed from harassing cares, may not the savage be the happier man of the two?" Such were the thoughts that arose in my mind as I gazed upon the novel spectacle before me. In truth it was an impressive one, and little likely to be effaced. I can recall even now with vivid distinctness every feature of the scene. The umbrageous shades where the interview took place—the glorious tropical vegetation around—the picturesque grouping of the mingled throng of soldiery and natives—and even the golden-hued bunch of bananas that I held in my hand at the time, and of which I occasionally partook while making the aforesaid philosophical reflections.

v

Having fully resolved to leave the vessel clandestinely, and having acquired all the knowledge concerning the bay that I could obtain under the circumstances in which I was placed, I now deliberately turned over in my mind every plan of escape that suggested itself, being determined to act with all possible prudence in an attempt where failure would be attended with so many disagreeable consequences. The idea of being taken and brought back ignominiously to the ship was so inexpressibly repulsive to me that I was determined by no hasty and imprudent measures to render such an event probable.

I knew that our worthy captain, who felt such a paternal solicitude for the welfare of his crew, would not willingly consent that one of his best hands should encounter the perils of a sojourn among the natives of a barbarous island; and I was certain that in the event of my disappearance, his fatherly anxiety would prompt him to offer, by way of a reward, yard upon yard of gaily printed calico for my apprehension. He might even have appreciated my services at the value of a musket, in which case I felt perfectly certain that the whole population of the bay would be immediately upon my track, incited by the prospect of so magnificent a bounty.

Having ascertained the fact before alluded to, that the islanders, from motives of precaution, dwelt altogether in the depths of the valleys, and avoided wandering about the more elevated portions of the shore, unless bound on some expedition of war or plunder, I concluded that if I could effect unperceived a passage to the mountains, I might easily remain among them, supporting myself by such fruits as came in my way until the sailing of the ship, an event of which I could not fail to be immediately apprised, as from my lofty position I should command a view of the entire harbor.

The idea pleased me greatly. It seemed to combine a great deal of practicability with no inconsiderable enjoyment in a quiet way; for how delightful it would be to look down upon the detested old vessel from the height of some thousand feet, and contrast the verdant scenery about me with the recollection of her narrow decks and gloomy forecastle! Why, it was really refreshing even to think of it; and so I straightway fell to picturing myself seated beneath a coco-nut tree on the brow of the mountain, with a cluster of plantains within easy reach, criticizing her nautical evolutions as she was working her way out of the harbor.

To be sure there was one rather unpleasant drawback to these agreeable anticipations—the possibility of falling in with a foraging party of these same bloody-minded Typees, whose appetites, edged perhaps by the air of so elevated a region, might prompt them to devour one. This, I must confess, was a most disagreeable view of the matter.

Just to think of a party of these unnatural gourmands taking it into their heads to make a convivial meal of a poor devil, who would have no means of escape or defense; however, there was no help for it. I was willing to encounter some risks in order to accomplish my object, and counted much upon my ability to elude these prowling cannibals amongst the many coverts which the mountains afforded. Besides, the chances were ten to one in my favor that they would none of them quit their own fastnesses.

I had determined not to communicate my design of withdrawing from the vessel to any of my shipmates, and least of all to solicit any one to accompany me in my flight. But it so happened one night that being upon deck, revolving over in my mind various plans of escape, I perceived one of the ship's company leaning over the bulwarks, apparently plunged in a profound reverie. He was a young fellow about my own age, for whom I had all along entertained a great regard, and Toby, such was the name by which he went among us, for his real name he would never tell us, was every way worthy of it. He was active, ready, and obliging, of dauntless courage, and singularly open and fearless in the expression of his feelings. I had on more than one occasion got him out of scrapes into which this had led him; and I know not whether it was from this cause, or a certain congeniality of sentiment between us, that he had always shown a partiality for my society. We had battled out many a long watch together, beguiling the weary hours with chat, song, and story, mingled with a good many imprecations upon the hard destiny it seemed our common fortune to encounter.

Toby, like myself, had evidently moved in a different sphere of life, and his conversation at times betrayed this, although he was anxious to conceal it. He was one of that class of rovers you sometimes meet at sea, who never reveal their origin, never allude to home, and go rambling over the world as if pursued by some mysterious fate they cannot possibly elude.

There was much even in the appearance of Toby calculated to draw me towards him, for while the greater part of the crew were as coarse in person as in mind, Toby was endowed with a remarkably prepossessing exterior. Arrayed in his blue frock and duck trousers, he was as smart a looking sailor as ever stepped upon a deck; he was singularly small and slightly made, with great flexibility of limb. His naturally dark complexion had been deepened by exposure to the tropical sun, and a mass of jetty locks clustered about his temples and threw a darker shade into his large black eyes. He was a strange, wayward being, moody, fitful, and melancholy —at times almost morose. He had a quick and fiery temper too, which, when thoroughly roused, transported him into a state bordering on delirium.

It is strange the power that a mind of deep passion has over feebler natures. I have seen a brawny fellow, with no lack of ordinary courage, fairly quail before this slender stripling, when in one of his furious fits. But these paroxysms seldom occurred, and in them my big-hearted shipmate vented the bile which more calm-tempered individuals get rid of by a continual pettishness at trivial annoyances.

No one ever saw Toby laugh; I mean in the hearty abandonment of broad-mouthed mirth. He did smile sometimes, it is true; and there was a good deal of dry sarcastic humor about him, which told the more from the imperturbable gravity of his tone and manner.

Latterly I had observed that Toby's melancholy had greatly increased, and I had frequently seen him since our arrival at the island gazing wistfully upon the shore, when the remainder of the crew would be rioting below. I was aware that he entertained a cordial detestation of the ship, and believed that, should a fair chance of escape present itself, he would embrace it willingly. But the attempt was so perilous in the place where we then lay, that I supposed myself the only individual on board the ship who was sufficiently reckless to think of it. In this, however, I was mistaken.

When I perceived Toby leaning, as I have mentioned, against the bulwarks and buried in thought, it struck me at once that the subject of his meditations might be the same as my own. And if it be so, thought I, is he not the very one of all my shipmates whom I would choose for the partner of my adventure? and why should I not have some comrade with me to divide its dangers and alleviate its hardships? Perhaps I might be obliged to lie concealed among the mountains for weeks. In such an event what a solace would a companion be!

These thoughts passed rapidly through my mind, and I wondered why I had not before considered the matter in this light. But it was not too late. A tap upon the shoulder served to rouse Toby from his reverie; I found him ripe for the enterprise, and a very few words sufficed for a mutual understanding between us. In an hour's time we had arranged all the preliminaries, and decided upon our plan of action. We then ratified our engagement with an affectionate wedding of palms, and to elude suspicion repaired each to his hammock, to spend the last night on board the *Dolly*.

The next day the starboard watch, to which we both belonged, was to be sent ashore on liberty; and, availing ourselves of this opportunity, we determined, as soon after landing as possible, to separate ourselves from the rest of the men without exciting their suspicions, and strike back at once for the mountains. Seen from the ship, their summits appeared inaccessible, but here and there sloping spurs extended from them almost

into the sea, buttressing the lofty elevations with which
they were connected, and forming those radiating valleys I have before described. One of these ridges, which
appeared more practicable than the rest, we determined
to climb, convinced that it would conduct us to the
heights beyond. Accordingly, we carefully observed its
bearings and locality from the ship, so that when ashore
we should run no chance of missing it.

In all this the leading object we had in view was to
seclude ourselves from sight until the departure of the
vessel; then to take our chance as to the reception the
Nukuheva natives might give us; and, after remaining
upon the island as long as we found our stay agreeable,
to leave it the first favorable opportunity that offered.

VI

Early the next morning the starboard watch were
mustered upon the quarter-deck, and our worthy captain, standing in the cabin gangway, harangued us as
follows:—

"Now, men, as we are just off a six months' cruise,
and have got through most all our work in port here,
I suppose you want to go ashore. Well, I mean to give
your watch liberty to-day, so you may get ready as
soon as you please, and go; but understand this, I am
going to give you liberty because I suppose you would
growl like so many old quarter gunners if I didn't; at
the same time, if you'll take my advice, every mother's
son of you will stay aboard, and keep out of the way of
the bloody cannibals altogether. Ten to one, men, if
you go ashore, you will get into some infernal row, and
that will be the end of you; for if those tattooed
scoundrels get you a little ways back into their valleys,
they'll nab you—that you may be certain of. Plenty

of white men have gone ashore here and never been seen any more. There was the old *Dido,* she put in here about two years ago, and sent one watch off on liberty; they never were heard of again for a week— the natives swore they didn't know where they were— and only three of them ever got back to the ship again, and one with his face damaged for life, for the cursed heathens tattooed a broad patch clean across his figurehead. But it will be no use talking to you, for go you will, that I see plainly; so all I have to say is, that you need not blame me if the islanders make a meal of you. You may stand some chance of escaping them though, if you keep close about the French encampment, and are back to the ship again before sunset. Keep that much in your mind, if you forget all the rest I've been saying to you. There, go forward; bear a hand and rig yourselves, and stand by for a call. At two bells the boat will be manned to take you off, and the Lord have mercy on you!"

Various were the emotions depicted upon the countenances of the starboard watch whilst listening to this address; but on its conclusion there was a general move towards the forecastle, and we soon were all busily engaged in getting ready for the holiday so auspiciously announced by the skipper. During these preparations his harangue was commented upon in no very measured terms; and one of the party, after denouncing him as a lying old son of a sea-cook who begrudged a fellow a few hours' liberty, exclaimed with an oath, "But you don't bounce me out of my liberty, old chap, for all your yarns; for I would go ashore if every pebble on the beach was a live coal, and every stick a gridiron, and the cannibals stood ready to broil me on landing."

The spirit of this sentiment was responded to by all

hands, and we resolved that in spite of the captain's croakings we would make a glorious day of it.

But Toby and I had our own game to play, and we availed ourselves of the confusion which always reigns among a ship's company preparatory to going ashore, to confer together and complete our arrangements. As our object was to effect as rapid a flight as possible to the mountains, we determined not to encumber ourselves with any superfluous apparel; and, accordingly, while the rest were rigging themselves out with some idea of making a display, we were content to put on new stout duck trousers, serviceable pumps, and heavy Havre-frocks which, with a Payta hat, completed our equipment.

When our shipmates wondered at this, Toby exclaimed in his odd grave way that the rest might do as they liked, but that he for one preserved his go-ashore traps for the Spanish Main, where the tie of a sailor's neckerchief might make some difference; but as for a parcel of unbreeched heathen, he wouldn't go to the bottom of his chest for any of them, and was half disposed to appear among them in buff himself. The men laughed at what they thought was one of his strange conceits, and so we escaped suspicion.

It may appear singular that we should have been thus on our guard with our own shipmates; but there were some among us who, had they possessed the least inkling of our project, would, for a paltry hope of reward, have immediately communicated it to the captain.

As soon as two bells were struck, the word was passed for the liberty-men to get into the boat. I lingered behind in the forecastle a moment to take a parting glance at its familiar features, and just as I was about to ascend to the deck my eye happened to light on the bread-barge and beef-kid, which contained the remnants of our hasty meal. Although I had never before thought of providing anything in the way of food for our expedition, as I fully relied upon the fruits of the island to sustain us wherever we might wander, yet I could not resist the inclination I felt to provide luncheon from the relics before me. Accordingly I took a double handful of these small, broken, flinty bits of biscuit which generally go by the name of "midshipmen's nuts," and thrust them into the bosom of my frock; in which same ample receptacle I had previously stowed away several pounds of tobacco and a few yards of cotton cloth—articles with which I intended to purchase the good-will of the natives as soon as we should appear among them after the departure of our vessel.

This last addition to my stock caused a considerable protuberance in front, which I abated in a measure by shaking the bits of bread around my waist, and distributing the plugs of tobacco among the folds of the garment.

Hardly had I completed these arrangements when my name was sung out by a dozen voices, and I sprung upon the deck, where I found all the party in the boat, and impatient to shove off. I dropped over the side and seated myself with the rest of the watch in the stern sheets, while the poor larboarders shipped their oars, and commenced pulling us ashore.

This happened to be the rainy season at the islands, and the heavens had nearly the whole morning betokened one of those heavy showers which during this period so frequently occur. The large drops fell bubbling into the water shortly after our leaving the ship, and by the time we had effected a landing it poured down in torrents. We fled for shelter under cover of an immense canoe-house which stood hard by the beach, and waited for the first fury of the storm to pass.

It continued, however, without cessation; and the monotonous beating of the rain overhead began to exert a drowsy influence upon the men, who, throwing themselves here and there upon the large war-canoes, after chatting awhile, all fell asleep.

This was the opportunity we desired, and Toby and I availed ourselves of it at once by stealing out of the canoe-house and plunging into the depths of an extensive grove that was in its rear. After ten minutes' rapid progress we gained an open space from which we could just descry the ridge we intended to mount looming dimly through the mists of the tropical shower, and distant from us, as we estimated, something more than a mile. Our direct course towards it lay through a rather populous part of the bay; but desirous as we were of evading the natives, and securing an unmolested retreat to the mountains, we determined, by taking a circuit through some extensive thickets, to avoid their vicinity altogether.

The heavy rain that still continued to fall without intermission favored our enterprise, as it drove the islanders into their houses, and prevented any casual meeting with them. Our heavy frocks soon became completely saturated with water, and by their weight, and that of the articles we had concealed beneath them, not a little impeded our progress. But it was no time to pause when at any moment we might be surprised by a body of the savages, and forced at the very outset to relinquish our undertaking.

Since leaving the canoe-house we had scarcely exchanged a single syllable with one another; but when we entered a second narrow opening in the wood, and again caught sight of the ridge before us, I took Toby by the arm and, pointing along its sloping outline to the lofty heights at its extremity, said in a low tone, "Now, Toby, not a word, nor a glance backward, till we stand on the summit of yonder mountain—so no more lingering, but let us shove ahead while we can, and in a few hours' time we may laugh aloud. You are the lightest and the nimblest, so lead on, and I will follow."

"All right, brother," said Toby, "quick's our play; only let's keep close together, that's all;" and so saying, with a bound like a young roe, he cleared a brook which ran across our path, and rushed forward with a quick step.

When we arrived within a short distance of the ridge, we were stopped by a mass of tall yellow reeds, growing together as thickly as they could stand, and as tough and stubborn as so many rods of steel; and we perceived, to our chagrin, that they extended midway up the elevation we purposed to ascend.

For a moment we gazed about us in quest of a more practicable route; it was, however, at once apparent that there was no resource but to pierce this thicket of canes at all hazards. We now reversed our order of march, I, being the heaviest, taking the lead, with a view of breaking a path through the obstruction, while Toby fell into the rear.

Two or three times I endeavored to insinuate myself between the canes and by dint of coaxing and bending them to make some progress; but a bull-frog might as well have tried to work a passage through the teeth of a comb, and I gave up the attempt in despair.

Half wild with meeting an obstacle we had so little anticipated, I threw myself desperately against it, crushing to the ground the canes with which I came in contact; and, rising to my feet again, repeated the action with like effect. Twenty minutes of this violent exercise almost exhausted me, but it carried us some way into the thicket; when Toby, who had been reaping the benefit of my labors by following close at my heels, proposed to become pioneer in turn, and accordingly passed ahead with a view of affording me a respite from my exertions. As however with his slight frame he made but bad work of it, I was soon obliged to resume my old place again.

On we toiled, the perspiration starting from our bodies in floods, our limbs torn and lacerated with the splintered fragments of the broken canes, until we had proceeded perhaps as far as the middle of the brake, when suddenly it ceased raining, and the atmosphere around us became close and sultry beyond expression. The elasticity of the reeds, quickly recovering from the temporary pressure of our bodies, caused them to spring back to their original position; so that they closed in upon us as we advanced, and prevented the circulation of the little air which might otherwise have reached us. Besides this, their great height completely shut us out from the view of surrounding objects, and we were not certain but that we might have been going all the time in a wrong direction.

Fatigued with my long-continued efforts, and panting for breath, I felt myself completely incapacitated for any further exertion. I rolled up the sleeve of my frock, and squeezed the moisture it contained into my parched mouth. But the few drops I managed to obtain gave me little relief, and I sank down for a moment with a sort of dogged apathy, from which I was aroused by Toby, who had devised a plan to free us from the net in which we had become entangled.

He was laying about him lustily with his sheath-knife, lopping the canes right and left, like a reaper, and soon made quite a clearing around us. This sight reanimated me, and seizing my own knife, I hacked and hewed away without mercy. But alas! the farther we advanced, the thicker and taller, and apparently the more interminable, the reeds became.

I began to think we were fairly snared, and had almost made up my mind that without a pair of wings we should never be able to escape from the toils, when all at once I discerned a peep of daylight through the canes on my right, and, communicating the joyful tidings to Toby, we both fell to with fresh spirit, and speedily opening a passage towards it we found ourselves clear of perplexities, and in the near vicinity of the ridge.

After resting for a few moments we began the ascent, and after a little vigorous climbing found ourselves close to its summit. Instead however of walking along its ridge, where we should have been in full view of the natives in the vales beneath, and at a point where they could easily intercept us were they so inclined, we cautiously advanced on one side, crawling on our hands and knees, and screened from observation by the grass through which we glided, much in the fashion of a couple of serpents. After an hour employed in this unpleasant kind of locomotion, we started to our feet again and pursued our way boldly along the crest of the ridge.

This salient spur of the lofty elevations that encompassed the bay rose with a sharp angle from the valleys at its base, and presented, with the exception of a few steep acclivities, the appearance of a vast inclined plane, sweeping down towards the sea from the heights in the distance. We had ascended it near the place of its termination and at its lowest point, and now saw our route to the mountains distinctly defined along its narrow crest, which was covered with a soft carpet of verdure, and was in many parts only a few feet wide.

Elated with the success which had so far attended our enterprise, and invigorated by the refreshing atmosphere we now inhaled, Toby and I in high spirits were making our way rapidly along the ridge when suddenly from the valleys below which lay on either side of us we heard the distant shouts of the natives, who had just descried us, and to whom our figures, brought in bold relief against the sky, were plainly revealed.

Glancing our eyes into these valleys, we perceived their savage inhabitants hurrying to and fro, seemingly under the influence of some sudden alarm, and appearing to the eye scarcely bigger than so many pygmies; while their white-thatched dwellings, dwarfed by the distance, looked like baby-houses. As we looked down upon the islanders from our lofty elevation, we experienced a sense of security; feeling confident that, should they undertake a pursuit, it would, from the start we now had, prove entirely fruitless, unless they followed us into the mountains, where we knew they cared not to venture.

However, we thought it as well to make the most of our time; and accordingly, where the ground would admit of it, we ran swiftly along the summit of the ridge, until we were brought to a stand by a steep cliff, which at first seemed to interpose an effectual barrier to our further advance. By dint of much hard scrambling, however, and at some risk to our necks, we at last surmounted it, and continued our flight with unabated celerity.

We had left the beach early in the morning, and after an uninterrupted, though at times difficult and dangerous ascent, during which we had never once turned our

faces to the sea, we found ourselves, about three hours
before sunset, standing on the top of what seemed to
be the highest land on the island, an immense overhanging cliff composed of basaltic rocks, hung round
with parasitical plants. We must have been more than
three thousand feet above the level of the sea, and the
scenery viewed from this height was magnificent.

The lonely bay of Nukuheva, dotted here and there
with the black hulls of the vessels composing the French
squadron, lay reposing at the base of a circular range
of elevations, whose verdant sides, perforated with
deep glens or diversified with smiling valleys, formed
altogether the loveliest view I ever beheld, and were
I to live a hundred years, I should never forget the feeling of admiration which I then experienced.

VII

My curiosity had been not a little raised with regard
to the description of country we should meet on the
other side of the mountains; and I supposed, with Toby,
that immediately on gaining the heights we should be
enabled to view the large bays of Happar and Typee
reposing at our feet on one side, in the same way that
Nukuheva lay spread out below on the other. But here
we were disappointed. Instead of finding the mountain
we had ascended sweeping down in the opposite direction into broad and capacious valleys, the land appeared
to retain its general elevation, only broken into a series
of ridges and inter-vales, which as far as the eye could
reach stretched away from us, with their precipitous
sides covered with the brightest verdure, and waving
here and there with the foliage of clumps of woodland;
among which, however, we perceived none of those

trees upon whose fruit we had relied with such certainty.

This was a most unlooked-for discovery, and one that promised to defeat our plans altogether, for we could not think of descending the mountain on the Nukuheva side in quest of food. Should we for this purpose be induced to retrace our steps, we should run no small chance of encountering the natives, who in that case, if they did nothing worse to us, would be certain to convey us back to the ship for the sake of the reward in calico and trinkets, which we had no doubt our skipper would hold out to them as an inducement to our capture.

What was to be done? The *Dolly* would not sail perhaps for ten days, and how were we to sustain life during this period? I bitterly repented our improvidence in not providing ourselves, as we easily might have done, with a supply of biscuit. With a rueful visage I now bethought me of the scanty handful of bread I had stuffed into the bosom of my frock, and felt somewhat desirous to ascertain what part of it had weathered the rather rough usage it had experienced in ascending the mountain. I accordingly proposed to Toby that we should enter into a joint examination of the various articles we had brought from the ship. With this intent we seated ourselves upon the grass; and a little curious to see with what kind of judgment my companion had filled his frock—which I remarked seemed about as well lined as my own—I requested him to commence operations by spreading out its contents.

Thrusting his hand, then, into the bosom of this capacious receptacle, he first brought to light about a pound of tobacco, whose component parts still adhered together, the whole outside being covered with soft particles of sea-bread. Wet and dripping, it had the appearance of having been just recovered from the bottom of the sea. But I paid slight attention to a substance of so little value to us in our present situation, as soon I perceived the indications it gave of Toby's foresight in laying in a supply of food for the expedition.

I eagerly inquired what quantity he had brought with him, when, rummaging once more beneath his garment, he produced a small handful of something so soft, pulpy, and discolored, that for a few moments he was as much puzzled as myself to tell by what possible instrumentality such a villainous compound had become engendered in his bosom. I can only describe it as a hash of soaked bread and bits of tobacco, brought to a doughy consistency by the united agency of perspiration and rain. But repulsive as it might otherwise have been, I now regarded it as an invaluable treasure, and proceeded with great care to transfer this pastelike mass to a large leaf which I had plucked from a bush beside me. Toby informed me that in the morning he had placed two whole biscuits in his bosom, with a view of munching them, should he feel so inclined, during our flight. These were now reduced to the equivocal substance which I had just placed on the leaf.

Another dive into the frock brought to view some four or five yards of calico print, whose tasteful pattern was rather disfigured by the yellow stains of the tobacco with which it had been brought in contact. In drawing this calico slowly from his bosom inch by inch, Toby reminded me of a juggler performing the feat of the endless ribbon. The next cast was a small one, being a sailor's little "ditty-bag," containing needles, thread, and other sewing utensils; then came a razor-case followed by two or three separate plugs of negrohead, which were fished up from the bottom of the now empty receptacle. These various matters being inspected, I produced the few things that I had myself brought.

As might have been anticipated from the state of my companion's edible supplies, I found my own in a deplorable condition, and diminished to a quantity that would not have formed half a dozen mouthfuls for a hungry man who was partial enough to tobacco not to mind swallowing it. A few morsels of bread, with a fathom or two of white cotton cloth, and several pounds of choice pigtail, composed the extent of my possessions.

Our joint stock of miscellaneous articles was now made up into a compact bundle, which it was agreed we should carry alternately. But the sorry remains of the biscuit were not to be disposed of so summarily: the precarious circumstances in which we were placed made us regard them as something on which very probably depended the fate of our adventure. After a brief discussion in which we both of us expressed our resolution of not descending into the bay until the ship's departure, I suggested to my companion that little of it as there was, we should divide the bread into six equal portions, each of which should be a day's allowance for both of us. This proposition he assented to; so I took the silk kerchief from my neck, and, cutting it with my knife into half a dozen equal pieces, proceeded to make an exact division.

At first, Toby, with a degree of fastidiousness that seemed to me ill-timed, was for picking out the minute particles of tobacco with which the spongy mass was mixed; but against this proceeding I protested, as by such an operation we must have greatly diminished its quantity.

When the division was accomplished, we found that a day's allowance for the two was not a great deal more than what a table-spoon might hold. Each separate portion we immediately rolled up in the bit of silk prepared for it, and joining them altogether into a small package, I committed them, with solemn injunctions of fidelity, to the custody of Toby. For the remainder of that day we resolved to fast, as we had been fortified by a breakfast in the morning; and now starting again to our feet, we looked about us for a shelter during the night, which, from the appearance of the heavens, promised to be a dark and tempestuous one.

There was no place near us which would in any way answer our purpose; so turning our backs upon Nukuheva, we commenced exploring the unknown regions which lay upon the other side of the mountain.

In this direction, as far as our vision extended, not a sign of life, nor anything that denoted even the transient residence of man, could be seen. The whole landscape seemed one unbroken solitude, the interior of the island having apparently been untenanted since the morning of the creation; and as we advanced through this wilderness, our voices sounded strangely in our ears, as though human accents had never before disturbed the fearful silence of the place, interrupted only by the low murmurings of distant waterfalls.

Our disappointment, however, in not finding the various fruits with which we had intended to regale ourselves during our stay in these wilds, was a good deal lessened by the consideration that from this very circumstance we should be much less exposed to a casual meeting with the savage tribes about us, who we knew always dwelt beneath the shadows of those trees which supplied them with food.

We wandered along, casting eager glances into every bush we passed, until just as we had succeeded in mounting one of the many ridges that intersected the ground, I saw in the grass before me something like an indistinctly traced footpath, which appeared to lead along the top of the ridge, and to descend with it into a deep ravine about half a mile in advance of us.

Robinson Crusoe could not have been more startled at the footprint in the sand than we were at this unwelcome discovery. My first impulse was to make as rapid a retreat as possible, and bend our steps in some other direction; but our curiosity to see whither this path might lead, prompted us to pursue it. So on we went, the track becoming more and more visible the farther we proceeded, until it conducted us to the verge of the ravine, where it abruptly terminated.

"And so," said Toby, peering down into the chasm, "every one that travels this path takes a jump here, eh?"

"Not so," said I, "for I think they might manage to descend without it; what say you—shall we attempt the feat?"

"And what, in the name of caves and coal-holes, do you expect to find at the bottom of that gulf but a broken neck—why it looks blacker than our ship's hold, and the roar of those waterfalls down there would batter one's brains to pieces."

"Oh, no, Toby," I exclaimed, laughing; "but there's something to be seen here, that's plain, or there would have been no path, and I am resolved to find out what it is."

"I will tell you what, my pleasant fellow," rejoined Toby quickly, "if you are going to pry into everything you meet with here that excites your curiosity, you will marvelously soon get knocked on the head; to a dead certainty you will come bang upon a party of these savages in the midst of your discovery-makings, and I doubt whether such an event would particularly delight you. Just take my advice for once, and let us 'bout ship and steer in some other direction: besides, it's getting late, and we ought to be mooring ourselves for the night."

"That is just the thing I have been driving at," replied I; "and I am thinking that this ravine will exactly answer our purpose, for it is roomy, secluded, well watered, and may shelter us from the weather."

"Aye, and from sleep too, and by the same token will give us sore throats and rheumatisms into the bargain," cried Toby with evident dislike at the idea.

"Oh, very well then, my lad," said I, "since you will not accompany me, here I go alone. You will see me in the morning;" and advancing to the edge of the cliff upon which we had been standing, I proceeded to lower myself down by the tangled roots which clustered about all the crevices of the rock. As I had anticipated, Toby, in spite of his previous remonstrances, followed my example, and dropping himself with the activity of a squirrel from point to point, he quickly outstripped me, and effected a landing at the bottom before I had accomplished two-thirds of the descent.

The sight that now greeted us was one that will ever be vividly impressed upon my mind. Five foaming streams, rushing through as many gorges, and swelled and turbid by the recent rains, united together in one mad plunge of nearly eighty feet, and fell with wild uproar into a deep black pool scooped out of the gloomy-looking rocks that lay piled around, and thence in one collected body dashed down a narrow sloping channel which seemed to penetrate into the very bowels of the earth. Overhead, vast roots of trees hung down from the sides of the ravine, dripping with moisture, and trembling with the concussions produced by the fall. It was now sunset, and the feeble uncertain light that found its way into these caverns and woody depths heightened their strange appearance, and reminded us that in a short time we should find ourselves in utter darkness.

As soon as I had satisfied my curiosity by gazing at this scene, I fell to wondering how it was that what we had taken for a path should have conducted us to so singular a place, and began to suspect that after all I might have been deceived in supposing it to have been a track formed by the islanders. This was rather an agreeable reflection than otherwise, for it diminished our dread of accidentally meeting with any of them, and I came to the conclusion that perhaps we could not have selected a more secure hiding-place than this very spot we had so accidentally hit upon. Toby agreed with me in this view of the matter, and we immediately began gathering together the limbs of trees which lay scattered about, with the view of constructing a temporary hut for the night. This we were obliged to build close to the foot of the cataract, for the current of water extended very nearly to the sides of the gorge. The few moments of light that remained we employed in covering our hut with a species of broad-bladed grass that grew in every fissure of the ravine. Our hut, if it deserved to be called one, consisted of six or eight of the straightest branches we could find laid obliquely against the steep wall of rock, with their lower ends within a foot of the stream. Into the space thus covered over we managed to crawl, and dispose our wearied bodies as best we could.

Shall I ever forget that horrid night? As for poor Toby, I could scarcely get a word out of him. It would have been some consolation to have heard his voice, but he lay shivering the livelong night like a man afflicted with the palsy, with his knees drawn up to his head, while his back was supported against the dripping side of the rock. During this wretched night there seemed nothing wanting to complete the perfect misery of our condition. The rain descended in such torrents that our poor shelter proved a mere mockery. In vain did I try to elude the incessant streams that poured upon me; by protecting one part I only exposed another, and the water was continually finding some new opening through which to drench us.

I have had many a ducking in the course of my life, and in general cared little about it; but the accumulated horrors of that night, the deathlike coldness of the place, the appalling darkness and the dismal sense of our forlorn condition, almost unmanned me.

It will not be doubted that the next morning we were early risers, and as soon as I could catch the faintest glimpse of anything like daylight I shook my companion by the arm, and told him it was sunrise. Poor Toby lifted up his head, and after a moment's pause said in a husky voice. "Then, shipmate, my toplights have gone out, for it appears darker now with my eyes open than it did when they were shut."

"Nonsense!" exclaimed I, "you are not awake yet."

"Awake!" roared Toby in a rage, "awake! You mean to insinuate I've been asleep, do you? It is an insult to a man to suppose he could sleep in such an infernal place as this."

By the time I had apologized to my friend for having misconstrued his silence, it had become somewhat more light, and we crawled out of our lair. The rain had ceased, but everything around us was dripping with moisture. We stripped off our saturated garments, and wrung them as dry as we could. We contrived to make the blood circulate in our benumbed limbs by rubbing them vigorously with our hands; and after performing our ablutions in the stream, and putting on our still wet clothes, we began to think it advisable to break our long fast, it being now twenty-four hours since we had tasted food.

Accordingly our day's ration was brought out, and seating ourselves on a detached fragment of rock, we proceeded to discuss it. First we divided it into two equal portions, and, carefully rolling one of them up for our evening's repast, divided the remainder again as equally as possible, and then drew lots for the first choice. I could have placed the morsel that fell to my share upon the tip of my finger; but notwithstanding this I took care that it should be full ten minutes before I had swallowed the last crumb. What a true saying it is that "appetite furnishes the best sauce." There was a flavor and a relish to this small particle of food that under other circumstances it would have been impossible for the most delicate viands to have imparted. A copious draught of the pure water which flowed at our feet served to complete the meal, and after it we rose sensibly refreshed, and prepared for whatever might befall us.

We now carefully examined the chasm in which we had passed the night. We crossed the stream, and gaining the farther side of the pool I have mentioned, discovered proofs that the spot must have been visited by some one but a short time previous to our arrival. Further observation convinced us that it had been regularly frequented, and, as we afterwards conjectured from particular indications, for the purpose of obtaining a certain root, from which the natives obtain a kind of ointment.

These discoveries immediately determined us to abandon a place which had presented no inducement for us to remain, except the promise of security; and as we looked about us for the means of ascending again into the upper regions, we at last found a practicable part of the rock, and half an hour's toil carried us to the summit of the same cliff from which the preceding evening we had descended.

I now proposed to Toby that instead of rambling about the island, exposing ourselves to discovery at every turn, we should select some place as our fixed abode for as long a period as our food should hold out, build ourselves a comfortable hut, and be as prudent and circumspect as possible. To all this my companion assented, and we at once set about carrying the plan into execution.

With this view, after exploring without success a little glen near us, we crossed several of the ridges of which I have before spoken; and about noon found ourselves ascending a long and gradually rising slope, but still without having discovered any place adapted to our purpose. Low and heavy clouds betokened an approaching storm, and we hurried on to gain a covert in a clump of thick bushes which appeared to terminate the long ascent. We threw ourselves under the lee of these bushes, and pulling up the long grass that grew around, covered ourselves completely with it, and awaited the shower.

But it did not come as soon as we had expected, and before many minutes my companion was fast asleep, and I was rapidly falling into the same state of happy forgetfulness. Just at this juncture, however, down came the rain with a violence that put all thoughts of slumber to flight. Although in some measure sheltered, our clothes soon became as wet as ever: this, after all the trouble we had taken to dry them, was provoking enough: but there was no help for it; and I recommend all adventurous youths who abandon vessels in romantic islands during the rainy season to provide themselves with umbrellas.

After an hour or so the shower passed away. My companion slept through it all, or at least appeared so to do; and now that it was over I had not the heart to awaken him. As I lay on my back completely shrouded with verdure, the leafy branches drooping over me, and my limbs buried in grass, I could not avoid comparing our situation with that of the interesting babes in the wood. Poor little sufferers!—no wonder their constitutions broke down under the hardships to which they were exposed.

During the hour or two spent under the shelter of these bushes, I began to feel symptoms which I at once attributed to the exposure of the preceding night. Cold shiverings and a burning fever succeeded one another at intervals, while one of my legs was swelled to such a degree, and pained me so acutely, that I half suspected I had been bitten by some venomous reptile, the congenial inhabitant of the chasm from which we had lately emerged. I may here remark by the way—what I subsequently learned—that all the islands of Polynesia enjoy the reputation, in common with the Hibernian isle, of being free from the presence of any vipers; though whether Saint Patrick ever visited them is a question I shall not attempt to decide.

As the feverish sensation increased upon me, I tossed about, still unwilling to disturb my slumbering companion, from whose side I removed two or three yards. I chanced to push aside a branch, and by so doing suddenly disclosed to my view a scene which even now I can recall with all the vividness of the first impression. Had a glimpse of the gardens of Paradise been revealed to me I could scarcely have been more ravished with the sight.

From the spot where I lay transfixed with surprise and delight, I looked straight down into the bosom of a valley, which swept away in long wavy undulations to the blue waters in the distance. Midway towards the sea, and peering here and there amidst the foliage, might be seen the palmetto-thatched houses of its inhabitants glistening in the sun that had bleached them to a dazzling whiteness. The vale was more than three leagues in length, and about a mile across at its greatest width.

On either side it appeared hemmed in by steep and green acclivities, which, uniting near the spot where I lay, formed an abrupt and semicircular termination of grassy cliffs and precipices hundreds of feet in height, over which flowed numberless small cascades. But the crowning beauty of the prospect was its universal verdure; and in this indeed consists, I believe, the peculiar charm of every Polynesian landscape. Everywhere below me, from the base of the precipice upon whose very verge I had been unconsciously reposing, the surface of the vale presented a mass of foliage, spread with such rich profusion that it was impossible to determine of what description of trees it consisted.

But perhaps there was nothing about the scenery I beheld more impressive than those silent cascades, whose slender threads of water, after leaping down the steep cliffs, were lost amidst the rich herbage of the valley.

Over all the landscape there reigned the most hushed repose, which I almost feared to break, lest, like the enchanted gardens in the fairy tale, a single syllable might dissolve the spell. For a long time, forgetful alike of my own situation and the vicinity of my still slumbering companion, I remained gazing around me, hardly able to comprehend by what means I had thus suddenly been made a spectator of such a scene.

VIII

Recovering from my astonishment at the beautiful scene before me, I quickly awakened Toby, and informed him of the discovery I had made. Together we now repaired to the border of the precipice, and my companion's admiration was equal to my own. A little reflection, however, abated our surprise at coming so unexpectedly upon this valley, since the large vales of Happar and Typee, lying upon this side of Nukuheva, and extending a considerable distance from the sea towards the interior, must necessarily terminate somewhere about this point.

The question now was as to which of those two places we were looking down upon. Toby insisted that it was the abode of the Happars, and I that it was tenanted by their enemies the ferocious Typees. To be sure I was not entirely convinced by my own arguments, but Toby's proposition to descend at once into the valley, and partake of the hospitality of its inmates, seemed to me to be risking so much upon the strength of a mere supposition, that I resolved to oppose it until we had more evidence to proceed upon.

The point was one of vital importance, as the natives of Happar were not only at peace with Nukuheva, but cultivated with its inhabitants the most friendly relations, and enjoyed beside a reputation for gentleness and humanity which led us to expect from them, if not a cordial reception, at least a shelter during the short period we should remain in their territory.

On the other hand, the very name of Typee struck a panic into my heart which I did not attempt to disguise. The thought of voluntarily throwing ourselves into the hands of these cruel savages, seemed to me an act of mere madness; and almost equally so the idea of venturing into the valley, uncertain by which of these two tribes it was inhabited. That the vale at our feet was tenanted by one of them, was a point that appeared to us past all doubt, since we knew that they resided in this quarter, although our information did not enlighten us further.

My companion, however, incapable of resisting the tempting prospect which the place held out of an abundant supply of food and other means of enjoyment, still clung to his own inconsiderate view of the subject, nor could all my reasoning shake it. When I reminded him that it was impossible for either of us to know anything with certainty, and when I dwelt upon the horrible fate we should encounter were we rashly to descend into the valley, and discover too late the error we had committed, he replied by detailing all the evils of our present condition, and the sufferings we must undergo should we continue to remain where we then were.

Anxious to draw him away from the subject, if possible—for I saw that it would be in vain to attempt changing his mind—I directed his attention to a long bright unwooded tract of land which, sweeping down from the elevations in the interior, descended into the valley before us. I then suggested to him that beyond this ridge might lie a capacious and untenanted valley, abounding with all manner of delicious fruits; for I had heard that there were several such upon the island, and proposed that we should endeavor to reach it, and if we found our expectations realized we should at once take refuge in it and remain there as long as we pleased.

He acquiesced in the suggestion; and we immediately, therefore, began surveying the country lying before us, with a view of determining upon the best route for us to pursue; but it presented little choice, the whole interval being broken into steep ridges, divided by dark ravines, extending in parallel lines at right angles to our direct course. All these we would be obliged to cross before we could hope to arrive at our destination.

A weary journey! But we decided to undertake it, though, for my own part, I felt little prepared to encounter its fatigues, shivering and burning by turns with the ague and fever; for I know not how else to describe the alternate sensations I experienced, and suffering not a little from the lameness which afflicted me. Added to this was the faintness consequent on our meager diet—a calamity in which Toby participated to the same extent as myself.

These circumstances, however, only augmented my anxiety to reach a place which promised us plenty and repose, before I should be reduced to a state which would render me altogether unable to perform the journey. Accordingly we now commenced it by descending the almost perpendicular side of a steep and narrow gorge, bristling with a thick growth of reeds. Here there was but one mode for us to adopt. We seated ourselves upon the ground, and guided our descent by catching at the canes in our path. The velocity with which we thus slid down the side of the ravine soon brought us to a point where we could use our feet, and in a short time we arrived at the edge of the torrent, which rolled impetuously along the bed of the chasm.

After taking a refreshing draught from the water of the stream, we addressed ourselves to a much more difficult undertaking than the last. Every foot of our late descent had to be regained in ascending the opposite side of the gorge—an operation rendered the less agreeable from the consideration that in these perpendicular episodes we did not progress a hundred yards on our journey. But, ungrateful as the task was, we set about it with exemplary patience, and, after a snail-like progress of an hour or more, had scaled perhaps one half of the distance, when the fever which had left me for awhile returned with such violence, and accompanied by so raging a thirst, that it required all the entreaties of Toby to prevent me from losing all the fruits of my late exertion, by precipitating myself madly down the cliffs we had just climbed in quest of the water which flowed so temptingly at their base. At the moment all my hopes and fears appeared to be merged in this one desire, careless of the consequences that might result from its gratification. I am aware of no feeling, either of pleasure or of pain, that so completely deprives one of all power to resist its impulses as this same raging thirst.

Toby earnestly conjured me to continue the ascent, assuring me that a little more exertion would bring us to the summit, and that then in less than five minutes we should find ourselves at the brink of the stream, which must necessarily flow on the other side of the ridge.

"Do not," he exclaimed, "turn back, now that we have proceeded thus far; for I tell you that neither of us will have the courage to repeat the attempt, if once more we find ourselves looking up to where we now are from the bottom of these rocks!"

I was not yet so perfectly beside myself as to be heedless of these representations, and therefore toiled on, ineffectually endeavoring to appease the thirst which consumed me, by thinking that in a short time I should be able to gratify it to my heart's content.

At last we gained the top of the second elevation, the loftiest of those I have described as extending in parallel lines between us and the valley we desired to reach. It commanded a view of the whole intervening distance; and, discouraged as I was by other circumstances, this prospect plunged me into the very depths of despair. Nothing but dark and fearful chasms, separated by sharp-crested and perpendicular ridges as far as the eye could reach. Could we have stepped from summit to summit of these steep but narrow elevations we could easily have accomplished the distance; but we must penetrate to the bottom of every yawning gulf, and scale in succession every one of the eminences before us. Even Toby, although not suffering as I did, was not proof against the disheartening influences of the sight.

But we did not long stand to contemplate it, impatient as I was to reach the waters of the torrent which flowed beneath us. With an insensibility to danger which I cannot call to mind without shuddering, we threw ourselves down the depths of the ravine, startling its savage solitudes with the echoes produced by the falling fragments of rock we every moment dislodged from their places, careless of the insecurity of our footing, and reckless whether the slight roots and twigs we clutched at sustained us for the while, or treacherously yielded to our grasp. For my own part I scarcely knew whether I was helplessly falling from the heights above, or whether the fearful rapidity with which I descended was an act of my own volition.

In a few minutes we reached the foot of the gorge, and, kneeling upon a small ledge of dripping rocks, I bent over to the stream. What a delicious sensation was I now to experience! I paused for a second to concentrate all my capabilities of enjoyment, and then immerged my lips in the clear element before me. Had the apples of Sodom turned to ashes in my mouth, I could not have felt a more startling revulsion. A single drop of the cold fluid seemed to freeze every drop of blood in my body; the fever that had been burning in my veins gave place on the instant to death-like chills, which shook me one after another like so many shocks of electricity, while the perspiration produced by my late violent exertions congealed in icy beads upon my forehead. My thirst was gone, and I fairly loathed the water. Starting to my feet, the sight of those dank rocks, oozing forth moisture at every crevice, and the dark stream shooting along its dismal channel, sent fresh chills through my shivering frame, and I felt as uncontrollable a desire to climb up towards the genial sunlight as I before had to descend the ravine.

After two hours' perilous exertions we stood upon the summit of another ridge, and it was with difficulty I could bring myself to believe that we had ever penetrated the black and yawning chasm which then gaped at our feet. Again we gazed upon the prospect which the height commanded, but it was just as depressing as the one which had before met our eyes. I now felt that in our present situation it was in vain for us to think of ever overcoming the obstacles in our way, and I gave up all thoughts of reaching the vale which lay beyond this series of impediments; while at the same time I could not devise any scheme to extricate ourselves from the difficulties in which we were involved.

The remotest idea of returning to Nukuheva, unless assured of our vessel's departure, never once entered my mind, and indeed it was questionable whether we could have succeeded in reaching it, divided as we were from the bay by a distance we could not compute, and perplexed too in our remembrance of localities by our recent wanderings. Besides, it was unendurable the thought of retracing our steps and rendering all our painful exertions of no avail.

There is scarcely anything when a man is in difficul-

ties that he is more disposed to look upon with abhorrence than a right-about retrograde movement—a
systematic going over of the already trodden ground;
and, especially if he has a love of adventure, such a
course appears indescribably repulsive, so long as there
remains the least hope to be derived from braving un-
tried difficulties.

It was this feeling that prompted us to descend the
opposite side of the elevation we had just scaled, although with what definite object in view it would have
been impossible for either of us to tell.

Without exchanging a syllable upon the subject,
Toby and myself simultaneously renounced the design
which had lured us thus far—perceiving in each other's
countenances that desponding expression which speaks
more eloquently than words.

Together we stood towards the close of this weary
day in the cavity of the third gorge we had entered,
wholly incapacitated for any further exertion, until restored to some degree of strength by food and repose.

We seated ourselves upon the least uncomfortable
spot we could select, and Toby produced from the
bosom of his frock the sacred package. In silence we
partook of the small morsel of refreshment that had
been left from the morning's repast, and, without once
proposing to violate the sanctity of our engagement
with respect to the remainder, we rose to our feet and
proceeded to construct some sort of shelter under which
we might obtain the sleep we so greatly needed.

Fortunately the spot was better adapted to our purpose than the one in which we had passed the las'
wretched night. We cleared away the tall reeds from
a small but almost level bit of ground, and twisted
them into a low basket-like hut, which we covered with
a profusion of long thick leaves, gathered from a tree

near at hand. We disposed them thickly all around, reserving only a slight opening that barely permitted us to crawl under the shelter we had thus obtained.

These deep recesses, though protected from the winds that assail the summits of their lofty sides, are damp and chill to a degree that one would hardly anticipate in such a climate; and being unprovided with anything but our woollen frocks and thin duck trousers to resist the cold of the place, we were the more solicitous to render our habitation for the night as comfortable as we could. Accordingly, in addition to what we had already done, we plucked down all the leaves within our reach and threw them in a heap over our little hut, into which we now crept, raking after us a reserved supply to form our couch.

That night nothing but the pain I suffered prevented me from sleeping most refreshingly. As it was, I caught two or three naps, while Toby slept away at my side as soundly as though he had been sandwiched between two Holland sheets. Luckily it did not rain, and we were preserved from the misery which a heavy shower would have occasioned us.

In the morning I was awakened by the sonorous voice of my companion ringing in my ears and bidding me rise. I crawled out from our heap of leaves and was astonished at the change which a good night's rest had wrought in his appearance. He was as blithe and joyous as a young bird, and was staying the keenness of his morning's appetite by chewing the soft bark of a delicate branch he held in his hand, and he recommended the like to me as an admirable antidote against the gnawings of hunger.

For my own part, though feeling materially better than I had done the preceding evening, I could not look at the limb that had pained me so violently at intervals during the last twenty-four hours without experiencing a sense of alarm that I strove in vain to shake off. Unwilling to disturb the flow of my comrade's spirits, I managed to stifle the complaints to which I might otherwise have given vent, and calling upon him good-humoredly to speed our banquet, I prepared myself for it by washing in the stream. This operation concluded, we swallowed, or rather absorbed, by a peculiar kind of slow sucking process, our respective morsels of nourishment, and then entered into a discussion as to the steps it was necessary for us to pursue.

"What's to be done now?" inquired I, rather dolefully.

"Descend into that same valley we descried yesterday," rejoined Toby, with a rapidity and loudness of utterance that almost led me to suspect he had been slyly devouring the broadside of an ox in some of the adjoining thickets. "What else," he continued, "remains for us to do but that, to be sure? Why, we shall both starve to a certainty if we remain here; and as to your fears of those Typees—depend upon it, it is all nonsense.

"It is impossible that the inhabitants of such a lovely place as we saw can be anything else but good fellows; and if you choose rather to perish with hunger in one of these soppy caverns, I for one prefer to chance a bold descent into the valley, and risk the consequences."

"And who is to pilot us thither," I asked, "even if we should decide upon the measure you propose? Are we to go again up and down those precipices that we crossed yesterday, until we reach the place we started from, and then take a flying leap from the cliffs to the valley?"

" 'Faith, I didn't think of that," said Toby; "sure enough both sides of the valley appeared to be hemmed in by precipices, didn't they?"

"Yes," answered I, "as steep as the sides of a line-of-battle ship, and about a hundred times as high." My companion sank his head upon his breast and remained for a while in deep thought. Suddenly he sprang to his feet, while his eyes lighted up with that gleam of intelligence that marks the presence of some bright idea.

"Yes, yes," he exclaimed; "the streams all run in the same direction, and must necessarily flow into the valley before they reach the sea; all we have to do is just to follow this stream, and sooner or later it will lead us into the vale."

"You are right, Toby," I exclaimed, "you are right; it must conduct us thither, and quickly too; for see with what a steep inclination the water descends."

"It does, indeed," burst forth my companion, over-joyed at my verification of his theory, "it does indeed; why, it is as plain as a pikestaff. Let us proceed at once; come, throw away all those stupid ideas about the Typees, and hurrah for the lovely valley of the Happars!"

"You will have it to be Happar, I see, my dear fellow; pray Heaven you may find not yourself deceived," observed I, with a shake of my head.

"Amen to all that, and much more," shouted Toby, rushing forward; "but Happar it is, for nothing else than Happar can it be. So glorious a valley—such forests of breadfruit-trees—such groves of coco-nut—such wildernesses of guava-bushes! Ah, shipmate! don't linger behind: in the name of all delightful fruits, I am dying to be at them. Come on, come on; shove ahead, there's a lively lad; never mind the rocks; kick them out of the way, as I do; and tomorrow, old fellow, take my word for it, we shall be in clover. Come on;" and so saying, he dashed along the ravine like a madman, forgetting my inability to keep up with him. In a few minutes, however, the exuberance of his spirits abated, and, pausing for a while, he permitted me to overtake him.

IX

The fearless confidence of Toby was contagious, and I began to adopt the Happar side of the question. I could not, however, overcome a certain feeling of trepidation as we made our way along these gloomy solitudes. Our progress, at first comparatively easy, became more and more difficult. The bed of the watercourse was covered with fragments of broken rocks, which had fallen from above, offering so many obstructions to the course of the rapid stream, which vexed and fretted about them—forming at intervals small waterfalls, pouring over into deep basins, or splashing wildly upon heaps of stones.

From the narrowness of the gorge, and the steepness of its sides, there was no mode of advancing but by wading through the water; stumbling every moment over the impediments which lay hidden under its surface, or tripping against the huge roots of trees. But the most annoying hindrance we encountered was from a multitude of crooked boughs, which, shooting out almost horizontally from the sides of the chasm, twisted themselves together in fantastic masses almost to the surface of the stream, affording us no passage except under the low arches which they formed. Under these we were obliged to crawl on our hands and feet, sliding along the oozy surface of the rocks, or slipping into the deep pools, and with scarce light enough to guide us.

Occasionally we would strike our heads against some projecting limb of a tree; and while imprudently engaged in rubbing the injured part, would fall sprawling amongst flinty fragments, cutting and bruising ourselves, whilst the unpitying waters flowed over our prostrate bodies. Belzoni, worming himself through the subterranean passages of the Egyptian catacombs, could not have met with greater impediments than those we here encountered. But we struggled against them manfully, well knowing our only hope lay in advancing.

Towards sunset we halted at a spot where we made preparations for passing the night. Here we constructed a hut, in much the same way as before, and crawling into it, endeavored to forget our sufferings. My companion, I believe, slept pretty soundly; but at daybreak, when we rolled out of our dwelling, I felt nearly disqualified for any further efforts. Toby prescribed as a remedy for my illness the contents of one of our little silk packages, to be taken at once in a single dose. To this species of medical treatment, however, I would by no means accede, much as he insisted upon it; and so we partook of our usual morsel, and silently resumed our journey. It was now the fourth day since we left Nukuheva, and the gnawings of hunger became painfully acute. We were fain to pacify them by chewing the tender bark of roots and twigs, which, if they did not afford us nourishment, were at least sweet and pleasant to the taste.

Our progress along the steep watercourse was necessarily slow, and by noon we had not advanced more than a mile. It was somewhere near this part of the day that the noise of falling waters, which we had faintly caught in the early morning, became more distinct; and it was not long before we were arrested by a rocky precipice of nearly a hundred feet in depth, that extended all across the channel, and over which the wild stream poured in an unbroken leap. On either hand the walls of the ravine presented their overhanging sides both above and below the fall, affording no means whatever of avoiding the cataract by taking a circuit round it.

"What's to be done now, Toby?" said I.

"Why," rejoined he, "as we cannot retreat, I suppose we must keep shoving along."

"Very true, my dear Toby; but how do you purpose accomplishing that desirable object?"

"By jumping from the top of the fall, if there be no other way," unhesitatingly replied my companion: "it will be much the quickest way of descent; but as you are not quite as active as I am, we will try some other way."

And, so saying, he crept cautiously along and peered over into the abyss, while I remained wondering by what possible means we could overcome this apparently insuperable obstruction. As soon as my companion had completed his survey, I eagerly inquired the result.

"The result of my observations you wish to know, do you?" began Toby, deliberately, with one of his odd looks: "Well, my lad, the result of my observations is very quickly imparted. It is at present uncertain which of our two necks will have the honor to be broken first; but about a hundred to one would be a fair bet in favor of the man who takes the first jump."

"Then it is an impossible thing, is it?" inquired I, gloomily.

"No, shipmate; on the contrary, it is the easiest thing in life: the only awkward point is the sort of usage which our unhappy limbs may receive when we arrive at the bottom and what sort of traveling trim we shall be in afterwards. But follow me now, and I will show you the only chance we have."

With this he conducted me to the verge of the cataract, and pointed along the side of the ravine to a number of curious-looking roots, some three or four inches in thickness, and several feet long, which, after twisting among the fissures of the rock, shot perpendicularly from it and ran tapering to a point in the air, hanging over the gulf like so many dark icicles. They covered nearly the entire surface of one side of the gorge, the lowest of them reaching even to the water. Many were moss-grown and decayed, with their extremities snapped short off, and those in the immediate vicinity of the fall were slippery with moisture.

Toby's scheme, and it was a desperate one, was to entrust ourselves to these treacherous-looking roots, and by slipping down from one to another to gain the bottom.

"Are you ready to venture it?" asked Toby, looking at me earnestly, but without saying a word as to the practicability of the plan.

"I am," was my reply; for I saw it was our only resource if we wished to advance, and as for retreating, all thoughts of that sort had been long abandoned.

After I had signified my assent, Toby, without uttering a single word, crawled along the dripping ledge until he gained a point from whence he could just reach one of the largest of the pendant roots; he shook it—it quivered in his grasp, and when he let it go it twanged in the air like a strong wire sharply struck. Satisfied by his scrutiny, my light-limbed companion swung himself nimbly upon it, and twisting his legs round it in sailor fashion, slipped down eight or ten feet, where his weight gave it a motion not unlike that of a pendulum. He could not venture to descend any further; so holding on with one hand, he with the other shook one by one all the slender roots around him, and at last, finding one which he thought trustworthy, shifted himself to it and continued his downward progress.

So far so well; but I could not avoid comparing my heavier frame and disabled condition with his light figure and remarkable activity; but there was no help for it, and in less than a minute's time I was swinging directly over his head. As soon as his upturned eyes caught a glimpse of me, he exclaimed in his usual dry tone, for the danger did not seem to daunt him in the least, "Mate, do me the kindness not to fall until I get out of your way"; and then swinging himself more on one side, he continued his descent. In the meantime I cautiously transferred myself from the limb down which I had been slipping to a couple of others that were near it, deeming two strings to my bow better than one, and taking care to test their strength before I trusted my weight to them.

On arriving towards the end of the second stage in this vertical journey, and shaking the long roots which were round me, to my consternation they snapped off one after another like so many pipe stems, and fell in fragments against the side of the gulf, splashing at last into the waters beneath.

As one after another the treacherous roots yielded to my grasp, and fell into the torrent, my heart sunk within me. The branches on which I was suspended over the yawning chasm swung to and fro in the air, and I expected them every moment to snap in twain. Appalled at the dreadful fate that menaced me, I clutched at the only large root which remained near me, but in vain; I could not reach it, though my fingers were within a few inches of it. Again and again I tried to reach it, until at length, maddened with the thought of my situation, I swayed myself violently by striking my foot against the side of the rock, and at the instant that I approached the large root caught desperately at it, and transferred myself to it. It vibrated violently under the sudden weight, but fortunately did not give way.

My brain grew dizzy with the idea of the frightful risk I had just run, and I involuntarily closed my eyes to shut out the view of the depth beneath me. For the instant I was safe, and I uttered a devout ejaculation of thanksgiving for my escape.

"Pretty well done," shouted Toby underneath me; "you are nimbler than I thought you to be—hopping about up there from root to root like any young squirrel. As soon as you have diverted yourself sufficiently, I would advise you to proceed."

"Aye, aye, Toby, all in good time: two or three more such famous roots as this, and I shall be with you."

The residue of my downward progress was comparatively easy; the roots were in greater abundance, and in one or two places jutting out points of rock assisted me greatly. In a few moments I was standing by the side of my companion.

Substituting a stout stick for the one I had thrown aside at the top of the precipice, we now continued our course along the bed of the ravine. Soon we were saluted by a sound in advance, that grew by degrees louder and louder, as the noise of the cataract we were leaving behind gradually died on our ears.

"Another precipice for us, Toby."

"Very good; we can descend them, you know—come on."

Nothing indeed appeared to depress or intimidate this intrepid fellow. Typees or Niagaras, he was as ready to engage one as the other, and I could not avoid a thousand times congratulating myself upon having such a companion in an enterprise like the present.

After an hour's painful progress, we reached the verge of another fall, still loftier than the preceding, and flanked both above and below with the same steep masses of rock, presenting, however, here and there narrow irregular ledges, supporting a shallow soil, on which grew a variety of bushes and trees, whose bright verdure contrasted beautifully with the foamy waters that flowed between them.

Toby, who invariably acted as pioneer, now proceeded to reconnoiter. On his return, he reported that the shelves of rock on our right would enable us to gain with little risk the bottom of the cataract. Accordingly, leaving the bed of the stream at the very point where it thundered down, we began crawling along one of these sloping ledges until it carried us to within a few feet of another that inclined downward at a still sharper angle, and upon which, by assisting each other, we managed to alight in safety. We warily crept along this, steadying ourselves by the naked roots of the shrubs that clung to every fissure. As we proceeded, the narrow path became still more contracted, rendering it difficult for us to maintain our footing, until suddenly, as we reached an angle of the wall of rock where we had expected it to widen, we perceived to our consternation that a yard or two farther on it abruptly terminated at a place we could not possibly hope to pass.

Toby as usual led the van, and in silence I waited to learn from him how he proposed to extricate us from this new difficulty.

"Well, my boy," I exclaimed, after the expiration of several minutes, during which time my companion had not uttered a word, "what's to be done now?"

He replied in a tranquil tone, that probably the best

thing we could do in our present strait was to get out of it as soon as possible.

"Yes, my dear Toby, but tell me *how* we are to get out of it."

"Something in this sort of style," he replied; and at the same moment to my horror he slipped sideways off the rock, and, as I then thought, by good fortune merely, alighted among the spreading branches of a species of palm tree, that, shooting its hardy roots along a ledge below, curved its trunk upwards into the air, and presented a thick mass of foliage about twenty feet below the spot where we had thus suddenly been brought to a standstill. I involuntarily held my breath, expecting to see the form of my companion, after being sustained for a moment by the branches of the tree, sink through their frail support, and fall headlong to the bottom. To my surprise and joy, however, he recovered himself, and disentangling his limbs from the fractured branches, he peered out from his leafy bed, and shouted lustily, "Come on, my hearty, there is no other alternative!" and with this he ducked beneath the foliage, and slipping down the trunk, stood in a moment at least fifty feet beneath me, upon the broad shelf of rock from which sprung the tree he had descended.

What would I not have given at that moment to have been by his side! The feat he had just accomplished seemed little less than miraculous, and I could hardly credit the evidence of my senses when I saw the wide distance that a single daring act had so suddenly placed between us.

Toby's animating "Come on!" again sounded in my ears, and dreading to lose all confidence in myself if I remained meditating upon the step, I once more gazed down to assure myself of the relative bearing of the tree and my own position, and then, closing my eyes and uttering one comprehensive ejaculation of prayer, I inclined myself over towards the abyss, and after one breathless instant fell with a crash into the tree, the branches snapping and crackling with my weight, as I sunk lower and lower among them, until I was stopped by coming in contact with a sturdy limb.

In a few moments I was standing at the foot of the tree, manipulating myself all over with a view of ascertaining the extent of the injuries I had received. To my surprise the only effects of my feat were a few slight contusions too trifling to care about. The rest of our descent was easily accomplished, and in half an hour after regaining the ravine we had partaken of our evening morsel, built our hut as usual, and crawled under its shelter.

The next morning, in spite of our debility and the agony of hunger under which we were now suffering, though neither of us confessed to the fact, we struggled along our dismal and still difficult and dangerous path, cheered by the hope of soon catching a glimpse of the valley before us, and towards evening the voice of a cataract which had for some time sounded like a low deep bass to the music of the smaller waterfalls, broke upon our ears in still louder tones, and assured us that we were approaching its vicinity.

That evening we stood on the brink of a precipice, over which the dark stream bounded in one final leap of full 300 feet. The sheer descent terminated in the region we so long had sought. On either side of the fall, two lofty and perpendicular bluffs buttressed the sides of the enormous cliff, and projected into the sea of verdure with which the valley waved, and a range of similar projecting eminences stood disposed in a half circle about the head of the vale. A thick canopy of trees hung over the very verge of the fall, leaving an arched aperture for the passage of the waters, which imparted a strange picturesqueness to the scene.

The valley was now before us; but instead of being conducted into its smiling bosom by the gradual descent of the deep watercourse we had thus far pursued, all our labors now appeared to have been rendered futile by its abrupt termination. But, bitterly disappointed, we did not entirely despair.

As it was now near sunset we determined to pass the night where we were, and on the morrow, refreshed by sleep and by eating at one meal all our stock of food, to accomplish a descent into the valley, or perish in the attempt.

We laid ourselves down that night on a spot, the recollection of which still makes me shudder. A small table of rock which projected over the precipice on one side of the stream, and was drenched by the spray of the fall, sustained a huge trunk of a tree which must have been deposited there by some heavy freshet. It lay obliquely, with one end resting on the rock and the other supported by the side of the ravine. Against it we placed in a sloping direction a number of the half-decayed boughs that were strewn about, and covering the whole with twigs and leaves, awaited the morning's light beneath such shelter as it afforded.

During the whole of this night the continual roaring of the cataract—the dismal moaning of the gale through the trees—the pattering of the rain—and the profound darkness, affected my spirits to a degree which nothing had ever before produced. Wet, half famished, and chilled to the heart with the dampness of the place, and nearly wild with the pain I endured, I fairly cowered down to the earth under this multiplication of hardships, and abandoned myself to frightful anticipations of evil; and my companion, whose spirit at last was a good deal broken, scarcely uttered a word during the whole night.

At length the day dawned upon us, and, rising from our miserable pallet, we stretched our stiffened joints, and after eating all that remained of our bread, prepared for the last stage of our journey.

I will not recount every hairbreadth escape, and every fearful difficulty that occurred before we succeeded in reaching the bosom of the valley. As I have already described similar scenes, it will be sufficient to say that at length after great toil and great dangers, we both stood with no limbs broken at the head of that magnificent vale which five days before had so suddenly burst upon my sight, and almost beneath the shadows of those very cliffs from whose summits we had gazed upon the prospect.

x

How to obtain the fruit which we felt convinced must grow near at hand was our first thought.

Typee or Happar? A frightful death at the hands of the fiercest of cannibals, or a kindly reception from a gentler race of savages? Which? But it was too late now to discuss a question which would so soon be answered.

The part of the valley in which we found ourselves appeared to be altogether uninhabited. An almost impenetrable thicket extended from side to side, without presenting a single plant affording the nourishment we had confidently calculated upon; and with this object, we followed the course of the stream, casting quick glances as we proceeded into the thick jungles on either hand.

My companion—to whose solicitations I had yielded in descending into the valley—now that the step was taken, began to manifest a degree of caution I had little expected from him. He proposed that, in the event of our finding an adequate supply of fruit, we should remain in this unfrequented portion of the country—where we should run little chance of being surprised by its occupants, whoever they might be—until sufficiently recruited to resume our journey; when, laying in a store of food equal to our wants, we might easily regain the bay of Nukuheva, after the lapse of a sufficient interval to ensure the departure of our vessel.

I objected strongly to this proposition, plausible as it was, as the difficulties of the route would be almost insurmountable, unacquainted as we were with the general bearings of the country, and I reminded my companion of the hardships which we had already encountered in our uncertain wanderings; in a word, I said that since we had deemed it advisable to enter the valley, we ought manfully to face the consequences, whatever they might be; the more especially as I was convinced there was no alternative left us but to fall in with the natives at once, and boldly risk the reception they might give us; and that, as to myself, I felt the necessity of rest and shelter, and that until I had obtained them I should be wholly unable to encounter such sufferings as we had lately passed through. To the justice of these observations Toby somewhat reluctantly assented.

We were surprised that, after moving as far as we had along the valley, we should still meet with the same impervious thickets; and thinking that although the borders of the stream might be lined for some distance with them, yet beyond there might be more open ground, I requested Toby to keep a bright look-out upon one side, while I did the same on the other, in order to discover some opening in the bushes, and especially to watch for the slightest appearance of a path or anything else that might indicate the vicinity of the islanders.

What furtive and anxious glances we cast into those dim-looking shades! With what apprehensions we proceeded, ignorant at what moment we might be greeted by the javelin of some ambushed savage! At last my companion paused, and directed my attention to a narrow opening in the foliage. We struck into it and it soon brought us by an indistinctly traced path to a comparatively clear space, at the further end of which we descried a number of the trees, the native name of which is "annuee," and which bear a most delicious fruit.

What a race! I hobbling over the ground like some decrepit wretch, and Toby leaping forward like a greyhound. He quickly cleared one of the trees on which there were two or three of the fruit, but to our chagrin they proved to be much decayed; the rinds partly opened by the birds, and their hearts half devoured. However, we quickly dispatched them, and no ambrosia could have been more delicious.

We looked about us uncertain whither to direct our steps, since the path we had so far followed appeared to be lost in the open space around us. At last we resolved to enter a grove near at hand, and had advanced a few rods when, just upon its skirts, I picked up a slender breadfruit shoot perfectly green, and with the tender bark freshly stripped from it. It was still slippery with moisture, and appeared as if it had been but that moment thrown aside. I said nothing, but merely held it up to Toby, who started at this undeniable evidence of the vicinity of the savages.

The plot was now thickening. A short distance further lay a little fagot of the same shoots bound together with a strip of bark. Could it have been thrown down by some solitary native who, alarmed at seeing us, had hurried forward to carry the tidings of our approach to his countrymen?—Typee or Happar?—But it was too late to recede, so we moved on slowly, my companion in advance casting eager glances under the trees on either side, until all at once I saw him recoil as if stung by an adder. Sinking on his knee, he waved me off with one hand, while with the other he held aside some intervening leaves and gazed intently at some object.

Disregarding his injunction, I quickly approached him and caught a glimpse of two figures partly hidden by the dense foliage; they were standing close together, and were perfectly motionless. They must have previously perceived us, and withdrawn into the depths of the wood to elude our observation.

My mind was at once made up. Dropping my staff, and tearing open the package of things we had brought from the ship, I unrolled the cotton cloth, and holding it in one hand plucked with the other a twig from the bushes beside me, and, telling Toby to follow my example, I broke through the covert and advanced, waving the branch in token of peace towards the shrinking forms before me.

They were a boy and girl, slender and graceful, and completely naked, with the exception of a slight girdle of bark, from which depended at opposite points two of the russet leaves of the breadfruit-tree. An arm of the boy, half screened from sight by her wild tresses, was thrown about the neck of the girl, while with the other he held one of her hands in his; and thus they stood together, their heads inclined forward, catching the faint noise we made in our progress, and with one foot in advance, as if half inclined to fly from our presence.

As we drew near, their alarm evidently increased. Apprehensive that they might fly from us altogether, I stopped short and motioned them to advance and receive the gift I extended towards them, but they would not; I then uttered a few words of their language with which I was acquainted, scarcely expecting that they would understand me, but to show that we had not dropped from the clouds upon them. This appeared to give them a little confidence, so I approached nearer, presenting the cloth with one hand and holding the bough with the other, while they slowly retreated. At last they suffered us to approach so near to them that we were enabled to throw the cotton cloth across their shoulders, giving them to understand that it was theirs, and by a variety of gestures endeavoring to make them understand that we entertained the highest possible regard for them.

The frightened pair now stood still, whilst we endeavored to make them comprehend the nature of our wants. In doing this Toby went through with a complete series of pantomimic illustrations—opening his mouth from ear to ear, and thrusting his fingers down his throat, gnashing his teeth and rolling his eyes about, till I verily believe the poor creatures took us for a couple of white cannibals who were about to make a meal of them. When, however, they understood us, they showed no inclination to relieve our wants. At this juncture it began to rain violently, and we motioned them to lead us to some place of shelter. With this request they appeared willing to comply, but nothing could evince more strongly the apprehension with which they regarded us, than the way in which, whilst walking before us, they kept their eyes constantly turned back to watch every movement we made, and even our very looks.

"Typee or Happar, Toby?" asked I as we walked after them.

"Of course Happar," he replied with a show of confidence which was intended to disguise his doubts.

"We shall soon know," I exclaimed; and at the same moment I stepped forward towards our guides, and pronouncing the two names interrogatively and pointing to the lowest part of the valley, endeavored to come to the point at once. They repeated the words after me again and again, but without giving any peculiar emphasis to either, so that I was completely at a loss to understand them; for a couple of wilier young things than we afterwards found them to have been on this particular occasion never probably fell in any traveler's way.

More and more curious to ascertain our fate, I now threw together in the form of a question the words "Happar" and "Mortarkee," the latter being equivalent to the word "good." The two natives interchanged glances of peculiar meaning with one another at this, and manifested no little surprise; but on the repetition of the question, after some consultation together, to the great joy of Toby, they answered in the affirmative. Toby was now in ecstasies, especially as the young savages continued to reiterate their answer with great energy, as though desirous of impressing us with the idea that being among the Happars, we ought to consider ourselves perfectly secure.

Although I had some lingering doubts, I feigned great delight with Toby at this announcement, while my companion broke out into a pantomimic abhorrence of Typee, and immeasurable love for the particular valley in which we were; our guides all the while gazing uneasily at one another as if at a loss to account for our conduct.

They hurried on, and we followed them; until suddenly they set up a strange halloo, which was answered from beyond the grove through which we were passing, and the next moment we entered upon some open ground, at the extremity of which we descried a long, low hut and in front of it were several young girls. As soon as they perceived us they fled with wild screams into the adjoining thickets, like so many startled fawns. A few moments after the whole valley resounded with savage outcries, and the natives came running towards us from every direction.

Had an army of invaders made an irruption into their territory they could not have evinced greater excitement. We were soon completely encircled by a dense throng, and in their eager desire to behold us they almost arrested our progress; an equal number surrounding our youthful guides, who with amazing volubility appeared to be detailing the circumstances which had attended their meeting with us. Every item of intelligence appeared to redouble the astonishment of the islanders, and they gazed at us with inquiring looks.

At last we reached a large and handsome building of bamboos, and were by signs told to enter it, the natives opening a lane for us through which to pass; on entering without ceremony, we threw our exhausted frames upon the mats that covered the floor. In a moment the slight tenement was completely full of people, whilst those who were unable to obtain admittance gazed at us through its open cane-work.

It was now evening, and by the dim light we could just discern the savage countenances around us, gleaming with wild curiosity and wonder; the naked forms and tattooed limbs of brawny warriors, with here and there the slighter figures of young girls, all engaged in a perfect storm of conversation, of which we were of course the one only theme; whilst our recent guides were fully occupied in answering the innumerable questions which every one put to them. Nothing can exceed the fierce gesticulation of these people when animated in conversation, and on this occasion they gave loose to all their natural vivacity, shouting and dancing about in a manner that well-nigh intimidated us.

Close to where we lay, squatting upon their haunches, were some eight or ten noble-looking chiefs—for such they subsequently proved to be—who, more reserved than the rest, regarded us with a fixed and stern attention, which not a little discomposed our equanimity. One of them in particular, who appeared to be the highest in rank, placed himself directly facing me; looking at me with a rigidity of aspect under which I absolutely quailed. He never once opened his lips, but maintained his severe expression of countenance, without turning his face aside for a single moment. Never before had I been subjected to so strange and steady a glance; it revealed nothing of the mind of the savage, but it appeared to be reading my own.

After undergoing this scrutiny till I grew absolutely nervous, with a view of diverting it if possible, and conciliating the good opinion of the warrior, I took some tobacco from the bosom of my frock and offered it to him. He quietly rejected the proffered gift, and, without speaking, motioned me to return it to its place.

In my previous intercourse with the natives of Nukuheva and Tior, I had found that the present of a small piece of tobacco would have rendered any of them devoted to my service. Was this act of the chief a token of his enmity? Typee or Happar? I asked within myself. I started, for at the same moment this identical question was asked by the strange being before me. I turned to Toby; the flickering light of a native taper showed me his countenance pale with trepidation at this fatal question. I paused for a second, and I know not by what impulse it was that I answered "Typee." The piece of dusky statuary nodded in approval, and then murmured "Mortarkee!" "Mortarkee," said I, without further hesitation—"Typee mortarkee."

What a transition! The dark figures around us leaped to their feet, clapped their hands in transport, and shouted again and again the talismanic syllables, the utterance of which appeared to have settled everything.

When this commotion had a little subsided, the principal chief squatted once more before me, and throwing himself into a sudden rage, poured forth a string of philippics, which I was at no loss to understand, from the frequent recurrence of the word Happar, as being directed against the natives of the adjoining valley. In all these denunciations my companion and I acquiesced while we extolled the character of the warlike Typees. To be sure our panegyrics were somewhat laconic, consisting in the repetition of that name, united with the potent adjective "mortarkee." But this was sufficient, and served to conciliate the good will of the natives, with whom our congeniality of sentiment on this point did more towards inspiring a friendly feeling than anything else that could have happened.

At last the wrath of the chief evaporated, and in a few moments he was as placid as ever. Laying his hand upon his breast, he now gave me to understand that his name was Mehevi, and that, in return, he wished me to communicate my appellation. I hesitated for an instant, thinking that it might be difficult for him to pronounce my real name, and then with the most praiseworthy intentions intimated that I was known as Tom. But I could not have made a worse selection; the chief could not master it: "Tommo," "Tomma," "Tommee," everything but plain "Tom." As he persisted in garnishing the word with an additional syllable, I compromised the matter with him at the word "Tommo;" and by that name I went during the entire period of my stay in the valley. The same proceeding was gone through with Toby whose mellifluous appellation was more easily caught.

An exchange of names is equivalent to a ratification of good-will and amity among these simple people; and as we were aware of this fact, we were delighted that it had taken place on the present occasion.

Reclining upon our mats, we now held a kind of levee, giving audience to successive troops of the natives, who introduced themselves to us by pronouncing their respective names, and retired in high good humor on receiving ours in return. During this ceremony the greatest merriment prevailed, nearly every announcement on the part of the islanders being followed by a fresh sally of gaiety which induced me to believe that some of them at least were innocently diverting the company at our expense, by bestowing upon themselves a string of absurd titles, of the humor of which we were of course entirely ignorant.

All this occupied about an hour, when the throng having a little diminished, I turned to Mehevi and gave him to understand that we were in need of food and sleep. Immediately the attentive chief addressed a few words to one of the crowd who disappeared and returned in a few moments with a calabash of "poee-poee," and two or three young coco-nuts stripped of their husks, and with their shells partly broken. We both of us forthwith placed one of these natural goblets to our lips, and drained it in a moment of the refreshing draught it contained. The poee-poee was then placed

before us, and even famished as I was, I paused to consider in what manner to convey it to my mouth.

This staple article of food among the Marquese islanders is manufactured from the produce of the breadfruit-tree. It somewhat resembles in its plastic nature
our bookbinder's paste, is of a yellow color, and somewhat tart to the taste.

Such was the dish, the merits of which I was now
eager to discuss. I eyed it wistfully for a moment, and
then unable any longer to stand on ceremony, plunged
my hand into the yielding mass, and to the boisterous
mirth of the natives drew it forth laden with the poee-
poee, which adhered in lengthy strings to every finger.
So stubborn was its consistency, that in conveying my
heavily freighted hand to my mouth, the connecting
links almost raised the calabash from the mats on which
it had been placed. This display of awkwardness—in
which, by the by, Toby kept me company—convulsed
the bystanders with uncontrollable laughter.

As soon as their merriment had somewhat subsided,
Mehevi, motioning us to be attentive, dipped the fore-
finger of his right hand in the dish, and giving it a rapid
and scientific twirl, drew it out coated smoothly with
the preparation. With a second peculiar flourish he prevented the poee-poee from dropping to the ground as
he raised it to his mouth, into which the finger was
inserted and drawn forth perfectly free from any ad-
hesive matter. This performance was evidently intended
for our instruction; so I again essayed the feat on the
principles inculcated, but with very ill success.

A starving man, however, little heeds conventional
proprieties, especially on a South-Sea island, and accordingly Toby and I partook of the dish after our own
clumsy fashion, beplastering our faces all over with the

glutinous compound, and daubing our hands nearly to the wrist. This kind of food is by no means disagreeable to the palate of a European, though at first the mode of eating it may be. For my own part, after the lapse of a few days I became accustomed to its singular flavor, and grew remarkably fond of it.

So much for the first course; several other dishes followed it, some of which were positively delicious. We concluded our banquet by tossing off the contents of two more young coco-nuts, after which we regaled ourselves with the soothing fumes of tobacco, inhaled from a quaintly carved pipe which passed round the circle.

During the repast, the natives eyed us with intense curiosity, observing our minutest motions, and appearing to discover abundant matter for comment in the most trifling occurrence. Their surprise mounted the highest when we began to remove our uncomfortable garments, which were saturated with rain. They scanned the whiteness of our limbs, and seemed utterly unable to account for the contrast they presented to the swarthy hue of our faces, embrowned from a six months' exposure to the scorching sun of the Line. They felt our skin, much in the same way that a silk mercer would handle a remarkably fine piece of satin; and some of them went so far in their investigation as to apply the olfactory organ.

Their singular behavior almost led me to imagine that they never before had beheld a white man; but a few moments' reflection convinced me that this could not have been the case; and a more satisfactory reason for their conduct has since suggested itself to my mind.

Deterred by the frightful stories related of its inhabitants, ships never enter this bay, while their hostile relations with the tribes in the adjoining valleys prevent the Typees from visiting that section of the island where vessels occasionally lie. At long intervals, however, some intrepid captain will touch on the skirts of the bay, with two or three armed boats' crews, and accompanied by an interpreter. The natives who live near the sea descry the strangers long before they reach their waters, and aware of the purpose for which they come, proclaim loudly the news of their approach. By a species of vocal telegraph the intelligence reaches the inmost recesses of the vale in an inconceivably short space of time, drawing nearly its whole population down to the beach laden with every variety of fruit. The interpreter, who is invariably a "tabooed Kannaka," [1] leaps ashore with the goods intended for barter, while the boats, with their oars shipped, and every man on his thwart, lie just outside the surf, heading off from the shore, in readiness at the first untoward event to escape to the open sea. As soon as the traffic is concluded, one of the boats pulls in under cover of the muskets of the others, the fruit is quickly thrown into her, and the transient visitors precipitately retire from what they justly consider so dangerous a vicinity.

The intercourse occurring with Europeans being so restricted, no wonder that the inhabitants of the valley manifested so much curiosity with regard to us, appearing as we did among them under such singular circumstances. I have no doubt that we were the first white

[1] The word "Kannaka" is at the present day universally used in the South Seas by Europeans to designate the Islanders. In the various dialects of the principal groups it is simply a sexual designation applied to the males; but it is now used by the natives in their intercourse with foreigners in the same sense in which the latter employ it.

A "tabooed Kannaka" is an islander whose person has been made to a certain extent sacred by the operation of a singular custom hereafter to be explained.—*H.M.*

men who ever penetrated thus far back into their territories, or at least the first who had ever descended from
the head of the vale. What had brought us thither must
have appeared a complete mystery to them, and from
our ignorance of the language it was impossible for us
to enlighten them. In answer to inquiries which the
eloquence of their gestures enabled us to comprehend,
all that we could reply was, that we had come from
Nukuheva, a place, be it remembered, with which they
were at open war. This intelligence appeared to affect
them with the most lively emotions. "Nukuheva mortarkee?" they asked. Of course we replied most energet-
ically in the negative.

They then plied us with a thousand questions, of
which we could understand nothing more than that they
had reference to the recent movements of the French,
against whom they seemed to cherish the most fierce
hatred. So eager were they to obtain information on
this point, that they still continued to propound their
queries long after we had shown that we were utterly
unable to answer them. Occasionally we caught some
indistinct idea of their meaning, when we would endeavor by every method in our power to communicate
the desired intelligence. At such times their gratification
was boundless, and they would redouble their efforts
to make us comprehend them more perfectly. But all in
vain; and in the end they looked at us despairingly, as
if we were the receptacles of invaluable information, but
how to come at it they knew not.

After a while the group around us gradually dispersed, and we were left about midnight (as we conjectured) with those who appeared to be permanent
residents of the house. These individuals now provided
us with fresh mats to lie upon, covered us with several
folds of tappa, and then, extinguishing the tapers that

had been burning, threw themselves down beside us, and after a little desultory conversation were soon sound asleep.

XI

Various and conflicting were the thoughts which oppressed me during the silent hours that followed the events related in the preceding chapter. Toby, wearied with the fatigues of the day, slumbered heavily by my side; but the pain under which I was suffering effectually prevented my sleeping, and I remained distressingly alive to all the fearful circumstances of our present situation. Was it possible that, after all our vicissitudes, we were really in the terrible valley of Typee, and at the mercy of its inmates, a fierce and unrelenting tribe of savages?

Typee or Happar? I shuddered when I reflected that there was no longer any room for doubt; and that beyond all hope of escape, we were now placed in those very circumstances from the bare thought of which I had recoiled with such abhorrence but a few days before. What might not be our fearful destiny? To be sure, as yet we had been treated with no violence; nay, had been even kindly and hospitably entertained. But what dependence could be placed upon the fickle passions which sway the bosom of a savage? His inconstancy and treachery are proverbial. Might it not be that beneath these fair appearances the islanders covered some perfidious design, and that their friendly reception of us might only precede some horrible catastrophe? How strongly did these forebodings spring up in my mind as I lay restlessly upon a couch of mats, surrounded by the dimly revealed forms of those whom I so greatly dreaded.

From the excitement of these fearful thoughts I sank

towards morning into an uneasy slumber; and on awaking, with a start, in the midst of an appalling dream, looked up into the eager countenances of a number of the natives, who were bending over me.

It was broad day; and the house was nearly filled with young females, fancifully decorated with flowers, who gazed upon me as I rose with faces in which childish delight and curiosity were vividly portrayed. After waking Toby, they seated themselves round us on the mats, and gave full play to that prying inquisitiveness which time out of mind has been attributed to the adorable sex.

As these unsophisticated young creatures were attended by no jealous duennas, their proceedings were altogether informal, and void of artificial restraint. Long and minute was the investigation with which they honored us, and so uproarious their mirth, that I felt infinitely sheepish; and Toby was immeasurably outraged at their familiarity.

These lively young ladies were at the same time wonderfully polite and humane; fanning aside the insects that occasionally lighted on our brows; presenting us with food; and compassionately regarding me in the midst of my afflictions. But in spite of all their blandishments, my feelings of propriety were exceedingly shocked, for I could not but consider them as having overstepped the due limits of female decorum.

Having diverted themselves to their hearts' content, our young visitants now withdrew, and gave place to successive troops of the other sex, who continued flocking towards the house until near noon; by which time I have no doubt that the greater part of the inhabitants of the valley had bathed themselves in the light of our benignant countenances.

At last, when their numbers began to diminish, a

superb-looking warrior stooped the towering plumes of his head-dress beneath the low portal, and entered the house. I saw at once that he was some distinguished personage, the natives regarding him with the utmost deference, and making room for him as he approached. His aspect was imposing. The splendid long drooping tail-feathers of the tropical bird, thickly interspersed with the gaudy plumage of the cock, were disposed in an immense upright semicircle upon his head, their lower extremities being fixed in a crescent of guinea-beads which spanned the forehead. Around his neck were several enormous necklaces of boars' tusks, polished like ivory, and disposed in such a manner as that the longest and largest were upon his capacious chest. Thrust forward through the large apertures in his ears were two small and finely shaped sperm-whale teeth, presenting their cavities in front, stuffed with freshly plucked leaves, and curiously wrought at the other end into strange little images and devices. These barbaric trinkets, garnished in this manner at their open extremities, and tapering and curving round to a point behind the ear, resembled not a little a pair of cornucopias.

The loins of the warrior were girt about with heavy folds of a dark-colored tappa, hanging before and behind in clusters of braided tassels, while anklets and bracelets of curling human hair completed his unique costume. In his right hand he grasped a beautifully carved paddle-spear, nearly fifteen feet in length, made of the bright koar-wood, one end sharply pointed, and the other flattened like an oar-blade. Hanging obliquely from his girdle by a loop of sinnate, was a richly decorated pipe; the slender reed forming its stem was colored with a red pigment, and round it, as well as the idol-bowl, fluttered little streamers of the thinnest tappa.

But that which was most remarkable in the appear-

ance of the splendid islander was the elaborate tattooing displayed on every noble limb. All imaginable lines
and curves and figures were delineated over his whole
body, and in their grotesque variety and infinite profusion I could only compare them to the crowded group-
ings of quaint patterns we sometimes see in costly pieces
of lacework. The most simple and remarkable of all
these ornaments was that which decorated the countenance of the chief. Two broad stripes of tattooing, diverg-
ing from the center of his shaven crown, obliquely
crossed both eyes—staining the lids—to a little below
either ear, where they united with another stripe which
swept in a straight line along the lips and formed the
base of the triangle. The warrior, from the excellence of
his physical proportions, might certainly have been
regarded as one of Nature's noblemen, and the lines
drawn upon his face may possibly have denoted his
exalted rank.

This warlike personage upon entering the house
seated himself at some distance from the spot where
Toby and myself reposed, while the rest of the savages
looked alternately from us to him, as if in expectation
of something they were disappointed in not perceiving.
Regarding the chief attentively, I thought his lineaments
appeared familiar to me. As soon as his full face was
turned upon me and I again beheld its extraordinary
embellishment, and met the strange gaze to which I had
been subjected the preceding night, I immediately, in
spite of the alteration in his appearance, recognized
the noble Mehevi. On addressing him, he advanced at
once in the most cordial manner, and, greeting me
warmly, seemed to enjoy not a little the effect his
barbaric costume had produced on me.

I forthwith determined to secure, if possible, the good
will of this individual, as I easily perceived he was a

man of great authority in his tribe, and one who might exert a powerful influence upon our subsequent fate. In the endeavor I was not repulsed; for nothing could surpass the friendliness he manifested towards both my companion and myself. He extended his sturdy limbs by our side, and endeavored to make us comprehend the full extent of the kindly feelings by which he was actuated. The almost insuperable difficulty in communicating to one another our ideas affected the chief with no little mortification. He evinced a great desire to be enlightened with regard to the customs and peculiarities of the far-off country we had left behind us, and to which under the name of Maneeka he frequently alluded.

But that which more than any other subject engaged his attention was the late proceedings of the "Franee," as he called the French, in the neighboring bay of Nukuheva. This seemed a never-ending theme with him, and one concerning which he was never weary of interrogating us. All the information we succeeded in imparting to him on this subject was little more than that we had seen six men-of-war lying in the hostile bay at the time we had left it. When he received this intelligence, Mehevi, by the aid of his fingers, went through a long numerical calculation, as if estimating the number of Frenchmen the squadron might contain.

It was just after employing his faculties in this way that he happened to notice the swelling in my limb. He immediately examined it with the utmost attention, and after doing so dispatched a boy who happened to be standing by with some message.

After a lapse of a few moments the stripling re-entered the house with an aged islander who might have been taken for old Hippocrates himself. His head was as bald as the polished surface of a coco-nut shell, which article it precisely resembled in smoothness and color, while a long silvery beard swept almost to his girdle of bark. Encircling his temples was a bandeau of the twisted leaves of the Omoo tree, pressed closely over the brows to shield his feeble vision from the glare of the sun. His tottering steps were supported by a long slim staff, resembling the wand with which a theatrical magician appears on the stage, and in one hand he carried a freshly plaited fan of the green leaflets of the coco-nut tree. A flowing robe of tappa, knotted over the shoulder, hung loosely round his stooping form, and heightened the venerableness of his aspect.

Mehevi, saluting this old gentleman, motioned him to a seat between us, and then uncovering my limb, desired him to examine it. The leech gazed intently from me to Toby, and then proceeded to business. After diligently observing the ailing member, he commenced manipulating it; and on the supposition probably that the complaint had deprived the leg of all sensation, began to pinch and hammer it in such a manner that I absolutely roared with the pain. Thinking that I was as capable of making an application of thumps and pinches to the part as any one else, I endeavored to resist this species of medical treatment. But it was not so easy a matter to get out of the clutches of the old wizard; he fastened on the unfortunate limb as if it were something for which he had been long seeking, and muttering some kind of incantation continued his discipline, pounding it after a fashion that set me wellnigh crazy; while Mehevi, upon the same principle which prompts an affectionate mother to hold a struggling child in a dentist's chair, restrained me in his powerful grasp, and actually encouraged the wretch in this infliction of torture.

Almost frantic with rage and pain, I yelled like a

Bedlamite; while Toby, throwing himself into all the attitudes of a posture-master, vainly endeavored to expostulate with the natives by signs and gestures. To have looked at my companion, as, sympathizing with my sufferings, he strove to put an end to them, one would have thought he was the deaf and dumb alphabet incarnated. Whether my tormentor yielded to Toby's entreaties, or paused from sheer exhaustion, I do not know; but all at once he ceased his operations, and at the same time the chief relinquishing his hold upon me, I fell back, faint and breathless with the agony I had endured.

My unfortunate limb was now left much in the same condition as a rump-steak after undergoing the castigating process which precedes cooking. My physician, having recovered from the fatigues of his exertions, as if anxious to make amends for the pain to which he had subjected me, now took some herbs out of a little wallet that was suspended from his waist, and moistening them in water, applied them to the inflamed part, stooping over it at the same time, and either whispering a spell, or having a little confidential chat with some imaginary demon located in the calf of my leg. My limb was now swathed in leafy bandages, and, grateful to Providence for the cessation of hostilities, I was suffered to rest.

Mehevi shortly after rose to depart; but before he went he spoke authoritatively to one of the natives whom he addressed as Kory-Kory; and from the little I could understand of what took place, pointed him out to me as a man whose peculiar business thenceforth would be to attend upon my person. I am not certain that I comprehended as much as this at the time, but the subsequent conduct of my trusty body-servant fully assured me that such must have been the case.

I could not but be amused at the manner in which the chief addressed me upon this occasion, talking to me for at least fifteen or twenty minutes as calmly as if I could understand every word that he said. I remarked this peculiarity very often afterwards in many other of the islanders.

Mehevi having now departed, and the family physician having likewise made his exit, we were left about sunset with the ten or twelve natives, who by this time I had ascertained composed the household of which Toby and I were members. As the dwelling to which we had been first introduced was the place of my permanent abode while I remained in the valley, and as I was necessarily placed upon the most intimate footing with its occupants, I may as well here enter into a little description of it and its inhabitants. This description will apply also to nearly all the other dwelling-places in the vale, and will furnish some idea of the generality of the natives.

Near one side of the valley, and about midway up the ascent of a rather abrupt rise of ground waving with the richest verdure, a number of large stones were laid in successive courses, to the height of nearly eight feet, and disposed in such a manner that their level surface corresponded in shape with the habitation which was perched upon it. A narrow space, however was reserved in front of the dwelling, upon the summit of this pile of stones (called by the natives a "pi-pi"), which being enclosed by a little picket of canes, gave it somewhat the appearance of a verandah. The frame of the house was constructed of large bamboos planted uprightly, and secured together at intervals by transverse stalks of the light wood of the hibiscus, lashed with thongs of bark. The rear of the tenement—built up with successive ranges of coco-nut boughs bound one upon another,

with their leaflets cunningly woven together—inclined
a little from the vertical, and extended from the extreme
edge of the "pi-pi" to about twenty feet from its surface; whence the shelving roof—thatched with the long
tapering leaves of the palmetto—sloped steeply off to
within about five feet of the floor; leaving the eaves
drooping with tassel-like appendages over the front of
the habitation. This was constructed of light and elegant
canes, in a kind of open screen work, tastefully adorned
with bindings of variegated sinnate, which served to
hold together its various parts. The sides of the house
were similarly built; thus presenting three quarters for
the circulation of the air, while the whole was impervious to the rain.

In length this picturesque building was perhaps
twelve yards, while in breadth it could not have exceeded as many feet. So much for the exterior; which,
with its wire-like reed-twisted sides, not a little reminded me of an immense aviary.

Stooping a little, you passed through a narrow aperture in its front; and facing you, on entering, lay two
long, perfectly straight, and well-polished trunks of the
coco-nut tree, extending the full length of the dwelling;
one of them placed closely against the rear, and the
other lying parallel with it some two yards distant, the
interval between them being spread with a multitude
of gaily worked mats, nearly all of a different pattern.
This space formed the common couch and lounging
place of the natives, answering the purpose of a divan in
Oriental countries. Here would they slumber through
the hours of the night, and recline luxuriously during
the greater part of the day. The remainder of the floor
presented only the cool shining surfaces of the large
stones of which the "pi-pi" was composed.

From the ridge-pole of the house hung suspended a

number of large packages enveloped in coarse tappa; some of which contained festival dresses, and various other matters of the wardrobe, held in high estimation. These were easily accessible by means of a line, which, passing over the ridge-pole, had one end attached to a bundle, while with the other, which led to the side of the dwelling and was there secured, the package could be lowered or elevated at pleasure.

Against the farther wall of the house were arranged in tasteful figures a variety of spears and javelins, and other implements of savage warfare. Outside of the habitation, and built upon the piazza-like area in its front, was a little shed used as a sort of larder or pantry, and in which were stored various articles of domestic use and convenience. A few yards from the "pi-pi" was a large shed built of coco-nut boughs, where the process of preparing the "poee-poee" was carried on, and all culinary operations attended to.

Thus much for the house, and its appurtenances; and it will be readily acknowledged that a more commodious and appropriate dwelling for the climate and the people could not possibly be devised. It was cool, free to admit the air, scrupulously clean, and elevated above the dampness and impurities of the ground.

But now to sketch the inmates; and here I claim for my tried servitor and faithful valet Kory-Kory the precedence of a first description. As his character will be gradually unfolded in the course of my narrative, I shall for the present content myself with delineating his personal appearance. Kory-Kory, though the most devoted and best-natured serving-man in the world, was, alas! a hideous object to look upon. He was some twenty-five years of age, and about six feet in height, robust and well made, and of the most extraordinary aspect. His head was carefully shaven, with the exception of two circular spots, about the size of a dollar, near the top of the cranium, where the hair, permitted to grow of an amazing length, was twisted up in two prominent knots, that gave him the appearance of being decorated with a pair of horns. His beard, plucked out by the roots from every other part of his face, was suffered to droop in hairy pendants, two of which garnished his upper lip, and an equal number hung from the extremity of his chin.

Kory-Kory, with a view of improving the handiwork of nature, and perhaps prompted by a desire to add to the engaging expression of his countenance, had seen fit to embellish his face with three broad longitudinal stripes of tattooing, which, like those country roads that go straight forward in defiance of all obstacles, crossed his nasal organ, descended into the hollow of his eyes, and even skirted the borders of his mouth. Each completely spanned his physiognomy; one extending in a line with his eyes, another crossing the face in the vicinity of the nose, and the third sweeping along his lips from ear to ear. His countenance thus triply hooped, as it were, with tattooing, always reminded me of those unhappy wretches whom I have sometimes observed gazing out sentimentally from behind the grated bars of a prison window; whilst the entire body of my savage valet, covered all over with representations of birds and fishes, and a variety of most unaccountable-looking creatures, suggested to me the idea of a pictorial museum of natural history, or an illustrated copy of Goldsmith's *Animated Nature.*

But it seems really heartless in me to write thus of the poor islander, when I owe perhaps to his unremitting attentions the very existence I now enjoy. Kory-Kory, I mean thee no harm in what I say in regard to thy outward adornings; but they were a little curious to my unaccustomed sight, and therefore I dilate upon them. But to underrate or forget thy faithful services is something I could never be guilty of, even in the giddiest moment of my life.

The father of my attached follower was a native of gigantic frame, and had once possessed prodigious physical powers; but the lofty form was now yielding to the inroads of time, though the hand of disease seemed never to have been laid upon the aged warrior. Marheyo —for such was his name—appeared to have retired from all active participation in the affairs of the valley, seldom or never accompanying the natives in their various expeditions; and employing the greater part of his time in throwing up a little shed just outside the house, upon which he was engaged to my certain knowledge for four months, without appearing to make any sensible advance. I suppose the old gentleman was in his dotage, for he manifested in various ways the characteristics which mark this particular stage of life.

I remember in particular his having a choice pair of ear-ornaments, fabricated from the teeth of some sea-monster. These he would alternately wear and take off at least fifty times in the course of the day, going and coming from his little hut on each occasion with all the tranquillity imaginable. Sometimes slipping them through the slits in his ears, he would seize his spear— which in length and slightness resembled a fishing-pole —and go stalking beneath the shadows of the neighboring groves, as if about to give a hostile meeting to some cannibal knight. But he would soon return again, and hiding his weapon under the projecting eaves of the house, and rolling his clumsy trinkets carefully in a piece of tappa, would resume his more pacific operations as quietly as if he had never interrupted them.

But despite his eccentricities, Marheyo was a most

paternal and warm-hearted old fellow, and in this particular not a little resembled his son Kory-Kory. The
mother of the latter was the mistress of the family, and
a notable housewife, and a most industrious old lady
she was. If she did not understand the art of making
jellies, jams, custards, tea-cakes, and suchlike trashy
affairs, she was profoundly skilled in the mysteries of
preparing "amar," "poee-poee," and "kokoo," with other
substantial matters. She was a genuine busybody; bustling about the house like a country landlady at an unexpected arrival; for ever giving the young girls tasks
to perform, which the little hussies as often neglected;
poking into every corner, and rummaging over bundles
of old tappa, or making a prodigious clatter among the
calabashes. Sometimes she might have been seen squatting upon her haunches in front of a huge wooden basin,
and kneading "poee-poee" with terrific vehemence, dashing the stone pestle about as if she would shiver the
vessel into fragments; on other occasions, galloping
about the valley in search of a particular kind of leaf
used in some of her recondite operations, and returning
home, toiling and sweating, with a bundle of it, under
which most women would have sunk.

To tell the truth, Kory-Kory's mother was the only
industrious person in all the valley of Typee; and she
could not have employed herself more actively had she
been left an exceedingly muscular and destitute widow,
with an inordinate supply of young children in the
bleakest part of the civilized world. There was not the
slightest necessity for the greater portion of the labor
performed by the old lady: but she seemed to work
from some irresistible impulse; her limbs continually
swaying to and fro, as if there were some indefatigable
engine concealed within her body which kept her in
perpetual motion.

Never suppose that she was a termagant or a shrew for all this: she had the kindliest heart in the world, and acted towards me in particular in a truly maternal manner, occasionally putting some little morsel of choice food into my hand, some outlandish kind of savage sweetmeat or pastry, like a doting mother petting a sickly urchin with tarts and sugar-plums. Warm indeed are my remembrances of the dear, good, affectionate old Tinor!

Besides the individuals I have mentioned, there belonged to the household three young men, dissipated, good-for-nothing, roystering blades of savages, who were either employed in prosecuting love-affairs with the maidens of the tribe, or grew boozy on "arva" and tobacco in the company of congenial spirits, the scapegraces of the valley.

Among the permanent inmates of the house were likewise several lovely damsels, who instead of thrumming pianos and reading novels, like more enlightened young ladies, substituted for these employments the manufacture of a fine species of tappa; but for the greater portion of the time were skipping from house to house, gadding and gossiping with their acquaintances.

From the rest of these, however, I must except the beauteous nymph Fayaway, who was my peculiar favorite. Her free, pliant figure was the very perfection of female grace and beauty. Her complexion was a rich and mantling olive, and when watching the glow upon her cheeks I could almost swear that beneath the transparent medium there lurked the blushes of a faint vermilion. The face of this girl was a rounded oval, and each feature as perfectly formed as the heart or imagination of man could desire. Her full lips, when parted with a smile, disclosed teeth of a dazzling whiteness;

and when her rosy mouth opened with a burst of merriment, they looked like the milk-white seeds of the "arta," a fruit of the valley, which, when cleft in twain, shows them reposing in rows on either side, imbedded in the rich and juicy pulp. Her hair of the deepest brown, parted irregularly in the middle, flowed in natural ringlets over her shoulders, and whenever she chanced to stoop, fell over and hid from view her lovely bosom. Gazing into the depths of her strange blue eyes, when she was in a contemplative mood, they seemed most placid yet unfathomable; but when illuminated by some lively emotion, they beamed upon the beholder like stars. The hands of Fayaway were as soft and delicate as those of any countess; for an entire exemption from rude labor marks the girlhood and even prime of a Typee woman's life. Her feet, though wholly exposed, were as diminutive and fairly shaped as those which peep from beneath the skirts of a Lima lady's dress. The skin of this young creature, from continual ablutions and the use of mollifying ointments, was inconceivably smooth and soft.

I may succeed, perhaps, in particularizing some of the individual features of Fayaway's beauty, but that general loveliness of appearance which they all contributed to produce I will not attempt to describe. The easy unstudied graces of a child of nature like this, breathing from infancy an atmosphere of perpetual summer, and nurtured by the simple fruits of the earth; enjoying a perfect freedom from care and anxiety, and removed effectually from all injurious tendencies, strike the eye in a manner which cannot be portrayed. This picture is no fancy sketch; it is drawn from the most vivid recollections of the person delineated.

Were I asked if the beauteous form of Fayaway was altogether free from the hideous blemish of tattooing,

I should be constrained to answer that it was not. But the practitioners of the barbarous art, so remorseless in their inflictions upon the brawny limbs of the warriors of the tribe, seem to be conscious that it needs not the resources of their profession to augment the charms of the maidens of the vale.

The females are very little embellished in this way, and Fayaway, with all the other young girls of her age, were even less so than those of their sex more advanced in years. The reason of this peculiarity will be alluded to hereafter. All the tattooing that the nymph in question exhibited upon her person may be easily described. Three minute dots, no bigger than pin-heads, decorated either lip, and at a little distance were not at all discernible. Just upon the fall of the shoulder were drawn two parallel lines half an inch apart, and perhaps three inches in length, the interval being filled with delicately executed figures. These narrow bands of tattooing, thus placed, always reminded me of those stripes of gold lace worn by officers in undress, and which are in lieu of epaulettes to denote their rank.

Thus much was Fayaway tattooed—the audacious hand which had gone so far in its desecrating work stopping short, apparently wanting the heart to proceed.

But I have omitted to describe the dress worn by this nymph of the valley.

Fayaway—I must avow the fact—for the most part clung to the primitive and summer garb of Eden. But how becoming the costume! It showed her fine figure to the best possible advantage; and nothing could have been better adapted to her peculiar style of beauty. On ordinary occasions she was habited precisely as I have described the two youthful savages whom we had met on first entering the valley. At other times, when rambling among the groves, or visiting at the houses of her acquaintances, she wore a tunic of white tappa, reaching from her waist to a little below the knees; and when exposed for any length of time to the sun, she invariably protected herself from its rays by a floating mantle of the same material, loosely gathered about the person. Her gala dress will be described hereafter.

As the beauties of our own land delight in bedecking themselves with fanciful articles of jewelry, suspending them from their ears, hanging them about their necks, and clasping them around their wrists, so Fayaway and her companions were in the habit of ornamenting themselves with similar appendages.

Flora was their jeweler. Sometimes they wore necklaces of small carnation flowers, strung like rubies upon a fiber of tappa, or displayed in their ears a single white bud, the stem thrust backward through the aperture, and showing in front the delicate petals folded together in a beautiful sphere, and looking like a drop of the purest pearl. Chaplets too, resembling in their arrangement the strawberry coronal worn by an English peeress, and composed of intertwined leaves and blossoms, often crowned their temples; and bracelets and anklets of the same tasteful pattern were frequently to be seen. Indeed, the maidens of the island were passionately fond of flowers, and never wearied of decorating their persons with them; a lovely trait in their character, and one that ere long will be more fully alluded to.

Though, in my eyes at least, Fayaway was indisputably the loveliest female I saw in Typee, yet the description I have given of her will in some measure apply to nearly all the youthful portion of her sex in the valley. Judge ye then, reader, what beautiful creatures they must have been.

XII

When Mehevi had departed from the house, as related in the preceding chapter, Kory-Kory commenced the functions of the post assigned him. He brought us various kinds of food; and, as if I were an infant, insisted upon feeding me with his own hands. To this procedure I, of course, most earnestly objected, but in vain; and having laid a calabash of kokoo before me, he washed his fingers in a vessel of water, and then putting his hand into the dish and rolling the food into little balls, put them one after another into my mouth. All my remonstrances against this measure only provoked so great a clamor on his part, that I was obliged to acquiesce; and the operation of feeding being thus facilitated, the meal was quickly dispatched. As for Toby, he was allowed to help himself after his own fashion.

The repast over, my attendant arranged the mats for repose, and, bidding me lie down, covered me with a large robe of tappa, at the same time looking approvingly upon me, and exclaiming, "Ki-ki, muee muee, ah! moee moee mortarkee" (Eat plenty, ah! sleep very good). The philosophy of this sentiment I did not pretend to question; for deprived of sleep for several preceding nights, and the pain in my limb having much abated, I now felt inclined to avail myself of the opportunity afforded me.

The next morning, on waking, I found Kory-Kory stretched out on one side of me, while my companion lay upon the other. I felt sensibly refreshed after a night of sound repose, and immediately agreed to the proposition of my valet that I should repair to the water and wash, although dreading the suffering that the exertion might produce. From this apprehension, however, I was quickly relieved; for Kory-Kory, leaping from the pi-pi, and then backing himself up against it, like a porter in readiness to shoulder a trunk, with loud vociferations and a superabundance of gestures, gave me to understand that I was to mount upon his back and be thus transported to the stream, which flowed perhaps two hundred yards from the house.

Our appearance upon the verandah in front of the habitation drew together quite a crowd, who stood looking on and conversing with one another in the most animated manner. They reminded one of a group of idlers gathered about the door of a village tavern when the equipage of some distinguished traveler is brought round previous to his departure. As soon as I clasped my arms about the neck of the devoted fellow, and he jogged off with me, the crowd—composed chiefly of young girls and boys—followed after, shouting and capering with infinite glee, and accompanied us to the banks of the stream.

On gaining it, Kory-Kory, wading up to his hips in the water, carried me half-way across, and deposited me on a smooth black stone which rose a few inches above the surface. The amphibious rabble at our heels plunged in after us, and, climbing to the summit of the grass-grown rocks with which the bed of the brook was here and there broken, waited curiously to witness our morning ablutions.

Somewhat embarrassed by the presence of the female portion of the company, and feeling my cheeks burning with bashful timidity, I formed a primitive basin by joining my hands together, and cooled my blushes in the water it contained; then removing my frock bent over and washed myself down to my waist in the stream. As soon as Kory-Kory comprehended from my motions that this was to be the extent of my performance, he appeared perfectly aghast with astonishment, and rushing towards me, poured out a torrent of words in eager deprecation of so limited an operation, enjoining me by unmistakable signs to immerse my whole body. To this I was forced to consent; and the honest fellow, regarding me as a froward, inexperienced child, whom it was his duty to serve at the risk of offending, lifted me from the rock, and tenderly bathed my limbs. This over, and resuming my seat, I could not avoid bursting into admiration of the scene around me.

From the verdant surfaces of the large stones that lay scattered about, the natives were now sliding off into the water, diving and ducking beneath the surface in all directions—the young girls springing buoyantly into the air, and revealing their naked forms to the waist, with their long tresses dancing about their shoulders, their eyes sparkling like drops of dew in the sun, and their gay laughter pealing forth at every frolicsome incident.

On the afternoon of the day that I took my first bath in the valley, we received another visit from Mehevi. The noble savage seemed to be in the same pleasant mood, and was quite as cordial in his manner as before. After remaining about an hour, he rose from the mats, and motioning to leave the house, invited Toby and myself to accompany him. I pointed to my leg; but Mehevi in his turn pointed to Kory-Kory, and removed that objection; so, mounting upon the faithful fellow's shoulders again—like the old man of the sea astride of Sindbad—I followed after the chief.

The nature of the route we now pursued struck me more forcibly than anything I had yet seen, as illustrating the indolent disposition of the islanders. The path was obviously the most beaten one in the valley, several others leading from either side into it, and perhaps for successive generations it had formed the principal avenue of the place. And yet, until I grew more familiar with its impediments, it seemed as difficult to travel as the recesses of a wilderness. Part of it swept round an abrupt rise of ground, the surface of which was broken by frequent inequalities, and thickly strewn with projecting masses of rocks, whose summits were often hidden from view by the drooping foliage of the luxuriant vegetation. Sometimes directly over, sometimes evading these obstacles with a wide circuit, the path wound along—one moment climbing over a sudden eminence smooth with continued wear, then descending on the other side into a steep glen, and crossing the flinty channel of a brook. Here it pursued the depths of a glade, occasionally obliging you to stoop beneath vast horizontal branches; and now you stepped over huge trunks and boughs that lay rotting across the track.

Such was the grand thoroughfare of Typee. After proceeding a little distance along it—Kory-Kory panting and blowing with the weight of his burden—I dismounted from his back, and grasping the long spear of Mehevi in my hand, assisted my steps over the numerous obstacles of the road; preferring this mode of advance to one which, from the difficulties of the way, was equally painful to myself and my wearied servitor.

Our journey was soon at an end; for, scaling a sudden height, we came abruptly upon the place of our destination. I wish that it were possible to sketch in words this spot as vividly as I recollect it.

Here were situated the Taboo groves of the valley —the scene of many a prolonged feast, of many a horrid rite. Beneath the dark shadows of the consecrated breadfruit-trees there reigned a solemn twilight—a cathedral-like gloom. The frightful genius of pagan worship seemed to brood in silence over the place, breathing its spell upon every object around. Here and there, in the depths of these awful shades, half screened from sight by masses of overhanging foliage, rose the idolatrous altars of the savages, built of enormous blocks of black and polished stone, placed one upon another, without cement, to the height of twelve or fifteen feet, and surmounted by a rustic open temple, enclosed with a low picket of canes, within which might be seen, in various stages of decay, offerings of breadfruit and coconuts, and the putrefying relics of some recent sacrifice.

In the midst of the wood was the hallowed "Hoolah-Hoolah" ground—set apart for the celebration of the fantastic religious ritual of these people—comprising an extensive oblong "pi-pi," terminating at either end in a lofty terraced altar, guarded by ranks of hideous wooden idols, and with the two remaining sides flanked by ranges of bamboo sheds, opening towards the interior of the quadrangle thus formed. Vast trees, standing in the middle of this space, and throwing over it an umbrageous shade, had their massive trunks built round with slight stages, elevated a few feet above the ground, and railed in with canes, forming so many rustic pulpits, from which the priests harangued their devotees.

This holiest of spots was defended from profanation by the strictest edicts of the all-pervading "taboo," which condemned to instant death the sacrilegious female who should enter or touch its sacred precincts, or even so much as press with her feet the ground made holy by the shadows that it cast.

Access was had to the enclosure through an embowered entrance on one side, facing a number of towering coco-nut trees, planted at intervals along a level area of a hundred yards. At the further extremity of this space was to be seen a building of considerable size, reserved for the habitation of the priests and religious attendants of the groves.

In its vicinity was another remarkable edifice, built as usual upon the summit of a pi-pi, and at least two hundred feet in length, though not more than twenty in breadth. The whole front of this latter structure was completely open, and from one end to the other ran a narrow verandah, fenced in on the edge of the pi-pi with a picket of canes. Its interior presented the appearance of an immense lounging-place, the entire floor being strewn with successive layers of mats, lying between parallel trunks of coco-nut trees, selected for the purpose from the straightest and most symmetrical the vale afforded.

To this building, denominated in the language of the natives the "Ti," Mehevi now conducted us. Thus far we had been accompanied by a troop of the natives of both sexes; but as soon as we approached its vicinity, the females gradually separated themselves from the crowd, and standing aloof, permitted us to pass on. The merciless prohibitions of the taboo extended likewise to this edifice, and were enforced by the same dreadful penalty that secured the hoolah-hoolah ground from the imaginary pollution of a woman's presence.

On entering the house, I was surprised to see six muskets ranged against the bamboo on one side, from the barrels of which depended as many small canvas pouches, partly filled with powder. Disposed about these muskets, like the cutlasses that decorate the bulkhead of a man-of-war's cabin, were a great variety of rude spears and paddles, javelins, and war-clubs. This then, said I to Toby, must be the armory of the tribe.

As we advanced further along the building, we were struck with the aspect of four or five hideous old wretches, on whose decrepit forms time and tattooing seemed to have obliterated every trace of humanity. Owing to the continued operation of this latter process, which only terminates among the warriors of the island after all the figures stretched upon their limbs in youth have been blended together—an effect, however, produced only in cases of extreme longevity—the bodies of these men were of a uniform dull green color—the hue which the tattooing gradually assumes as the individual advances in age. Their skin had a frightful scaly appearance, which, united with its singular color, made their limbs not a little resemble dusty specimens of verd-antique. Their flesh, in parts, hung upon them in huge folds, like the overlapping pleats on the flank of a rhinoceros. Their heads were completely bald, whilst their faces were puckered into a thousand wrinkles, and they presented no vestige of a beard. But the most remarkable peculiarity about them was the appearance of their feet; the toes, like the radiating lines of the mariner's compass, pointed to every quarter of the horizon. This was doubtless attributable to the fact, that during nearly a hundred years of existence, the said toes never had been subjected to any artificial confinement, and in their old age, being averse to close neighborhood, bid one another keep open order.

These repulsive-looking creatures appeared to have lost the use of their lower limbs altogether; sitting upon the floor cross-legged in a state of torpor. They never heeded us in the least, scarcely looking conscious of our presence, while Mehevi seated us upon the mats, and Kory-Kory gave utterance to some unintelligible gibberish.

In a few moments a boy entered with a wooden trencher of poee-poee; and in regaling myself with its contents I was obliged again to submit to the officious intervention of my indefatigable servitor. Various other dishes followed, the chief manifesting the most hospitable importunity in pressing us to partake, and to remove all bashfulness on our part, set us no despicable example in his own person.

The repast concluded, a pipe was lighted, which passed from mouth to mouth, and yielding to its soporific influence, the quiet of the place, and the deepening shadows of approaching night, my companion and I sank into a kind of drowsy repose, while the chief and Kory-Kory seemed to be slumbering beside us.

I awoke from an uneasy nap, about midnight, as I supposed; and, raising myself partly from the mat, became sensible that we were enveloped in utter darkness. Toby lay still asleep, but our late companion had disappeared. The only sound that interrupted the silence of the place was the asthmatic breathing of the old men I have mentioned, who reposed at a little distance from us. Beside them, as well as I could judge, there was no one else in the house.

Apprehensive of some evil, I roused my comrade, and we were engaged in a whispered conference concerning the unexpected withdrawal of the natives when all at once, from the depth of the grove, in full view of us where we lay, shoots of flame were seen to rise, and in a few moments illuminated the surrounding trees, casting, by contrast, into still deeper gloom the darkness around us.

While we continued gazing at this sight, dark figures appeared moving to and fro before the flames; while others, dancing and capering about, looked like so many demons.

Regarding this new phenomenon with no small degree of trepidation, I said to my companion, "What can all this mean, Toby?"

"Oh, nothing," replied he; "getting the fire ready, I suppose."

"Fire!" exclaimed I, while my heart took to beating like a trip-hammer, "what fire?"

"Why, the fire to cook us, to be sure; what else would the cannibals be kicking up such a row about if it were not for that?"

"Oh, Toby! have done with your jokes; this is no time for them; something is about to happen, I feel confident."

"Jokes, indeed!" exclaimed Toby, indignantly. "Did you ever hear me joke? Why, for what do you suppose the devils have been feeding us up in this kind of style during the last three days, unless it were for something that you are too much frightened at to talk about? Look at that Kory-Kory there!—has he not been stuffing you with his confounded mushes, just in the way they treat swine before they kill them? Depend upon it, we will be eaten this blessed night, and there is the fire we shall be roasted by."

This view of the matter was not at all calculated to allay my apprehensions, and I shuddered when I reflected that we were indeed at the mercy of a tribe of cannibals, and that the dreadful contingency to which Toby had alluded was by no means removed beyond the bounds of possibility.

"There! I told you so! they are coming for us!" exclaimed my companion the next moment, as the forms of four of the islanders were seen in bold relief against the illuminated background, mounting the pi-pi and approaching towards us.

They came on noiselessly, nay stealthily, and glided along through the gloom that surrounded us as if about to spring upon some object they were fearful of disturbing before they should make sure of it.—Gracious heaven! the horrible reflections which crowded upon me that moment.—A cold sweat stood upon my brow, and spellbound with terror I awaited my fate!

Suddenly the silence was broken by the well-remembered tones of Mehevi, and at the kindly accents of his voice my fears were immediately dissipated. "Tommo, Toby, ki ki!" (eat).—He had waited to address us until he had assured himself that we were both awake, at which he seemed somewhat surprised.

"Ki ki! is it?" said Toby in his gruff tones; "well, cook us first, will you?—but what's this?" he added, as another savage appeared, bearing before him a large trencher of wood, containing some kind of steaming meat, as appeared from the odors it diffused, and which he deposited at the feet of Mehevi. "A baked baby, I dare say! but I will have none of it, never mind what it is.—A pretty fool I should make of myself, indeed, waked up here in the middle of the night, stuffing and guzzling, and all to make a fat meal for a parcel of bloody-minded cannibals one of these mornings!—No, I see what they are at very plainly, so I am resolved to starve myself into a bunch of bones and gristle, and then, if they serve me up, they are welcome! But I say, Tommo, you are not going to eat any of that mess there, in the dark, are you? Why, how can you tell what it is?"

"By tasting it, to be sure," said I, masticating a morsel that Kory-Kory had just put in my mouth; "and excellently good it is too, very much like veal."

"A baked baby, by the soul of Captain Cook!" burst forth Toby, with amazing vehemence; "Veal! why there never was a calf on the island till you landed.

I tell you you are bolting down mouthfuls from a dead Happar's carcass, as sure as you live, and no mistake!"

Emetics and lukewarm water! What a sensation in the abdominal regions! Sure enough, where could the fiends incarnate have obtained meat? But I resolved to satisfy myself at all hazards; and, turning to Mehevi, I soon made the ready chief understand that I wished a light to be brought. When the taper came, I gazed eagerly into the vessel, and recognized the mutilated remains of a juvenile porker! "Puarkee!" exclaimed Kory-Kory, looking complacently at the dish; and from that day to this I have never forgotten that such is the designation of a pig in the Typee lingo.

The next morning, after being again abundantly feasted by the hospitable Mehevi, Toby and myself arose to depart. But the chief requested us to postpone our intention. "Abo, abo" (Wait, wait), he said, and accordingly we resumed our seats, while, assisted by the zealous Kory-Kory, he appeared to be engaged in giving directions to a number of the natives outside, who were busily employed in making arrangements, the nature of which we could not comprehend. But we were not left long in our ignorance, for a few moments only had elapsed when the chief beckoned us to approach, and we perceived that he had been marshaling a kind of guard of honor to escort us on our return to the house of Marheyo.

The procession was led off by two venerable-looking savages, each provided with a spear, from the end of which streamed a pennon of milk-white tappa. After them went several youths, bearing aloft calabashes of poee-poee; and followed in their turn by four stalwart fellows, sustaining long bamboos, from the tops of which hung suspended, at least twenty feet from the ground, large baskets of green breadfruit. Then came a troop of boys, carrying bunches of ripe bananas, and baskets made of the woven leaflets of coco-nut boughs, filled with the young fruit of the tree, the naked shells stripped of their husks peeping forth from the verdant wicker-work that surrounded them. Last of all came a burly islander, holding over his head a wooden trencher, in which lay disposed the remnants of our midnight feast, hidden from view, however, by a covering of breadfruit leaves.

Astonished as I was at this exhibition, I could not avoid smiling at its grotesque appearance, and the associations it naturally called up. Mehevi, it seemed, was bent on replenishing old Marheyo's larder, fearful perhaps that without this precaution his guests might not fare as well as they could desire.

As soon as I descended from the pi-pi, the procession formed anew, enclosing us in its center; where I remained part of the time, carried by Kory-Kory, and occasionally relieving him from his burden by limping along with a spear. When we moved off in this order, the natives struck up a musical recitative, which, with various alternations, they continued until we arrived at the place of our destination.

As we proceeded on our way, bands of young girls, darting from the surrounding groves, hung upon our skirts, and accompanied us with shouts of merriment and delight, which almost drowned the deep notes of the recitative. On approaching old Marheyo's domicile, its inmates rushed out to receive us; and while the gifts of Mehevi were being disposed of, the superannuated warrior did the honors of his mansion with all the warmth of hospitality evinced by an English squire when he regales his friends at some fine old patrimonial mansion.

XIII

Amidst these novel scenes a week passed away almost imperceptibly. The natives, actuated by some mysterious impulse, day after day redoubled their attentions to us. Their manner towards us was unaccountable. Surely, thought I, they would not act thus if they meant us any harm. But why this excess of deferential kindness, or what equivalent can they imagine us capable of rendering them for it?

We were fairly puzzled. But despite the apprehensions I could not dispel, the horrible character imputed to these Typees appeared to me wholly undeserved.

"Why, they are cannibals!" said Toby on one occasion when I eulogized the tribe. "Granted," I replied, "but a more humane, gentlemanly, and amiable set of epicures do not probably exist in the Pacific."

But, notwithstanding the kind of treatment we received, I was too familiar with the fickle disposition of savages not to feel anxious to withdraw from the valley, and put myself beyond the reach of that fearful death which, under all these smiling appearances, might yet menace us. But here there was an obstacle in the way of doing so. It was idle for me to think of moving from the place until I should have recovered from the severe lameness that afflicted me; indeed my malady began seriously to alarm me; for, despite the herbal remedies of the natives, it continued to grow worse and worse. Their mild applications, though they soothed the pain, did not remove the disorder, and I felt convinced that without better aid I might anticipate long and acute suffering.

But how was this aid to be procured? From the surgeons of the French fleet, which probably still lay in the bay of Nukuheva, it might easily have been obtained, could I have made my case known to them. But how could that be effected?

At last, in the exigency to which I was reduced, I proposed to Toby that he should endeavor to go round to Nukuheva, and if he could not succeed in returning to the valley by water, in one of the boats of the squadron, and taking me off, he might at least procure me some proper medicines, and effect his return overland.

My companion listened to me in silence, and at first did not appear to relish the idea. The truth was he felt impatient to escape from the place, and wished to avail himself of our present high favor with the natives to make good our retreat, before we should experience some sudden alteration in their behavior. As he could not think of leaving me in my helpless condition, he implored me to be of good cheer, assured me that I should soon be better and enabled in a few days to return with him to Nukuheva.

Added to this, he could not bear the idea of again returning to this dangerous place; and as for the expectation of persuading the Frenchmen to detach a boat's crew for the purpose of rescuing me from the Typees, he looked upon it as idle; and, with arguments that I could not answer, urged the improbability of their provoking the hostilities of the clan by any such measure; especially as, for the purpose of quieting its apprehensions, they had as yet refrained from making any visit to the bay. "And even should they consent," said Toby, "they would only produce a commotion in the valley, in which we might both be sacrificed by these ferocious islanders." This was unanswerable; but still I clung to the belief that he might succeed in accomplishing the other part of my plan; and at last I overcame his scruples, and he agreed to make the attempt.

As soon as we succeeded in making the natives understand our intention, they broke out into the most vehement opposition to the measure, and for a while I almost despaired of obtaining their consent. At the bare thought of one of us leaving them, they manifested the most lively concern. The grief and consternation of Kory-Kory, in particular, was unbounded; he threw himself into a perfect paroxysm of gestures, which were intended to convey to us not only his abhorrence of Nukuheva and its uncivilized inhabitants, but also his astonishment that after becoming acquainted with the enlightened Typees, we should evince the least desire to withdraw, even for a time, from their agreeable society.

However, I overbore his objections by appealing to my lameness; from which I assured the natives I should speedily recover, if Toby were permitted to obtain the supplies I needed.

It was agreed that on the following morning my companion should depart, accompanied by some one or two of the household, who should point out to him an easy route, by which the bay might be reached before sunset.

At early dawn of the next day, our habitation was astir. One of the young men mounted into an adjoining coco-nut tree, and threw down a number of the young fruit, which old Marheyo quickly stripped of the green husks, and strung together upon a short pole. These were intended to refresh Toby on his route.

The preparations being completed, with no little emotion I bade my companion adieu. He promised to return in three days at farthest; and, bidding me keep up my spirits in the interval, turned round the corner of the pi-pi, and, under the guidance of the venerable Marheyo, was soon out of sight. His departure oppressed me with melancholy, and, re-entering the dwelling, I threw myself almost in despair upon the matting of the floor.

In two hours' time the old warrior returned, and gave me to understand that, after accompanying my companion a little distance, and showing him the route, he had left him journeying on his way.

It was about noon of this same day, a season which these people are wont to pass in sleep, that I lay in the house, surrounded by its slumbering inmates, and painfully affected by the strange silence which prevailed. All at once I thought I heard a faint shout, as if proceeding from some persons in the depth of the grove which extended in front of our habitation.

The sounds grew louder and nearer, and gradually the whole valley rang with wild outcries. The sleepers around me started to their feet in alarm, and hurried outside to discover the cause of the commotion. Kory-Kory, who had been the first to spring up, soon returned almost breathless and nearly frantic with the excitement under which he seemed to be laboring. All that I could understand from him was that some accident had happened to Toby. Apprehensive of some dreadful calamity, I rushed out of the house, and caught sight of a tumultuous crowd, who, with shrieks and lamentations, were just emerging from the grove bearing in their arms some object, the sight of which produced all this transport of sorrow. As they drew near, the men redoubled their cries, while the girls, tossing their bare arms in the air, exclaimed plaintively, "Awha! awha! Toby muckee moee!"—Alas! alas! Toby is killed!

In a moment the crowd opened, and disclosed the apparently lifeless body of my companion borne between two men, the head hanging heavily against the breast of the foremost. The whole face, neck, and bosom were covered with blood, which still trickled slowly from a wound behind the temple. In the midst of the greatest uproar and confusion the body was carried into the house and laid on a mat. Waving the natives off to give room and air, I bent eagerly over Toby, and, laying my hand upon the breast, ascertained that the heart still beat. Overjoyed at this, I seized a calabash of water, and dashed its contents upon his face, then wiping away the blood, anxiously examined the wound. It was about three inches long, and on removing the clotted hair from about it, showed the skull laid completely bare. Immediately with my knife I cut away the heavy locks, and bathed the part repeatedly in water.

In a few moments Toby revived, and, opening his eyes for a second, closed them again without speaking. Kory-Kory, who had been kneeling beside me, now chafed his limbs gently with the palms of his hands, while a young girl at his head kept fanning him, and I still continued to moisten his lips and brow. Soon my poor comrade showed signs of animation, and I succeeded in making him swallow from a coco-nut shell a few mouthfuls of water.

Old Tinor now appeared, holding in her hand some simples she had gathered, the juice of which she by signs besought me to squeeze into the wound. Having done so, I thought it best to leave Toby undisturbed until he should have had time to rally his faculties. Several times he opened his lips, but fearful for his safety I enjoined silence. In the course of two or three hours, however, he sat up, and was sufficiently recovered to tell me what had occurred.

"After leaving the house with Marheyo," said Toby, "we struck across the valley, and ascended the opposite heights. Just beyond them, my guide informed me, lay the valley of Happar, while along their summits, and skirting the head of the vale, was my route to Nukuheva. After mounting a little way up the elevation my guide paused, and gave me to understand that he could not accompany me any farther, and by various signs intimated that he was afraid to approach any nearer the territories of the enemies of his tribe. He, however, pointed out my path, which now lay clearly before me, and bidding me farewell hastily descended the mountain.

"Quite elated at being so near the Happars, I pushed up the acclivity, and soon gained its summit. It tapered up to a sharp ridge, from whence I beheld both the hostile valleys. Here I sat down and rested for a moment, refreshing myself with my coco-nuts. I was soon again pursuing my way along the height, when suddenly I saw three of the islanders, who must have just come out of Happar valley, standing in the path ahead of me. They were each armed with a heavy spear, and one from his appearance I took to be a chief. They sung out something, I could not understand what, and beckoned me to come on.

"Without the least hesitation I advanced towards them, and had approached within about a yard of the foremost, when, pointing angrily into the Typee valley, and uttering some savage exclamation, he wheeled round his weapon like lightning, and struck me in a moment to the ground. The blow inflicted this wound, and took away my senses. As soon as I came to myself, I perceived the three islanders standing a little distance off, and apparently engaged in some violent altercation respecting me.

"My first impulse was to run for it; but, in endeavoring to rise, I fell back, and rolled down a little grassy precipice. The shock seemed to rally my faculties; so, starting to my feet, I fled down the path I had just ascended. I had no need to look behind me, for, from the yells I heard, I knew that my enemies were in full pursuit. Urged on by their fearful outcries, and heedless of the injury I had received—though the blood flowing from the wound trickled over into my eyes and almost blinded me—I rushed down the mountain-side with the speed of the wind. In a short time I had descended nearly a third of the distance, and the savages had ceased their cries, when suddenly a terrific howl burst upon my ear, and at the same moment a heavy javelin darted past me as I fled, and stuck quivering in a tree close to me. Another yell followed, and a second spear and a third shot through the air within a few feet of my body, both of them piercing the ground obliquely in advance of me. The fellows gave a roar of rage and disappointment; but they were afraid, I suppose, of coming down further into the Typee valley, and so abandoned the chase. I saw them recover their weapons and turn back; and I continued my descent as fast as I could.

"What could have caused this ferocious attack on the part of these Happars I could not imagine, unless it were that they had seen me ascending the mountain with Marheyo, and that the mere fact of coming from the Typee valley was sufficient to provoke them.

"As long as I was in danger I scarcely felt the wound I had received; but when the chase was over I began to suffer from it. I had lost my hat in my flight, and the sun scorched my bare head. I felt faint and giddy; but, fearful of falling to the ground beyond the reach of assistance, I staggered on as well as I could, and at last gained the level of the valley and then down I sunk; and I knew nothing more until I found myself lying upon these mats, and you stooping over me with the calabash of water."

Such was Toby's account of this sad affair. I afterwards learned that fortunately he had fallen close to a spot where the natives go for fuel. A party of them caught sight of him as he fell, and sounding the alarm, had lifted him up; and, after ineffectually endeavoring to restore him at the brook, had hurried forward with him to the house.

This incident threw a dark cloud over our prospects. It reminded us that we were hemmed in by hostile tribes, whose territories we could not hope to pass, on our route to Nukuheva, without encountering the effects of their savage resentment. There appeared to be no avenue opened to our escape but the sea, which washed the lower extremity of the vale.

Our Typee friends availed themselves of the recent disaster of Toby to exhort us to a due appreciation of the blessings we enjoyed among them; contrasting their own generous reception of us with the animosity of their neighbors. They likewise dwelt upon the cannibal propensities of the Happars, a subject which they were perfectly aware could not fail to alarm us; while at the same time they earnestly disclaimed all participation in so horrid a custom. Nor did they omit to call upon us to admire the natural loveliness of their own abode, and the lavish abundance with which it produced all manner of luxuriant fruits; exalting it in this particular above any of the surrounding valleys.

Kory-Kory seemed to experience so heartfelt a desire to infuse into our minds proper views on these subjects that, assisted in his endeavors by the little knowledge of the language we had acquired, he actually succeeded in making us comprehend a considerable part of what he said. To facilitate our correct apprehension of his meaning, he at first condensed his ideas into the smallest possible compass.

"Happar keekeeno nuee," he exclaimed; "nuee, nuee, ki ki kannaka!—ah! owlee mortarkee!" which signifies, 'Terrible fellows those Happars!—devour an amazing quantity of men!—ah, shocking bad!" Thus far he explained himself by a variety of gestures, during the performance of which he would dart out of the house, and point abhorrently towards the Happar valley; running in to us again with a rapidity that showed he was fearful we would lose one part of his meaning before he could complete the other; and continuing his illustrations by seizing the fleshy part of my arm in his teeth, intimating by the operation that the people who lived over in that direction would like nothing better than to treat me in that manner.

Having assured himself that we were fully enlightened on this point, he proceeded to another branch of his subject. "Ah! Typee mortarkee!—nuee, nuee mioree —nuee, nuee wai—nuee, nuee poee-poee—nuee, nuee kokoo—ah! nuee, nuee ki ki—ah! nuee, nuee, nuee!" Which, literally interpreted as before, would imply, "Ah, Typee! isn't it a fine place though!—no danger of starving here, I tell you!—plenty of breadfruit—plenty of water—plenty of pudding—ah! plenty of everything!— ah! heaps, heaps, heaps!" All this was accompanied by a running commentary of signs and gestures which it was impossible not to comprehend.

As he continued his harangue, however, Kory-Kory, in emulation of our more polished orators, began to launch out rather diffusely into other branches of his subject, enlarging, probably, upon the moral reflections it suggested; and proceeded in such a strain of unintelligible and stunning gibberish, that he actually gave me the headache for the rest of the day.

XIV

In the course of a few days Toby had recovered from the effects of his adventure with the Happar warriors; the wound on his head rapidly healing under the vegetable treatment of the good Tinor. Less fortunate than my companion, however, I still continued to languish under a complaint the origin and nature of which were still a mystery. Cut off as I was from all intercourse with the civilized world, and feeling the inefficiency of anything the natives could do to relieve me; knowing too, that so long as I remained in my present condition, it would be impossible for me to leave the valley, whatever opportunity might present itself; and apprehensive that ere long we might be exposed to some caprice on the part of the islanders, I now gave up all hopes of recovery, and became a prey to the most gloomy thoughts. A deep dejection fell upon me, which neither the friendly remonstrances of my companion, the devoted attentions of Kory-Kory, nor all the soothing influences of Fayaway could remove.

One morning as I lay on the mats in the house, plunged in melancholy reverie, and regardless of everything around me, Toby, who had left me about an hour, returned in haste, and with great glee told me to cheer up and be of good heart: for he believed from what was going on among the natives, that there were boats approaching the bay.

These tidings operated upon me like magic. The hour of our deliverance was at hand, and starting up, I was soon convinced that something unusual was about to occur. The word "botee! botee!" was vociferated in all directions; and shouts were heard in the distance, at first feebly and faintly: but growing louder and nearer at each successive repetition, until they were caught up by a fellow in a coco-nut tree a few yards off, who sounding them in turn, they were reiterated from a neighboring grove, and so died away gradually from point to point, as the intelligence penetrated into the farthest recesses of the valley. This was the vocal telegraph of the islanders; by means of which condensed items of information could be carried in a very few minutes from the sea to their remotest habitation, a distance of at least eight or nine miles. On the present occasion it was in active operation; one piece of information following another with inconceivable rapidity.

The greatest commotion now appeared to prevail. At every fresh item of intelligence the natives betrayed the liveliest interest, and redoubled the energy with which they employed themselves in collecting fruit to sell to the expected visitors. Some were tearing off the husks from coco-nuts; some perched in the trees were throwing down breadfruit to their companions, who gathered them into heaps as they fell; while others were plying their fingers rapidly in weaving leafen baskets in which to carry the fruit.

There were other matters too going on at the same time. Here you would see a stout warrior polishing his spear with a bit of old tappa, or adjusting the folds of the girdle about his waist; and there you might descry a young damsel decorating herself with flowers, as if having in her eye some maidenly conquest; while, as in all cases of hurry and confusion in every part of the world, a number of individuals kept hurrying to and fro, with amazing vigor and perseverance, doing nothing themselves, and hindering others.

Never before had we seen the islanders in such a state of bustle and excitement; and the scene furnished abundant evidence of the fact—that it was only at long intervals any such events occur.

When I thought of the length of time that might intervene before a similar chance of escape would be presented, I bitterly lamented that I had not the power of availing myself effectually of the present opportunity.

From all that we could gather, it appeared that the natives were fearful of arriving too late upon the beach, unless they made extraordinary exertions. Sick and lame as I was, I could have started with Toby at once, had not Kory-Kory not only refused to carry me, but manifested the most invincible repugnance to our leaving the neighborhood of the house. The rest of the savages were equally opposed to our wishes, and seemed grieved and astonished at the earnestness of my solicitations. I clearly perceived that while my attendant avoided all appearance of constraining my movements, he was nevertheless determined to thwart my wish. He seemed to me on this particular occasion, as well as often afterwards, to be executing the orders of some other person with regard to me, though at the same time feeling towards me the most lively affection.

Toby, who had made up his mind to accompany the islanders if possible, as soon as they were in readiness to depart, and who for that reason had refrained from showing the same anxiety that I had done, now represented to me that it was idle for me to entertain the hope of reaching the beach in time to profit by any opportunity that might then be presented.

"Do you not see," said he, "the savages themselves are fearful of being too late, and I should hurry forward myself at once did I not think that if I showed too much eagerness I should destroy all our hopes of reaping any benefit from this fortunate event. If you will only endeavor to appear tranquil or unconcerned, you will quiet their suspicions, and I have no doubt they will then let me go with them to the beach, supposing that I merely go out of curiosity. Should I succeed in getting down to the boats, I will make known the condition in which I have left you, and measures may then be taken to secure our escape."

In the expediency of this I could not but acquiesce; and as the natives had now completed their preparations, I watched with the liveliest interest the reception that Toby's application might meet with. As soon as they understood from my companion that I intended to remain, they appeared to make no objection to his proposition, and even hailed it with pleasure. Their singular conduct on this occasion not a little puzzled me at the time, and imparted to subsequent events an additional mystery.

The islanders were now to be seen hurrying along the path which led to the sea. I shook Toby warmly by the hand, and gave him my Payta hat to shield his wounded head from the sun, as he had lost his own. He cordially returned the pressure of my hand, and solemnly promising to return as soon as the boats should leave the shore, sprang from my side, and the next minute disappeared in a turn of the grove.

In spite of the unpleasant reflections that crowded upon my mind, I could not but be entertained by the novel and animated sight which now met my view. One after another the natives crowded along the narrow path, laden with every variety of fruit. Here, you might have seen one, who, after ineffectually endeavoring to persuade a surly porker to be conducted in leading strings, was obliged at last to seize the perverse animal in his arms, and carry him struggling against his naked breast, and squealing without intermission. There went two, who at a little distance might have been taken for the Hebrew spies, on their return to Moses with the goodly bunch of grapes. One trotted before the other at a distance of a couple of yards, while between them, from a pole resting on their shoulders, was suspended a huge cluster of bananas, which swayed to and fro with the rocking gait at which they proceeded. Here ran another, perspiring with his exertions, and bearing before him a quantity of coco-nuts, who, fearful of being too late, heeded not the fruit that dropped from his basket, and appeared solely intent upon reaching his destination, careless how many of his coco-nuts kept company with him.

In a short time the last straggler was seen hurrying on his way, and the faint shouts of those in advance died insensibly upon the ear. Our part of the valley now appeared nearly deserted by its inhabitants, Kory-Kory, his aged father, and a few decrepit old people being all that were left.

Towards sunset the islanders in small parties began to return from the beach, and among them, as they drew near to the house, I sought to descry the form of my companion. But one after another they passed the dwelling, and I caught no glimpse of him. Supposing, however, that he would soon appear with some of the members of the household, I quieted my apprehensions, and waited patiently to see him advancing in company with the beautiful Fayaway. At last, I perceived Tinor coming forward, followed by the girls and young men who usually resided in the house of Marheyo; but with them came not my comrade, and, filled with a thousand alarms, I eagerly sought to discover the cause of his delay.

My earnest questions appeared to embarrass the

natives greatly. All their accounts were contradictory: one giving me to understand that Toby would be with me in a very short time; another that he did not know where he was; while a third, violently inveighing against him, assured me that he had stolen away, and would never come back. It appeared to me, at the time, that in making these various statements they endeavored to conceal from me some terrible disaster, lest the knowledge of it should overpower me.

Fearful lest some fatal calamity had overtaken him, I sought out young Fayaway, and endeavored to learn from her, if possible, the truth.

This gentle being had early attracted my regard, not only from her extraordinary beauty, but from the attractive cast of her countenance, singularly expressive of intelligence and humanity. Of all the natives she alone seemed to appreciate the effect which the peculiarity of the circumstances in which we were placed had produced upon the minds of my companion and myself. In addressing me—especially when I lay reclining upon the mats suffering from pain—there was a tenderness in her manner which it was impossible to misunderstand or resist. Whenever she entered the house, the expression of her face indicated the liveliest sympathy for me; and moving towards the place where I lay, with one arm slightly elevated in a gesture of pity, and her large glistening eyes gazing intently into mine, she would murmur plaintively, "Awha! awha! Tommo," and seat herself mournfully beside me.

Her manner convinced me that she deeply compassionated my situation, as being removed from my country and friends, and placed beyond the reach of all relief. Indeed, at times I was almost led to believe that her mind was swayed by gentle impulses hardly to be anticipated from one in her condition; that she appeared to be conscious there were ties rudely severed, which had once bound us to our homes; that there were sisters and brothers anxiously looking forward to our return, who were, perhaps, never more to behold us.

In this amiable light did Fayaway appear in my eyes; and reposing full confidence in her candor and intelligence, I now had recourse to her, in the midst of my alarm, with regard to my companion.

My questions evidently distressed her. She looked round from one to another of the bystanders, as if hardly knowing what answer to give me. At last, yielding to my importunities, she overcame her scruples, and gave me to understand that Toby had gone away with the boats which had visited the bay, but had promised to return at the expiration of three days. At first I accused him of perfidiously deserting me; but as I grew more composed, I upbraided myself for imputing so cowardly an action to him, and tranquillized myself with the belief that he had availed himself of the opportunity to go round to Nukuheva, in order to make some arrangement by which I could be removed from the valley. At any rate, thought I, he will return with the medicines I require, and then, as soon as I recover, there will be no difficulty in the way of our departure.

Consoling myself with these reflections, I lay down that night in a happier frame of mind than I had done for some time. The next day passed without any allusion to Toby on the part of the natives, who seemed desirous of avoiding all reference to the subject. This raised some apprehensions in my breast; but when night came, I congratulated myself that the second day had now gone by and that on the morrow Toby would again be with me. But the morrow came and went, and my companion did not appear. Ah! thought I, he reckons three days from the morning of his departure—tomorrow he will arrive. But that weary day also closed upon me, without his return. Even yet I would not despair; I thought that something detained him—that he was waiting for the sailing of a boat, at Nukuheva, and that in a day or two at farthest I should see him again. But day after day of renewed disappointment passed by; at last hope deserted me, and I fell a victim to despair.

Yes, thought I, gloomily, he has secured his own escape, and cares not what calamity may befall his unfortunate comrade. Fool that I was to suppose that any one would willingly encounter the perils of this valley, after having once got beyond its limits! He has gone, and has left me to combat alone all the dangers by which I am surrounded. Thus would I sometimes seek to derive a desperate consolation from dwelling upon the perfidy of Toby: whilst at other times I sunk under the bitter remorse which I felt as having by my own imprudence brought upon myself the fate which I was sure awaited me.

At other times I thought that perhaps after all these treacherous savages had made away with him, and thence the confusion into which they were thrown by my questions, and their contradictory answers, or he might be a captive in some other part of the valley; or, more dreadful still, might have met with that fate at which my very soul shuddered. But all these speculations were vain; no tidings of Toby ever reached me; he had gone never to return.

The conduct of the islanders appeared inexplicable. All reference to my lost comrade was carefully evaded, and if at any time they were forced to make some reply to my frequent inquiries on the subject, they would uniformly denounce him as an ungrateful runaway, who

had deserted his friend, and taken himself off to that
vile and detestable place Nukuheva.

But whatever might have been his fate, now that he
was gone, the natives multiplied their acts of kindness
and attention towards myself, treating me with a degree
of deference which could hardly have been surpassed
had I been some celestial visitant. Kory-Kory never for
one moment left my side, unless it were to execute my
wishes. The faithful fellow, twice every day, in the cool
of the morning and in the evening, insisted upon carrying me to the stream, and bathing me in its refreshing
water.

Frequently in the afternoon he would carry me to a
particular part of the stream, where the beauty of the
scene produced a soothing influence upon my mind.
At this place the waters flowed between grassy banks,
planted with enormous breadfruit-trees, whose vast
branches, interlacing overhead, formed a leafy canopy;
near the stream were several smooth black rocks. One of
these, projecting several feet above the surface of the
water, had upon its summit a shallow cavity, which,
filled with freshly gathered leaves, formed a delightful
couch.

Here I often lay for hours, covered with a gauze-like
veil of tappa, while Fayaway, seated beside me, and
holding in her hand a fan woven from the leaflets of a
young coco-nut bough, brushed aside the insects that
occasionally lighted on my face, and Kory-Kory, with a
view of chasing away my melancholy, performed a thousand antics in the water before us.

As my eye wandered along this romantic stream, it
would fall upon the half-immersed figure of a beautiful
girl, standing in the transparent water, and catching in
a little net a species of diminutive shell-fish, of which

these people are extravagantly fond. Sometimes a chattering group would be seated upon the edge of a low rock in the midst of the brook, busily engaged in thinning and polishing the shells of coco-nuts, by rubbing them briskly with a small stone in the water, an operation which soon converts them into a light and elegant drinking-vessel, somewhat resembling goblets made of tortoise-shell.

But the tranquilizing influences of beautiful scenery, and the exhibition of human life under so novel and charming an aspect, were not my only sources of consolation.

Every evening the girls of the house gathered about me on the mats, and after chasing away Kory-Kory from my side—who, nevertheless, retired only to a little distance and watched their proceedings with the most jealous attention—would anoint my whole body with a fragrant oil, squeezed from a yellow root, previously pounded between a couple of stones, and which in their language is denominated "aka." And most refreshing and agreeable are the juices of the "aka," when applied to one's limbs by the soft palms of sweet nymphs, whose bright eyes are beaming upon you with kindness; and I used to hail with delight the daily recurrence of this luxurious operation, in which I forgot all my troubles, and buried for the time every feeling of sorrow.

Sometimes in the cool of the evening my devoted servitor would lead me out upon the pi-pi in front of the house, and seating me near its edge, protect my body from the annoyances of the insects which occasionally hovered in the air, by wrapping me round with a large roll of tappa. He then bustled about, and employed himself at least twenty minutes in adjusting everything to secure my personal comfort.

Having perfected his arrangements, he would get my pipe, and, lighting it, would hand it to me. Often he was obliged to strike a light for the occasion, and as the mode he adopted was entirely different from what I had ever seen or heard of before, I will describe it.

A straight, dry, and partly decayed stick of the hibiscus, about six feet in length, and half as many inches in diameter, with a smaller bit of wood not more than a foot long, and scarcely an inch wide, is as invariably to be met with in every house in Typee as a box of lucifer matches in the corner of a kitchen cupboard at home.

The islander, placing the larger stick obliquely against some object, with one end elevated at an angle of forty-five degrees, mounts astride of it like an urchin about to gallop off upon a cane, and then, grasping the smaller one firmly in both hands, he rubs its pointed end slowly up and down the extent of a few inches on the principal stick, until at last he makes a narrow groove in the wood, with an abrupt termination at the point furthest from him, where all the dusty particles which the friction creates are accumulated in a little heap.

At first Kory-Kory goes to work quite leisurely, but gradually quickens his pace, and waxing warm in the employment, drives the stick furiously along the smoking channel, plying his hands to and fro with amazing rapidity, the perspiration starting from every pore. As he approaches the climax of his effort, he pants and gasps for breath, and his eyes almost start from their sockets with the violence of his exertions. This is the critical stage of the operation; all his previous labors are vain if he cannot sustain the rapidity of the movement until the reluctant spark is produced. Suddenly he stops, becomes perfectly motionless. His hands still retain their hold of the smaller stick, which is pressed convulsively against the further end of the channel among the fine powder there accumulated, as if he had just pierced through and through some little viper that was wriggling and struggling to escape from his clutches. The next moment a delicate wreath of smoke curls spirally into the air, the heap of dusty particles glows with fire, and Kory-Kory almost breathless, dismounts from his steed.

This operation appeared to me to be the most laborious species of work performed in Typee; and had I possessed a sufficient intimacy with the language to have conveyed my ideas upon the subject, I should certainly have suggested to the most influential of the natives the expediency of establishing a college of vestals to be centrally located in the valley, for the purpose of keeping alive the indispensable article of fire; so as to supersede the necessity of such a vast outlay of strength and good temper, as were usually squandered on these occasions. There might, however, be special difficulties in carrying this plan into execution.

What a striking evidence does this operation furnish of the wide difference between the extreme of savage and civilized life. A gentleman of Typee can bring up a numerous family of children and give them all a highly respectable cannibal education, with infinitely less toil and anxiety than he expends in the simple process of striking a light; whilst a poor European artisan, who through the instrumentality of a lucifer performs the same operation in one second, is put to his wits' end to provide for his starving offspring that food which the children of a Polynesian father, without troubling their parent, pluck from the branches of every tree around them.

XV

All the inhabitants of the valley treated me with great kindness; but as to the household of Marheyo, with whom I was now permanently domiciled, nothing could surpass their efforts to minister to my comfort. To the gratification of my palate they paid the most unwearied attention. They continually invited me to partake of food, and when after eating heartily I declined the viands they continued to offer me, they seemed to think that my appetite stood in need of some piquant stimulant to excite its activity.

In pursuance of this idea, old Marheyo himself would hie him away to the sea-shore by the break of day, for the purpose of collecting various species of rare seaweed; some of which among these people are considered a great luxury. After a whole day spent in this employment, he would return about nightfall with several coco-nut shells filled with different descriptions of kelp. In preparing these for me he manifested all the ostentation of a professed cook, although the chief mystery of the affair appeared to consist in pouring water in judicious quantities upon the slimy contents of his coco-nut shells.

The first time he submitted one of these saline salads to my critical attention I naturally thought that anything collected at such pains must possess peculiar merits; but one mouthful was a complete dose; and great was the consternation of the old warrior at the rapidity with which I ejected his epicurean treat.

How true it is, that the rarity of any particular article enhances its value amazingly. In some part of the valley—I know not where, but probably in the neighborhood of the sea—the girls were sometimes in the habit of procuring small quantities of salt, a thimble-full or so being the result of the united labors of a party of five or six employed for the greater part of the day. This precious commodity they brought to the house, enveloped in multitudinous folds of leaves; and as a special mark of the esteem in which they held me, would spread an immense leaf on the ground, and dropping one by one a few minute particles of the salt upon it, invite me to taste them.

From the extravagant value placed upon the article I verily believe, that with a bushel of common Liver-pool salt all the real estate in Typee might have been purchased. With a small pinch of it in one hand, and a quarter section of a breadfruit in the other, the great-est chief in the valley would have laughed at all the luxuries of a Parisian table.

The celebrity of the breadfruit-tree, and the con-spicuous place it occupies in a Typee bill of fare, in-duces me to give at some length a general description of the tree, and the various modes in which the fruit is prepared.

The breadfruit-tree, in its glorious prime, is a grand and towering object, forming the same feature in a Marquesan landscape that the patriarchal elm does in New England scenery. The latter tree it not a little resembles in height, in the wide spread of its stalwart branches, and in its venerable and imposing aspect.

The leaves of the breadfruit are of great size, and their edges are cut and scolloped as fantastically as those of a lady's lace collar. As they annually tend to-wards decay, they almost rival in the brilliant variety of their gradually changing hues the fleeting shades of the expiring dolphin. The autumnal tints of our American forests, glorious as they are, sink into nothing in com-parison with this tree.

The leaf, in one particular stage, when nearly all the prismatic colors are blended on its surface, is often converted by the natives into a superb and striking head-dress. The principal fiber traversing its length being split open a convenient distance, and the elastic sides of the aperture pressed apart, the head is inserted between them, the leaf drooping on one side, with its forward half turned jauntily up on the brows, and the remaining part spreading laterally behind the ears.

The fruit somewhat resembles in magnitude and general appearance one of our citron melons of ordinary size; but, unlike the citron it has no sectional lines drawn along the outside. Its surface is dotted all over with little conical prominences, looking not unlike the knobs on an antiquated church door. The rind is perhaps an eighth of an inch in thickness; and denuded of this, at the time when it is in the greatest perfection, the fruit presents a beautiful globe of white pulp, the whole of which may be eaten, with the exception of a slender core, which is easily removed.

The breadfruit, however, is never used, and is indeed altogether unfit to be eaten, until submitted in one form or other to the action of fire.

The most simple manner in which this operation is performed, and, I think, the best, consists in placing any number of the freshly plucked fruit, when in a particular stage of greenness, among the embers of a fire, in the same way that you would roast a potato. After the lapse of ten or fifteen minutes, the green rind embrowns and cracks, showing through the fissures in its sides the milk-white interior. As soon as it cools, the rind drops off, and you then have the soft round pulp in its purest and most delicious state. Thus eaten, it has a mild and pleasing flavor.

Sometimes, after having been roasted in the fire, the

natives snatch it briskly from the embers, and permitting it to slip out of the yielding rind into a vessel of cold water, stir up the mixture, which they call "bo-a-cho." I never could endure this compound, and indeed the preparation is not greatly in vogue among the more polite Typees.

There is one form, however, in which the fruit is occasionally served, that renders it a dish fit for a king. As soon as it is taken from the fire the exterior is removed, the core extracted, and the remaining part is placed in a sort of shallow stone mortar, and briskly worked with a pestle of the same substance. While one person is performing this operation, another takes a ripe coco-nut, and breaking it in half, which they also do very cleverly, proceeds to grate the juicy meat into fine particles. This is done by means of a piece of mother-of-pearl shell, lashed firmly to the extreme end of a heavy stick, with its straight side accurately notched like a saw. The stick is sometimes a grotesquely formed limb of a tree, with three or four branches twisting from its body like so many shapeless legs, and sustaining it two or three feet from the ground.

The native, first placing a calabash beneath the nose, as it were, of his curious-looking log-steed, for the purpose of receiving the grated fragments as they fall, mounts astride of it as if it were a hobby-horse, and twirling the inside of one of his hemispheres of coco-nut around the sharp teeth of the mother-of-pearl shell, the pure white meat falls in snowy showers into the receptacle provided. Having obtained a quantity sufficient for his purpose, he places it in a bag made of the net-like fibrous substance attached to all coco-nut trees, and compressing it over the breadfruit, which, being now sufficiently pounded, is put into a wooden bowl—extracts a thick creamy milk. The delicious liquid soon bubbles round the fruit, and leaves it at last just peeping above its surface.

This preparation is called "kokoo," and a most luscious preparation it is. The hobby-horse and the pestle and mortar were in great requisition during the time I remained in the house of Marheyo, and Kory-Kory had frequent occasion to show his skill in their use.

But the great staple articles of food into which the breadfruit is converted by these natives are known respectively by the names of amar and poee-poee.

At a certain season of the year, when the fruit of the hundred groves of the valley has reached its maturity, and hangs in golden spheres from every branch, the islanders assemble in harvest groups, and garner in the abundance which surrounds them. The trees are stripped of their nodding burdens, which, easily freed from the rind and core, are gathered together in capacious wooden vessels, where the pulpy fruit is soon worked by a stone pestle, vigorously applied, into a blended mass of a doughy consistency, called by the natives "tutao." This is then divided into separate parcels, which, after being made up into stout packages, enveloped in successive folds of leaves, and bound round with thongs of bark, are stored away in large receptacles hollowed in the earth, from whence they are drawn as occasion may require.

In this condition the tutao sometimes remains for years, and even is thought to improve by age. Before it is fit to be eaten, however, it has to undergo an additional process. A primitive oven is scooped in the ground, and its bottom being loosely covered with stones, a large fire is kindled within it. As soon as the requisite degree of heat is attained, the embers are removed, and the surface of the stones being covered with thick layers of leaves, one of the larger packages of tutao is deposited upon them, and overspread with another layer of leaves. The whole is then quickly heaped up with earth, and forms a sloping mound.

The tutao thus baked is called "amar"; the action of the oven having converted it into an amber-colored caky substance, a little tart, but not at all disagreeable to the taste.

By another and final process the "amar" is changed into "poee-poee." This transition is rapidly effected. The amar is placed in a vessel, and mixed with water until it gains a proper pudding-like consistency, when, without further preparation, it is in readiness for use. This is the form in which the tutao is generally consumed. The singular mode of eating it I have already described.

Were it not that the breadfruit is thus capable of being preserved for a length of time, the natives might be reduced to a state of starvation; for owing to some unknown cause the trees sometimes fail to bear fruit; and on such occasions the islanders chiefly depend upon the supplies they have been enabled to store away.

This stately tree, which is rarely met with upon the Sandwich Islands, and then only of a very inferior quality, and at Tahiti, does not abound to a degree that renders its fruit the principal article of food, attains its greatest excellence in the genial climate of the Marquesan group, where it grows to an enormous magnitude, and flourishes in the utmost abundance.

XVI

In looking back to this period, and calling to remembrance the numberless proofs of kindness and respect which I received from the natives of the valley, I can scarcely understand how it was that, in the midst of so many consolatory circumstances, my mind should still have been consumed by the most dismal forebodings, and have remained a prey to the profoundest melancholy. It is true that the suspicious circumstances which had attended the disappearance of Toby were enough of themselves to excite distrust with regard to the savages, in whose power I felt myself to be entirely placed, especially when it was combined with the knowledge that these very men, kind and respectful as they were to me, were, after all, nothing better than a set of cannibals.

But my chief source of anxiety, and that which poisoned every temporary enjoyment, was the mysterious disease in my leg, which still remained unabated. All the herbal applications of Tinor, united with the severer discipline of the old leech, and the affectionate nursing of Kory-Kory, had failed to relieve me. I was almost a cripple, and the pain I endured at intervals was agonizing. The unaccountable malady showed no signs of amendment; on the contrary, its violence increased day by day, and threatened the most fatal results, unless some powerful means were employed to counteract it. It seemed as if I were destined to sink under this grievous affliction, or at least that it would hinder me from availing myself of any opportunity of escaping from the valley.

An incident which occurred as nearly as I can estimate about three weeks after the disappearance of Toby convinced me that the natives, from some reason or other, would interpose every possible obstacle to my leaving them.

One morning there was no little excitement evinced by the people near my abode, and which I soon discovered proceeded from a vague report that boats had been seen at a great distance approaching the bay.

Immediately all was bustle and animation. It so happened that day that the pain I suffered having somewhat abated, and feeling in much better spirits than usual, I had complied with Kory-Kory's invitation to visit the chief Mehevi at the place called the "Ti," which I have before described as being situated within the precincts of the Taboo Groves. These sacred recesses were at no great distance from Marheyo's habitation, and lay between it and the sea; the path that conducted to the beach passing directly in front of the Ti, and thence skirting along the border of the groves.

I was reposing upon the mats, within the sacred building, in company with Mehevi and several other chiefs, when the announcement was first made. It sent a thrill of joy through my whole frame;—perhaps Toby was about to return. I rose at once to my feet, and my instinctive impulse was to hurry down to the beach, equally regardless of the distance that separated me from it and of my disabled condition. As soon as Mehevi noticed the effect the intelligence had produced upon me, and the impatience I betrayed to reach the sea, his countenance assumed that inflexible rigidity of expression which had so awed me on the afternoon of our arrival at the house of Marheyo. As I was proceeding to leave the Ti, he laid his hand upon my shoulder, and said gravely, "Abo, abo" (Wait, wait). Solely intent upon the one thought that occupied my mind, and heedless of his request, I was brushing past him, when suddenly he assumed a tone of authority, and told me to "moee" (sit down). Though struck by the alteration in his demeanor, the excitement under which I labored was too strong to permit me to obey the unexpected command, and I was still limping towards the edge of the pi-pi with Kory-Kory clinging to one arm in his efforts to restrain me, when the natives around starting to their feet, ranged themselves along the open front of the building, while Mehevi looked at me scowlingly, and reiterated his commands still more sternly.

It was at this moment, when fifty savage countenances were glaring upon me, that I first truly experienced I was indeed a captive in the valley. The conviction rushed upon me with staggering force, and I was overwhelmed by this confirmation of my worst fears. I saw at once that it was useless for me to resist, and sick at heart, I reseated myself upon the mats, and for the moment abandoned myself to despair.

I now perceived the natives one after the other hurrying past the Ti and pursuing the route that conducted to the sea. These savages, thought I, will soon be holding communication with some of my own countrymen perhaps, who with ease could restore me to liberty did they know of the situation I was in. No language can describe the wretchedness which I felt; and in the bitterness of my soul I imprecated a thousand curses on the perfidious Toby, who had thus abandoned me to destruction. It was in vain that Kory-Kory tempted me with food, or lighted my pipe, or sought to attract my attention by performing the uncouth antics that had sometimes diverted me. I was fairly knocked down by this last misfortune, which, much as I had feared it, I had never before had the courage calmly to contemplate.

Regardless of every thing but my own sorrow, I remained in the Ti for several hours, until shouts proceeding at intervals from the groves beyond the house proclaimed the return of the natives from the beach.

Whether any boats visited the bay that morning or not, I never could ascertain. The savages assured me that there had not—but I was inclined to believe that by deceiving me in this particular they sought to allay the violence of my grief. However that might be, this incident showed plainly that the Typees intended to hold me a prisoner. As they still treated me with the same sedulous attention as before, I was utterly at a loss how to account for their singular conduct. Had I been in a situation to instruct them in any of the rudiments of the mechanic arts, or had I manifested a disposition to render myself in any way useful among them, their conduct might have been attributed to some adequate motive, but as it was, the matter seemed to me inexplicable.

During my whole stay on the island there occurred but two or three instances where the natives applied to me with the view of availing themselves of my superior information. And these now appear so ludicrous that I cannot forbear relating them.

The few things we had brought from Nukuheva had been done up into a small bundle which we had carried with us in our descent to the valley. This bundle, the first night of our arrival, I had used as a pillow, but on the succeeding morning, opening it for the inspection of the natives, they gazed upon the miscellaneous contents as though I had just revealed to them a casket of diamonds, and they insisted that so precious a treasure should be properly secured. A line was accordingly attached to it, and the other end being passed over the ridge-pole of the house, it was hoisted up to the apex of the roof, where it hung suspended directly over the mats where I usually reclined. When I desired anything from it I merely raised my finger to a bamboo beside me, and taking hold of the string which was there fastened, lowered the package. This was exceedingly handy, and I took care to let the natives understand how much I applauded the invention. Of this package the chief contents were a razor with its case, a supply of needles and thread, a pound or two of tobacco, and a few yards of a bright-colored calico.

I should have mentioned that shortly after Toby's disappearance, perceiving the uncertainty of the time I might be obliged to remain in the valley—if, indeed, I ever should escape from it—and considering that my whole wardrobe consisted of a shirt and a pair of trousers, I resolved to doff these garments at once, in order to preserve them in a suitable condition for wear should I again appear among civilized beings. I was consequently obliged to assume the Typee costume, a little altered, however, to suit my own views of propriety, and in which I have no doubt I appeared to as much advantage as a senator of Rome enveloped in the folds of his toga. A few folds of yellow tappa tucked about my waist, descended to my feet in the style of a lady's petticoat, only I did not have recourse to those voluminous paddings in the rear with which our gentle dames are in the habit of augmenting the sublime rotundity of their figures. This usually comprised my indoor dress: whenever I walked out, I superadded to it an ample robe of the same material, which completely enveloped my person, and screened it from the rays of the sun.

One morning I made a rent in this mantle; and to show the islanders with what facility it could be repaired, I lowered my bundle, and taking from it a needle and thread, proceeded to stitch up the opening. They regarded this wonderful application of science with intense admiration; and whilst I was stitching away, old Marheyo, who was one of the lookers-on, suddenly clapped his hand to his forehead and rushing to a corner of the house, drew forth a soiled and tattered strip of faded calico—which he must have procured some time or other in traffic on the beach—and besought me eagerly to exercise a little of my art upon it. I willingly complied though certainly so stumpy a needle as mine never took such gigantic strides over calico before. The repairs completed, old Marheyo gave me a paternal hug; and divesting himself of his "maro" (girdle), swathed the calico about his loins, and slipped the beloved ornaments into his ears, grasped his spear and sailed out of the house, like a valiant Templar arrayed in a new and costly suit of armor.

I never used my razor during my stay in the island, but, although a very subordinate affair, it had been vastly admired by the Typees; and Narmonee, a great hero among them, who was exceedingly precise in the arrangements of his toilet and the general adjustment of his person, being the most accurately tattooed and laboriously horrified individual in all the valley, thought it would be a great advantage to have it applied to the already shaven crown of his head.

The implement they usually employ is a shark's tooth, which is about as well adapted to the purpose as a one-pronged fork for pitching hay. No wonder, then, that the acute Narmonee perceived the advantage my razor possessed over the usual implement. Accordingly, one day he requested as a personal favor that I would just run over his head with the razor. In reply, I gave him to understand that it was too dull, and could not be used to any purpose without being previously sharpened. To assist my meaning, I went through an imaginary honing process on the palm of my hand. Narmonee took my meaning in an instant, and running out of the house, returned the next moment with a huge rough mass of rock as big as a milestone, and indicated to me that that was exactly the thing I wanted. Of course there was nothing left for me but to proceed to business, and I began scraping away at a great rate. He writhed and wriggled under the infliction, but, fully convinced of my skill, endured the pain like a martyr.

Though I never saw Narmonee in battle, I will, from what I then observed, stake my life upon his courage and fortitude. Before commencing operations, his head had presented a surface of short bristling hairs, and by the time I had concluded my unskillful operation it resembled not a little a stubble field after being gone over with a harrow. However, as the chief expressed the liveliest satisfaction at the result, I was too wise to dissent from his opinion.

XVII

Day after day wore on, and still there was no perceptible change in the conduct of the islanders towards me. Gradually I lost all knowledge of the regular occurrence of the days of the week, and sunk insensibly into that kind of apathy which ensues after some violent outbreak of despair. My limb suddenly healed, the swelling went down, the pain subsided, and I had every reason to suppose I should soon completely recover from the affliction that had so long tormented me.

As soon as I was enabled to ramble about the valley in company with the natives, troops of whom followed me whenever I sallied out of the house, I began to experience an elasticity of mind which placed me beyond the reach of those dismal forebodings to which I had so lately been a prey. Received wherever I went with the most deferential kindness; regaled perpetually with the most delightful fruits; ministered to by dark-eyed nymphs; and enjoying besides all the services of the devoted Kory-Kory, I thought that for a sojourn among cannibals, no man could have well made a more agreeable one.

To be sure there were limits set to my wanderings.

Toward the sea my progress was barred by an express prohibition of the savages; and after having made two or three ineffectual attempts to reach it, as much to gratify my curiosity as anything else, I gave up the idea. It was in vain to think of reaching it by stealth, since the natives escorted me in numbers wherever I went, and not for one single moment that I can recall to mind was I ever permitted to be alone.

The green and precipitous elevations that stood ranged around the head of the vale where Marheyo's habitation was situated effectually precluded all hope of escape in that quarter, even if I could have stolen away from the thousand eyes of the savages.

But these reflections now seldom obtruded upon me; I gave myself up to the passing hour, and if ever disagreeable thoughts arose in my mind, I drove them away. When I looked around the verdant recess in which I was buried, and gazed up to the summits of the lofty eminence that hemmed me in, I was well disposed to think that I was in the "Happy Valley," and that beyond those heights there was naught but a world of care and anxiety.

As I extended my wanderings in the valley and grew more familiar with the habits of its inmates, I was fain to confess that, despite the disadvantages of his condition, the Polynesian savage, surrounded by all the luxurious provisions of nature, enjoyed an infinitely happier, though certainly a less intellectual existence, than the self-complacent European.

The naked wretch who shivers beneath the bleak skies, and starves among the inhospitable wilds of Tierra del Fuego, might indeed be made happier by civilization, for it would alleviate his physical wants. But the voluptuous Indian, with every desire supplied, whom

Providence has bountifully provided with all the sources
of pure and natural enjoyment, and from whom are removed so many of the ills and pains of life—what has
he to desire at the hands of Civilization? She may "cultivate his mind," may "elevate his thoughts"—these I believe are the established phrases—but will he be the
happier? Let the once smiling and populous Hawaiian
islands with their now diseased, starving, and dying
natives, answer the question. The missionaries may seek
to disguise the matter as they will, but the facts are
incontrovertible; and the devoutest Christian who visits
that group with an unbiased mind, must go away mournfully asking—"Are these, alas! the fruits of twenty-five
years of enlightening?"

In a primitive state of society, the enjoyments of
life, though few and simple, are spread over a great
extent, and are unalloyed; but Civilization, for every
advantage she imparts, holds a hundred evils in reserve
—the heart burnings, the jealousies, the social rivalries,
the family dissensions, and the thousand self-inflicted
discomforts of refined life, which make up in units the
swelling aggregate of human misery, are unknown
among these unsophisticated people.

But it will be urged that these shocking unprincipled
wretches are cannibals. Very true; and a rather bad trait
in their character it must be allowed. But they are such
only when they seek to gratify the passion of revenge
upon their enemies; and I ask whether the mere eating
of human flesh so very far exceeds in barbarity that
custom which only a few years since was practiced in
enlightened England—a convicted traitor, perhaps a
man found guilty of honesty, patriotism, and such-like
heinous crimes, had his head lopped off with a huge
axe, his bowels dragged out and thrown into a fire;

while his body, carved into four quarters, was with his head exposed upon pikes, and permitted to rot and fester among the public haunts of men!

The fiend-like skill we display in the invention of all manner of death-dealing engines, the vindictiveness with which we carry on our wars, and the misery and desolation that follow in their train, are enough of themselves to distinguish the white civilized man as the most ferocious animal on the face of the earth.

His remorseless cruelty is seen in many of the institutions of our own favored land. There is one in particular lately adopted in one of the States of the Union, which purports to have been dictated by the most merciful considerations. To destroy our malefactors piecemeal, drying up in their veins, drop by drop, the blood we are too chicken-hearted to shed by a single blow which would at once put a period to their sufferings, is deemed to be infinitely preferable to the old-fashioned punishment of gibbeting—much less annoying to the victim, and more in accordance with the refined spirit of the age; and yet how feeble is all language to describe the horrors we inflict upon these wretches, whom we mason up in the cells of our prisons, and condemn to perpetual solitude in the very heart of our population!

But it is needless to multiply the examples of civilized barbarity; they far exceed in the amount of misery they cause the crimes which we regard with such abhorrence in our less enlightened fellow-creatures.

The term "Savage" is, I conceive, often misapplied, and indeed when I consider the vices, cruelties, and enormities of every kind that spring up in the tainted atmosphere of a feverish civilization, I am inclined to think that so far as the relative wickedness of the parties is concerned, four or five Marquesan Islanders sent to the United States as Missionaries might be quite as useful as an equal number of Americans dispatched to the Islands in a similar capacity.

I once heard it given as an instance of the frightful depravity of a certain tribe in the Pacific, that they had no word in their language to express the idea of virtue. The assertion was unfounded; but were it otherwise, it might be met by stating that their language is almost entirely destitute of terms to express the delightful ideas conveyed by our endless catalogue of civilized crimes.

In the altered frame of mind to which I have referred, every object that presented itself to my notice in the valley struck me in a new light, and the opportunities I now enjoyed of observing the manners of its inmates tended to strengthen my favorable impressions. One peculiarity that fixed my admiration was the perpetual hilarity reigning through the whole extent of the vale. There seemed to be no cares, griefs, troubles, or vexations in all Typee. The hours tripped along as gaily as the laughing couples down a country dance.

There were none of those thousand sources of irritation that the ingenuity of civilized man has created to mar his own felicity. There were no foreclosures of mortgages, no protested notes, no bills payable, no debts of honor in Typee; no unreasonable tailors and shoemakers, perversely bent on being paid; no duns of any description; no assault and battery attorneys, to foment discord, backing their clients up to a quarrel, and then knocking their heads together; no poor relations, everlastingly occupying the spare bed-chamber, and diminishing the elbow room at the family table; no destitute widows with their children starving on the cold charities of the world; no beggars; no debtors' prisons; no proud and hard-hearted nabobs in Typee; or to sum up all in one word—no Money! "That root of all evil" was not to be found in the valley.

In this secluded abode of happiness there were no cross old women, no cruel step-dames, no withered spinsters, no love-sick maidens, no sour old bachelors, no inattentive husbands, no melancholy young men, no blubbering youngsters, and no squalling brats. All was mirth, fun, and high good humor. Blue devils, hypochondria, and doleful dumps, went and hid themselves among the nooks and crannies of the rocks.

Here you would see a parcel of children frolicking together the livelong day, and no quarrelling, no contention, among them. The same number in our own land could not have played together for the space of an hour without biting or scratching one another. There you might have seen a throng of young females, not filled with envyings of each other's charms, nor displaying the ridiculous affectations of gentility, nor yet moving in whalebone corsets, like so many automatons, but free, inartificially happy, and unconstrained.

There were some spots in that sunny vale where they would frequently resort to decorate themselves with garlands of flowers. To have seen them reclining beneath the shadows of one of the beautiful groves; the ground about them strewn with freshly gathered buds and blossoms, employed in weaving chaplets and necklaces, one would have thought that all the train of Flora had gathered together to keep a festival in honor of their mistress.

With the young men there seemed almost always some matter of diversion or business on hand that afforded a constant variety of enjoyment. But whether fishing, or carving canoes, or polishing their ornaments, never was there exhibited the least sign of strife or contention among them.

As for the warriors, they maintained a tranquil dignity of demeanor, journeying occasionally from house to house, where they were always sure to be received with the attention bestowed upon distinguished guests. The old men, of whom there were many in the vale, seldom stirred from their mats, where they would recline for hours and hours, smoking and talking to one another with all the garrulity of age.

But the continual happiness, which so far as I was able to judge appeared to prevail in the valley, sprung principally from that all-pervading sensation which Rousseau has told us he at one time experienced, the mere buoyant sense of a healthful physical existence. And indeed in this particular the Typees had ample reason to felicitate themselves, for sickness was almost unknown. During the whole period of my stay I saw but one invalid among them; and on their smooth clear skins you observed no blemish or mark of disease.

The general repose, however, upon which I have just been descanting, was broken in upon about this time by an event which proved that the islanders were not entirely exempt from those occurrences which disturb the quiet of more civilized communities.

Having now been a considerable time in the valley I began to feel surprised that the violent hostility, subsisting between its inhabitants, and those of the adjoining bay of Happar, should never have manifested itself in any warlike encounter. Although the valiant Typees would often by gesticulations declare their undying hatred against their enemies, and the disgust they felt at their cannibal propensities; although they dilated upon the manifold injuries they had received at their hands, yet with a forbearance truly commendable, they appeared patiently to sit down under their grievances, and to refrain from making any reprisals. The Happars, entrenched behind their mountains, and never even showing themselves on their summits, did not appear to me to furnish adequate cause for that excess of animosity evinced towards them by the heroic tenants of our vale, and I was inclined to believe that the deeds of blood attributed to them had been greatly exaggerated.

On the other hand, as the clamors of war had not up to this period disturbed the serenity of the tribe, I began to distrust the truth of those reports which ascribed so fierce and belligerent a character to the Typee nation. Surely, thought I, all these terrible stories I have heard about the inveteracy with which they carried on the feud, their deadly intensity of hatred, and the diabolical malice with which they glutted their revenge upon the inanimate forms of the slain, are nothing more than fables, and I must confess that I experienced something like a sense of regret at having my hideous anticipations thus disappointed. I felt in some sort like a 'prentice-boy who, going to the play in the expectation of being delighted with a cut-and-thrust tragedy, is almost moved to tears of disappointment at the exhibition of a genteel comedy.

I could not avoid thinking that I had fallen in with a greatly traduced people, and I moralized not a little upon the disadvantage of having a bad name, which in this instance had given a tribe of savages, who were as pacific as so many lambkins, the repuation of a confederacy of giant-killers.

But subsequent events proved that I had been a little too premature in coming to this conclusion. One day about noon, happening to be at the Ti, I had lain down on the mats with several of the chiefs, and had gradually sunk into a most luxurious siesta, when I was awakened by a tremendous outcry, and starting up beheld the natives seizing their spears and hurrying out, while the most puissant of the chiefs, grasping the six muskets which were ranged against the bamboos, followed after, and soon disappeared in the groves. These movements were accompanied by wild shouts, in which "Happar, Happar," greatly predominated. The islanders were now to be seen running past the Ti, and striking across the valley to the Happar side. Presently I heard the sharp report of a musket from the adjoining hills, and then a burst of voices in the same direction. At this the women, who had congregated in the groves, set up the most violent clamors, as they invariably do here as elsewhere on every occasion of excitement and alarm, with a view of tranquillizing their own minds and disturbing other people. On this particular occasion they made such an outrageous noise, and continued it with such perseverance, that for awhile, had entire volleys of musketry been fired off in the neighboring mountains, I should not have been able to have heard them.

When this female commotion had a little subsided I listened eagerly for further information. At last bang went another shot, and then a second volley of yells from the hills. Again all was quiet, and continued so for such a length of time that I began to think the contending armies had agreed upon a suspension of hostilities; when pop went a third gun, followed as before with a yell. After this, for nearly two hours nothing occurred worthy of comment, save some straggling shouts from the hill-side, sounding like the halloos of a parcel of truant boys who had lost themselves in the woods.

During this interval I had remained standing on the piazza of the Ti, which directly fronted the Happar mountain, and with no one near me but Kory-Kory and the old superannuated savages I have before described. These latter never stirred from their mats, and seemed altogether unconscious that anything unusual was going on.

As for Kory-Kory, he appeared to think that we were in the midst of great events, and sought most zealously to impress me with a due sense of their importance. Every sound that reached us conveyed some momentous item of intelligence to him. At such times, as if he were gifted with second sight, he would go through a variety of pantomimic illustrations, showing me the precise manner in which the redoubtable Typees were at that very moment chastising the insolence of the enemy. "Mehevi hanna pippee nuee Happar," he exclaimed every five minutes, giving me to understand that under that distinguished captain the warriors of his nation were performing prodigies of valor.

Having heard only four reports from the muskets I was led to believe that they were worked by the islanders in the same manner as the Sultan Solyman's ponderous artillery at the siege of Byzantium, one of them taking an hour or two to load and train. At last, no sound whatever proceeding from the mountains, I concluded that the contest had been determined one way or the other. Such appeared, indeed, to be the case, for in a little while a courier arrived at the Ti, almost breathless with his exertions, and communicated the news of a great victory having been achieved by his countrymen: "Happar poo arva!—Happar poo arva!" (The cowards had fled.) Kory-Kory was in ecstasies, and commenced a vehement harangue, which, so far as I understood it, implied that the result exactly agreed with his expectations, and which, moreover, was intended to convince me that it would be a perfectly useless undertaking, even for an army of fire-eaters, to offer battle to the irresistible heroes of our valley. In all this I of course acquiesced, and looked forward with no little interest to the return of the conquerors, whose victory I feared might not have been purchased without cost to themselves.

But here I was again mistaken; for Mehevi, in conducting his warlike operations, rather inclined to the Fabian than to the Bonapartean tactics, husbanding his resources and exposing his troops to no unnecessary hazards. The total loss of the victors in this obstinately contested affair was, in killed, wounded, and missing—one forefinger and part of a thumb-nail (which the late proprietor brought along with him in his hand), a severely contused arm, and a considerable effusion of blood flowing from the thigh of a chief, who had received an ugly thrust from a Happar spear. What the enemy had suffered I could not discover, but I presume they had succeeded in taking off with them the bodies of their slain.

Such was the issue of the battle, as far as its results came under my observation; and as it appeared to be considered an event of prodigious importance, I reasonably concluded that the wars of the natives were marked by no very sanguinary traits. I afterwards learned how the skirmish had originated. A number of the Happars had been discovered prowling for no good purpose on the Typee side of the mountain; the alarm was sounded, and the invaders, after a protracted resistance, had been chased over the frontier. But why had not the intrepid Mehevi carried the war into Happar? Why had he not made a descent into the hostile vale, and brought away some trophy of his victory—some materials for the cannibal entertainment which I had heard usually terminated every engagement? After all, I was much inclined to believe that such shocking festivals must occur very rarely among the islanders, if, indeed, they ever take place.

For two or three days the late event was the theme

of general comment; after which the excitement gradually wore away, and the valley resumed its accustomed tranquillity.

XVIII

Returning health and peace of mind gave a new interest to everything around me. I sought to diversify my time by as many enjoyments as lay within reach. Bathing in company with troops of girls formed one of my chief amusements. We sometimes enjoyed the recreation in the waters of a miniature lake, into which the central stream of the valley expanded. This lovely sheet of water was almost circular in figure, and about three hundred yards across. Its beauty was indescribable. All around its banks waved luxuriant masses of tropical foliage, soaring high above which were to be seen, here and there, the symmetrical shaft of the coconut tree, surmounted by its tuft of graceful branches, drooping in the air like so many waving ostrich plumes.

The ease and grace with which the maidens of the valley propelled themselves through the water, and their familiarity with the element, were truly astonishing. Sometimes they might be seen gliding along just under the surface, without apparently moving hand or foot— then throwing themselves on their sides, they darted through the water, revealing glimpses of their forms, as, in the course of their rapid progress, they shot for an instant partly into the air—at one moment they dived deep down into the water and the next they rose bounding to the surface.

I remember upon one occasion plunging in among a parcel of these river-nymphs, and counting vainly upon my superior strength, sought to drag some of them under the water, but I quickly repented my temerity. The amphibious young creatures swarmed about me like a shoal of dolphins, and seizing hold of my devoted limbs, tumbled me about and ducked me under the surface until from the strange noises which rang in my ears, and the supernatural visions dancing before my eyes, I thought I was in the land of spirits. I stood indeed as little chance among them as a cumbrous whale attacked on all sides by a legion of sword-fish. When at length they relinquished their hold of me, they swam away in every direction, laughing at my clumsy endeavors to reach them.

There was no boat on the lake; but at my solicitation and for my special use, some of the young men attached to Marheyo's household, under the direction of the indefatigable Kory-Kory, brought up a light and tastefully carved canoe from the sea. It was launched upon the sheet of water, and floated there as gracefully as a swan. But, melancholy to relate, it produced an effect I had not anticipated. The sweet nymphs, who had sported with me before in the lake, now all fled its vicinity. The prohibited craft, guarded by the edicts of the "taboo," extended the prohibition to the waters in which it lay.

For a few days, Kory-Kory, with one or two other youths, accompanied me in my excursions to the lake, and while I paddled about in my light canoe, would swim after me shouting and gamboling in pursuit. But I was ever partial to what is termed in the *Young Men's Own Book*—"the society of virtuous and intelligent young ladies"; and in the absence of the mermaids, the amusement became dull and insipid. One morning I expressed to my faithful servitor my desire for the return of the nymphs. The honest fellow looked at me bewildered for a moment, and then shook his head solemnly, and murmured *"Taboo! taboo!"* giving me to understand that unless the canoe was removed, I could not expect to have the young ladies back again. But to this procedure I was averse; I not only wanted the canoe to stay where it was, but I wanted the beauteous Fayaway to get into it, and paddle with me about the lake. This latter proposition completely horrified Kory-Kory's notions of propriety. He inveighed against it, as something too monstrous to be thought of. It not only shocked their established notions of propriety, but was at variance with all their religious ordinances.

However, although the "taboo" was a ticklish thing to meddle with, I determined to test its capabilities of resisting an attack. I consulted the chief Mehevi, who endeavored to dissuade me from my object: but I was not to be repulsed; and accordingly increased the warmth of my solicitations. At last he entered into a long, and I have no doubt a very learned and eloquent, exposition of the history and nature of the "taboo" as affecting this particular case; employing a variety of most extraordinary words, which, from their amazing length and sonorousness, I have every reason to believe were of a theological nature. But all that he said failed to convince me: partly, perhaps, because I could not comprehend a word that he uttered; but chiefly, that for the life of me I could not understand why a woman should not have as much right to enter a canoe as a man. At last he became a little more rational, and intimated that, out of the abundant love he bore me, he would consult with the priests and see what could be done.

How it was that the priesthood of Typee satisfied the affair with their consciences, I know not; but so it was, and Fayaway's dispensation from this portion of the taboo was at length procured. Such an event I believe never before had occurred in the valley; but it was high time the islanders should be taught a little gallantry, and I trust that the example I set them may produce bene-

ficial effects. Ridiculous, indeed, that the lovely creatures should be obliged to paddle about in the water,
like so many ducks, while a parcel of great strapping fellows skimmed over its surface in their canoes.

The first day after Fayaway's emancipation I had
a delightful little party on the lake—the damsel, Kory-
Kory, and myself. My zealous body-servant brought
from the house a calabash of poee-poee, half a dozen
young coco-nuts—stripped of their husks—three pipes,
as many yams, and me on his back a part of the way.
Something of a load; but Kory-Kory was a very strong
man for his size, and by no means brittle in the spine.
We had a very pleasant day; my trusty valet plied the
paddle and swept us gently along the margin of the
water, beneath the shades of the overhanging thickets.
Fayaway and I reclined in the stern of the canoe, on the
very best terms possible with one another; the gentle
nymph occasionally placing her pipe to her lip, and
exhaling the mild fumes of the tobacco, to which her
rosy breath added a fresh perfume. Strange as it may
seem, there is nothing in which a young and beautiful
female appears to more advantage than in the act of
smoking. How captivating is a Peruvian lady, swinging
in her gaily woven hammock of grass, extended between
two orange trees, and inhaling the fragrance of a choice
cigarro! But Fayaway, holding in her delicately formed
olive hand the long yellow reed of her pipe, with its
quaintly carved bowl, and every few moments languish-
ingly giving forth light wreaths of vapor from her mouth
and nostrils, looked still more engaging.

We floated about thus for several hours, when I
looked up to the warm, glowing, tropical sky, and then
down into the transparent depths below; and when my
eye, wandering from the bewitching scenery around, fell
upon the grotesquely-tattooed form of Kory-Kory, and

finally encountered the pensive gaze of Fayaway, I thought I had been transported to some fairy region, so unreal did everything appear.

This lovely piece of water was the coolest spot in all the valley, and I now made it a place of continual resort during the hottest period of the day. One side of it lay near the termination of a long, gradually expanding gorge, which mounted to the heights that environed the vale. The strong trade wind, met in its course by these elevations, circled and eddied about their summits, and was sometimes driven down the steep ravine and swept across the valley, ruffling in its passage the otherwise tranquil surface of the lake.

One day, after we had been paddling about for some time, I disembarked Kory-Kory, and paddled the canoe to the windward side of the lake. As I turned the canoe, Fayaway, who was with me, seemed all at once to be struck with some happy idea. With a wild exclamation of delight, she disengaged from her person the ample robe of tappa which was knotted over her shoulder (for the purpose of shielding her from the sun), and spreading it out like a sail, stood erect with upraised arms in the head of the canoe. We American sailors pride ourselves upon our straight clean spars, but a prettier little mast than Fayaway made was never shipped a-board of any craft.

In a moment the tappa was distended by the breeze —the long brown tresses of Fayaway streamed in the air—and the canoe glided rapidly through the water, and shot towards the shore. Seated in the stern, I directed its course with my paddle until it dashed up the soft sloping bank, and Fayaway, with a light spring, alighted on the ground; whilst Kory-Kory, who had watched our maneuvers with admiration, now clapped his hands in transport, and shouted like a madman. Many a time afterwards was this feat repeated.

If the reader have not observed ere this that I was the declared admirer of Miss Fayaway, all I can say is that he is little conversant with affairs of the heart, and I certainly shall not trouble myself to enlighten him any farther. Out of the calico I had brought from the ship I made a dress for this lovely girl. In it she looked, I must confess, something like an opera dancer. The drapery of the latter damsel generally commences a little above the elbows, but my island beauty's began at the waist, and terminated sufficiently far above the ground to reveal the most bewitching ankles in the universe.

The day that Fayaway first wore this robe was rendered memorable by a new acquaintance being introduced to me. In the afternoon I was lying in the house, when I heard a great uproar outside; but being by this time pretty well accustomed to the wild halloos which were almost continually ringing through the valley, I paid little attention to it, until old Marheyo, under the influence of some strange excitement, rushed into my presence and communicated the astounding tidings, "Marnoo pemi!" which being interpreted, implied that an individual by the name of Marnoo was approaching. My worthy old friend evidently expected that this intelligence would produce a great effect upon me, and for a time he stood earnestly regarding me, as if curious to see how I should conduct myself, but as I remained perfectly unmoved, the old gentleman darted out of the house again, in as great a hurry as he had entered it.

"Marnoo, Marnoo," cogitated I, "I have never heard that name before. Some distinguished character, I presume, from the prodigious riot the natives are making"; the tumultuous noise drawing nearer and nearer every moment, while "Marnoo!—Marnoo!" was shouted by every tongue.

I made up my mind that some savage warrior of consequence, who had not yet enjoyed the honor of an audience, was desirous of paying his respects on the present occasion. So vain had I become by the lavish attention to which I had been accustomed that I felt half inclined, as a punishment for such neglect, to give this Marnoo a cold reception, when the excited throng came within view, convoying one of the most striking specimens of humanity that I ever beheld.

The stranger could not have been more than twenty-five years of age, and was a little above the ordinary height; had he been a single hair's breadth taller, the matchless symmetry of his form would have been destroyed. His unclad limbs were beautifully formed; whilst the elegant outline of his figure, together with his beardless cheeks, might have entitled him to the distinction of standing for the statue of the Polynesian Apollo; and indeed the oval of his countenance and the regularity of every feature reminded me of an antique bust. But the marble repose of art was supplied by a warmth and liveliness of expression only to be seen in the South Sea Islander under the most favorable developments of nature. The hair of Marnoo was a rich curling brown, and twined about his temples and neck in little close curling ringlets, which danced up and down continually when he was animated in conversation. His cheek was of a feminine softness, and his face was free from the least blemish of tattooing, although the rest of his body was drawn all over with fanciful figures, which—unlike the unconnected sketching usual among these natives—appeared to have been executed in conformity with some general design.

The tattooing on his back in particular attracted my attention. The artist employed must indeed have excelled in his profession. Traced along the course of the spine was accurately delineated the slender, tapering, and diamond-checkered shaft of the beautiful "artu" tree. Branching from the stem on either side, and disposed alternately, were the graceful branches drooping with leaves all correctly drawn, and elaborately finished. Indeed, this piece of tattooing was the best specimen of the Fine Arts I had yet seen in Typee. A rear view of the stranger might have suggested the idea of a spreading vine tacked against a garden wall. Upon his breast, arms, and legs, were exhibited an infinite variety of figures; every one of which, however, appeared to have reference to the general effect sought to be produced. The tattooing I have described was of the brightest blue, and when contrasted with the light olive color of the skin, produced an unique and even elegant effect. A slight girdle of white tappa, scarcely two inches in width, but hanging before and behind in spreading tassels, composed the entire costume of the stranger.

He advanced surrounded by the islanders, carrying under one arm a small roll of the native cloth, and grasping in his other hand a long and richly decorated spear. His manner was that of a traveler conscious that he is approaching a comfortable stage in his journey. Every moment he turned good-humoredly to the throng around him, and gave some dashing sort of reply to their incessant queries, which appeared to convulse them with uncontrollable mirth.

Struck by his demeanor, and the peculiarity of his appearance, so unlike that of the shaven-crowned and face-tattooed natives in general, I involuntarily rose as he entered the house, and proffered him a seat on the mats beside me. But without deigning to notice the civility, or even the more incontrovertible fact of my existence, the stranger passed on, utterly regardless of me, and flung himself upon the further end of the long couch that traversed the sole apartment of Marheyo's habitation.

Had the belle of the season, in the pride of her beauty and power, been cut in a place of public resort by some supercilious exquisite, she could not have felt greater indignation than I did at this unexpected slight.

I was thrown into utter astonishment. The conduct of the savages had prepared me to anticipate from every new-comer the same extravagant expressions of curiosity and regard. The singularity of his conduct, however, only roused my desire to discover who this remarkable personage might be, who now engrossed the attention of every one.

Tinor placed before him a calabash of poee-poee, from which the stranger regaled himself, alternating every mouthful with some rapid exclamation which was eagerly caught up and echoed by the crowd that completely filled the house. When I observed the striking devotion of the natives to him, and their temporary withdrawal of all attention from myself I felt not a little piqued. The glory of Tommo is departed, thought I, and the sooner he removes from the valley the better. These were my feelings at the moment, and they were prompted by that glorious principle inherent in all heroic natures—the strong-rooted determination to have the biggest share of the pudding or go without any of it.

Marnoo, this all-attractive personage, having satisfied his hunger, and inhaled a few whiffs from a pipe which was handed to him, launched out into an harangue which completely enchained the attention of his auditors

Little as I understood of the language, yet from his animated gestures and the varying expression of his features—reflected as from so many mirrors in the countenances around him—I could easily discover the nature of those passions which he sought to arouse. From the frequent recurrence of the words "Nukuheva" and "Franee" (French), and some others with the meaning of which I was acquainted, he appeared to be rehearsing to his auditors events which had recently occurred in the neighboring bays. But how he had gained the knowledge of these matters I could not understand, un. less it were that he had just come from Nukuheva—a supposition which his travel-stained appearance not a little supported. But, if a native of that region, I could not account for his friendly reception at the hands of the Typees.

Never, certainly, had I beheld so powerful an exhibition of natural eloquence as Marnoo displayed during the course of his oration. The grace of the attitudes into which he threw his flexible figure, the striking gestures of his naked arms, and above all, the fire which shot from his brilliant eyes, imparted an effect to the continually changing accents of his voice, of which the most accomplished orator might have been proud. At one moment reclining sideways upon the mat, and leaning calmly upon his bended arm, he related circumstantially the aggressions of the French—their hostile visits to the surrounding bays, enumerating each one in succession—Happar, Pueearka, Nukuheva, Tior—and then, starting to his feet and precipitating himself forward with clenched hands and a countenance distorted with passion, he poured out a tide of invectives. Falling back into an attitude of lofty command, he exhorted the Typees to resist these encroachments; reminding them, with a fierce glance of exultation, that as yet the terror of their name had preserved them from attack, and with a scornful sneer he sketched in ironical terms the wondrous intrepidity of the French, who, with five warcanoes and hundreds of men, had not dared to assail the naked warriors of their valley.

The effect he produced upon his audience was electric; one and all they stood regarding him with sparkling eyes and trembling limbs, as though they were listening to the inspired voice of a prophet.

But it soon appeared that Marnoo's powers were as versatile as they were extraordinary. As soon as he had finished this vehement harangue, he threw himself again upon the mats, and, singling out individuals in the crowd, addressed them by name, in a sort of bantering style, the humor of which, though nearly hidden from me, filled the whole assembly with uproarious delight.

He had a word for everybody; and, turning rapidly from one to another, gave utterance to some hasty witticism, which was sure to be followed by peals of laughter. To the females, as well as to the men, he addressed his discourse. Heaven only knows what he said to them, but he caused smiles and blushes to mantle their ingenuous faces. I am, indeed, very much inclined to believe that Marnoo, with his handsome person and captivating manners, was a sad deceiver among the simple maidens of the island.

During all this time he had never, for one moment, deigned to regard me. He appeared, indeed, to be altogether unconscious of my presence. I was utterly at a loss how to account for this extraordinary conduct. I easily perceived that he was a man of no little consequence among the islanders; that he possessed uncommon talents; and was gifted with a higher degree of knowledge than the inmates of the valley. For these reasons, I therefore greatly feared lest having, from some cause or other, unfriendly feelings towards me, he might exert his powerful influence to do me mischief.

It seemed evident that he was not a permanent resident of the vale, and yet, whence could he have come? On all sides the Typees were girt in by hostile tribes, and how could he possibly, if belonging to any of these, be received with so much cordiality?

The personal appearance of the enigmatical stranger suggested additional perplexities. The face, free from tattooing, and the unshaven crown, were peculiarities I had never before remarked in any part of the island, and I had always heard that the contrary were considered the indispensable distinctions of a Marquesan warrior. Altogether the matter was perfectly incomprehensible to me, and I awaited its solution with no small degree of anxiety.

At length, from certain indications, I suspected that he was making me the subject of his remarks, although he appeared cautiously to avoid either pronouncing my name, or looking in the direction where I lay. All at once he rose from the mats where he had been reclining, and, still conversing, moved towards me, his eye purposely evading mine, and seated himself within less than a yard of me. I had hardly recovered from my surprise, when he suddenly turned round, and, with a most benignant countenance, extended his right hand gracefully towards me. Of course I accepted the courteous challenge, and as soon as our palms met, he bent towards me, and murmured in musical accents,—"How you do?" "How long you been in this bay?" "You like this bay?"

Had I been pierced simultaneously by three Happar spears, I could not have started more than I did at hearing these simple questions! For a moment I was overwhelmed with astonishment, and then answered something I know not what; but as soon as I regained my self-possession, the thought darted through my mind that from this individual I might obtain that information regarding Toby which I suspected the natives had purposely withheld from me. Accordingly I questioned him concerning the disappearance of my companion, but he denied all knowledge of the matter. I then inquired from whence he had come? He replied, from Nukuheva. When I expressed my surprise, he looked at me for a moment, as if enjoying my perplexity, and then, with his strange vivacity, exclaimed—"Ah! me taboo—me go Nukuheva—me go Tior—me go Typee—me go everywhere—nobody harm me—me taboo."

This explanation would have been altogether unintelligible to me, had it not recalled to my mind something I had previously heard concerning a singular custom among these islanders. Though the country is possessed by various tribes, whose mutual hostilities almost wholly preclude any intercourse between them, yet there are instances where a person having ratified friendly relations with some individual belonging to the valley, whose inmates are at war with his own, may, under particular restrictions, venture with impunity into the country of his friend, where, under other circumstances, he would have been treated as an enemy. In this light are personal friendships regarded among them, and the individual so protected is said to be "taboo," and his person, to a certain extent, is held as sacred. Thus the stranger informed me he had access to all the valleys in the island.

Curious to know how he had acquired his knowledge of English, I questioned him on the subject. At first, for some reason or other, he evaded the inquiry, but afterwards told me that, when a boy, he had been carried to sea by the captain of a trading vessel, with whom he had stayed three years, living part of the time with him at Sydney, in Australia, and that, at a subsequent visit to the island, the captain had, at his own request, permitted him to remain among his countrymen. The natural quickness of the savage had been wonderfully improved by his intercourse with the white men, and his partial knowledge of a foreign language gave him a great ascendancy over his less accomplished countrymen.

When I asked the now affable Marnoo why it was that he had not previously spoken to me, he eagerly inquired what I had been led to think of him from his conduct in that respect. I replied, that I had supposed him to be some great chief or warrior, who had seen plenty of white men before, and did not think it worth while to notice a poor sailor. At this declaration of the exalted opinion I had formed of him, he appeared vastly gratified, and gave me to understand that he had purposely behaved in that manner, in order to increase my astonishment, as soon as he should see proper to address me.

Marnoo now sought to learn my version of the story as to how I came to be an inmate of the Typee valley. When I related to him the circumstances under which Toby and I had entered it, he listened with evident interest; but as soon as I alluded to the absence, yet unaccounted for, of my comrade, he endeavored to change the subject, as if it were something he desired not to agitate. It seemed, indeed, as if everything connected with Toby was destined to beget distrust and anxiety in my bosom. Notwithstanding Marnoo's denial of any knowledge of his fate, I could not avoid suspecting that he was deceiving me; and this suspicion revived those frightful apprehensions with regard to my own fate, which, for a short time past, had subsided in my breast.

Influenced by these feelings, I now felt a strong desire to avail myself of the stranger's protection, and under his safeguard to return to Nukuheva. But as soon as I hinted at this, he unhesitatingly pronounced it to be entirely impracticable; assuring me that the Typees would never consent to my leaving the valley. Although what he said merely confirmed the impression which I had before entertained, still it increased my anxiety to escape from a captivity which, however endurable, nay, delightful it might be in some respects, involved in its issues a fate marked by the most frightful contingencies.

I could not conceal from my mind that Toby had been treated in the same friendly manner as I had been, and yet all their kindness had terminated in his mysterious disappearance. Might not the same fate await me?—a fate too dreadful to think of. Stimulated by these considerations, I urged anew my request to Marnoo; but he only set forth in stronger colors the impossibility of my escape and repeated his previous declaration that the Typees would never be brought to consent to my departure.

When I endeavored to learn from him the motives which prompted them to hold me a prisoner, Marnoo again assumed that mysterious tone which had tormented me with apprehensions when I had questioned him with regard to the fate of my companion.

Thus repulsed, in a manner which only served, by arousing the most dreadful forebodings, to excite me to renewed attempts, I conjured him to intercede for me with the natives, and endeavor to procure their consent to my leaving them. To this he appeared strongly averse; but, yielding at last to my importunities, he addressed several of the chiefs, who with the rest had been eying us intently during the whole of our conversation. His petition, however, was at once met with the most

violent disapprobation, manifesting itself in angry
glances and gestures, and a perfect torrent of passionate
words, directed to both him and myself. Marnoo, evidently repenting the step he had taken, earnestly dep-
recated the resentment of the crowd, and in a few
moments succeeded in pacifying to some extent the
clamors which had broken out as soon as his proposition
had been understood.

With the most intense interest had I watched the
reception his intercession might receive; and a bitter
pang shot through my heart at the additional evidence,
now furnished, of the unchangeable determination of
the islanders. Marnoo told me, with evident alarm in
his countenance, that although admitted into the bay on
a friendly footing with its inhabitants, he could not
presume to meddle with their concerns, as such a procedure, if persisted in, would at once absolve the Typees
from the restraints of the "Taboo," although so long as
he refrained from any such conduct, it screened him
effectually from the consequences of the enmity they
bore his tribe.

At this moment, Mehevi, who was present, angrily
interrupted him; and the words which he uttered, in a
commanding tone, evidently meant that he must at once
cease talking to me, and withdraw to the other part of
the house. Marnoo immediately started up, hurriedly
enjoining me not to address him again, and, as I valued
my safety, to refrain from all further allusion to the
subject of my departure; and then, in compliance with
the order of the determined chief, but not before it had
again been angrily repeated, he withdrew to a distance.

I now perceived, with no small degree of apprehension, the same savage expression in the countenance
of the natives which had startled me during the scene
at the Ti. They glanced their eyes suspiciously from

Marnoo to me, as if distrusting the nature of an intercourse carried on, as it was, in a language they could not understand, and they seemed to harbor the belief that already we had concerted measures calculated to elude their vigilance.

The lively countenances of these people are wonderfully indicative of the emotions of the soul, and the imperfections of their oral language are more than compensated for by the nervous eloquence of their looks and gestures. I could plainly trace, in every varying expression of their faces, all those passions which had been thus unexpectedly aroused in their bosoms.

It required no reflection to convince me, from what was going on, that the injunction of Marnoo was not to be rashly slighted; and accordingly, great as was the effort to suppress my feelings, I accosted Mehevi in a good-humored tone, with a view of dissipating any ill impression he might have received. But the ireful, angry chief was not so easily mollified. He rejected my advances with that peculiarly stern expression I have before described, and took care by the whole of his behavior towards me to show the displeasure and resentment which he felt.

Marnoo, at the other extremity of the house, apparently desirous of making a diversion in my favor, exerted himself to amuse with his pleasantries the crowd about him; but his lively attempts were not so successful as they had previously been, and, foiled in his efforts, he rose gravely to depart. No one expressed any regret at this movement, so seizing his roll of tappa, and grasping his spear, he advanced to the front of the pi-pi, and waving his hand in adieu to the now silent throng, cast upon me a glance of mingled pity and reproach, and flung himself into the path which led from the house. I watched his receding figure until it was lost in the obscurity of the grove and then gave myself up to the most desponding reflections.

XIX

The knowledge I had now obtained as to the intention of the savages deeply affected me.

Marnoo, I perceived, was a man who, by reason of his superior acquirements, and the knowledge he possessed of the events which were taking place in the different bays of the island, was held in no little estimation by the inhabitants of the valley. He had been received with the most cordial welcome and respect. The natives had hung upon the accents of his voice, and had manifested the highest gratification at being individually noticed by him. And yet, despite all this, a few words urged in my behalf, with the intent of obtaining my release from captivity, had sufficed not only to banish all harmony and good-will; but, if I could believe what he told me, had gone nigh to endanger his own personal safety.

How strongly rooted, then, must be the determination of the Typees with regard to me, and how suddenly could they display the strangest passions! The mere suggestion of my departure had estranged from me, for the time at least, Mehevi, who was the most influential of all the chiefs, and who had previously exhibited so many instances of his friendly sentiments. The rest of the natives had likewise evinced their strong repugnance to my wishes, and even Kory-Kory himself seemed to share in the general disapprobation bestowed upon me.

In vain I racked my invention to find out some motive for the strange desire these people manifested to retain me among them; but I could discover none.

But however this might be, the scene which had just

occurred admonished me of the danger of trifling with the wayward and passionate spirits against whom it was vain to struggle, and might even be fatal to do so. My only hope was to induce the natives to believe that I was reconciled to my detention in the valley, and, by assuming a tranquil and cheerful demeanor, to allay the suspicions which I had so unfortunately aroused. Their confidence revived, they might in a short time remit in some degree their watchfulness over my movements, and I should then be the better enabled to avail myself of any opportunity which presented itself for escape. I determined, therefore, to make the best of a bad bargain, and to bear up manfully against whatever might betide. In this endeavor I succeeded beyond my own expectations. At the period of Marnoo's visit, I had been in the valley, as nearly as I could conjecture, some two months. Although not completely recovered from my strange illness which still lingered about me, I was free from pain and able to take exercise. In short, I had every reason to anticipate a perfect recovery. Freed from apprehensions on this point, and resolved to regard the future without flinching, I flung myself anew into all the social pleasures of the valley, and sought to bury all regrets, and all remembrances of my previous existence, in the wild enjoyments it afforded.

In my various wanderings through the vale, and as I became better acquainted with the character of its inhabitants, I was more and more struck with the light-hearted joyousness that everywhere prevailed. The minds of these simple savages, unoccupied by matters of graver moment, were capable of deriving the utmost delight from circumstances which would have passed unnoticed in more intelligent communities. All their enjoyment, indeed, seemed to be made up of the little trifling incidents of the passing hour; but these diminu-

tive items swelled altogether to an amount of happiness
seldom experienced by more enlightened individuals,
whose pleasures are drawn from more elevated but rarer
sources.

What community, for instance, of refined and intellectual mortals would derive the least satisfaction from
shooting pop-guns? The mere supposition of such a thing
being possible would excite their indignation, and yet
the whole population of Typee did little else for ten
days but occupy themselves with that childish amusement, fairly screaming, too, with the delight it afforded
them.

One day I was frolicking with a little spirited urchin,
some six years old, who chased me with a piece of bamboo about three feet long, with which he occasionally
belabored me. Seizing the stick from him, the idea
happened to suggest itself that I might make for the
youngster, out of the slender tube, one of those nursery
muskets with which I had sometimes seen children
playing. Accordingly, with my knife I made two parallel
slits in the cane several inches in length, and cutting
loose at one end the elastic strip between them, bent
it back and slipped the point into a little notch made
for the purpose. Any small substance placed against
this would be projected with considerable force through
the tube, by merely springing the bent strip out of
the notch.

Had I possessed the remotest idea of the sensation
this piece of ordnance was destined to produce, I should
certainly have taken out a patent for the invention.
The boy scampered away with it, half delirious with
ecstasy, and in twenty minutes afterwards I might have
been seen surrounded by a noisy crowd—venerable
old graybeards—responsible fathers of families—valiant
warriors—matrons—young men—girls and children, all

holding in their hand bits of bamboo, and each clamoring to be served first.

For three or four hours I was engaged in manufacturing pop-guns, but at last made over my goodwill and interest in the concern to a lad of remarkable quick parts, whom I soon initiated into the art and mystery.

Pop, pop, pop, pop, now resounded all over the valley. Duels, skirmishes, pitched battles, and general engagements were to be seen on every side. Here, as you walked along a path which led through a thicket, you fell into a cunningly laid ambush, and became a target for a body of musketeers whose tattooed limbs you could just see peeping into view through the foliage. There, you were assailed by the intrepid garrison of a house, who leveled their bamboo rifles at you from between the upright canes which composed its sides. Farther on you were fired upon by a detachment of sharpshooters, mounted upon the top of a pi-pi.

Pop, pop, pop, pop! Green guavas, seeds, and berries were flying about in every direction, and during this dangerous state of affairs I was half afraid that, like the man and his brazen bull, I should fall a victim to my own ingenuity. Like everything else, however, the excitement gradually wore away, though ever after occasional pop-guns might be heard at all hours of the day.

It was towards the close of the pop-gun war, that I was infinitely diverted with a strange freak of Marheyo's.

I had worn, when I quitted the ship, a pair of thick pumps, which, from the rough usage they had received in scaling precipices and sliding down gorges, were so dilapidated as to be altogether unfit for use—so, at least, would have thought the generality of people, and so they most certainly were, when considered in the light of shoes. But things unserviceable in one way, may with advantage be applied in another, that is, if one have genius enough for the purpose. This genius Marheyo possessed in a superlative degree, as he abundantly evinced by the use to which he put these sorely bruised and battered old shoes.

Every article, however trivial, which belonged to me, the natives appeared to regard as sacred; and I observed that for several days after becoming an inmate of the house, my pumps were suffered to remain, untouched, where I had first happened to throw them. I remembered, however, that after awhile I had missed them from their accustomed place; but the matter gave me no concern, supposing that Tinor—like any other tidy housewife, having come across them in some of her domestic occupations—had pitched the useless things out of the house. But I was soon undeceived.

One day I observed old Marheyo bustling about me with unusual activity, and to such a degree as almost to supersede Kory-Kory in the functions of his office. One moment he volunteered to trot off with me on his back to the stream; and when I refused, noways daunted by the repulse, he continued to frisk about me like a superannuated house-dog. I could not for the life of me conjecture what possessed the old gentleman, until all at once, availing himself of the temporary absence of the household, he went through a variety of uncouth gestures, pointing eagerly down to my feet, and then up to a little bundle which swung from the ridge-pole overhead. At last I caught a faint idea of his meaning, and motioned him to lower the package. He executed the order in the twinkling of an eye, and unrolling a piece of tappa displayed to my astonished gaze the identical pumps which I thought had been destroyed long before.

I immediately comprehended his desires, and very

generously gave him the shoes, which had become quite moldy, wondering for what earthly purpose he could want them.

The same afternoon I described the venerable warrior approaching the house, with a slow, stately gait, earrings in ears, and spear in hand, with this highly ornamental pair of shoes suspended from his neck by a strip of bark, and swinging backwards and forwards on his capacious chest. In the gala costume of the tasteful Marheyo, these calf-skin pendants ever after formed the most striking feature.

But to turn to something a little more important. Although the whole existence of the inhabitants of the valley seemed to pass away exempt from toil, yet there were some light employments which, although amusing rather than laborious as occupations, contributed to their comfort and luxury. Among these, the most important was the manufacture of the native cloth—"tappa"—so well known, under various modifications, throughout the whole Polynesian Archipelago. As is generally understood, this useful and sometimes elegant article is fabricated from the bark of different trees. But, as I believe that no description of its manufacture has ever been given, I shall state what I know regarding it.

In the manufacture of the beautiful white tappa generally worn on the Marquesan Islands, the preliminary operation consists in gathering a certain quantity of the young branches of the cloth-tree. The exterior green bark being pulled off as worthless, there remains a slender fibrous substance, which is carefully stripped from the stick, to which it closely adheres. When a sufficient quantity of it has been collected, the various strips are enveloped in a covering of large leaves, which the natives use precisely as we do wrapping-paper, and which are secured by a few turns of a line passed round them. The package is then laid in the bed of some running stream, with a heavy stone placed over it, to prevent its being swept away. After it has remained for two or three days in this state, it is drawn out, and exposed, for a short time, to the action of the air, every distinct piece being attentively inspected, with a view of ascertaining whether it has yet been sufficiently affected by the operation. This is repeated again and again, until the desired result is obtained.

When the substance is in a proper state for the next process, it betrays evidences of incipient decomposition; the fibers are relaxed and softened, and rendered perfectly malleable. The different strips are now extended, one by one, in successive layers, upon some smooth surface—generally the prostrate trunk of a cocoanut tree—and the heap thus formed is subjected, at every new increase, to a moderate beating, with a sort of wooden mallet, leisurely applied. The mallet is made of a hard heavy wood resembling ebony, is about twelve inches in length, and perhaps two in breadth, with a rounded handle at one end, and in shape is the exact counterpart of one of our four-sided razor-strops. The flat surfaces of the implement are marked with shallow parallel indentations, varying in depth on the different sides, so as to be adapted to the several stages of the operation. These marks produce the corduroy sort of stripes discernible in the tappa in its finished state. After being beaten in the manner I have described, the material soon becomes blended in one mass, which, moistened occasionally with water, is at intervals hammered out, by a kind of gold-beating process, to any degree of thinness required. In this way the cloth is easily made to vary in strength and thickness, so as to suit the numerous purposes to which it is applied.

When the operation last described has been concluded the new-made tappa is spread out on the grass to bleach and dry, and soon becomes of a dazzling whiteness. Sometimes, in the first stages of the manufacture, the substance is impregnated with a vegetable juice, which gives it a permanent color. A rich brown and a bright yellow are occasionally seen, but the simple taste of the Typee people inclines them to prefer the natural tint.

The notable wife of Kamehameha, the renowned conqueror and king of the Sandwich Islands, used to pride herself in the skill she displayed in dyeing her tappa with contrasting colors disposed in regular figures; and, in the midst of the innovations of the times, was regarded, towards the decline of her life, as a lady of the old school, clinging as she did to the national cloth, in preference to the frippery of the European calicoes. But the art of printing the tappa is unknown upon the Marquesan Islands.

In passing along the valley, I was often attracted by the noise of the mallet, which, when employed in the manufacture of the cloth, produces at every stroke of its hard, heavy wood, a clear, ringing, and musical sound, capable of being heard at a great distance. When several of these implements happen to be in operation at the same time, and near one another, the effect upon the ear of a person at a little distance is really charming.

XX

Nothing can be more uniform and undiversified than the life of the Typees; one tranquil day of ease and happiness follows another in quiet succession; and with these unsophisticated savages the history of a day is the history of a life. I will, therefore, as briefly as I can, describe one of our days in the valley.

To begin with the morning. We were not very early risers—the sun would be shooting his golden spikes above the Happar mountain, ere I threw aside my tappa robe, and girding my long tunic about my waist, sallied out with Fayaway and Kory-Kory and the rest of the household, and bent my steps towards the stream. Here we found congregated all those who dwelt in our section of the valley; and here we bathed with them. The fresh morning air and the cool flowing waters put both soul and body in a glow, and after a half-hour employed in this recreation, we sauntered back to the house—Tinor and Marheyo gathering dry sticks by the way for firewood; some of the young men laying the coco-nut trees under contribution as they passed beneath them; while Kory-Kory played his outlandish pranks for my particular diversion, and Fayaway and I, not arm in arm to be sure, but sometimes hand in hand, strolled along, with feelings of perfect charity for all the world, and especial good-will towards each other.

Our morning meal was soon prepared. The islanders are somewhat abstemious at this repast; reserving the more powerful efforts of their appetite to a later period of the day. For my own part, with the assistance of my valet, who, as I have before stated, always officiated as spoon on these occasions, I ate sparingly from one of Tinor's trenchers of poee-poee; which was devoted exclusively for my own use, being mixed with the milky meat of ripe coco-nut. A section of a roasted breadfruit, a small cake of "amar," or a mess of "kokoo," two or three bananas, or a mawmee apple; an annuee, or some other agreeable and nutritious fruit served from day to day to diversify the meal, which was finished

by tossing off the liquid contents of a young coco-nut
or two.

While partaking of this simple repast, the inmates
of Marheyo's house, after the style of the indolent
Romans, reclined in sociable groups upon the divan
of mats, and digestion was promoted by cheerful conversation.

After the morning meal was concluded, pipes were
lighted; and among them my own especial pipe, a
present from the noble Mehevi. The islanders, who
only smoke a whiff or two at a time, and at long intervals, and who keep their pipes going from hand to
hand continually, regarded my systematic smoking of
four or five pipefuls of tobacco in succession as something quite wonderful. When two or three pipes had
circulated freely, the company gradually broke up.
Marheyo went to the little hut he was for ever building.
Tinor began to inspect her rolls of tappa, or employed
her busy fingers in plaiting grass-mats. The girls
anointed themselves with their fragrant oils, dressed their
hair, or looked over their curious finery, and compared
together their ivory trinkets, fashioned out of boars'
tusks or whales' teeth. The young men and warriors
produced their spears, paddles, canoe-gear, battle-clubs,
and war-conchs, and occupied themselves in carving all
sorts of figures upon them with pointed bits of shell or
flint, and adorning them, especially the war-conchs, with
tassels of braided bark and tufts of human hair. Some,
immediately after eating, threw themselves once more
upon the inviting mats, and resumed the employment
of the previous night, sleeping as soundly as if they had
not closed their eyes for a week. Others sallied out into
the groves, for the purpose of gathering fruit or fibers
of bark and leaves; the last two being in constant requisition, and applied to a hundred uses. A few, per-

haps, among the girls, would slip into the woods after flowers, or repair to the stream with small calabashes and coco-nut shells, in order to polish them by friction with a smooth stone in the water. In truth these innocent people seemed to be at no loss for something to occupy their time; and it would be no light task to enumerate all their employments, or rather pleasures.

My own mornings I spent in a variety of ways. Sometimes I rambled about from house to house, sure of receiving a cordial welcome wherever I went; or from grove to grove, and from one shady place to another, in company with Kory-Kory and Fayaway, and a rabble rout of merry young idlers. Sometimes I was too indolent for exercise, and accepting one of the many invitations I was continually receiving, stretched myself out on the mats of some hospitable dwelling, and occupied myself pleasantly either in watching the proceedings of those around me or taking part in them myself. Whenever I chose to do the latter, the delight of the islanders was boundless; and there was always a throng of competitors for the honor of instructing me in any particular craft. I soon became quite an accomplished hand at making tappa—could braid a grass sling as well as the best of them—and once, with my knife, carved the handle of a javelin so exquisitely, that I have no doubt, to this day, Karnoonoo, its owner, preserves it as a surprising specimen of my skill. As noon approached, all those who had wandered forth from our habitation began to return; and when mid-day was fairly come scarcely a sound was to be heard in the valley: a deep sleep fell upon all. The luxurious siesta was hardly ever omitted, except by old Marheyo, who was so eccentric a character, that he seemed to be governed by no fixed principles whatever; but, acting just according to the humor of the moment, slept, ate, or tinkered away at his little hut, without regard to the proprieties of time or place. Frequently he might have been seen taking a nap in the sun at noonday, or a bath in the stream at midnight. Once I beheld him perched eighty feet from the ground, in the tuft of a coco-nut tree, smoking; and often I saw him standing up to the waist in water, engaged in plucking out the stray hairs of his beard, using a piece of mussel-shell for tweezers.

The noontide slumber lasted generally an hour and a half; very often longer; and after the sleepers had arisen from their mats they again had recourse to their pipes, and then made preparations for the most important meal of the day.

I, however, like those gentlemen of leisure who breakfast at home and dine at their club, almost invariably, during my intervals of health, enjoyed the afternoon repast with the bachelor chiefs of the Ti, who were always rejoiced to see me, and lavishly spread before me all the good things which their larder afforded. Mehevi generally produced among other dainties a baked pig, an article which I have every reason to suppose was provided for my sole gratification.

The Ti was a right jovial place. It did my heart, as well as my body, good to visit it. Secure from female intrusion, there was no restraint upon the hilarity of the warriors, who, like the gentlemen of Europe after the cloth is drawn and the ladies retire, freely indulged their mirth.

After spending a considerable portion of the afternoon at the Ti, I usually found myself, as the cool of the evening came on, either sailing on the little lake with Fayaway, or bathing in the waters of the stream with a number of the savages, who, at this hour, always repaired thither. As the shadows of night approached, Marheyo's household were once more assembled under his roof: tapers were lit, long and curious chants were raised, interminable stories were told (for which one present was little the wiser), and all sorts of social festivities served to while away the time.

The young girls very often danced by moonlight in front of their dwellings. There are a great variety of these dances, in which, however, I never saw the men take part. They all consist of active, romping, mischievous evolutions, in which every limb is brought into requisition. Indeed, the Marquesan girls dance all over, as it were; not only do their feet dance, but their arms, hands, fingers, aye, their very eyes, seem to dance in their heads. In good sooth, they so sway their floating forms, arch their necks, toss aloft their naked arms, and glide, and swim, and whirl, that it was almost too much for a quiet, sober-minded, modest young man like myself.

The damsels wear nothing but flowers and their compendious gala tunics; and when they plume themselves for the dance, they look like a band of olive-colored Sylphides on the point of taking wing. [In an instant, two of them, taller than their companions, were standing, side by side, in the middle of a ring, formed by the clasped hands of the rest. This movement was made in perfect silence.

Presently the two girls join hands overhead, and, crying out, "Ahloo! ahloo!" wave them to and fro. Upon which, the ring begins to circle slowly; the dancers moving sideways, with their arms a little drooping. Soon they quicken their pace; and, at last, fly round and round: bosoms heaving, hair streaming, flowers dropping, and every sparkling eye circling in what seemed a line of light.

Meanwhile, the pair within are passing and repassing each other incessantly. Inclining sideways, so that their

long hair falls far over, they glide this way and that,
one foot continually in the air, and their fingers thrown
forth, and twirling in the moonbeams.

"Ahloo! ahloo!" again cry the dance queens; and,
coming together in the middle of the ring, they once
more lift up the arch, and stand motionless.

"Ahloo! ahloo!" Every link of the circle is broken;
and the girls, deeply breathing, stand perfectly still.
They pant hard and fast, a moment or two; and then,
just as the deep flush is dying away from their faces,
slowly recede, all round; thus enlarging the ring.

Again the two leaders wave their hands, when the
rest pause, and now, far apart, stand in the still moonlight, like a circle of fairies. Presently, raising a strange
chant, they softly sway themselves, gradually quicken-
ing the movement, until, at length, for a few passionate
moments, with throbbing bosoms and glowing cheeks,
they abandon themselves to all the spirit of the dance,
apparently lost to everything around. But soon subsiding
again into the same languid measure, as before, they
become motionless; and then, reeling forward on all
sides, their eyes swimming in their heads, join in one
wild chorus, and sink into each other's arms.] [1]

Unless some particular festivity was going forward,
the inmates of Marheyo's house retired to their mats
rather early in the evening; but not for the night,
since, after slumbering lightly for a while, they rose

---

[1] Melville later published this bracketed passage in Chapter LXIII of *Omoo*, explaining to John Murray: "This discrip-
tion has been modified & adapted from a certain chapter
which it was thought best to exclude from *Typee*. In their
dances the Tahitians much resembled the Marquesans. . . ."
Though neither its exact location in *Typee* nor the reason
for its omission is known, the passage may have assisted the
above description of a Typee dance, left curiously undeveloped.—*J.L.*

again, relit their tapers, partook of the third and last
meal of the day, at which poee-poee alone was eaten,
and then, after inhaling a narcotic whiff from a pipe of
tobacco, disposed themselves for the great business of
night, sleep. With the Marquesans it might almost be
styled the great business of life, for they pass a large
portion of their time in the arms of Somnus. The native
strength of their constitutions is no way shown more
emphatically than in the quantity of sleep they can
endure. To many of them, indeed, life is little else
than an often interrupted and luxurious nap.

XXI

Almost every country has its medicinal springs famed
for their healing virtues. The Cheltenham of Typee is
embosomed in the deepest solitude, and but seldom
receives a visitor. It is situated remote from any dwelling,
a little way up the mountain, near the head of the valley;
and you approach it by a pathway shaded by the most
beautiful foliage and adorned with a thousand fragrant
plants.

The mineral waters of Arva Wai[1] ooze forth from
the crevices of a rock, and gliding down its mossy side,
fall at last, in many clustering drops, into a natural
basin of stone fringed round with grass and dewy-
looking little violet-colored flowers, as fresh and beautiful as the perpetual moisture they enjoy can make them.

The water is held in high estimation by the islanders,
some of whom consider it an agreeable as well as a
medicinal beverage; they bring it from the mountain

---

[1] I presume this might be translated into "Strong Waters."
"Arva" is the name bestowed upon a root the properties of
which are both inebriating and medicinal. "Wai" is the
Marquesan word for water.—*H.M.*

in their calabashes, and store it away beneath heaps
of leaves in some shady nook near the house. Old Marheyo had a great love for the waters of the spring. Every
now and then he lugged off to the mountain a great
round demijohn of a calabash, and, panting with his
exertions, brought it back filled with his darling fluid.

The water tasted like a solution of a dozen disagreeable things, and was sufficiently nauseous to have made
the fortune of the proprietor, had the spa been situated
in the midst of any civilized community.

As I am no chemist, I cannot give a scientific analysis
of the water. All I know about the matter is, that one
day Marheyo in my presence poured out the last drop
from his huge calabash, and I observed at the bottom
of the vessel a small quantity of gravelly sediment very
much resembling our common sand. Whether this is always found in the water, and gives it its peculiar flavor
and virtues, or whether its presence was merely incidental, I was not able to ascertain.

One day in returning from this spring by a circuitous
path, I came upon a scene which reminded me of
Stonehenge and the architectural labors of the Druid.

At the base of one of the mountains, and surrounded
on all sides by dense groves, a series of vast terraces of
stone rises, step by step, for a considerable distance up
the hill-side. These terraces cannot be less than one
hundred yards in length and twenty in width. Their
magnitude, however, is less striking than the immense
size of the blocks composing them. Some of the stones,
of an oblong shape, are from ten to fifteen feet in length,
and five or six feet thick. Their sides are quite smooth,
but though square, and of pretty regular formation, they
bear no mark of the chisel. They are laid together without cement, and here and there show gaps between.

The topmost terrace and the lower one are somewhat peculiar in their construction. They have both a quadrangular depression in the center, leaving the rest of the terrace elevated several feet above it. In the intervals of the stones immense trees have taken root, and their broad boughs stretching far over, and interlacing together, support a canopy almost impenetrable to the sun. Overgrowing the greater part of them, and climbing from one to another, is a wilderness of vines, in whose sinewy embrace many of the stones lie half hidden, while in some places a thick growth of bushes entirely covers them. There is a wild pathway which obliquely crosses two of these terraces; and so profound is the shade, so dense the vegetation, that a stranger to the place might pass along it without being aware of their existence.

These structures bear every indication of a very high antiquity, and Kory-Kory, who was my authority in all matters of scientific research, gave me to understand that they were coeval with the creation of the world; that the great gods themselves were the builders; and that they would endure until time shall be no more. Kory-Kory's prompt explanation, and his attributing the work to a divine origin, at once convinced me that neither he nor the rest of his countrymen knew anything about them.

As I gazed upon this monument, doubtless the work of an extinct and forgotten race, thus buried in the green nook of an island at the ends of the earth, the existence of which was yesterday unknown, a stronger feeling of awe came over me than if I had stood musing at the mighty base of the Pyramid of Cheops. There are no inscriptions, no sculpture, no clue, by which to conjecture its history: nothing but the dumb stones. How many generations of those majestic trees which over-shadow them have grown and flourished and decayed since first they were erected!

These remains naturally suggest many interesting reflections. They establish the great age of the island, an opinion which the builders of theories concerning the creation of the various groups in the South Seas are not always inclined to admit. For my own part, I think it just as probable that human beings were living in the valleys of the Marquesas three thousand years ago as that they were inhabiting the land of Egypt. The origin of the island of Nukuheva cannot be imputed to the coral insect; for indefatigable as that wonderful creature is, it would be hardly muscular enough to pile rocks one upon the other more than three thousand feet above the level of the sea. That the land may have been thrown up by a submarine volcano is as possible as anything else. No one can make an affidavit to the contrary, and therefore I will say nothing against the supposition: indeed, were geologists to assert that the whole continent of America had in like manner been formed by the simultaneous explosion of a train of Etnas laid under the water all the way from the North Pole to the parallel of Cape Horn, I am the last man in the world to contradict them.

I have already mentioned that the dwellings of the islanders were almost invariably built upon massive stone foundations, which they call pi-pis. The dimensions of these, however, as well as of the stones composing them, are comparatively small: but there are other and larger erections of a similar description comprising the "morais," or burying-grounds, and festival-places, in nearly all the valleys of the island. Some of these piles are so extensive, and so great a degree of labor and skill must have been requisite in constructing them, that I can scarcely believe they were built by the ancestors of the present inhabitants. If indeed they were, the race has sadly deteriorated in their knowledge of the mechanic arts. To say nothing of their habitual indolence, by what contrivance within the reach of so simple a people could such enormous masses have been moved or fixed in their places? and how could they with their rude implements have chiseled and hammered them into shape?

All of these larger pi-pis—like that of the Hoolah-Hoolah ground in the Typee valley—bore incontestable marks of great age; and I am disposed to believe that their erection may be ascribed to the same race of men who were the builders of the still more ancient remains I have just described.

According to Kory-Kory's account, the pi-pi upon which stands the Hoolah-Hoolah ground was built a great many moons ago, under the direction of Monoo, a great chief and warrior, and, as it would appear, master-mason among the Typees. It was erected for the express purpose to which it is at present devoted in the incredibly short period of one sun; and was dedicated to the immortal wooden idols by a grand festival, which lasted ten days and nights.

Among the smaller pi-pis, upon which stand the dwelling-houses of the natives, I never observed any which intimated a recent erection. There are in every part of the valley a great many of these massive stone foundations which have no houses upon them. This is vastly convenient, for whenever an enterprising islander chooses to emigrate a few hundred yards from the place where he was born, all he has to do in order to establish himself in some new locality, is to select one of the many unappropriated pi-pis, and without farther cere-mony pitch his bamboo tent upon it.

XXII

From the time that my lameness had decreased, I had made a daily practice of visiting Mehevi at the Ti, who invariably gave me a most cordial reception. I was always accompanied in these excursions by Fayaway and the ever-present Kory-Kory. The former, as soon as we reached the vicinity of the Ti—which was rigorously tabooed to the whole female sex—withdrew to a neighboring hut, as if her feminine delicacy restrained her from approaching a habitation which might be regarded as a sort of Bachelors' Hall.

And in good truth it might well have been so considered. Although it was the permanent residence of several distinguished chiefs, and of the noble Mehevi in particular, it was still at certain seasons the favorite haunt of all the jolly, talkative, and elderly savages of the vale, who resorted thither in the same way that similar characters frequent a tavern in civilized countries. There they would remain hour after hour, chatting, smoking, eating poee-poee, or busily engaged in sleeping for the good of their constitutions.

This building appeared to be the headquarters of the valley, where all flying rumors concentrated; and to have seen it filled with a crowd of the natives, all males, conversing in animated clusters, while multitudes were continually coming and going, one would have thought it a kind of savage Exchange, where the rise and fall of Polynesian Stock was discussed.

Mehevi acted as supreme lord over the place, spending the greater portion of his time there: and often when, at particular hours of the day, it was deserted by nearly every one else except the verd-antique looking centenarians, who were fixtures in the building, the chief himself was sure to be found enjoying his "otium cum dignitate," upon the luxurious mats which covered the floor. Whenever I made my appearance he invariably rose, and, like a gentleman doing the honors of his mansion, invited me to repose myself wherever I pleased, and calling out "Tammaree!" (Boy), a little fellow would appear, and then retiring for an instant, return with some savory mess, from which the chief would press me to regale myself. To tell the truth, Mehevi was indebted to the excellence of his viands for the honor of my repeated visits—a matter which cannot appear singular when it is borne in mind that bachelors, all the world over, are famous for serving up unexceptionable repasts.

One day, on drawing near to the Ti, I observed that extensive preparations were going forward, plainly betokening some approaching festival. Some of the symptoms reminded me of the stir produced among the scullions of a large hotel where a grand jubilee dinner is about to be given. The natives were hurrying about hither and thither, engaged in various duties; some lugging off to the stream enormous hollow bamboos, for the purpose of filling them with water; others chasing furious-looking hogs through the bushes, in their endeavors to capture them; and numbers employed in kneading great mountains of poee-poee heaped up in huge wooden vessels.

After observing these lively indications for a while, I was attracted to a neighboring grove by a prodigious squeaking which I heard there. On reaching the spot I found it proceeded from a large hog which a number of natives were forcibly holding to the earth, while a muscular fellow, armed with a bludgeon, was ineffectually aiming murderous blows at the skull of the unfortunate porker. Again and again he missed his writhing and struggling victim, but though puffing and panting with his exertions, he still continued them; and after striking a sufficient number of blows to have demolished an entire drove of oxen, with one crashing stroke he laid him dead at his feet.

Without letting any blood from the body, it was immediately carried to a fire which had been kindled near at hand, and four savages taking hold of the carcass by its legs, passed it rapidly to and fro in the flames. In a moment the smell of burning bristles betrayed the object of this procedure. Having got thus far in the matter, the body was removed to a little distance; and, being disembowelled, the entrails were laid aside as choice parts, and the whole carcass thoroughly washed with water. An ample thick green cloth, composed of the long thick leaves of a species of palm-tree, ingeniously tacked together with little pins of bamboo, was now spread upon the ground, in which the body being carefully rolled, it was borne to an oven previously prepared to receive it. Here it was at once laid upon the heated stones at the bottom, and covered with thick layers of leaves, the whole being quickly hidden from sight by a mound of earth raised over it.

Such is the summary style in which the Typees convert perverse-minded and rebellious hogs into the most docile and amiable pork; a morsel of which placed on the tongue melts like a soft smile from the lips of Beauty.

I commend their peculiar mode of proceeding to the consideration of all butchers, cooks, and housewives. The hapless porker whose fate I have just rehearsed, was not the only one who suffered on that memorable day. Many a dismal grunt, many an imploring squeak, proclaimed what was going on throughout the whole extent of the valley; and I verily believe the first-born of every litter perished before the setting of that fatal sun.

The scene around the Ti was now most animated. Hogs and poee-poee were baking in numerous ovens, which, heaped up with fresh earth into slight elevations, looked like so many ant-hills. Scores of the savages were vigorously plying their stone pestles in preparing masses of poee-poee, and numbers were gathering green bread-fruit and young coco-nuts in the surrounding groves; while an exceeding great multitude, with a view of encouraging the rest in their labors, stood still, and kept shouting most lustily without intermission.

It is a peculiarity among these people, that when engaged in any employment they always make a pro-digious fuss about it. So seldom do they ever exert themselves, that when they do work they seem de-termined that so meritorious an action shall not escape the observation of those around. If, for example, they have occasion to remove a stone to a little distance, which perhaps might be carried by two able-bodied men, a whole swarm gather about it, and, after a vast deal of palavering, lift it up among them, every one struggling to get hold of it, and bear it off yelling and panting as if accomplishing some mighty achievement. Seeing them on these occasions, one is reminded of an infinity of black ants clustering about and dragging away to some hole the leg of a deceased fly.

Having for some time attentively observed these demonstrations of good cheer, I entered the Ti, where Mehevi sat complacently looking out upon the busy scene, and occasionally issuing his orders. The chief appeared to be in an extraordinary flow of spirits, and gave me to understand that on the morrow there would be grand doings in the Groves generally, and at the Ti in particular; and urged me by no means to absent myself. In commemoration of what event, however, or in honor of what distinguished personage, the feast was to be given, altogether passed my comprehension. Mehevi sought to enlighten my ignorance, but he failed as signally as when he had endeavored to initiate me into the perplexing arcana of the taboo.

On leaving the Ti, Kory-Kory, who had as a matter of course accompanied me, observing that my curiosity remained unabated, resolved to make everything plain and satisfactory. With this intent, he escorted me through the Taboo Groves, pointing out to my notice a variety of objects, and endeavored to explain them in such an indescribable jargon of words, that it almost put me in bodily pain to listen to him. In particular, he led me to a remarkable pyramidical structure some three yards square at the base, and perhaps ten feet in height, which had lately been thrown up, and occupied a very conspicuous position. It was composed principally of large empty calabashes, with a few polished coco-nut shells, and looked not unlike a cenotaph of skulls. My cicerone perceived the astonishment with which I gazed at this monument of savage crockery, and immediately addressed himself to the task of enlightening me: but all in vain; and to this hour the nature of the monument remains a complete mystery to me. As, however, it formed so prominent a feature in the approaching revels, I bestowed upon the latter, in my own mind, the title of the "Feast of Calabashes."

The following morning, awaking rather late, I perceived the whole of Marheyo's family busily engaged in preparing for the festival. The old warrior himself was arranging in round balls the two gray locks of hair that were suffered to grow from the crown of his head; his earrings and spear, both well polished, lay beside him, while the highly decorative pair of shoes hung suspended from a projecting cane against the side of the house. The young men were similarly employed; and the fair damsels, including Fayaway, were anointing themselves with "aka," arranging their long tresses, and performing other matters connected with the duties of the toilet.

Having completed their preparations, the girls now exhibited themselves in gala costume; the most conspicuous feature of which was a necklace of beautiful white flowers, with the stems removed, and strung closely together upon a single fiber of tappa. Corresponding ornaments were inserted in their ears, and woven garlands upon their heads. About their waist they wore a short tunic of spotless white tappa, and some of them superadded to this a mantle of the same material, tied in an elaborate bow upon the left shoulder, and falling about the figure in picturesque folds.

Thus arrayed, I would have matched the charming Fayaway against any beauty in the world.

People may say what they will about the taste evinced by our fashionable ladies in dress. Their jewels, their feathers, their silks, and their furbelows would have sunk into utter insignificance beside the exquisite simplicity of attire adopted by the nymphs of the vale on this festive occasion. I should like to have seen a gallery of coronation beauties, at Westminster Abbey, confronted for a moment by this band of Island girls; their stiffness, formality, and affectation contrasted with the artless vivacity and unconcealed natural graces of these savage maidens. It would be the Venus de' Medici placed beside a milliner's doll.

It was not long before Kory-Kory and myself were left alone in the house, the rest of its inmates having departed for the Taboo Groves. My valet was all impatience to follow them, and was as fidgety about my dilatory movements as a diner-out waiting hat in hand at the bottom of the stairs for some lagging companion. At last, yielding to his importunities, I set out for the Ti. As we passed the houses peeping out from the groves through which our route lay, I noticed that they were entirely deserted by their inhabitants.

When we reached the rock that abruptly terminated the path, and concealed from us the festive scene, wild shouts and a confused blending of voices assured me that the occasion, whatever it might be, had drawn together a great multitude. Kory-Kory, previous to mounting the elevation, paused for a moment, like a dandy at a ballroom door, to put a hasty finish to his toilet. During this short interval, the thought struck me that I ought myself perhaps to be taking some little pains with my appearance. But as I had no holiday raiment, I was not a little puzzled to devise some means of decorating myself. However, as I felt desirous to create a sensation, I determined to do all that lay in my power; and knowing that I could not delight the savages more than by conforming to their style of dress, I removed from my person the large robe of tappa which I was accustomed to wear over my shoulders whenever I sallied into the open air, and remained merely girt about with a short tunic descending from my waist to my knees.

My quick-witted attendant fully appreciated the compliment I was paying to the costume of his race, and began more sedulously to arrange the folds of the one only garment which remained to me. Whilst he was doing this, I caught sight of a knot of young lasses, who were sitting near us on the grass surrounded by heaps of flowers which they were forming into garlands. I motioned to them to bring some of their handiwork to me; and in an instant a dozen wreaths were at my disposal. One of them I put round the apology of a hat which I had been forced to construct for myself out of palmetto-leaves, and some of the others I converted into a splendid girdle. These operations finished, with the slow and dignified step of a full-dressed beau I ascended the rock.

XXIII

The whole population of the valley seemed to be gathered within the precincts of the grove. In the distance could be seen the long front of the Ti, its immense piazza swarming with men, arrayed in every variety of fantastic costume, and all vociferating with animated gestures; while the whole interval between it and the place where I stood was enlivened by groups of females fancifully decorated, dancing, capering, and uttering wild exclamations. As soon as they descried me they set up a shout of welcome; and a band of them came dancing towards me chanting, as they approached, some wild recitative. The change in my garb seemed to transport them with delight, and clustering about me on all sides, they accompanied me towards the Ti. When, however, we drew near it these joyous nymphs paused in their career, and parting on either side, permitted me to pass on to the now densely thronged building.

So soon as I mounted to the pi-pi I saw at a glance that the revels were fairly under way.

What lavish plenty reigned around!—Warwick feasting his retainers with beef and ale was a niggard to the noble Mehevi!—All along the piazza of the Ti were arranged elaborately carved canoe-shaped vessels, some twenty feet in length, filled with newly made poee-poee, and sheltered from the sun by the broad leaves of the banana. At intervals were heaps of green breadfruit,

raised in pyramidical stacks, resembling the regular
piles of heavy shot to be seen in the yard of an arsenal.
Inserted into the interstices of the huge stones which
formed the pi-pi were large boughs of trees; hanging
from the branches of which, and screened from the sun
by their foliage, were innumerable little packages with
leafy coverings, containing the meat of the numerous
hogs which had been slain, done up in this manner to
make it more accessible to the crowd. Leaning against
the railing of the piazza were an immense number of
long, heavy bamboos, plugged at the lower end, and
with their projecting muzzles stuffed with a wad of
leaves. These were filled with water from the stream,
and each of them might hold from four to five gallons.

The banquet being thus spread, nought remained
but for every one to help himself at his pleasure. Accordingly not a moment passed but the transplanted
boughs I have mentioned were rifled by the throng of
the fruit they certainly had never borne before. Calabashes of poee-poee were continually being replenished
from the extensive receptacle in which that article was
stored, and multitudes of little fires were kindled abou⁺
the Ti for the purpose of roasting the breadfruit.

Within the building itself was presented a most extraordinary scene. The immense lounge of mats lying between the parallel rows of the trunks of coco-nut trees,
and extending the entire length of the house, at least
two hundred feet, was covered by the reclining forms
of a host of chiefs and warriors, who were eating at a
great rate, or soothing the cares of Polynesian life in
the sedative fumes of tobacco. The smoke was inhaled
from large pipes, the bowls of which, made out of
small coco-nut shells, were curiously carved in strange
heathenish devices. These were passed from mouth to
mouth by the recumbent smokers, who, taking two or

three prodigious whiffs, handed the pipe to his neighbor; sometimes for that purpose stretching indolently across the body of some dozing individual whose exertions at the dinner-table had already induced sleep.

The tobacco used among the Typees was of a very mild and pleasing flavor, and as I always saw it in leaves, and the natives appeared pretty well supplied with it, I was led to believe that it must have been the growth of the valley. Indeed Kory-Kory gave me to understand that this was the case; but I never saw a single plant growing on the island. At Nukuheva, and, I believe, in all the other valleys, the weed is very scarce, being only obtained in small quantities from foreigners, and smoking is consequently with the inhabitants of these places a very great luxury. How it was that the Typees were so well furnished with it I cannot divine. I should think them too indolent to devote any attention to its culture; and, indeed, as far as my observation extended, not a single atom of the soil was under any other cultivation than that of shower and sunshine. The tobacco-plant, however, like the sugar-cane, may grow wild in some remote part of the vale.

There were many in the Ti for whom the tobacco did not furnish a sufficient stimulus, and who accordingly had recourse to "arva," as a more powerful agent in producing the desired effect.

"Arva" is a root very generally dispersed over the South Seas, and from it is extracted a juice, the effects of which upon the system are at first stimulating in a moderate degree; but it soon relaxes the muscles, and exerting a narcotic influence produces a luxurious sleep. In the valley this beverage was universally prepared in the following way:—Some half-dozen young boys seated themselves in a circle around an empty wooden vessel, each one of them being supplied with a certain quantity of the roots of the "arva," broken into small bits and laid by his side. A coco-nut goblet of water was passed around the juvenile company, who, rinsing their mouths with its contents, proceeded to the business before them. This merely consisted in thoroughly masticating the "arva," and throwing it mouthful after mouthful into the receptacle provided. When a sufficient quantity had been thus obtained water was poured upon the mass, and being stirred about with the forefinger of the right hand, the preparation was soon in readiness for use. The "arva" has medicinal qualities.

Upon the Sandwich Islands it has been employed with no small success in the treatment of scrofulous affections, and in combatting the ravages of a disease for whose frightful inroads the ill-starred inhabitants of that group are indebted to their foreign benefactors. But the tenants of the Typee valley, as yet exempt from these inflictions, generally employ the "arva" as a minister to social enjoyment, and a calabash of the liquid circulates among them as the bottle with us.

Mehevi, who was greatly delighted with the change in my costume, gave me a cordial welcome. He had reserved for me a most delectable mess of "kokoo," well knowing my partiality for that dish; and had likewise selected three or four young coco-nuts, several roasted breadfruit, and a magnificent bunch of bananas, for my especial comfort and gratification. These various matters were at once placed before me; but Kory-Kory deemed the banquet entirely insufficient for my wants until he had supplied me with one of the leafy packages of pork, which, notwithstanding the somewhat hasty manner in which it had been prepared, possessed a most excellent flavor, and was surprisingly sweet and tender.

Pork is not a staple article of food among the people

of the Marquesas; consequently they pay little attention to the *breeding* of the swine. The hogs are permitted to roam at large in the groves, where they obtain no small part of their nourishment from the coco-nuts which continually fall from the trees. But it is only after infinite labor and difficulty, that the hungry animal can pierce the husk and shell so as to get at the meat. I have frequently been amused at seeing one of them, after crunching the obstinate nut with his teeth for a long time unsuccessfully, get into a violent passion with it. He would then root furiously under the coco-nut, and, with a fling of his snout, toss it before him on the ground. Following it up he would crunch at it again savagely for a moment, and the next knock it on one side, pausing immediately after, as if wondering how it could so suddenly have disappeared. In this way the persecuted coco-nuts were often chased half across the valley.

The second day of the Feast of Calabashes was ushered in by still more uproarious noises than the first. The skins of innumerable sheep seemed to be resounding to the blows of an army of drummers. Startled from my slumbers by the din, I leaped up, and found the whole household engaged in making preparations for immediate departure. Curious to discover of what strange events these novel sounds might be the precursors, and not a little desirous to catch a sight of the instruments which produced the terrific noise, I accompanied the natives as soon as they were in readiness to depart for the Taboo Groves.

The comparatively open space that extended from the Ti towards the rock, to which I have before alluded as forming the ascent to the place, was, with the building itself, now altogether deserted by the men, the whole distance being filled by bands of females, shouting and dancing under the influence of some strange excitement.

I was amused at the appearance of four or five old women who, in a state of utter nudity, with their arms extended flatly down their sides, and holding themselves perfectly erect, were leaping stiffly into the air, like so many sticks bobbing to the surface after being pressed perpendicularly into the water. They preserved the utmost gravity of countenance, and continued their extraordinary movements without a single moment's cessation. They did not appear to attract the observation of the crowd around them, but I must candidly confess that, for my own part, I stared at them most pertinaciously.

Desirous of being enlightened with regard to the meaning of this peculiar diversion, I turned inquiringly to Kory-Kory; that learned Typee immediately proceeded to explain the whole matter thoroughly. But all that I could comprehend from what he said was, that the leaping figures before me were bereaved widows, whose partners had been slain in battle many moons previously; and who, at every festival, give public evidence in this manner of their calamities. It was evident that Kory-Kory considered this an all-sufficient reason for so indecorous a custom; but I must say that it did not satisfy me as to its propriety.

Leaving these afflicted females, we passed on to the Hoolah-Hoolah ground. Within the spacious quadrangle, the whole population of the valley seemed to be assembled, and the sight presented was truly remarkable. Beneath the sheds of bamboo which opened towards the interior of the square, reclined the principal chiefs and warriors, while a miscellaneous throng lay at their ease under the enormous trees which spread a majestic canopy overhead. Upon the terraces of the gigantic altars, at either end, were deposited green breadfruit in baskets of coco-nut leaves, large rolls of tappa, bunches of ripe bananas, clusters of mawmee-apples, the golden-hued fruit of the artu-tree, and baked hogs, laid out in large wooden trenchers, fancifully decorated with freshly plucked leaves, whilst a variety of rude implements of war were piled in confused heaps before the ranks of hideous idols. Fruits of various kinds were likewise suspended in leafen baskets, from the tops of poles planted uprightly, and at regular intervals, along the lower terraces of both altars. At their base were arranged two parallel rows of cumbersome drums, standing at least fifteen feet in height, and formed from the hollow trunks of large trees. Their heads were covered with shark-skins, and their barrels were elaborately carved with various quaint figures and devices. At regular intervals they were bound round by a species of sinnate of various colors, and strips of native cloth flattened upon them here and there. Behind these instruments were built slight platforms, upon which stood a number of young men who, beating violently with the palms of their hands upon the drumheads, produced those outrageous sounds which had awakened me in the morning. Every few minutes these musical performers hopped down from their elevation into the crowd below, and their places were immediately supplied by fresh recruits. Thus an incessant din was kept up that might have startled Pandemonium.

Precisely in the middle of the quadrangle were placed perpendicularly in the ground a hundred or more slender, fresh-cut poles, stripped of their bark, and decorated at the end with a floating pennon of white tappa; the whole being fenced about with a little picket of canes. For what purpose these singular ornaments were intended I in vain endeavored to discover.

Another most striking feature of the performance was exhibited by a score of old men, who sat cross-legged in the little pulpits, which encircled the trunks of the immense trees growing in the middle of the enclosure. These venerable gentlemen, who I presume were the priests, kept up an uninterrupted monotonous chant, which was nearly drowned in the roar of drums. In the right hand they held a finely woven grass fan, with a heavy black wooden handle curiously chased: these fans they kept in continual motion.

But no attention whatever seemed to be paid to the drummers or to the old priests; the individuals who composed the vast crowd present being entirely taken up in chatting and laughing with one another, smoking, drinking arva, and eating. For all the observation it attracted, or the good it achieved, the whole savage orchestra might, with great advantage to its own members and the company in general, have ceased the prodigious uproar they were making.

In vain I questioned Kory-Kory and others of the natives, as to the meaning of the strange things that were going on; all their explanations were conveyed in such a mass of outlandish gibberish and gesticulation that I gave up the attempt in despair. All that day the drums resounded, the priests chanted, and the multitude feasted and roared till sunset, when the throng dispersed, and the Taboo Groves were again abandoned to quiet and repose. The next day the same scene was repeated until night, when this singular festival terminated.

XXIV

Although I had been baffled in my attempts to learn the origin of the Feast of Calabashes, yet it seemed very plain to me that it was principally, if not wholly, of a religious character. As a religious solemnity, however, it had not at all corresponded with the horrible descriptions of Polynesian worship which we have received in some published narratives, and especially in those accounts of the evangelized islands with which the missionaries have favored us. Did not the sacred character of these persons render the purity of their intentions unquestionable, I should certainly be led to suppose that they had exaggerated the evils of Paganism, in order to enhance the merit of their own disinterested labors.

In a certain work incidentally treating of the "Washington, or Northern Marquesas Islands," I have seen the frequent immolation of human victims upon the altars of their gods, positively and repeatedly charged upon the inhabitants. The same work gives also a rather minute account of their religion—enumerates a great many of their superstitions—and makes known the particular designations of numerous orders of the priesthood. One would almost imagine from the long list that is given of cannibal primates, bishops, archdeacons, prebendaries, and other inferior ecclesiastics, that the sacerdotal order far outnumbered the rest of the population, and that the poor natives were more severely priest-ridden than even the inhabitants of the papal states. These accounts are likewise calculated to leave upon the reader's mind an impression that human victims are daily cooked and served up upon the altars; that heathenish cruelties of every description are continually practiced; and that these ignorant Pagans are in a state of the extremest wretchedness in consequence of the grossness of their superstitions. Be it observed, however, that all this information is given by a man who, according to his own statement, was only at one of the islands, and remained there but two weeks, sleeping every night on board his ship, and taking little kidglove excursions ashore in the daytime, attended by an armed party.

Now, all I can say is, that in all my excursions through the valley of Typee, I never saw any of these alleged enormities. If any of them are practiced upon the Marquesas Islands they must certainly have come to my knowledge while living for months with a tribe of savages, wholly unchanged from their original primitive condition, and reputed the most ferocious in the South Seas.

The fact is that there is a vast deal of unintentional humbuggery in some of the accounts we have from scientific men concerning the religious institutions of Polynesia. These learned tourists generally obtain the greater part of their information from the retired old South-Sea rovers, who have domesticated themselves among the barbarous tribes of the Pacific. Jack, who has long been accustomed to the long-bow, and to spin tough yarns on a ship's forecastle, invariably officiates as showman of the island on which he has settled, and having mastered a few dozen words of the language, is supposed to know all about the people who speak it. A natural desire to make himself of consequence in the eyes of the strangers prompts him to lay claim to a much greater knowledge of such matters than he actually possesses. In reply to incessant queries, he communicates not only all he knows but a good deal more, and if there be any information deficient still he is at no loss to supply it. The avidity with which his anecdotes are noted down tickles his vanity, and his powers of invention increase with the credulity of his auditors. He knows just the sort of information wanted, and furnishes it to any extent.

This is not a supposed case; I have met with several individuals like the one described, and I have been present at two or three of their interviews with strangers.

Now when the scientific voyager arrives at home with his collection of wonders, he attempts, perhaps, to give a description of some of the strange people he has been visiting. Instead of representing them as a community of lusty savages, who are leading a merry, idle, innocent life, he enters into a very circumstantial and learned narrative of certain unaccountable superstitions and practices, about which he knows as little as the islanders do themselves. Having had little time, and scarcely any opportunity, to become acquainted with the customs he pretends to describe, he writes them down one after another in an off-hand, haphazard style; and were the book thus produced to be translated into the tongue of the people of whom it purports to give the history, it would appear quite as wonderful to them as it does to the American public, and much more improbable.

For my own part, I am free to confess my almost entire inability to gratify any curiosity that may be felt with regard to the theology of the valley. I doubt whether the inhabitants themselves could do so. They are either too lazy or too sensible to worry themselves about abstract points of religious belief. While I was among them they never held any synods or councils to settle the principles of their faith by agitating them. An unbounded liberty of conscience seemed to prevail. Those who pleased to do so were allowed to repose implicit faith in an ill-favored god with a large bottle-nose and fat shapeless arms crossed upon his breast; whilst others worshiped an image which, having no likeness either in heaven or on earth, could hardly be called an idol. As the islanders always maintained a discreet reserve with regard to my own peculiar views on religion, I thought it would be excessively ill-bred in me to pry into theirs.

But, although my knowledge of the religious faith of the Typees was unavoidably limited, one of their superstitious observances with which I became acquainted interested me greatly.

In one of the most secluded portions of the valley, within a stone's cast of Fayaway's Lake—for so I christened the scene of our island yachting—and hard by a growth of palms, which stood ranged in order along both banks of the stream, waving their green arms as if to do honor to its passage, was the mausoleum of a deceased warrior-chief. Like all the other edifices of any note, it was raised upon a small pi-pi of stones, which, being of unusual height, was a conspicuous object from a distance. A light thatching of bleached palmetto-leaves hung over it like a self-supported canopy; for it was not until you came very near that you saw it was supported by four slender columns of bamboo rising at each corner to a little more than the height of a man. A clear area of a few yards surrounded the pi-pi, and was enclosed by four trunks of coco-nut trees resting at the angles on massive blocks of stone. The place was sacred. The sign of the inscrutable taboo was seen in the shape of a mystic roll of white tappa,[1] suspended by a twisted cord of the same material from the top of a slight pole planted within the enclosure. The sanctity of the spot appeared never to have been violated. The stillness of the grave was there, and the calm solitude around was beautiful and touching. The soft shadows of those lofty palm-trees!—I can see them

[1] White appears to be the sacred color among the Marquesans.—H.M.

now—hanging over the little temple, as if to keep out the intrusive sun.

On all sides as you approached this silent spot you caught sight of the dead chief's effigy, seated in the stern of a canoe, which was raised on a light frame a few inches above the level of the pi-pi. The canoe was about seven feet in length; of a rich, dark-colored wood, handsomely carved and adorned in many places with variegated bindings of stained sinnate, into which were ingeniously wrought a number of sparkling seashells, and a belt of the same shells ran all round it. The body of the figure—of whatever material it might have been made—was effectually concealed in a heavy robe of brown tappa, revealing only the hands and head; the latter skillfully carved in wood, and surmounted by a superb arch of plumes. These plumes, in the subdued and gentle gales which found access to this sequestered spot, were never for one moment at rest, but kept nodding and waving over the chief's brow. The long leaves of the palmetto drooped over the eaves, and through them you saw the warrior holding his paddle with both hands in the act of rowing, leaning forward and inclining his head, as if eager to hurry on his voyage. Glaring at him for ever, and face to face, was a polished human skull, which crowned the prow of the canoe. The spectral figurehead, reversed in its position, glancing backwards, seemed to mock the impatient attitude of the warrior.

When I first visited this singular place with Kory-Kory, he told me—or at least I so understood him—that the chief was paddling his way to the realms of bliss and breadfruit—the Polynesian heaven—where every moment the breadfruit trees dropped their ripened spheres to the ground, and where there was no end to the coco-nuts and bananas; there they reposed through the livelong eternity upon mats much finer than those of Typee; and every day bathed their glowing limbs in rivers of coco-nut oil. In that happy land there were plenty of plumes and feathers, and boars' tusks and sperm-whale teeth, far preferable to all the shining trinkets and gay tappa of the white men; and, best of all, women far lovelier than the daughters of earth were there in abundance. "A very pleasant place," Kory-Kory said it was; but after all, not much pleasanter, he thought, than Typee. "Did he not then," I asked him, "wish to accompany the warrior?" "Oh, no: he was very happy where he was; but supposed that some time or other he would go in his own canoe."

Thus far, I think, I clearly comprehended Kory-Kory. But there was a singular expression he made use of at the time, enforced by as singular a gesture, the meaning of which I would have given much to penetrate. I am inclined to believe it must have been a proverb he uttered; for I afterwards heard him repeat the same words several times and in what appeared to me to be a somewhat similar sense. Indeed, Kory-Kory had a great variety of short, smart-sounding sentences, with which he frequently enlivened his discourse; and he introduced them with an air which plainly intimated, that in his opinion, they settled the matter in question, whatever it might be.

Could it have been then, that when I asked him whether he desired to go to this heaven of breadfruit, coco-nuts, and young ladies, which he had been describing, he answered by saying something equivalent to our old adage—"A bird in the hand is worth two in the bush?"—if he did, Kory-Kory was a discreet and sensible fellow, and I cannot sufficiently admire his shrewdness.

Whenever in the course of my rambles through the valley I happened to be near the chief's mausoleum, I always turned aside to visit it. The place had a peculiar charm for me; I hardly know why; but so it was. As I leaned over the railing and gazed upon the strange effigy and watched the play of the feathery head-dress, stirred by the same breeze which in low tones breathed amidst the lofty palm-trees, I loved to yield myself up to the fanciful superstition of the islanders, and could almost believe that the grim warrior was bound heavenward. In this mood when I turned to depart, I bade him "God speed, and a pleasant voyage." Aye, paddle away, brave chieftain, to the land of spirits! To the material eye thou makest but little progress; but with the eye of faith, I see thy canoe cleaving the bright waves, which die away on those dimly looming shores of Paradise.

This strange superstition affords another evidence of the fact, that however ignorant man may be, he still feels within him his immortal spirit yearning after the unknown future.

Although the religious theories of the islands were a complete mystery to me, their practical every-day operation could not be concealed. I frequently passed the little temples reposing in the shadows of the Taboo Groves and beheld the offerings—mouldy fruit spread out upon a rude altar, or hanging in half-decayed baskets around some uncouth jolly-looking image; I was present during the continuance of the festival; I daily beheld the grinning idols marshaled rank and file in the Hoolah-Hoolah ground, and was often in the habit of meeting those whom I supposed to be the priests. But the temples seemed abandoned to solitude; the festival had been nothing more than a jovial mingling of the tribe; the idols were quite as harmless as any other logs of wood; and the priests were the merriest dogs in the valley.

In fact religious affairs in Typee were at a very low ebb: all such matters sat very lightly upon the thoughtless inhabitants; and, in the celebration of many of their strange rites, they appeared merely to seek a sort of childish amusement.

A curious evidence of this was given in a remarkable ceremony in which I frequently saw Mehevi and several other chiefs and warriors of note take part; but never a single female.

Among those whom I looked upon as forming the priesthood of the valley, there was one in particular who often attracted my notice, and whom I could not help regarding as the head of the order. He was a noble-looking man, in the prime of his life, and of a most benignant aspect. The authority this man, whose name was Kolory, seemed to exercise over the rest, the episcopal part he took in the Feast of Calabashes, his sleek and complacent appearance, the mystic characters which were tattooed upon his chest, and above all the miter he frequently wore, in the shape of a towering headdress, consisting of part of a coco-nut branch, the stalk planted uprightly on his brow, and the leaflets gathered together and passed round the temples and behind the ears, all these pointed him out as Lord Primate of Typee. Kolory was a sort of Knight Templar—a soldier-priest; for he often wore the dress of a Marquesan warrior, and always carried a long spear, which, instead of terminating in a paddle at the lower end, after the general fashion of these weapons, was curved into a heathenish-looking little image. This instrument, however, might perhaps have been emblematic of his double functions. With one end in carnal combat he transfixed the enemies of his tribe; and with the other as a pastoral crook he kept in order his spiritual flock. But this is not all I have to say about Kolory. His martial grace very often carried about with him what seemed to me the half of a broken war-club. It was swathed round with ragged bits of white tappa, and the upper part, which was intended to represent a human head, was embellished with a strip of scarlet cloth of European manufacture. It required little observation to discover that this strange object was revered as a god. By the side of the big and lusty images standing sentinel over the altars of the Hoolah-Hoolah ground, it seemed a mere pigmy in tatters. But appearances all the world over are deceptive. Little men are sometimes very potent, and rags sometimes cover very extensive pretensions. In fact, this funny little image was the "crack" god of the island; lording it over all the wooden lubbers who looked so grim and dreadful; its name was Moa Artua.[2] And it was in honor of Moa Artua, and for the entertainment of those who believe in him, that the curious ceremony I am about to describe was observed.

Mehevi and the chieftains of the Ti have just risen from their noontide slumbers. There are no affairs of state to dispose of; and having eaten two or three breakfasts in the course of the morning, the magnates of the valley feel no appetite as yet for dinner. How are their leisure moments to be occupied? They smoke, they chat, and at last one of their number makes a proposition to the rest, who joyfully acquiescing, he darts out of the house, leaps from the pi-pi, and disappears in the grove. Soon you see him returning with Kolory, who bears the god Moa Artua in his arms, and carries in one

---

[2] The word "Artua," although having some other significations, is in nearly all the Polynesian dialects used as the general designation of the gods.—*H.M.*

hand a small trough, hollowed out in the likeness of a canoe. The priest comes along dandling his charge as if it were a lachrymose infant he was endeavoring to put into a good humor. Presently, entering the Ti, he seats himself on the mats as composedly as a juggler about to perform his sleight-of-hand tricks; and with the chiefs disposed in a circle around him, commences his ceremony.

In the first place he gives Moa Artua an affectionate hug, then caressingly lays him to his breast, and, finally, whispers something in his ear; the rest of the company listening eagerly for a reply. But the baby-god is deaf or dumb—perhaps both, for never a word does he utter. At last Kolory speaks a little louder, and soon growing angry, comes boldly out with what he has to say and bawls to him. He put me in mind of a choleric fellow, who, after trying in vain to communicate a secret to a deaf man, all at once flies into a passion and screams it out so that every one may hear. Still Moa Artua remains as quiet as ever; and Kolory, seemingly losing his temper, fetches him a box over the head, strips him of his tappa and red cloth, and laying him in a state of nudity in the little trough, covers him from sight. At this proceeding all present loudly applaud and signify their approval by uttering the adjective "mortarkee" with violent emphasis. Kolory, however, is so desirous his conduct should meet with unqualified approbation, that he inquires of each individual separately whether, under existing circumstances, he has not done perfectly right in shutting up Moa Artua. The invariable response is "Aa, aa" (Yes, yes), repeated over again and again in a manner which ought to quiet the scruples of the most conscientious. After a few moments Kolory brings forth his doll again, and while arraying it very carefully in the tappa and red cloth, alternately fondles and chides it. The toilet being completed, he once more speaks to

it aloud. The whole company hereupon show the greatest interest; while the priest holding Moa Artua to his
ear interprets to them what he pretends the god is
confidentially communicating to him. Some items of
intelligence appear to tickle all present amazingly; for
one claps his hands in a rapture; another shouts with
merriment; and a third leaps to his feet and capers
about like a madman.

What under the sun Moa Artua on these occasions
had to say to Kolory I never could find out: but I
could not help thinking that the former showed a sad
want of spirit in being disciplined into making those
disclosures, which at first he seemed bent on withhold-
ing. Whether the priest honestly interpreted what he
believed the divinity said to him or whether he was not
all the while guilty of a vile humbug, I shall not presume to decide. At any rate whatever as coming from
the god was imparted to those present seemed to be
generally of a complimentary nature: a fact which illus-
trates the sagacity of Kolory, or else the time-serving
disposition of this hardly used deity.

Moa Artua having nothing more to say, his bearer
goes to nursing him again, in which occupation, however, he is soon interrupted by a question put by one
of the warriors to the god. Kolory hereupon snatches it
up to his ear again, and after listening attentively,
once more officiates as the organ of communication. A
multitude of questions and answers having passed between the parties, much to the satisfaction of those
who propose them, the god is put tenderly to bed in
the trough, and the whole company unite in a long
chant, led off by Kolory. This ended, the ceremony is
over; the chiefs rise to their feet in high good humor,
and my Lord Archbishop, after chatting awhile, and
regaling himself with a whiff or two from a pipe of

tobacco, tucks the canoe under his arm and marches off with it.

The whole of these proceedings were like those of a parcel of children playing with dolls and baby houses.

For a youngster scarcely ten inches high, and with so few early advantages as he doutless had had, Moa Artua was certainly a precocious little fellow if he really said all that was imputed to him; but for what reason this poor devil of a deity, thus cuffed about, cajoled and shut up in a box, was held in greater estimation than the full-grown and dignified personages of the Taboo Groves, I cannot divine. And yet Mehevi, and other chiefs of unquestionable veracity—to say nothing of the Primate himself—assured me over and over again that Moa Artua was the tutelary deity of Typee, and was more to be held in honor than a whole battalion of the clumsy idols in the Hoolah-Hoolah grounds. Kory-Kory—who seemed to have devoted considerable attention to the study of theology, as he knew the names of all the graven images in the valley, and often repeated them over to me—likewise entertained some rather enlarged ideas with regard to the character and pretensions of Moa Artua. He once gave me to understand, with a gesture there was no misconceiving, that if he (Moa Artua) were so minded, he could cause a coco-nut tree to sprout out of his (Kory-Kory's) head; and that it would be the easiest thing in life for him (Moa Artua) to take the whole island of Nukuheva in his mouth and dive down to the bottom of the sea with it.

But in sober seriousness, I hardly knew what to make of the religion of the valley. There was nothing that so much perplexed the illustrious Cook, in his intercourse with the South Sea islanders, as their sacred rites. Although this prince of navigators was in many instances assisted by interpreters in the prosecution of his researches, he still frankly acknowledges that he was at a loss to obtain anything like a clear insight into the puzzling arcana of their faith. A similar admission has been made by other eminent voyagers: by Carteret, Byron, Kotzebue, and Vancouver.

For my own part, although hardly a day passed while I remained upon the island that I did not witness some religious ceremony or other, it was very much like seeing a parcel of "Freemasons" making secret signs to each other; I saw everything, but could comprehend nothing.

On the whole, I am inclined to believe that the islanders in the Pacific have no fixed and definite ideas whatever on the subject of religion. I am persuaded that Kolory himself would be effectually posed were he called upon to draw up the articles of his faith and pronounce the creed by which he hoped to be saved. In truth, the Typees, so far as their actions evince, submitted to no laws, human or divine—always excepting the thrice mysterious Taboo. The "independent electors" of the valley were not to be brow-beaten by chiefs, priests, idols, or devils. As for the luckless idols, they received more hard knocks than supplications. I do not wonder that some of them looked so grim, and stood so bolt upright, as if fearful of looking to the right or the left lest they should give any one offense. The fact is, they had to carry themselves *"pretty straight,"* or suffer the consequences. Their worshipers were such a precious set of fickle-minded and irreverent heathens, that there was no telling when they might topple one of them over, break it to pieces, and making a fire with it on the very altar itself, fall to roasting the offerings of breadfruit, and eat them in spite of its teeth.

In how little reverence these unfortunate deities were

held by the natives was on one occasion most convincingly proved to me. Walking with Kory-Kory through the deepest recesses of the groves, I perceived a curious-looking image, about six feet in height, which originally had been placed upright against a low pi-pi, surmounted by a ruinous bamboo temple, but having become fatigued and weak in the knees, was now carelessly leaning against it. The idol was partly concealed by the foliage of a tree which stood near, and whose leafy boughs drooped over the pile of stones, as if to protect the rude fane from the decay to which it was rapidly hastening. The image itself was nothing more than a grotesquely shaped log, carved in the likeness of a portly, naked man with the arms clasped over the head, the jaws thrown wide apart, and its thick, shapeless legs bowed into an arch. It was much decayed. The lower part was overgrown with a bright silky moss. Thin spears of grass sprouted from the distended mouth and fringed the outline of the head and arms. His godship had literally attained a green old age. All its prominent points were bruised and battered, or entirely rotted away. The nose had taken its departure, and from the general appearance of the head it might have been supposed that the wooden divinity, in despair at the neglect of its worshipers, had been trying to beat its own brains out against the surrounding trees.

I drew near to inspect more closely this strange object of idolatry; but halted reverently at the distance of two or three paces, out of regard to the religious prejudices of my valet. As soon, however, as Kory-Kory perceived that I was in one of my inquiring, scientific moods, to my astonishment, he sprang to the side of the idol, and pushing it away from the stones against which it rested, endeavored to make it stand upon its legs. But the divinity had lost the use of them altogether; and while Kory-Kory was trying to prop it up, by placing a stick between it and the pi-pi, the monster fell clumsily to the ground, and would infallibly have broken its neck had not Kory-Kory providentially broken its fall by receiving its whole weight on his own half-crushed back. I never saw the honest fellow in such a rage before. He leaped furiously to his feet, and seizing the stick, began beating the poor image: every moment or two pausing and talking to it in the most violent manner, as if upbraiding it for the accident. When his indignation had subsided a little he whirled the idol about most profanely, so as to give me an opportunity of examining it on all sides. I am quite sure I never should have presumed to have taken such liberties with the god myself, and I was not a little shocked at Kory-Kory's impiety.

This anecdote speaks for itself. When one of the inferior order of natives could show such contempt for a venerable and decrepit God of the Groves, what the state of religion must be among the people in general is easily to be imagined. In truth, I regard the Typees as a back-slidden generation. They are sunk in religious sloth, and require a spiritual revival. A long prosperity of breadfruit and coco-nuts has rendered them remiss in the performance of their higher obligations. The wood-rot malady is spreading among the idols—the fruit upon their altars is becoming offensive—the temples themselves need re-thatching—the tattooed clergy are altogether too light-hearted and lazy—and their flocks are going astray.

XXV

Although I had been unable during the late festival to obtain information on many interesting subjects which had much excited my curiosity, still that important event had not passed by without adding materially to my general knowledge of the islanders.

I was especially struck by the physical strength and beauty which they displayed, by their great superiority in these respects over the inhabitants of the neighboring bay of Nukuheva, and by the singular contrasts they presented among themselves in their various shades of complexion.

In beauty of form they surpassed anything I had ever seen. Not a single instance of natural deformity was observable in all the throng attending the revels. Occasionally I noticed among the men the scars of wounds they had received in battle; and sometimes, though very seldom, the loss of a finger, an eye, or an arm, attributable to the same cause. With these exceptions, every individual appeared free from those blemishes which sometimes mar the effect of an otherwise perfect form. But their physical excellence did not merely consist in an exemption from these evils; nearly every individual of their number might have been taken for a sculptor's model.

When I remembered that these islanders derived no advantage from dress, but appeared in all the naked simplicity of nature, I could not avoid comparing them with the fine gentlemen and dandies who promenade such unexceptionable figures in our frequented thoroughfares. Stripped of the cunning artifices of the tailor, and standing forth in the garb of Eden—what a sorry set of round-shouldered, spindle-shanked, crane-necked varlets would civilized men appear! Stuffed calves, padded breasts, and scientifically cut pantaloons would then avail them nothing, and the effect would be truly deplorable.

Nothing in the appearance of the islanders struck

me more forcibly than the whiteness of their teeth. The novelist always compares the masticators of his heroine to ivory; but I boldly pronounce the teeth of the Typees to be far more beautiful than ivory itself. The jaws of the oldest graybeards among them were much better garnished than those of most of the youths of civilized countries; while the teeth of the young and middle-aged, in their purity and whiteness, were actually dazzling to the eye. This marvelous whiteness of the teeth is to be ascribed to the pure vegetable diet of these people, and the uninterrupted healthfulness of their natural mode of life.

The men, in almost every instance, are of lofty stature, scarcely ever less than six feet in height, while the other sex are uncommonly diminutive. The early period of life at which the human form arrives at maturity in this generous tropical climate, likewise deserves to be mentioned. A little creature, not more than thirteen years of age, and who in other particulars might be regarded as a mere child, is often seen nursing her own baby; whilst lads who, under less ripening skies, would be still at school, are here responsible fathers of families.

On first entering the Typee Valley, I had been struck with the marked contrast presented by its inhabitants with those of the bay I had previously left. In the latter place, I had not been favorably impressed with the personal appearance of the male portion of the population; although with the females, excepting in some truly melancholy instances, I had been wonderfully pleased. I had observed that even the little intercourse Europeans had carried on with the Nukuheva natives had not failed to leave its traces amongst them. One of the most dreadful curses under which humanity labors had commenced its havocs, and betrayed, as it ever does among the South Sea islanders, the most aggravated symptoms.

From this, as from all other foreign inflictions, the yet uncontaminated tenants of the Typee Valley were wholly exempt; and long may they continue so. Better will it be for them for ever to remain the happy and innocent heathens and barbarians that they now are, than, like the wretched inhabitants of the Sandwich Islands, to enjoy the mere name of Christians without experiencing any of the vital operations of true religion, whilst, at the same time, they are made the victims of the worst vices and evils of civilized life.

Apart, however, from these considerations, I am inclined to believe that there exists a radical difference between the two tribes, if indeed they are not distinct races of men. To those who have merely touched at Nukuheva Bay, without visiting other portions of the island, it would hardly appear credible the diversities presented between the various small clans inhabiting so diminutive a spot. But the hereditary hostility which has existed between them for ages fully accounts for this.

Not so easy, however, is it to assign an adequate cause for the endless variety of complexions to be seen in the Typee Valley. During the festival, I had noticed several young females whose skins were almost as white as any Saxon damsels; a slight dash of the mantling brown being all that marked the difference. This comparative fairness of complexion, though in a great degree perfectly natural, is partly the result of an artificial process, and of an entire exclusion from the sun. The juice of the "papa" root, found in great abundance at the head of the valley, is held in great esteem as a cosmetic, with which many of the females daily anoint their whole person. The habitual use of it whitens and beautifies the skin. Those of the young girls who resort to this method of heightening their charms, never expose themselves to the rays of the sun; an observance, however, that produces little or no inconvenience, since there are but few of the inhabited portions of the vale which are not shaded over with a spreading canopy of boughs, so that one may journey from house to house, scarcely deviating from the direct course, and yet never once see his shadow cast upon the ground.

The "papa," when used, is suffered to remain upon the skin for several hours; being of a light green color, it consequently imparts for the time a similar hue to the complexion. Nothing, therefore, can be imagined more singular than the appearance of these nearly naked damsels immediately after the application of the cosmetic. To look at one of them you would almost suppose she was some vegetable in an unripe state; and that, instead of living in the shade for ever, she ought to be placed out in the sun to ripen.

All the islanders are more or less in the habit of anointing themselves; the women preferring the "aka" or "papa," and the men using the oil of the coco-nut. Mehevi was remarkably fond of mollifying his entire cuticle with this ointment. Sometimes he might be seen, with his whole body fairly reeking with the perfumed oil of the nut, looking as if he had just emerged from a soap-boiler's vat or had undergone the process of dipping in a tallow-chandlery. To this cause perhaps, united to their frequent bathing and extreme cleanliness, is ascribable, in a great measure, the marvelous purity and smoothness of skin exhibited by the natives in general.

The prevailing tint among the women of the valley was a light olive, and of this style of complexion Fayaway afforded the most beautiful example. Others were still darker, while not a few were of a genuine golden color, and some of a swarthy hue.

As agreeing with much previously mentioned in this

narrative, I may here observe, that Mendana, their discoverer, in his account of the Marquesas, described the natives as wonderously beautiful to behold, and as nearly resembling the people of southern Europe. The first of these islands seen by Mendana was La Madalena, which is not far distant from Nukuheva; and its inhabitants in every respect resemble those dwelling on that and the other islands of the group. Figueroa, the chronicler of Mendana's voyage, says that on the morning the land was descried, when the Spaniards drew near the shore, there sallied forth, in rude procession, about seventy canoes, and at the same time many of the inhabitants (females, I presume) made towards the ships by swimming. He adds, that "in complexion they were nearly white; of good stature, and finely formed; and on their faces and bodies were delineated representations of fishes and other devices." The old Don then goes on to say, "There came, among others, two lads paddling their canoe, whose eyes were fixed on the ship; they had beautiful faces and the most promising animation of countenance; and were in all things so becoming, that the pilor-mayor (Quiros) affirmed nothing in his life ever caused him so much regret as the leaving such fine creatures to be lost in that country." [1] More than two hundred years have gone by since the passage of which the above translation was written; and it appears to me now, as I read it, as fresh and true as if written but yesterday. The islanders are still the same; and I have

[1] This passage, which is cited as an almost literal translation from the original, I found in a small volume entitled *Circumnavigation of the Globe*, in which volume are several extracts from Dalrymple's *Historical Collection*. The last-mentioned work I have never seen, but it is said to contain a very correct English version of great part of the learned Doctor Christoval Suarez de Figueroa's *History of Mendana's Voyage*, published at Madrid A.D. 1613.—*H.M.*

seen boys in the Typee Valley of whose "beautiful faces" and "promising animation of countenance" no one who has not beheld them can form any adequate idea. Cook, in the account of his voyages, pronounces the Marquesans as by far the most splendid islanders in the South Seas. Stewart, the chaplain of the U.S. ship *Vincennes*, in his *Visit to the South Seas*, expresses, in more than one place, his amazement at the surpassing loveliness of the women; and says that many of the Nukuheva damsels reminded him forcibly of the most celebrated beauties in his own land. Fanning, a Yankee mariner of some reputation, likewise records his lively impressions of the physical appearance of these people; and Commodore David Porter of the U.S. frigate *Essex*, is said to have been vastly smitten by the beauty of the ladies. Their great superiority over all other Polynesians cannot fail to attract the notice of those who visit the principal groups in the Pacific. The voluptuous Tahitians are the only people who at all deserve to be compared with them; while the dark-hued Hawaiians and the woolly-headed Feejees are immeasurably inferior to them. The distinguishing characteristic of the Marquesan islanders, and that which at once strikes you, is the European cast of their features—a peculiarity seldom observable among other uncivilized people. Many of their faces present a profile classically beautiful, and in the valley of Typee, I saw several who, like the stranger Marnoo, were in every respect models of beauty.

Some of the natives present at the Feast of Calabashes had displayed a few articles of European dress; disposed, however, about their persons after their own peculiar fashion. Among these I perceived the two pieces of cotton-cloth which poor Toby and myself had bestowed upon our youthful guides the afternoon we entered the valley. They were evidently reserved for gala days; and during those of the festival they rendered the young islanders who wore them very distinguished characters. The small number who were similarly adorned, and the great value they appeared to place upon the most common and most trivial articles, furnished ample evidence of the very restricted intercourse they held with vessels touching at the island. A few cotton handkerchiefs, of a gay pattern, tied about the neck, and suffered to fall over the shoulders; strips of fanciful calico, swathed about the loins, were nearly all I saw.

Indeed, throughout the valley, there were few things of any kind to be seen of European origin. All I ever saw beside the articles just alluded to, were the six muskets preserved in the Ti, and three or four similar implements of warfare hung up in other houses; some small canvas bags, partly filled with bullets and powder, and half a dozen old hatchet-heads, with the edges blunted and battered to such a degree as to render them utterly useless. These last seemed to be regarded as nearly worthless by the natives; and several times they held up one of them before me, and throwing it aside with a gesture of disgust, manifested their contempt for anything that could so soon become unserviceable.

But the muskets, the powder, and the bullets were held in most extravagant esteem. The former, from their great age and the peculiarities they exhibited, were well worth a place in any antiquarian's armory. I remember in particular one that hung in the Ti, and which Mehevi —supposing as a matter of course that I was able to repair it—had put into my hands for that purpose. It was one of those clumsy, old-fashioned, English pieces known generally as Tower Hill muskets, and, for aught I know, might have been left on the island by Wallace,

Carteret, Cook, or Vancouver. The stock was half-rotten and worm-eaten; the lock was as rusty and about as well adapted to its ostensible purpose as an old door-hinge; the threading of the screws about the trigger was completely worn away; while the barrel shook in the wood. Such was the weapon the chief desired me to restore to its original condition. As I did not possess the accomplishments of a gunsmith, and was likewise destitute of the necessary tools, I was reluctantly obliged to signify my inability to perform the task. At this unexpected communication Mehevi regarded me, for a moment, as if he half suspected I was some inferior sort of white man, who after all did not know much more than a Typee. However, after a most labored explanation of the matter, I succeeded in making him understand the extreme difficulty of the task. Scarcely satisfied with my apologies, however, he marched off with the superannuated musket in something of a huff as if he would no longer expose it to the indignity of being manipulated by such unskillful fingers.

During the festival I had not failed to remark the simplicity of manner, the freedom from all restraint, and, to a certain degree, the quality of condition manifested by the natives in general. No one appeared to assume any arrogant pretensions. There was little more than a slight difference in costume to distinguish the chiefs from the other natives. All appeared to mix together freely, and without any reserve; although I noticed that the wishes of a chief, even when delivered in the mildest tone, received the same immediate obedience which elsewhere would have been only accorded to a peremptory command. What may be the extent of the authority of the chiefs over the rest of the tribe, I will not venture to assert; but from all I saw during my stay in the valley, I was induced to believe that in matters concerning the general welfare it was very limited. The required degree of deference towards them, however, was willingly and cheerfully yielded; and as all authority is transmitted from father to son, I have no doubt that one of the effects here, as elsewhere, of high birth, is to induce respect and obedience.

The civil institutions of the Marquesas Islands appear to be in this, as in other respects, directly the reverse of those of the Tahitian and Hawaiian groups, where the original power of the king and chiefs was far more despotic than that of any tyrant in civilized countries. At Tahiti it used to be death for one of the inferior orders to approach, without permission, under the shadow of the king's house; or to fail in paying the customary reverence when food destined for the king was borne past them by his messengers. At the Sandwich Islands, Kaahumanu, the gigantic old dowager queen—a woman of nearly four hundred pounds weight, and who is said to be still living at Mowee—was accustomed, in some of her terrific gusts of temper, to snatch up an ordinary-sized man who had offended her, and snap his spine across her knee. Incredible as this may seem, it is a fact. While at Lahainaluna—the residence of this monstrous Jezebel—a humpbacked wretch was pointed out to me, who, some twenty-five years previously, had had the vertebræ of his backbone very seriously discomposed by his gentle mistress.

The particular grades of rank existing among the chiefs of Typee, I could not in all cases determine. Previous to the Feast of Calabashes I had been puzzled what particular station to assign to Mehevi. But the important part he took upon that occasion convinced me that he had no superior among the inhabitants of the valley. I had invariably noticed a certain degree of deference paid to him by all with whom I had ever seen him brought in contact; but when I remembered that my wanderings had been confined to a limited portion of the valley, and that towards the sea a number of distinguished chiefs resided, some of whom had separately visited me at Marheyo's house, and whom, until the festival, I had never seen in the company of Mehevi, I felt disposed to believe that his rank after all might not be particularly elevated.

The revels, however, had brought together all the warriors whom I had seen individually and in groups at different times and places. Among them Mehevi moved with an easy air of superiority which was not to be mistaken; and he whom I had only looked at as the hospitable host of the Ti, and one of the military leaders of the tribe, now assumed in my eyes the dignity of royal station. His striking costume, no less than his naturally commanding figure, seemed indeed to give him pre-eminence over the rest. The towering helmet of feathers that he wore raised him in height above all who surrounded him; and though some others were similarly adorned, the length and luxuriance of their plumes were far inferior to his.

Mehevi was in fact the greatest of the chiefs—the head of his clan—the sovereign of the valley; and the simplicity of the social institutions of the people could not have been more completely proved than by the fact, that after having been several weeks in the valley, and almost in daily intercourse with Mehevi, I should have remained until the time of the festival ignorant of his regal character. But a new light had now broken in upon me. The Ti was the palace—and Mehevi the king. Both the one and the other of a most simple and patriarchal nature it must be allowed, and wholly unattended by the ceremonious pomp which usually surrounds the purple.

After having made this discovery I could not avoid congratulating myself that Mehevi had from the first taken me as it were under his royal protection, and that he still continued to entertain for me the warmest regard, as far at least as I was enabled to judge from appearances. For the future I determined to pay most assiduous court to him, hoping that eventually through his kindness I might obtain my liberty.

XXVI

King Mehevi!—A goodly sounding title!—and why should I not bestow it upon the foremost man in the valley of Typee? The republican missionaries of Oahu cause to be gazetted in the Court Journal, published at Honolulu, the most trivial movements of "his gracious majesty" King Kamehameha III, and "their highnesses the princes of the blood royal." [1] —And who is his "gra-

[1] Accounts like these are sometimes copied into English and American journals. They lead the reader to infer that the arts and customs of civilized life are rapidly refining the natives of the Sandwich Islands. But let no one be deceived by these accounts. The chiefs swagger about in gold lace and broadcloth, while the great mass of the common people are nearly as primitive in their appearance as in the days of Cook. In the progress of events at these Islands, the two classes are receding from each other: the chiefs are daily becoming more luxurious and extravagant in their style of living, and the common people more and more destitute of the necessaries and decencies of life. But the end to which both will arrive at last will be the same: the one are fast destroying themselves by sensual indulgences, and the other are fast *being* destroyed by a complication of disorders, and the want of wholesome food. The resources of the domineering chiefs are wrung from the starving serfs, and every additional bauble with which they bedeck themselves

cious majesty," and what the quality of this "blood-royal?"—His "gracious majesty" is a fat, lazy, Negro-looking blockhead, with as little character as power. He has lost the noble traits of the barbarian, without acquiring the redeeming graces of a civilized being; and, although a member of the Hawaiian Temperence Society, is a most inveterate dram-drinker.

The "blood royal" is an extremely thick, depraved fluid; formed principally of raw fish, bad brandy, and European sweetmeats, and is charged with a variety of eruptive humors, which are developed in sundry blotches and pimples upon the august face of "majesty itself," and the angelic countenances of the "princes and princess of the blood royal"!

Now, if the farcical puppet of a chief magistrate in the Sandwish Islands be allowed the title of King, why should it be withheld from the noble savage Mehevi, who is a thousand times more worthy of the appellation? All hail, therefore, Mehevi, King of the Cannibal Valley, and long life and prosperity to his Typeean majesty! May Heaven for many a year preserve him, the uncompromising foe of Nukuheva and the French, if a hostile attitude will secure his lovely domain from the remorseless inflictions of South Sea civilization.

.   .   .   .   .   .

Previously to seeing the Dancing Widows I had little idea that there were any matrimonial relations subsisting in Typee, and I should as soon have thought of a Platonic affection being cultivated between the sexes, as of the solemn connection of man and wife.

---

is purchased by the sufferings of their bondsmen; so that the measure of gew-gaw refinement attained by the chiefs is only an index to the actual state of degradation in which the greater portion of the population lie groveling.—*H.M.*

To be sure, there were old Marheyo and Tinor, who seemed to have a sort of nuptial understanding with one another; but for all that, I had sometimes observed a comical-looking old gentleman dressed in a suit of shabby tattooing, who had the audacity to take various liberties with the lady, and that too in the very presence of the old warrior her husband, who looked on, as good-naturedly as if nothing was happening. This behavior, until subsequent discoveries enlightened me, puzzled me more than anything else I witnessed in Typee.

As for Mehevi, I had supposed him a confirmed bachelor, as well as most of the principal chiefs. At any rate, if they had wives and families, they ought to have been ashamed of themselves; for sure I am, they never troubled themselves about any domestic affairs. In truth, Mehevi seemed to be the president of a club of hearty fellows, who kept "Bachelors' Hall" in fine style at the Ti. I had no doubt but that they regarded children as odious encumbrances; and their ideas of domestic felicity were sufficiently shown in the fact, that they allowed no meddlesome housekeepers to turn topsy-turvy those snug little arrangements they had made in their comfortable dwelling. I strongly suspected, however, that some of these jolly bachelors were carrying on love intrigues with the maidens of the tribe; although they did not appear publicly to acknowledge them. I happened to pop upon Mehevi three or four times when he was romping—in a most undignified manner for a warrior king—with one of the prettiest little witches in the valley. She lived with an old woman and a young man in a house near Marheyo's; and although in appearance a mere child herself, had a noble boy about a year old, who bore a marvelous resemblance to Mehevi, whom

I should certainly have believed to have been the father, were it not that the little fellow had no triangle on his face—but on second thoughts, tattooing is not hereditary. Mehevi, however, was not the only person upon whom the damsel Moonoony smiled—the young fellow of fifteen, who permanently resided in the house with her, was decidedly in her good graces. I sometimes beheld both him and the chief making love at the same time. Is it possible, thought I, that the valiant warrior can consent to give up a corner in the thing he loves? This too was a mystery which, with others of the same kind, was afterwards satisfactorily explained.

During the second day of the Feast of Calabashes, Kory-Kory—being determined that I should have some understanding on these matters—had, in the course of his explanations, directed my attention to a peculiarity I had frequently remarked among many of the females —principally those of a mature age and rather matronly appearance. This consisted in having the right hand and the left foot most elaborately tattooed; while the rest of the body was wholly free from the operation of the art, with the exception of the minutely dotted lips and slight marks on the shoulders, to which I have previously referred as comprising the sole tattooing exhibited by Fayaway, in common with other young girls of her age. The hand and foot thus embellished were, according to Kory-Kory, the distinguishing badge of wedlock, so far as that social and highly commendable institution is known among these people. It answers, indeed, the same purpose as the plain gold ring worn by our fairer spouses.

After Kory-Kory's explanation of the subject, I was for some time studiously respectful in the presence of all females thus distinguished, and never ventured to indulge in the slightest approach to flirtation with any of their number. Married women, to be sure!—I knew better than to offend them.

A further insight however into the peculiar domestic customs of the inmates of the valley did away in a measure with the severity of my scruples, and convinced me that I was deceived in some at least of my conclusions. A regular system of polygamy exists among the islanders; but of a most extraordinary nature—a plurality of husbands, instead of wives; and this solitary fact speaks volumes for the gentle disposition of the male population. Where else, indeed, could such a practice exist, even for a single day?—Imagine a revolution brought about in a Turkish seraglio, and the harem rendered the abode of bearded men; or conceive some beautiful woman in our own country running distracted at the sight of her numerous lovers murdering one another before her eyes, out of jealousy for the unequal distribution of her favors!—Heaven defend us from such a state of things!—We are scarcely amiable and forbearing enough to submit to it.

I was not able to learn what particular ceremony was observed in forming the marriage contract, but am inclined to think that it must have been of a very simple nature. Perhaps the mere "popping the question," as it is termed with us, might have been followed by an immediate nuptial alliance. At any rate, I have more than one reason to believe that tedious courtships are unknown in the valley of Typee.

The males considerably outnumber the females. This holds true of many of the islands of Polynesia, although the reverse of what is the case in most civilized countries. The girls are first wooed and won, at a very tender age, by some stripling in the household in which they reside. This, however, is a mere frolic of the affections, and no formal engagement is contracted. By the time this first love has a little subsided a second suitor presents himself, of graver years, and carries both boy and girl away to his own habitation. This disinterested and generous-hearted fellow now weds the young couple— marrying damsel and lover at the same time—and all three thenceforth live together as harmoniously as so many turtles. I have heard of some men who in civilized countries rashly marry large families with their wives, but had no idea that there was any place where people married supplementary husbands with them. Infidelity on either side is very rare. No man has more than one wife, and no wife of mature years has less than two husbands—sometimes she has three, but such instances are not frequent. The marriage tie, whatever it may be, does not appear to be indissoluble; for separations occasionally happen. These, however, when they do take place, produce no unhappiness, and are preceded by no bickerings; for the simple reason, that an ill-used wife or a henpecked husband is not obliged to file a bill in Chancery to obtain a divorce. As nothing stands in the way of a separation, the matrimonial yoke sits easily and lightly, and a Typee wife lives on very pleasant and sociable terms with her husbands. On the whole, wedlock, as known among these Typees, seems to be of a more distinct and enduring nature than is usually the case with barbarous people. A baneful promiscuous intercourse of the sexes is hereby avoided, and virtue, without being clamorously invoked, is, as it were, unconsciously practiced.

The contrast exhibited between the Marquesas and other islanders of the Pacific in this respect, is worthy of being noticed. At Tahiti the marriage tie was altogether unknown; and the relation of husband and wife, father and son, could hardly be said to exist. The Arreory Society—one of the most singular institutions that ever existed in any part of the world—spread universal licentiousness over the island. It was the voluptuous character of these people which rendered the disease introduced among them by De Bougainville's ships, in 1768, doubly destructive. It visited them like a plague, sweeping them off by hundreds.

Notwithstanding the existence of wedlock among the Typees, the Scriptural injunction to increase and multiply seems to be but indifferently attended to. I never saw any of those large families in arithmetical or step-ladder progression which one often meets with at home. I never knew of more than two youngsters living together in the same home, and but seldom even that number. As for the women it was very plain that the anxieties of the nursery but seldom disturbed the serenity of their souls; and they were never to be seen going about the valley with half a score of little ones tagging at their apron-strings, or rather at the breadfruit-leaf they usually wore in the rear.

The ratio of increase among all the Polynesian nations is very small; and in some places as yet uncorrupted by intercourse with Europeans, the births would appear but very little to outnumber the deaths; the population in such instances remaining nearly the same for several successive generations, even upon those islands seldom or never desolated by wars, and among people with whom the crime of infanticide is altogether unknown. This would seem expressly ordained by Providence to prevent the overstocking of the islands with a race too indolent to cultivate the ground, and who, for that reason alone, would, by any considerable increase in their numbers, be exposed to the most deplorable misery. During the entire period of my stay in the valley of Typee, I never saw more than ten or twelve children under the age of six months, and only became aware of two births.

It is to the absence of the marriage tie that the late rapid decrease of the population of the Sandwich Islands and of Tahiti is in part to be ascribed. The vices and diseases introduced among these unhappy people annually swell the ordinary mortality of the islands, while, from the same cause, the originally small number of births is proportionally decreased. Thus the progress of the Hawaiians and Tahitians to utter extinction is accelerated in a sort of compound ratio.

I have before had occasion to remark that I never saw any of the ordinary signs of a place of sepulture in the valley, a circumstance which I attributed, at the time, to my living in a particular part of it, and being forbidden to extend my rambles to any considerable distance towards the sea. I have since thought it probable, however, that the Typees, either desirous of removing from their sight the evidences of mortality, or prompted by a taste for rural beauty, may have some charming cemetery situated in the shadowy recesses along the base of the mountains. At Nukuheva, two or three large quadrangular "pi-pis," heavily flagged, enclosed with regular stone walls and shaded over and almost hidden from view by the interlacing branches of enormous trees, were pointed out to me as burial-places. The bodies, I understood, were deposited in rude vaults beneath the flagging, and were suffered to remain there without being disinterred. Although nothing could be more strange and gloomy than the aspect of these places where the lofty trees threw their dark shadows over rude blocks of stone, a stranger in looking at them would have discerned none of the ordinary evidences of a place of sepulture.

During my stay in the valley, as none of its inmates

were so accommodating as to die and be buried in order to gratify my curiosity with regard to their funeral rites, I was reluctantly obliged to remain in ignorance of them. As I have reason to believe, however, that the observances of the Typees in these matters are the same with those of all the other tribes on the island, I will here relate a scene I chanced to witness at Nukuheva.

A young man had died, about daybreak, in a house near the beach. I had been sent ashore that morning, and saw a good deal of the preparations they were making for his obsequies. The body, neatly wrapped in new white tappa, was laid out in an open shed of coconut boughs, upon a bier constructed of elastic bamboos ingeniously twisted together. This was supported, about two feet from the ground, by large canes planted upright in the earth. Two females, of a dejected appearance, watched by its side, plaintively chanting and beating the air with large grass fans whitened with pipeclay. In the dwelling-house adjoining a numerous company were assembled, and various articles of food were being prepared for consumption. Two or three individuals, distinguished by head-dresses of beautiful tappa, and wearing a great number of ornaments, appeared to officiate as masters of the ceremonies. By noon the entertainment had fairly begun, and we were told that it would last during the whole of the two following days. With the exception of those who mourned by the corpse, every one seemed disposed to drown the sense of the late bereavement in convivial indulgence. The girls, decked out in their savage finery, danced; the old men chanted; the warriors smoked and chatted; and the young and lusty, of both sexes, feasted plentifully and seemed to enjoy themselves as pleasantly as they could have done had it been a wedding.

The islanders understand the art of embalming, and

practice it with such success that the bodies of their great chiefs are frequently preserved for many years in the very houses where they died. I saw three of these in my visit to the Bay of Tior. One was enveloped in immense folds of tappa, with only the face exposed, and hung erect against the side of the dwelling. The others were stretched out upon biers of bamboo, in open, elevated temples, which seemed consecrated to their memory. The heads of enemies killed in battle are invariably preserved and hung up as trophies in the house of the conqueror. I am not acquainted with the process which is in use, but believe that fumigation is the principal agency employed. All the remains which I saw presented the appearance of a ham after being suspended for some time in a smoky chimney.

But to return from the dead to the living. The late festival had drawn together, as I had every reason to believe, the whole population of the vale, and consequently I was enabled to make some estimate with regard to its numbers. I should imagine that there were about two thousand inhabitants in Typee; and no number could have been better adapted to the extent of the valley. The valley is some nine miles in length, and may average one in breadth; the houses being distributed at wide intervals throughout its whole extent, principally, however, towards the head of the vale. There are no villages: the houses stand here and there in the shadow of the groves, or are scattered along the banks of the winding stream; their golden-hued bamboo sides and gleaming white thatch forming a beautiful contrast to the perpetual verdure in which they are embowered. There are no roads of any kind in the valley—nothing but a labyrinth of footpaths twisting and turning among the thickets without end.

The penalty of the Fall presses very lightly upon

the valley of Typee; for, with the one solitary exception of striking a light, I scarcely saw any piece of work performed there which caused the sweat to stand upon a single brow. As for digging and delving for a livelihood, the thing is altogether unknown. Nature had planted the breadfruit and the banana, and in her own good time she brings them to maturity, when the idle savage stretches forth his hand, and satisfies his appetite.

Ill-fated people! I shudder when I think of the change a few years will produce in their paradisaical abode; and probably when the most destructive vices, and the worst attendances on civilization, shall have driven all peace and happiness from the valley, the magnanimous French will proclaim to the world that the Marquesas Islands have been converted to Christianity! and this the Catholic world will doubtless consider as a glorious event. Heaven help the "Isles of the Sea"!—The sympathy which Christendom feels for them has, alas! in too many instances proved their bane.

How little do some of these poor islanders comprehend when they look around them, that no inconsiderable part of their disasters originate in certain tea-party excitements, under the influence of which benevolent-looking gentlemen in white cravats solicit alms, and old ladies in spectacles, and young ladies in sober russet low gowns, contribute sixpences towards the creation of a fund, the object of which is to ameliorate the spiritual condition of the Polynesians, but whose end has almost invariably been to accomplish their temporal destruction!

Let the savages be civilized, but civilize them with benefits, and not with evils; and let heathenism be destroyed, but not by destroying the heathen. The Anglo-Saxon hive have extirpated Paganism from the greater part of the North American continent; but with it they have likewise extirpated the greater portion of the Red race. Civilization is gradually sweeping from the earth the lingering vestiges of Paganism, and at the same time the shrinking forms of its unhappy worshipers.

Among the islands of Polynesia, no sooner are the images overturned, the temples demolished, and the idolaters converted into *nominal* Christians, than disease, vice, and premature death make their appearance. The depopulated land is then recruited from the rapacious hordes of enlightened individuals who settle themselves within its borders, and clamorously announce the progress of the Truth. Neat villas, trim gardens, shaven lawns, spires, and cupolas arise, while the poor savage soon finds himself an interloper in the country of his fathers, and that too on the very site of the hut where he was born. The spontaneous fruits of the earth, which God in his wisdom had ordained for the support of the indolent natives, remorselessly seized upon and appropriated by the stranger, are devoured before the eyes of the starving inhabitants, or sent on board the numerous vessels which now touch at their shores.

When the famished wretches are cut off in this manner from their natural supplies, they are told by their benefactors to work and earn their support by the sweat of their brows! But to no fine gentleman born to hereditary opulence does manual labor come more unkindly than to the luxurious Indian when thus robbed of the bounty of Heaven. Habituated to a life of indolence, he cannot and will not exert himself; and want, disease, and vice, all evils of foreign growth, soon terminate his miserable existence.

But what matters all this? Behold the glorious result!—The abominations of Paganism have given way to the pure rites of the Christian worship, the ignorant savage has been supplanted by the refined European! Look at Honolulu, the metropolis of the Sandwich Islands!—A community of disinterested merchants, and devoted self-exiled heralds of the Cross, located on the very spot that twenty years ago was defiled by the presence of idolatry. What a subject for an eloquent Bible-meeting orator! Nor has such an opportunity for a display of missionary rhetoric been allowed to pass by unimproved!—But when these philanthropists send us such glowing accounts of one half of their labors, why does their modesty restrain them from publishing the other half of the good they have wrought?—Not until I visited Honolulu was I aware of the fact that the small remnant of the natives had been civilized into draught horses, and evangelized into beasts of burden. But so it is. They have been literally broken into the traces, and are harnessed to the vehicles of their spiritual instructors like so many dumb brutes!

Among a multitude of similar exhibitions that I saw, I shall never forget a robust, red-faced, and very lady-like personage, a missionary's spouse, who day after day for months together took her regular airings in a little go-cart drawn by two of the islanders, one an old gray-headed man, and the other a roguish stripling, both being, with the exception of the fig-leaf, as naked as when they were born. Over a level piece of ground this pair of *draught* bipeds would go with a shambling, unsightly trot, the youngster hanging back all the time like a knowing horse, while the old hack plodded on and did all the work.

Rattling along through the streets of the town in this stylish equipage, the lady looks about her as magnificently as any queen driven in state to her coronation. A sudden elevation, and a sandy road however, soon disturb her serenity. The small wheels become imbedded in the loose soil—the old stager stands tugging and sweating, while the young one frisks about and does nothing; not an inch does the chariot budge. Will the tender-hearted lady, who has left friends and home for the good of the souls of the poor heathen, will she think a little about their bodies and get out, and ease the wretched old man until the ascent is mounted? Not she; she could not dream of it. To be sure, she used to think nothing of driving the cows to pasture on the old farm in New England; but times have changed since then. So she retains her seat and bawls out, "Hookee! hookee!" (Pull, pull.) The old gentleman, frightened at the sound, labors away harder than ever; and the younger one makes a great show of straining himself, but takes care to keep one eye on his mistress, in order to know when to dodge out of harm's way. At last the good lady loses all patience; "Hookee! hookee!" and rap goes the heavy handle of her huge fan over the naked skull of the old savage; while the young one shies to one side and keeps beyond its range. "Hookee! hookee!" again she cries—"Hookee tata kannaka!" (Pull strong, men,)—but all in vain, and she is obliged in the end to dismount and, sad necessity! actually to walk to the top of the hill.

At the town where this paragon of humility resides, is a spacious and elegant American chapel, where divine service is regularly performed. Twice every Sabbath towards the close of the exercises may be seen a score or two of little wagons ranged along the railing in front of the edifice, with two squalid native footmen in the livery of nakedness standing by each, and waiting for the dismission of the congregation to draw their superiors home.

Lest the slightest misconception should arise from anything thrown out of this chapter, or indeed in any other part of the volume, let me here observe, that against the cause of missions in the abstract no Christian can possibly be opposed: it is in truth a just and holy cause. But if the great end proposed by it be spiritual, the agency employed to accomplish that end is purely earthly; and, although the object in view be the achievement of much good, that agency may nevertheless be productive of evil. In short, missionary undertaking, however it may be blessed of Heaven, is in itself but human; and subject, like everything else, to errors and abuses. And have not errors and abuses crept into the most sacred places, and may there not be unworthy or incapable missionaries abroad, as well as ecclesiastics of a similiar character at home? May not the unworthiness or incapacity of those who assume apostolic functions upon the remote islands of the sea more easily escape detection by the world at large than if it were displayed in the heart of a city? An unwarranted confidence in the sanctity of its apostles—a proneness to regard them as incapable of guile—and an impatience of the least suspicion as to their rectitude as men or Christians, have ever been prevailing faults in the Church. Nor is this to be wondered at: for subject as Christianity is to the assaults of unprincipled foes, we are naturally disposed to regard everything like an exposure of ecclesiastical misconduct as the offspring of malevolence or irreligious feeling. Not even this last consideration, however, shall deter me from the honest expression of my sentiments.

There is something decidedly wrong in the practical operations of the Sandwich Island Missions. Those who from pure religious motives contribute to the support of this enterprise, should take care to ascertain that their donations, flowing through many devious channels, at last effect their legitimate object, the conversion of the Hawaiians. I urge this not because I doubt the moral probity of those who disburse these funds, but because I know that they are not rightly applied. To read pathetic accounts of missionary hardships, and glowing descriptions of conversions, and baptisms taking place beneath palm-trees, is one thing; and to go to the Sandwich Islands and see the missionaries dwelling in picturesque and prettily furnished coral-rock villas, whilst the miserable natives are committing all sorts of immoralities around them, is quite another.

In justice to the missionaries, however, I will willingly admit, that whatever evils may have resulted from their collective mismanagement of the business of the mission, and from the want of vital piety evinced by some of their number, still the present deplorable condition of the Sandwich Islands is by no means wholly chargeable against them. The demoralizing influence of a dissolute foreign population, and the frequent visits of all descriptions of vessels, have tended not a little to increase the evils alluded to. In a word, here, as in every case where Civilization has in any way been introduced among those whom we call savages, she has scattered her vices, and withheld her blessings.

As wise a man as Shakespeare has said, that the bearer of evil tidings hath but a losing office; and so I suppose will it prove with me, in communicating to the trusting friends of the Hawaiian Mission what has been disclosed in various portions of this narrative. I am persuaded, however, that as these disclosures will by their very nature attract attention, so they will lead to something which will not be without ultimate benefit to the cause of Christianity in the Sandwich Islands.

I have but one thing more to add in connection with this subject—those things which I have stated as facts will remain facts, in spite of whatever the bigoted or incredulous may say or write against them. My reflections, however, on those facts may not be free from error. If such be the case, I claim no further indulgence than should be conceded to every man whose object is to do good.

XXVII

I have already mentioned that the influence exerted over the people of the valley by their chiefs was mild in the extreme: and as to any general rule or standard of conduct by which the commonalty were governed in their intercourse with each other, so far as my observation extended, I should be almost tempted to say that none existed on the island, except, indeed, the mysterious "Taboo" be considered as such. During the time I lived among the Typees, no one was ever put upon his trial for any offense against the public. To all appearances there were no courts of law or equity. There was no municipal police for the purpose of apprehending vagrants and disorderly characters. In short, there were no legal provisions whatever for the well-being and conservation of society, the enlightened end of civilized legislation. And yet everything went on in the valley with a harmony and smoothness unparalleled, I will venture to assert, in the most select, refined, and pious associations of mortals in Christendom. How are we to explain this enigma? These islanders were heathens! savages! aye, cannibals! and how came they, without the aid of established law, to exhibit, in so eminent a degree, that social order which is the greatest blessing and highest pride of the social state?

It may reasonably be inquired, how were these

people governed? How were their passions controlled
in their everyday transactions? It must have been by
an inherent principle of honesty and charity towards
each other. They seemed to be governed by that sort
of tacit common-sense law which, say what they will
of the inborn lawlessness of the human race, has its
precepts graven on every breast. The grand principles
of virtue and honor, however they may be distorted
by arbitrary codes, are the same all the world over:
and where these principles are concerned, the right or
wrong of any action appears the same to the uncultivated
as to the enlightened mind. It is to this indwelling, this
universally diffused perception of what is *just* and *noble,*
that the integrity of the Marquesans in their intercourse
with each other is to be attributed. In the darkest nights
they slept securely, with all their worldly wealth around
them, in houses the doors of which were never fastened.
The disquieting ideas of theft or assassination never
disturbed them. Each islander reposed beneath his own
palmetto thatching, or sat under his own breadfruit-
tree, with none to molest or alarm him. There was not
a padlock in the valley, nor anything that answered
the purpose of one: still there was no community of
goods. This long spear, so elegantly carved and highly
polished, belongs to Warmoonoo: it is far handsomer
than the one which old Marheyo so greatly prizes; it is
the most valuable article belonging to its owner. And
yet I have seen it leaning against a coco-nut tree in
the grove, and there it was found when sought for.
Here is a sperm-whale tooth, graven all over with cunning devices: it is the property of Karluna: it is the most
precious of the damsel's ornaments. In her estimation
its price is far above rubies—and yet there hangs the
dental jewel by its cord of braided bark, in the girl's

house, which is far back in the valley; the door is left open, and all the inmates have gone off to bathe in the stream.[1]

So much for the respect in which "personal property" is held in Typee; how secure an investment of "real property" may be, I cannot take upon me to say. Whether the land of the valley was the joint property of its inhabitants, or whether it was parceled out among a certain number of landed proprietors who allowed everybody to "squat" and "poach" as much as he or she pleased, I never could ascertain. At any rate, musty parchments and title-deeds there were none on the island; and I am half inclined to believe that its inhabitants hold their broad valleys in fee simple from Nature herself; to have and to hold, so long as grass grows and water runs; or until their French visitors, by a summary mode of conveyancing, shall appropriate them to their own benefit and behoof.

Yesterday I saw Kory-Kory hie him away, armed with a long pole, with which, standing on the ground, he knocked down the fruit from the topmost boughs of the trees, and brought them home in his basket of coco-nut leaves. To-day I see an islander, whom I know

[1] The strict honesty which the inhabitants of nearly all the Polynesian Islands manifest towards each other, is in striking contrast with the thieving propensities some of them evince in their intercourse with foreigners. It would almost seem that, according to their peculiar code of morals, the pilfering of a hatchet or a wrought nail from a European is looked upon as a praiseworthy action. Or rather, it may be presumed, that bearing in mind the wholesale forays made upon them by their nautical visitors, they consider the property of the latter as a fair object of reprisal. This consideration, while it serves to reconcile an apparent contradiction in the moral character of the islanders, should in some measure alter that low opinion of it which the reader of South Sea voyages is too apt to form.—*H.M.*

to reside in a distant part of the valley, doing the self-same thing. On the sloping bank of the stream are a number of banana-trees. I have often seen a score or two of young people making a merry foray on the great golden clusters, and bearing them off, one after another, to different parts of the vale, shouting and tramping as they went. No churlish old curmudgeon could have been the owner of that grove of breadfruit trees, or of these gloriously yellow bunches of bananas.

From what I have said it will be perceived that there is a vast difference between "personal property" and "real estate" in the valley of Typee. Some individuals, of course, are more wealthy than others. For example: the ridge-pole of Marheyo's house bends under the weight of many a huge package of tappa; his long couch is laid with mats placed one upon the other seven deep. Outside, Tinor has ranged along in her bamboo cupboard—or whatever the place may be called—a goodly array of calabashes and wooden trenchers. Now, the house just beyond the grove, and next to Marheyo's, occupied by Ruaruga, is not quite so well furnished. There are only three moderate-sized packages swinging overhead: there are only two layers of mats beneath, and the calabashes and trenchers are not so numerous, nor so tastefully stained and carved. But then, Ruaruga has a house—not so pretty a one, to be sure—but just as commodious as Marheyo's; and, I suppose, if he wished to vie with his neighbor's establishment, he could do so with very little trouble. These, in short, constituted the chief differences perceivable in the relative wealth of the people in Typee.

Civilization does not engross all the virtues of humanity: she has not even her full share of them. They flourish in greater abundance and attain greater strength among many barbarous people. The hospitality of the wild Arab, the courage of the North American Indian and the faithful friendships of some of the Polynesian nations, far surpass any thing of a similar kind among the polished communities of Europe. If truth and justice, and the better principles of our nature, cannot exist unless enforced by the statute-book, how are we to account for the social condition of the Typees? So pure and upright were they in all the relations of life, that entering their valley, as I did, under the most erroneous impressions of their character, I was soon led to exclaim in amazement: "Are these the ferocious savages, the bloodthirsty cannibals of whom I have heard such frightful tales! They deal more kindly with each other, and are more humane, than many who study essays on virtue and benevolence, and who repeat every night that beautiful prayer breathed first by the lips of the divine and gentle Jesus." I will frankly declare, that after passing a few weeks in this valley of the Marquesas, I formed a higher estimate of human nature than I had ever before entertained. But alas! since then I have been one of the crew of a man-of-war, and the pent-up wickedness of five hundred men has nearly overturned all my previous theories.

There was one admirable trait in the general character of the Typees which, more than anything else secured my admiration: it was the unanimity of feeling they displayed on every occasion. With them there hardly appeared to be any difference of opinion upon any subject whatever. They all thought and acted alike. I do not conceive that they could support a debating society for a single night: there would be nothing to dispute about; and were they to call a convention to take into consideration the state of the tribe, its session would be a remarkably short one. They showed this spirit of unanimity in every action of life: everything was done in concert and good fellowship. I will give an instance of this fraternal feeling.

One day, in returning with Kory-Kory from my accustomed visit to the Ti, we passed by a little opening in the grove; on one side of which, my attendant informed me, was that afternoon to be built a dwelling of bamboo. At least a hundred of the natives were bringing materials to the ground, some carrying in their hands one or two of the canes which were to form the sides, others slender rods of the hibiscus, strung with palmetto leaves, for the roof. Every one contributed something to the work; and by the united, but easy, and even indolent, labors of all, the entire work was completed before sunset. The islanders, while employed in erecting this tenement, reminded me of a colony of beavers at work. To be sure, they were hardly as silent and demure as those wonderful creatures, nor were they by any means as diligent. To tell the truth, they were somewhat inclined to be lazy, but a perfect tumult of hilarity prevailed; and they worked together so unitedly, and seemed actuated by such an instinct of friendliness that it was truly beautiful to behold.

Not a single female took part in this employment: and if the degree of consideration in which the ever-adorable sex is held by the men be—as the philosophers affirm—a just criterion of the degree of refinement among a people, then I may truly pronounce the Typees to be as polished a community as ever the sun shone upon. The religious restrictions of the taboo alone excepted, the women of the valley were allowed every possible indulgence. Nowhere are the ladies more assiduously courted; nowhere are they better appreciated as the contributors to our highest enjoyments; and nowhere are they more sensible of their power. Far different from their condition among many rude nations, where the women are made to perform all the work while their ungallant lords and masters lie buried in sloth, the gentle sex in the valley of Typee were exempt from toil, if toil it might be called that, even in that tropical climate, never distilled one drop of perspiration. Their light household occupations, together with the manufacture of tappa, the platting of mats, and the polishing of drinking-vessels, were the only employments pertaining to the women. And even these resembled those pleasant avocations which fill up the elegant morning leisure of our fashionable ladies at home. But in these occupations, slight and agreeable though they were, the giddy young girls very seldom engaged. Indeed these wilful, care-killing damsels were averse to all useful employment. Like so many spoiled beauties, they ranged through the groves—bathed in the stream —danced—flirted—played all manner of mischievous pranks, and passed their days in one merry round of thoughtless happiness.

During my whole stay on the island I never witnessed a single quarrel, nor anything that in the slightest degree approached even to a dispute. The natives appeared to form one household, whose members were bound together by the ties of strong affection. The love of kindred I did not so much perceive, for it seemed blended in the general love; and where all were treated as brothers and sisters, it was hard to tell who were actually related to each other by blood.

Let it not be supposed that I have overdrawn this picture. I have not done so. Nor let it be urged, that the hostility of this tribe to foreigners, and the hereditary feuds they carry on against their fellow-islanders beyond the mountains, are facts which contradict me. Not so: these apparent discrepancies are easily reconciled. By many a legendary tale of violence and wrong, as well as by events which have passed before their eyes, these people have been taught to look upon white men with abhorrence. The cruel invasion of their country by Porter has alone furnished them with ample provocation; and I can sympathize in the spirit which prompts the Typee warrior to guard all the passes to his valley with the point of his leveled spear, and, standing upon the beach, with his back turned upon his green home, to hold at bay the intruding European.

As to the origin of the enmity of this particular clan towards the neighboring tribes, I cannot so confidently speak. I will not say that their foes are the aggressors, nor will I endeavor to palliate their conduct. But surely, if our evil passions must find vent, it is far better to expend them on strangers and aliens, than in the bosom of the community in which we dwell. In many polished countries civil contentions, as well as domestic enmities, are prevalent at the same time that the most atrocious foreign wars are waged. How much less guilty, then, are our islanders, who of these three sins are only chargeable with one, and that the least criminal!

The reader will erelong have reason to suspect that the Typees are not free from the guilt of cannibalism; and he will then, perhaps, charge me with admiring a people against whom so odious a crime is chargeable. But this only enormity in their character is not half so horrible as it is usually described. According to the popular fictions, the crews of vessels, shipwrecked on some barbarous coast, are eaten alive like so many dainty joints by the uncivil inhabitants; and unfortunate voyagers are lured into smiling and treacherous bays, knocked in the head with outlandish war-clubs, and served up without any preliminary dressing. In truth, so horrific and improbable are these accounts that many sensible and well-informed people will not believe that any cannibals exist, and place every book of voyages which purports to give any account of them, on the same shelf with *Blue-Beard* and *Jack the Giant-Killer;* while others, implicitly crediting the most extravagant fictions, firmly believe that there are people in the world with tastes so depraved that they would infinitely prefer a single mouthful of material humanity to a good dinner of roast beef and plum pudding. But here Truth, who loves to be centrally located, is again found between the two extremes; for cannibalism to a certain moderate extent is practiced among several of the primitive tribes in the Pacific, but it is upon the bodies of slain enemies alone; and horrible and fearful as the custom is, immeasurably as it is to be abhorred and condemned, still I assert that those who indulge in it are in other respects humane and virtuous.

XXVIII

There was no instance in which the social and kindly dispositions of the Typees were more forcibly evinced than in the manner they conducted their great fishing parties. Four times during my stay in the valley the young men assembled near the full of the moon, and went together on these excursions. As they were generally absent about forty-eight hours, I was led to believe that they went out towards the open sea, some distance from the bay. The Polynesians seldom use a hook and line, almost always employing large well-made nets, most ingeniously fabricated from the twisted fibers of a certain bark. I examined several of them which had been spread to dry upon the beach at Nukuheva. They resemble very much our own seines, and I should think were very nearly as durable.

All the South-Sea Islanders are passionately fond of

fish; but none of them can be more so than the inhabitants of Typee. I could not comprehend, therefore, why they so seldom sought it in their waters, for it was only at stated times that the fishing parties were formed, and these occasions were always looked forward to with no small degree of interest.

During their absence the whole population of the place were in a ferment, and nothing was talked of but "pehee, pehee" (fish, fish). Towards the time when they were expected to return the vocal telegraph was put into operation—the inhabitants, who were scattered throughout the length of the valley, leaped upon rocks and into trees, shouting with delight at the thoughts of the anticipated treat. As soon as the approach of the party was announced, there was a general rush of the men towards the beach; some of them remaining, however, about the Ti, in order to get matters in readiness for the reception of the fish, which were brought to the Taboo groves in immense packages of leaves, each one of them being suspended from a pole carried on the shoulders of two men.

I was present at the Ti on one of these occasions, and the sight was most interesting. After all the packages had arrived, they were laid in a row under the verandah of the building and opened. The fish were all quite small, generally about the size of a herring, and of every variety of color. About one-eighth of the whole being reserved for the use of the Ti itself, the remainder was divided into numerous smaller packages, which were immediately dispatched in every direction to the remotest parts of the valley. Arrived at their destination, these were in turn portioned out, and equally distributed among the various houses of each particular district. The fish were under a strict Taboo, until the distribution was completed, which seemed to be effected in the most impartial manner. By the operation of this system every man, woman, and child in the vale were at one and the same time partaking of this favorite article of food.

Once I remember the party arrived at midnight; but the unseasonableness of the hour did not repress the impatience of the islanders. The carriers dispatched from the Ti were to be seen hurrying in all directions through the deep groves; each individual preceded by a boy bearing a flaming torch of dried coco-nut boughs, which from time to time was replenished from the materials scattered along the path. The wild glare of these enormous flambeaux, lighting up with a startling brilliancy the innermost recesses of the vale, and seen moving rapidly along beneath the canopy of leaves, the savage shout of the excited messengers sounding the news of their approach, which was answered on all sides, and the strange appearance of their naked bodies, seen against the gloomy background, produced altogether an effect upon my mind that I shall long remember.

It was on this same occasion that Kory-Kory awakened me at the dead hour of night, and in a sort of transport communicated the intelligence contained in the words "pehee pemi" (fish come). As I happened to have been in a remarkably sound and refreshing slumber, I could not imagine why the information had not been deferred until morning; indeed, I felt very much inclined to fly into a passion and box my valet's ears; but on second thoughts I got quietly up, and on going outside the house was not a little interested by the moving illumination which I beheld.

When old Marheyo received his share of the spoils, immediate preparations were made for a midnight banquet; calabashes of poee-poee were filled to the brim; green breadfruit were roasted; and a huge cake of "amar" was cut up with a sliver of bamboo and laid out on an immense banana-leaf.

At this supper we were lighted by several of the native tapers, held in the hands of young girls. These tapers are most ingeniously made. There is a nut abounding in the valley, called by the Typees "armor," closely resembling our common horse-chestnut. The shell is broken, and the contents extracted whole. Any number of these are strung at pleasure upon the long elastic fiber that traverses the branches of the coco-nut tree. Some of these tapers are eight and ten feet in length; but being perfectly flexible, one end is held in a coil, while the other is lighted. The nut burns with a fitful bluish flame, and the oil that it contains is exhausted in about ten minutes. As one burns down, the next becomes ignited, and the ashes of the former are knocked into a coco-nut shell kept for the purpose. This primitive candle requires continual attention, and must be constantly held in the hand. The person so employed marks the lapse of time by the number of nuts consumed, which is easily learned by counting the bits of tappa distributed at regular intervals along the string.

I grieve to state so distressing a fact, but the inhabitants of Typee were in the habit of devouring fish much in the same way that a civilized being would eat a radish, and without any more previous preparation. They eat it raw: scales, bones, gills, and all the inside. The fish is held by the tail, and the head being introduced into the mouth, the animal disappears with a rapidity that would at first nearly lead one to imagine it had been launched bodily down the throat.

Raw fish! Shall I ever forget my sensations when I first saw my island beauty devour one? Oh, heavens! Fayaway, how could you ever have contracted so vile a habit? However, after the first shock had subsided, the custom grew less odious in my eyes, and I soon accustomed myself to the sight. Let no one imagine, however, that the lovely Fayaway was in the habit of swallowing great vulgar-looking fishes: oh, no; with her beautiful small hand she would clasp a delicate, little, golden-hued love of a fish, and eat it as elegantly and as innocently as though it were a Naples biscuit. But, alas! it was after all a raw fish; and all I can say is, that Fayaway ate it in a more lady-like manner than any other girl of the valley.

When at Rome do as the Romans do, I held to be so good a proverb, that being in Typee I made a point of doing as the Typees did. Thus I ate poee-poee as they did; I walked about in a garb striking for its simplicity; and I reposed on a community of couches; besides doing many other things in conformity with their peculiar habits; but the farthest I ever went in the way of conformity was on several occasions to regale myself with raw fish. These being remarkably tender, and quite small, the undertaking was not so disagreeable in the main, and after a few trials I positively began to relish them; however, I subjected them to a slight operation with my knife previously to making my repast.

XXIX

I think I must enlighten the reader a little about the natural history of the valley.

Whence, in the name of Count Buffon and Baron Cuvier, came those dogs that I saw in Typee? Dogs!— Big hairless rats rather; all with smooth, shining, speckled hides, fat sides, and very disagreeable faces. Whence could they have come? That they were not the indigenous production of the region, I am firmly convinced.

Indeed they seemed aware of their being interlopers, looking fairly ashamed, and always trying to hide themselves in some dark corner. It was plain enough they did not feel at home in the vale—that they wished themselves well out of it, and back to the ugly country from which they must have come.

Scurvy curs! they were my abhorrence; I should have liked nothing better than to have been the death of every one of them. In fact, on one occasion, I intimated the propriety of a canine crusade to Mehevi; but the benevolent king would not consent to it. He heard me very patiently; but when I had finished, shook his head, and told me, in confidence, that they were "taboo."

As for the animal that made the fortune of the ex-lord-mayor Whittington: I shall never forget the day that I was lying in the house about noon, everybody else being fast asleep; and happening to raise my eyes, met those of a big black spectral cat, which sat erect in the doorway, looking at me with its frightful goggling green orbs, like one of those monstrous imps that torment some of the olden saints! I am one of those unfortunate persons to whom the sight of these animals is at any time an insufferable annoyance.

Thus constitutionally averse to cats in general, the unexpected apparition of this one in particular utterly confounded me. When I had a little recovered from the fascination of its glance, I started up; the cat fled, and emboldened by this, I rushed out of the house in pursuit; but it had disappeared. It was the only time I ever saw one in the valley, and how it got there I cannot imagine. It is just possible that it might have escaped from one of the ships at Nukuheva. It was in vain to seek information on the subject from the natives; since none of them had seen the animal, the appearance of which remains a mystery to me to this day.

Among the few animals which are to be met with in Typee, there were none which I looked upon with more interest than a beautiful golden-hued species of lizard. It measured perhaps five inches from head to tail, and was most gracefully proportioned. Numbers of these creatures were to be seen basking in the sunshine upon the thatching of the houses, and multitudes at all hours of the day showed their glittering sides as they ran frolicking between the spears of grass or raced in troops up and down the tall shafts of the coco-nut trees. But the remarkable beauty of these little animals and their lively ways were not their only claims upon my admiration. They were perfectly tame and insensible to fear. Frequently after seating myself upon the ground in some shady place during the heat of the day, I would be completely overrun with them. If I brushed one off my arm, it would leap perhaps into my hair: when I tried to frighten it away by gently pinching its leg, it would turn for protection to the very hand that attacked it.

The birds are also remarkably tame. If you happened to see one perched upon a branch within reach of your arm, and advanced towards it, it did not fly away immediately, but waited quietly looking at you, until you could almost touch it, and then took wing slowly, less alarmed at your presence, it would seem, than desirous of removing itself from your path. Had salt been less scarce in the valley than it was, this was the very place to have gone birding with it.

I remember that once, on an uninhabited island of the Galápagos, a bird alighted on my outstretched arm, while its mate chirped from an adjoining tree. Its tameness, far from shocking me, as a similar occurrence did Selkirk, imparted to me the most exquisite thrill of delight I ever experienced; and with somewhat of the same pleasure did I afterwards behold the birds and lizards of the valley show their confidence in the kindliness of man.

Among the numerous afflictions which the Europeans have entailed upon some of the natives of the South Seas, is the accidental introduction among them of that enemy of all repose and ruffler of even tempers—the Mosquito. At the Sandwich Islands and at two or three of the Society group there are now thriving colonies of these insects, who promise ere long to supplant altogether the aboriginal sand-flies. They sting, buzz, and torment, from one end of the year to the other, and by incessantly exasperating the natives materially obstruct the benevolent labors of the missionaries.

From this grievous visitation, however, the Typees are as yet wholly exempt; but its place is unfortunately in some degree supplied by the occasional presence of a minute species of fly, which, without stinging, is nevertheless productive of no little annoyance. The tameness of the birds and lizards is as nothing when compared to the fearless confidence of this insect. He will perch upon one of your eyelashes, and go to roost there, if you do not disturb him, or force his way through your hair, or along the cavity of the nostril, till you almost fancy he is resolved to explore the very brain itself. On one occasion I was so inconsiderate as to yawn while a number of them were hovering around me. I never repeated the act. Some half-dozen darted into the open apartment, and began walking about its ceiling; the sensation was dreadful. I involuntarily closed my mouth, and the poor creatures being enveloped in inner darkness, must in their consternation have stumbled over my palate, and been precipitated into the gulf beneath. At any rate, though I afterwards charitably held my mouth open for at least five minutes, with a view of affording egress to the stragglers, none of them ever availed themselves of the opportunity.

There are no wild animals of any kind on the island, unless it be decided that the natives themselves are such. The mountains and the interior present to the eye nothing but silent solitudes, unbroken by the roar of beasts of prey, and enlivened by few tokens even of minute animated existence. There are no venomous reptiles, and no snakes of any description to be found in any of the valleys.

In a company of Marquesan natives the weather affords no topic of conversation. It can hardly be said to have any vicissitudes. The rainy season, it is true, brings frequent showers, but they are intermitting and refreshing. When an islander bound on some expedition rises from his couch in the morning, he is never solicitous to peep out and see how the sky looks, or ascertain from what quarter the wind blows. He is always sure of a "fine day," and the promise of a few genial showers he hails with pleasure. There is never any of that "remarkable weather" on the island which from time immemorial has been experienced in America, and still continues to call forth the wondering conversational exclamations of its elderly citizens. Nor do there even occur any of those eccentric meteorological changes which elsewhere surprise us. In the valley of Typee ice-creams would never be rendered less acceptable by sudden frosts, nor would picnic parties be deferred on account of inauspicious snow-storms: for there day follows day in one unvarying round of summer and sunshine, and the whole year is one long tropical month of June just melting into July.

It is this genial climate which causes the coco-nuts to flourish as they do. This invaluable fruit, brought to perfection by the rich soil of the Marquesas, and borne aloft on a stately column more than a hundred feet from the ground, would seem at first almost inaccessible to the simple natives. Indeed the slender, smooth, and soaring shaft, without a single limb or protuberance of any kind to assist one in mounting it, presents an obstacle only to be overcome by the surprising agility and ingenuity of the islanders. It might be supposed that their indolence would lead them patiently to await the period when the ripened nuts, slowly parting from their stems, fall one by one to the ground. This certainly would be the case, were it not that the young fruit, encased in a soft green husk, with the incipient meat adhering in a jelly-like pellicle to its sides, and containing a bumper of the most delicious nectar, is what they chiefly prize. They have at least twenty different terms to express as many progressive stages in the growth of the nut. Many of them reject the fruit altogether except at a particular period of its growth, which, incredible as it may appear, they seemed to me to be able to ascertain within an hour or two. Others are still more capricious in their tastes; and after gathering together a heap of the nuts of all ages, and ingeniously tapping them, will sip first from one and then from another, as fastidiously as some delicate wine-bibber experimenting glass in hand among his dusty demijohns of different vintages.

Some of the young men, with more flexible frames than their comrades, and perhaps with more courageous souls, had a way of walking up the trunk of the coconut trees which to me seemed little less than miraculous; and when looking at them in the act, I experienced that curious perplexity a child feels when he beholds a fly moving feet uppermost along a ceiling.

I will endeavor to describe the way in which Narnee, a noble young chief, sometimes performed this feat for my peculiar gratification; but his preliminary performances must also be recorded. Upon my signifying my desire that he should pluck me the young fruit of some particular tree, the handsome savage, throwing himself into a sudden attitude of surprise, feigns astonishment at the apparent absurdity of the request. Maintaining this position for a moment, the strange emotions depicted on his countenance soften down into one of humorous resignation to my will, and then looking wistfully up to the tufted top of the tree, he stands on tiptoe, straining his neck and elevating his arm, as though endeavoring to reach the fruit from the ground where he stands. As if defeated in this childish attempt, he now sinks to the earth despondingly, beating his breast in well-acted despair; and then, starting to his feet all at once, and throwing back his head, raises both hands, like a schoolboy about to catch a falling ball. After continuing this for a moment or two, as if in expectation that the fruit was going to be tossed down to him by some good spirit in the tree-top, he turns wildly round in another fit of despair, and scampers off to the distance of thirty or forty yards. Here he remains awhile, eyeing the tree, the very picture of misery; but the next moment, receiving, as it were, a flash of inspiration, he rushes again towards it, and clasping both arms about the trunk, with one elevated a little above the other, he presses the soles of his feet close together against the tree, extending his legs from it until they are nearly horizontal, and his body becomes doubled into an arch; then, hand over hand and foot after foot, he rises from the earth with steady rapidity, and almost before you are aware of it, has gained the cradled and embowered nest of nuts, and with boisterous glee flings the fruit to the ground.

This mode of walking the tree is only practicable where the trunk declines considerably from the perpen-

:cular. This, however, is almost always the case; some
i the perfectly straight shafts of the trees leaning at an
angle of thirty degrees.

The less active among the men, and many of the
children of the valley, have another method of climbing. They take a broad and stout piece of bark, and
secure either end of it to their ankles; so that when the
feet thus confined are extended apart, a space of little
more than twelve inches is left between them. This contrivance greatly facilitates the act of climbing. The band
pressed against the tree, and closely embracing it, yields
a pretty firm support; while with the arms clasped about
the trunk, and at regular intervals sustaining the body,
the feet are drawn up nearly a yard at a time, and a
corresponding elevation of the hands immediately suc-
ceeds. In this way I have seen little children, scarcely
five years of age, fearlessly climbing the slender pole of
a young coco-nut tree, and while hanging perhaps fifty
feet from the ground, received the plaudits of their par-
ents beneath, who clapped their hands, and encouraged them to mount still higher.

What, thought I, on first witnessing one of these
exhibitions, would the nervous mothers of America and
England say to a similar display of hardihood in any
of their children? The Lacedemonian nations might
have approved of it, but most modern dames would
have gone into hysterics at the sight.

At the top of the coco-nut tree the numerous
branches, radiating on all sides from a common center,
form a sort of green and waving basket, between the
leaflets of which you just discern the nuts thickly clustering together, and on the loftier trees looking no
bigger from the ground than bunches of grapes. I remember one adventurous little fellow—Too-Too was
the rascal's name—who had built himself a sort of aerial

baby-house in the picturesque tuft of a tree adjoinin Marheyo's habitation. He used to spend hours there— rustling among the branches, and shouting with delight every time the strong gusts of wind rushing down from the mountain's side swayed to and fro the tall and flexible column on which he was perched. Whenever I heard Too-Too's musical voice, sounding strangely to the ear from so great a height, and beheld him peeping down upon me from out his leafy covert, he always recalled to my mind Dibdin's lines—

> There's a sweet little cherub that sits up aloft,
> To look out for the life of poor Jack.

Birds—bright and beautiful birds—fly over the valley of Typee. You see them perched aloft among the immovable boughs of the majestic breadfruit trees, or gently swaying on the elastic branches of the Omoo; skimming over the palmetto thatching of the bamboo huts; passing like spirits on the wing through the shadows of the grove, and sometimes descending into the bosom of the valley in gleaming flights from the mountains. Their plumage is purple and azure, crimson and white, black and gold; with bills of every tint:—bright bloody-red, jet black, and ivory white; and their eyes are bright and sparkling; they go sailing through the air in starry throngs; but alas! the spell of dumbness is upon them all—there is not a single warbler in the valley!

I know not why it was, but the sight of these birds, generally the ministers of gladness, always oppressed me with melancholy. As in their dumb beauty they hovered by me whilst I was walking, or looked down upon me with steady curious eyes from out the foliage, I was almost inclined to fancy that they knew they were gazing upon a stranger, and that they commiserated his fate.

XXX

In one of my strolls with Kory-Kory, in passing along the border of a thick growth of bushes, my attention was arrested by a singular noise. On entering the thicket I witnessed for the first time the operation of tattooing as performed by these islanders.

I beheld a man extended flat upon his back on the ground, and, despite the forced composure of his countenance, it was evident that he was suffering agony. His tormentor bent over him, working away for all the world like a stone-cutter with mallet and chisel. In one hand he held a short slender stick, pointed with a shark's tooth, on the upright end of which he tapped with a small hammer-like piece of wood, thus puncturing the skin, and charging it with the coloring matter in which the instrument was dipped. A coco-nut shell containing this fluid was placed upon the ground. It is prepared by mixing with a vegetable juice the ashes of the "armor," or candle-nut, always preserved for the purpose. Beside the savage, and spread out upon a piece of soiled tappa, were a great number of curious black-looking little implements of bone and wood, used in the various divisions of his art. A few terminated in a single fine point, and, like very delicate pencils, were employed in giving the finishing touches, or in operating upon the more sensitive portions of the body, as was the case in the present instance. Others presented several points distributed in a line, somewhat resembling the teeth of a saw. These were employed in the coarser parts of the work, and particularly in pricking in straight marks. Some presented their points disposed in small figures, and being placed upon the body, were, by a single blow of the hammer, made to leave their indelible impression. I observed a few the handles of which were mysteriously curved, as if intended to be introduced into the orifice of the ear, with a view perhaps of beating the tattoo upon the tympanum. Altogether, the sight of these strange instruments recalled to mind that display of cruel-looking mother-of-pearl-handled things which one sees in their velvet-lined cases at the elbow of a dentist.

The artist was not at this time engaged on an original sketch, his subject being a venerable savage, whose tattooing had become somewhat faded with age and needed a few repairs, and accordingly he was merely employed in touching up the works of some of the old masters of the Typee school, as delineated upon the human canvas before him. The parts operated upon were the eyelids, where a longitudinal streak, like the one which adorned Kory-Kory, crossed the countenance of the victim.

In spite of all the efforts of the poor old man, sundry twitchings and screwings of the muscles of the face denoted the exquisite sensibility of these shutters to the windows of his soul, which he was now having repainted. But the artist, with a heart as callous as that of an army surgeon, continued his performance, enlivening his labors with a wild chant, tapping away the while as merrily as a woodpecker.

So deeply engaged was he in his work, that he had not observed our approach, until, after having enjoyed an unmolested view of the operation, I chose to attract his attention. As soon as he perceived me, supposing that I sought him in his professional capacity, he seized hold of me in a paroxysm of delight, and was all eagerness to begin the work. When, however, I gave him to understand that he had altogether mistaken my views, nothing could exceed his grief and disappointment. But recovering from this, he seemed determined not to credit my assertion and grasping his implements, he flourished them about in fearful vicinity to my face, going through an imaginary performance of his art, and every moment bursting into some admiring exclamation at the beauty of his designs.

Horrified at the bare thought of being rendered hideous for life if the wretch were to execute his purpose upon me, I struggled to get away from him, while Kory-Kory, turning traitor, stood by, and besought me to comply with the outrageous request.

On my reiterated refusals, the excited artist got half beside himself, and was overwhelmed with sorrow at losing so noble an opportunity of distinguishing himself in his profession.

The idea of engrafting his tattooing upon my white skin filled him with all a painter's enthusiasm: again and again he gazed into my countenance, and every fresh glimpse seemed to add to the vehemence of his ambition. Not knowing to what extremities he might proceed, and shuddering at the ruin he might inflict upon my figure-head, I now endeavored to draw off his attention from it, and holding out my arm in a fit of desperation, signed to him to commence operations. But he rejected the compromise indignantly, and still continued his attack on my face, as though nothing short of that would satisfy him. When his fore-finger swept across my features, in laying out the borders of those parallel bands which were to encircle my countenance, the flesh fairly crawled upon my bones. At last, half wild with terror and indignation, I succeeded in breaking away from the three savages, and fled towards old Marheyo's house, pursued by the indomitable artist, who ran after me, implements in hand. Kory-Kory, however, at last interfered, and drew him off from the chase.

This incident opened my eyes to a new danger; and I now felt convinced that in some luckless hour I should be disfigured in such a manner as never more to have the *face* to return to my countrymen, even should an opportunity offer.

These apprehensions were greatly increased by the desire which King Mehevi and several of the inferior chiefs now manifested that I should be tattooed. The pleasure of the king was first signified to me some three days after my casual encounter with Karky the artist. Heavens! what imprecations I showered upon that Karky! Doubtless he had plotted a conspiracy against me and my countenance, and would never rest until his diabolical purpose was accomplished. Several times I met him in various parts of the valley, and, invariably, whenever he descried me, he came running after me with his mallet and chisel, flourishing them about my face as if he longed to begin. What an object he would have made of me!

When the king first expressed his wish to me, I made known to him my utter abhorrence of the measure, and worked myself into such a state of excitement, that he absolutely stared at me in amazement. It evidently surpassed his majesty's comprehension how any sober-minded and sensible individual could entertain the least possible objection to so beautifying an operation.

Soon afterwards he repeated his suggestion, and meeting with a like repulse, showed some symptoms of displeasure at my obduracy. On his a third time renewing his request, I plainly perceived that something must be done, or my visage was ruined for ever; I therefore screwed up my courage to the sticking point, and declared my willingness to have both arms tattooed from just above the wrist to the shoulder. His majesty was greatly pleased at the proposition, and I was congratulating myself with having thus compromised the matter, when he intimated that as a thing of course my face was first to undergo the operation. I was fairly driven to despair; nothing but the utter ruin of my "face divine," as the poets call it, would, I perceived, satisfy the inexorable Mehevi and his chiefs, or rather, that infernal Karky, for he was at the bottom of it all.

The only consolation afforded me was a choice of patterns: I was at perfect liberty to have my face spanned by three horizontal bars, after the fashion of my serving-man's; or to have as many oblique stripes slanting across it; or if, like a true courtier, I chose to model my style on that of royalty, I might wear a sort of freemason badge upon my countenance in the shape of a mystic triangle. However, I would have none of these, though the king most earnestly impressed upon my mind that my choice was wholly unrestricted. At last, seeing my unconquerable repugnance, he ceased to importune me.

But not so some other of the savages. Hardly a day passed but I was subjected to their annoying requests, until at last my existence became a burden to me; the pleasures I had previously enjoyed no longer afforded me delight, and all my former desire to escape from the valley now revived with additional force.

A fact which I soon afterwards learned augmented my apprehension. The whole system of tattooing was, I found, connected with their religion; and it was evident, therefore, that they were resolved to make a convert of me.

In the decoration of the chiefs it seems to be necessary to exercise the most elaborate penciling; while some of the inferior natives looked as if they had been daubed over indiscriminately with a house-painter's brush. I remember one fellow who prided himself hugely upon a great oblong patch, placed high upon his back, and who always reminded me of a man with a blister of Spanish flies stuck between his shoulders. Another whom I frequently met had the hollow of his eyes tattooed in two regular squares, and his visual organs being remarkably brilliant, they gleamed forth from out this setting like a couple of diamonds inserted in ebony.

Although convinced that tattooing was a religious observance, still the nature of the connection between it and the superstitious idolatry of the people was a point upon which I could never obtain any information. Like the still more important system of the "Taboo," it always appeared inexplicable to me.

There is a marked similarity, almost an identity, between the religious institutions of most of the Polynesian islands, and in all exists the mysterious "Taboo," restricted in its uses to a greater or less extent. So strange and complex in its arrangements is this remarkable system, that I have in several cases met with individuals who, after residing for years among the islands in the Pacific, and acquiring a considerable knowledge of the language, have nevertheless been altogether unable to give any satisfactory account of its operations. Situated as I was in the Typee valley, I perceived every hour the effects of this all-controlling power, without in the least comprehending it. Those effects were, indeed, widespread and universal, pervading the most important as well as the minutest transactions of life. The savage, in short, lives in the continual observance of its dictates, which guide and control every action of his being.

For several days after entering the valley I had been saluted at least fifty times in the twenty-four hours with the talismanic word "Taboo" shrieked in my ears, at some gross violation of its provisions, of which I had

unconsciously been guilty. The day after our arrival I
happened to hand some tobacco to Toby over the head
of a native who sat between us. He started up, as if
stung by an adder; while the whole company, manifesting an equal degree of horror, simultaneously screamed
out "Taboo!" I never again perpetrated a similar piece
of ill-manners, which, indeed, was forbidden by the
canons of good breeding, as well as by the mandates of
the taboo. But it was not always so easy to perceive
wherein you had contravened the spirit of this institution. I was many times called to order, if I may use the
phrase, when I could not for the life of me conjecture
what particular offense I had committed.

One day I was strolling through a secluded portion
of the valley, and hearing the musical sound of the
cloth-mallet at a little distance, I turned down a path
that conducted me in a few moments to a house where
there were some half-dozen girls employed in making
tappa. This was an operation I had frequently witnessed, and had handled the bark in all the various
stages of its preparation. On the present occasion the
females were intent upon their occupation, and after
looking up and talking gaily to me for a few moments,
they resumed their employment. I regarded them for
awhile in silence, and then carelessly picking up a handful of the material that lay around, proceeded unconsciously to pick it apart. While thus engaged, I was
suddenly startled by a scream, like that of a whole
boarding-school of young ladies just on the point of
going into hysterics. Leaping up with the idea of seeing
a score of Happar warriors about to perform anew the
Sabine atrocity, I found myself confronted by the company of girls, who, having dropped their work, stood before me with starting eyes, swelling bosoms, and fingers
pointed in horror towards me.

Thinking that some venomous reptile must be concealed in the bark which I held in my hand, I began cautiously to separate and examine it. Whilst I did so the horrified girls redoubled their shrieks. Their wild cries and frightened motions actually alarmed me, and throwing down the tappa, I was about to rush from the house, when in the same instant their clamors ceased, and one of them seizing me by the arm, pointed to the broken fibers that had just fallen from my grasp, and screamed in my ears the fatal word "Taboo!"

I subsequently found out that the fabric they were engaged in making was of a peculiar kind, destined to be worn on the heads of the females, and through every stage of its manufacture was guarded by a vigorous taboo, which interdicted the whole masculine gender from even so much as touching it.

Frequently in walking through the groves I observed breadfruit and coco-nut trees, with a wreath of leaves twined in a peculiar fashion about their trunks. This was the mark of the taboo. The trees themselves, their fruit, and even the shadows they cast upon the ground, were consecrated by its presence. In the same way a pipe, which the king had bestowed upon me, was rendered sacred in the eyes of the natives, none of whom could I ever prevail upon to smoke from it. The bowl was encircled by a woven band of grass, somewhat resembling those Turks' heads occasionally worked in the handles of our whip-stalks.

A similar badge was once braided about my wrist by the royal hand of Mehevi himself, who, as soon as he had concluded the operation, pronounced me "Taboo." This occurred shortly after Toby's disappearance; and were it not that from the first moment I had entered the valley the natives had treated me with uniform kindness, I should have supposed that their conduct afterwards was to be ascribed to the fact that I had received this sacred investiture.

The capricious operations of the taboo is not its least remarkable feature: to enumerate them all would be impossible. Black hogs—infants to a certain age— women in an interesting situation—young men while the operation of tattooing their faces is going on—and certain parts of the valley during the continuance of a shower—are alike fenced about by the operation of the taboo.

I witnessed a striking instance of its effects in the bay of Tior, my visit to which place has been alluded to in a former part of this narrative. On that occasion our worthy captain formed one of the party. He was a most insatiable sportsman. Outward bound, and off the pitch of Cape Horn, he used to sit on the taffrail, and keep the steward loading three or four old fowling-pieces, with which he would bring down albatrosses, Cape pigeons, jays, petrels, and divers other marine fowl, who followed chattering in our wake. The sailors were struck aghast at his impiety, and one and all attributed our forty days' beating about that horrid headland to his sacrilegious slaughter of these inoffensive birds.

At Tior he evinced the same disregard for the religious prejudices of the islanders, as he had previously shown for the superstitions of the sailors. Having heard that there were a considerable number of fowls in the valley—the progeny of some cocks and hens accidentally left there by an English vessel, and which being strictly tabooed, flew about almost in a wild state—he determined to break through all restraints, and be the death of them. Accordingly, he provided himself with a most formidable-looking gun, and announced his landing on the beach by shooting down a noble cock that was crowing what proved to be his own funeral dirge, on the limb of an adjoining tree. "Taboo," shrieked the affrighted savages. "Oh, hang your taboo," says the nautical sportsman; "talk taboo to the marines"; and bang went the piece again, and down came another victim. At this the natives ran scampering through the groves, horror-struck at the enormity of the act.

All that afternoon the rocky sides of the valley rang with successive reports, and the superb plumage of many a beautiful fowl was ruffled by the fatal bullet. Had it not been that the French admiral, with a large party, were then in the glen, I have no doubt that the natives, although their tribe was small and dispirited, would have inflicted summary vengeance upon the man who thus outraged their most sacred institutions; as it was, they contrived to annoy him not a little.

Thirsting with his exertions, the skipper directed his steps to a stream; but the savages, who had followed at a little distance, perceiving his object, rushed towards him and forced him away from its bank—his lips would have polluted it. Wearied at last, he sought to enter a house, that he might rest for a while on the mats; its inmates gathered tumultuously about the door and denied him admittance. He coaxed and blustered by turns, but in vain; the natives were neither to be intimidated nor appeased, and as a final resort he was obliged to call together his boat's crew, and pull away from what he termed the most infernal place he ever stepped upon.

Lucky was it for him and for us that we were not honored on our departure by a salute of stones from the hands of the exasperated Tiors. In this way, on the neighboring island of Ropo, were killed, but a few weeks previously, and for a nearly similar offense, the master and three of the crew of the K——.

I cannot determine with anything approaching to certainty, what power it is that imposes the taboo. When

I consider the slight disparity of condition among the islanders—the very limited and inconsiderable prerogatives of the king and chiefs—and the loose and indefinite functions of the priesthood, most of whom were hardly to be distinguished from the rest of their countrymen, I am wholly at a loss where to look for the authority which regulates this potent institution. It is imposed upon something today, and withdrawn to-morrow; while its operations in other cases are perpetual. Sometimes its restrictions only affect a single individual —sometimes a particular family—sometimes a whole tribe; and in a few instances they extend not merely over the various clans on a single island, but over all the inhabitants of an entire group. In illustration of this latter peculiarity I may cite the law which forbids a female to enter a canoe—a prohibition which prevails upon all the northern Marquesas Islands.

The word itself (taboo) is used in more than one signification. It is sometimes used by a parent to his child, when in the exercise of parental authority he forbids it to perform a particular action. Anything opposed to the ordinary customs of the islanders, although not expressly prohibited, is said to be "taboo."

The Typee language is one very difficult to be acquired; it bears a close resemblance to the other Polynesian dialects, all of which show a common origin. The duplication of words, as "lumee lumee," "poee poee," "muee muee," is one of their peculiar features. But another, and a more annoying one, is the different senses in which one and the same word is employed; its various meanings all have a certain connection, which only makes the matter more puzzling. So one brisk, lively little word is obliged, like a servant in a poor family, to perform all sorts of duties; for instance, one particular combination of syllables expresses the ideas of sleep, rest, reclining, sitting, leaning, and all other things anywise analogous thereto, the particular meaning being shown chiefly by a variety of gestures and the eloquent expression of the countenance.

The intricacy of these dialects is another peculiarity. In the Missionary College at Lahainaluna, or Mowee, one of the Sandwich Islands, I saw a tabular exhibition of a Hawaiian verb, conjugated through all its moods and tenses. It covered the side of a considerable apartment, and I doubt whether Sir William Jones himself would have not despaired of mastering it.

XXXI

Sadly discursive as I have already been, I must still further entreat the reader's patience, as I am about to string together, without any attempt at order, a few odds and ends of things not hitherto mentioned, but which are either curious in themselves or peculiar to the Typees.

There was one singular custom, observed in old Marheyo's domestic establishment, which often excited my surprise. Every night, before retiring, the inmates of the house gathered together on the mats, and squatting upon their haunches, after the universal practice of these islanders, would commence a low, dismal, and monotonous chant, accompanying the voice with the instrumental melody produced by two small half-rotten sticks tapped slowly together, a pair of which were held in the hands of each person present. Thus would they employ themselves for an hour or two, sometimes longer. Lying in the gloom which wrapped the further end of the house, I could not avoid looking at them, although the spectacle suggested nothing but unpleasant reflections. The flickering rays of the "armor" nut just served to reveal their savage lineaments, without dispelling the darkness that hovered about them.

Sometimes when, after falling into a kind of doze, and awaking suddenly in the midst of these doleful chantings, my eye would fall upon the wild-looking group engaged in their strange occupation, with their naked tattooed limbs, and shaven heads disposed in a circle, I was almost tempted to believe that I gazed upon a set of evil beings in the act of working a frightful incantation.

What was the meaning or purpose of this custom, whether it was practiced merely as a diversion, or whether it was a religious exercise, a sort of family prayers, I never could discover.

The sounds produced by the natives on these occasions were of a most singular description; and had I not actually been present, I never would have believed that such curious noises could have been produced by human beings.

To savages generally is imputed a guttural articulation. This, however, is not always the case, especially among the inhabitants of the Polynesian Archipelago. The labial melody with which the Typee girls carry on an ordinary conversation, giving a musical prolongation to the final syllable of every sentence, and chirping out some of the words with a liquid, bird-like accent, was singularly pleasing.

The men, however, are not quite so harmonious in their utterance, and when excited upon any subject, would work themselves up into a sort of wordy paroxysm, during which all descriptions of rough-sided sounds were projected from their mouths, with a force and rapidity which was absolutely astonishing.

Although these savages are remarkably fond of chanting, still they appear to have no idea whatever of singing, at least as that art is practiced among other nations.

I never shall forget the first time I happened to roar out a stave in the presence of the noble Mehevi. It was a stanza from the "Bavarian Broom-seller." His Typeean majesty, with all his court, gazed upon me in amazement, as if I had displayed some preternatural faculty which Heaven had denied to them. The king was delighted with the verse; but the chorus fairly transported him. At his solicitation I sang it again and again, and nothing could be more ludicrous than his vain attempts to catch the air and the words. The royal savage seemed to think that by screwing all the features of his face into the end of his nose, he might possibly succeed in the undertaking, but it failed to answer the purpose, and in the end he gave it up, and consoled himself by listening to my repetition of the sounds fifty times over.

Previous to Mehevi's making the discovery, I had never been aware that there was anything of the nightingale about me; but I was now promoted to the place of court-minstrel, in which capacity I was afterwards perpetually called upon to officiate.

.   .   .   .   .   .

Besides the sticks and the drums, there are no other musical instruments among the Typees, except one which might appropriately be denominated a nasal flute. It is somewhat longer than an ordinary fife; is made of a beautiful scarlet-colored reed; and has four or five stops, with a large hole near one end, which latter is held just beneath the left nostril. The other nostril being closed by a peculiar movement of the muscles about the nose, the breath is forced into the tube, and produces a soft dulcet sound, which is varied by the fingers running at random over the stops. This is a favorite recreation with the females, and one in which Fayaway greatly excelled. Awkward as such an instrument may appear, it was, in Fayaway's delicate little hands, one of the most graceful I have ever seen. A young lady in the act of tormenting a guitar strung about her neck by a couple of yards of blue ribbon is not half so engaging.

·　　·　　·　　·　　·　　·

Singing was not the only means I possessed of diverting the royal Mehevi and his easy-going subjects. Nothing afforded them more pleasure than to see me go through the attitudes of a pugilistic encounter. As not one of the natives had soul enough in him to stand up like a man, and allow me to hammer away at him, for my own personal gratification and that of the king, I was necessitated to fight with an imaginary enemy, whom I invariably made to knock under to my superior prowess. Sometimes when this sorely battered shadow retreated precipitately towards a group of the savages, and, following him up, I rushed among them, dealing my blows right and left, they would disperse in all directions, much to the enjoyment of Mehevi, the chiefs, and themselves.

The noble art of self-defense appeared to be regarded by them as the peculiar gift of the white man; and I make little doubt but that they supposed armies of Europeans were drawn up provided with nothing else but bony fists and stout hearts, with which they set to in column, and pummeled one another at the word of command.

·　　·　　·　　·　　·　　·

One day, in company with Kory-Kory, I had repaired to the stream for the purpose of bathing, when I observed a woman sitting upon a rock in the midst of the current, and watching with the liveliest interest the gambols of something, which at first I took to be an uncommonly large species of frog that was sporting in the water near her. Attracted by the novelty of the sight, I waded towards the spot where she sat, and could hardly credit the evidence of my senses when I beheld a little infant, the period of whose birth could not have extended back many days, paddling about as if it had just risen to the surface, after being hatched into existence at the bottom. Occasionally the delighted parent reached out her hands towards it, when the little thing, uttering a faint cry, and striking out its tiny limbs, would sidle for the rock, and the next moment be clasped to its mother's bosom. This was repeated again and again, the baby remaining in the stream about a minute at a time. Once or twice it made wry faces at swallowing a mouthful of water, and choked and spluttered as if on the point of strangling. At such times, however, the mother snatched it up, and by a process scarcely to be mentioned obliged it to eject the fluid. For several weeks afterwards I observed this woman bringing her child down to the stream regularly every day, in the cool of the morning and evening, and treating it to a bath. No wonder that the South Sea Islanders are so amphibious a race, when they are thus launched into the water as soon as they see the light. I am convinced that it is as natural for a human being to swim as it is for a duck. And yet in civilized communities how many able-bodied individuals die, like so many drowning kittens, from the occurrence of the most trivial accidents!

.   .   .   .   .   .

The long, luxuriant, and glossy tresses of the Typee damsels often attracted my admiration. A fine head of hair is the pride and joy of every woman's heart. Whether, against the express will of Providence, it is twisted up on the crown of the head and there coiled away like a rope on a ship's deck; whether it be stuck behind the ears and hangs down like the swag of a small window-curtain; or whether it be permitted to flow over the shoulders in natural ringlets, it is always the pride of the owner, and the glory of the toilette.

The Typee girls devote much of their time to the dressing of their fair and redundant locks. After bathing, as they sometimes do five or six times every day, the hair is carefully dried, and if they have been in the sea, invariably washed in fresh water, and anointed with a highly scented oil extracted from the meat of the coco-nut. This oil is obtained in great abundance by the following very simple process:

A large vessel of wood, with holes perforated in the bottom, is filled with the pounded meat, and exposed to the rays of the sun. As the oleaginous matter exudes, it falls in drops through the apertures into a wide-mouthed calabash placed underneath. After a sufficient quantity has been thus collected, the oil undergoes a purifying process, and is then poured into the small spherical shells of the nuts of the omoo-tree, which are hollowed out to receive it. These nuts are then hermetically sealed with a resinous gum, and the vegetable fragrance of their green rind soon imparts to the oil a delightful odor. After the lapse of a few weeks the exterior shell of the nuts becomes quite dry and hard, and assumes a beautiful carnation tint; and when opened they are found to be about two-thirds full of an ointment of a light yellow color, and diffusing the sweetest perfume. This elegant little odorous globe would not be out of place even upon the toilette of a queen. Its merits as a preparation for the hair are undeniable—it imparts to it a superb gloss and a silky fineness.

XXXII

From the time of my casual encounter with Karky the artist, my life was one of absolute wretchedness. Not a day passed but I was persecuted by the solicitations of some of the natives to subject myself to the odious operation of tattooing. Their importunities drove me half wild, for I felt how easily they might work their will upon me regarding this or anything else which they took into their heads. Still, however, the behavior of the islanders towards me was as kind as ever. Fayaway was quite as engaging; Kory-Kory as devoted; and Mehevi the king just as gracious and condescending as before. But I had now been three months in their valley, as nearly as I could estimate; I had grown familiar with the narrow limits to which my wanderings had been confined; and I began bitterly to feel the state of captivity in which I was held. There was no one with whom I could freely converse; no one to whom I could communicate my thoughts; no one who could sympathize with my sufferings. A thousand times I thought how much more endurable would have been my lot had Toby still been with me. But I was left alone, and the thought was terrible to me. Still, despite my griefs, I did all in my power to appear composed and cheerful, well knowing that by manifesting any uneasiness, or any desire to escape, I should only frustrate my object.

It was during the period I was in this unhappy frame of mind that the painful malady under which I had been laboring—after having almost completely subsided—began again to show itself, and with symptoms as violent as ever. This added calamity nearly unmanned me; the recurrence of the complaint proved that without powerful remedial applications all hope of cure was futile; and when I reflected that just beyond the elevations which bound me in, was the medical relief I needed, and that, although so near, it was impossible for me to avail myself of it, the thought was misery.

In this wretched situation, every circumstance which evinced the savage nature of the beings at whose mercy I was, augmented the fearful apprehensions that consumed me. An occurrence which happened about this time affected me most powerfully.

I have already mentioned that from the ridge-pole of Marheyo's house were suspended a number of packages enveloped in tappa. Many of these I had often seen in the hands of the natives, and their contents had been examined in my presence. But there were three packages hanging very nearly over the place where I lay, which from their remarkable appearance had often excited my curiosity. Several times I had asked Kory-Kory to show me their contents; but my servitor, who in almost every other particular had acceded to my wishes, always refused to gratify me in this.

One day, returning unexpectedly from the Ti, my arrival seemed to throw the inmates of the house into the greatest confusion. They were seated together on the mats, and by the lines which extended from the roof to the floor I immediately perceived that the mysterious packages were for some purpose or other under inspection. The evident alarm the savages betrayed filled me with forebodings of evil, and with an uncontrollable desire to penetrate the secret so jealously guarded. Despite the efforts of Marheyo and Kory-Kory to restrain me, I forced my way into the midst of the circle, and just caught a glimpse of three human heads, which others of the party were hurriedly enveloping in the coverings from which they had been taken.

One of the three I distinctly saw. It was in a state of perfect preservation, and, from the slight glimpse I had of it, seemed to have been subjected to some smoking operation which had reduced it to the dry, hard, and mummy-like appearance it presented. The two long scalp-locks were twisted up into balls upon the crown of the head in the same way that the individual had worn them during life. The sunken cheeks were rendered yet more ghastly by the rows of glistening teeth which protruded from between the lips, while the sockets of the eyes—filled with oval bits of mother-of-pearl shell, with a black spot in the center—heightened the hideousness of its aspect.

Two of the three were heads of the islanders; but the third, to my horror, was that of a white man. Although it had been quickly removed from my sight, still the glimpse I had of it was enough to convince me that I could not be mistaken.

Gracious God! what dreadful thoughts entered my mind! In solving this mystery perhaps I had solved another, and the fate of my lost companion might be revealed in the shocking spectacle I had just witnessed. I longed to have torn off the folds of cloth, and satisfied the awful doubts under which I labored. But before I had recovered from the consternation into which I had been thrown, the fatal packages were hoisted aloft and once more swung over my head. The natives now gathered round me tumultuously, and labored to convince me that what I had just seen were the heads of three Happar warriors, who had been slain in battle. This glaring falsehood added to my alarm, and it was not until I reflected that I had observed the packages swinging from their elevation before Toby's disappearance, that I could at all recover my composure.

But although this horrible apprehension had been dispelled, I had discovered enough to fill me, in my present state of mind, with the most bitter reflections. It was plain that I had seen the last relic of some unfortunate wretch, who must have been massacred on the beach by the savages, in one of those perilous trading adventures which I have before described.

It was not, however, alone the murder of the stranger that overcame me with gloom. I shuddered at the idea of the subsequent fate his inanimate body might have met with. Was the same doom reserved for me? Was I destined to perish like him—like him, perhaps, to be devoured, and my head to be preserved as a fearful memento of the event? My imagination ran riot in these horrid speculations, and I felt certain that the worst possible evils would befall me. But whatever were my misgivings, I studiously concealed them from the islanders, as well as the full extent of the discovery I had made.

Although the assurances which the Typees had often given me, that they never eat human flesh, had not convinced me that such was the case, yet, having been so long a time in the valley without witnessing anything which indicated the existence of the practice, I began to hope that it was an event of very rare occurrence, and that I should be spared the horror of witnessing it during my stay among them; but, alas! these hopes were soon destroyed.

It is a singular fact that in all our accounts of cannibal tribes we have seldom received the testimony of an eye-witness to the revolting practice. The horrible conclusion has almost always been derived either from the second-hand evidence of Europeans, or else from the admissions of the savages themselves, after they have in some degree become civilized. The Polynesians are aware of the detestation in which Europeans hold this custom, and therefore invariably deny its existence, and, with the craft peculiar to savages, endeavor to conceal every trace of it.

The excessive unwillingness betrayed by the Sandwich Islanders, even at the present day, to allude to the unhappy fate of Cook, has been often remarked. And so well have they succeeded in covering that event with mystery, that to this very hour, despite all that has been said and written on the subject, it still remains doubtful whether they wreaked upon his murdered body the vengeance they sometimes inflicted upon their enemies.

At Karakikova, the scene of that tragedy, a strip of ship's copper nailed against an upright post in the ground used to inform the traveler that beneath reposed the "remains" of the great circumnavigator. But I am strongly inclined to believe not only that the corpse was refused Christian burial, but that the heart which was brought to Vancouver some time after the event, and which the Hawaiians stoutly maintained was that of Captain Cook, was no such thing; and that the whole affair was a piece of imposture which was sought to be palmed off upon the credulous Englishman.

A few years since there was living on the island of Mowee (one of the Sandwich group) an old chief, who, actuated by a morbid desire for notoriety, gave himself out among the foreign residents of the place as the living tomb of Captain Cook's big toe!—affirming, that at the cannibal entertainment which ensued after the lamented Briton's death, that particular portion of his body had fallen to his share. His indignant countrymen actually caused him to be prosecuted in the native courts, on a charge nearly equivalent to what we term defamation of character; but the old fellow persisting in his assertion, and no invalidating proof being adduced, the plaintiffs were cast in the suit, and the cannibal reputation of the defendant fully established. This result was the making of his fortune; ever afterwards he was in the habit of giving very profitable audiences to all curious travelers who were desirous of beholding the man who had eaten the great navigator's great toe.

About a week after my discovery of the contents of the mysterious packages, I happened to be at the Ti, when another war-alarm was sounded, and the natives rushing to their arms, sallied out to resist a second incursion of the Happar invaders. The same scene was again repeated, only that on this occasion I heard at least fifteen reports of muskets from the mountains during the time that the skirmish lasted. An hour or two after its termination, loud pæans chanted through the valley announced the approach of the victors. I stood with Kory-Kory leaning against the railing of the pi-pi awaiting their advance, when a tumultuous crowd of islanders emerged with wild clamors from the neighboring groves. In the midst of them marched four men, one preceding the other at regular intervals of eight or ten feet, with poles of corresponding length, extended from shoulder to shoulder, to which were lashed with thongs of bark three long narrow bundles, carefully wrapped in ample coverings of freshly plucked palm-leaves, tacked together with slivers of bamboo. Here and there upon these green winding-sheets might be seen the stains of blood, while the warriors who carried the frightful burdens displayed upon their naked limbs similar sanguinary marks. The shaven head of the foremost had a deep gash upon it, and the clotted gore which had flowed from the wound remained in dry patches around it. This savage seemed to be sinking under the weight he bore. The bright tattooing upon his body was covered with blood and dust; his inflamed eyes rolled in their sockets, and his whole appearance denoted extraordinary suffering and exertion; yet, sustained by some powerful impulse, he continued to advance, while the throng around him with wild cheers sought to encourage him. The other three men were marked about the arms and breasts with several slight wounds, which they somewhat ostentatiously displayed.

These four individuals, having been the most active in the late encounter, claimed the honor of bearing the bodies of their slain enemies to the Ti. Such was the conclusion I drew from my own observations, and, as far as I could understand, from the explanation which Kory-Kory gave me.

The royal Mehevi walked by the side of these heroes. He carried in one hand a musket, from the barrel of which was suspended a small canvas pouch of powder, and in the other he grasped a short javelin, which he held before him and regarded with fierce exultation. This javelin he had wrested from a celebrated champion of the Happars, who had ignominiously fled, and was pursued by his foe beyond the summit of the mountain.

When within a short distance of the Ti, the warrior with the wounded head, who proved to be Narmonee, tottered forward two or three steps, and fell helplessly to the ground; but not before another had caught the end of the pole from his shoulder, and placed it upon his own.

The excited throng of islanders, who surrounded the person of the king and the dead bodies of the enemy, approached the spot where I stood, brandishing their rude implements of warfare, many of which were bruised and broken, and uttered continual shouts of triumph. When the crowd drew up opposite the Ti, I set myself to watch their proceedings most attentively; but scarcely had they halted when my servitor, who had left my side for an instant, touched my arm, and proposed our returning to Marheyo's house. To this I objected; but, to my surprise, Kory-Kory reiterated his request, and with an unusual vehemence of manner. Still, however, I refused to comply, and was retreating before him, as in his importunity he pressed upon me, when I felt a heavy hand laid upon my shoulder, and turning round, encountered the bulky form of Mow-Mow, a one-eyed chief, who had just detached himself from the crowd below, and had mounted the rear of the pi-pi upon which we stood. His cheek had been pierced by the point of a spear, and the wound imparted a still more frightful expression to his hideously tattooed face, already deformed by the loss of an eye. The warrior, without uttering a syllable, pointed fiercely in the direction of Marheyo's house, while Kory-Kory, at the same time presenting his back, desired me to mount.

I declined this offer, but intimated my willingness to withdraw, and moved slowly along the piazza, wondering what could be the cause of this unusual treatment. A few minutes' consideration convinced me that the savages were about to celebrate some hideous rite in connection with their peculiar customs, and at which they were determined I should not be present. I descended from the pi-pi, and attended by Kory-Kory, who on this occasion did not show his usual commiseration for my lameness, but seemed only anxious to hurry me on, walked away from the place. As I passed through the noisy throng, which by this time completely environed the Ti, I looked with fearful curiosity at the three packages, which now were deposited upon the ground;

but although I had no doubt as to their contents, still their thick coverings prevented my actually detecting the form of a human body.

The next morning, shortly after sunrise, the same thundering sounds which had awakened me from sleep on the second day of the Feast of Calabashes, assured me that the savages were on the eve of celebrating another, and, as I fully believed, a horrible solemnity.

All the inmates of the house, with the exception of Marheyo, his son, and Tinor, after assuming their gala dresses, departed in the direction of the Taboo Groves.

Although I did not anticipate a compliance with my request, still, with a view of testing the truth of my suspicions, I proposed to Kory-Kory that, according to our usual custom in the morning, we should take a stroll to the Ti: he positively refused; and when I renewed the request, he evinced his determination to prevent my going there; and, to divert my mind from the subject, he offered to accompany me to the stream. We accordingly went, and bathed. On our coming back to the house, I was surprised to find that all its inmates had returned, and were lounging upon the mats as usual, although the drums still sounded from the groves.

The rest of the day I spent with Kory-Kory and Fayaway, wandering about a part of the valley situated in an opposite direction from the Ti; and whenever I so much as looked towards that building, although it was hidden from view by intervening trees, and at the distance of more than a mile, my attendant would exclaim, "Taboo, taboo!"

At the various houses where we stopped, I found many of the inhabitants reclining at their ease, or pursuing some light occupation, as if nothing unusual were going forward; but amongst them all I did not perceive a single chief or warrior. When I asked several of the people why they were not at the Hoolah Hoolah (the feast), they uniformly answered the question in a manner which implied that it was not intended for them, but for Mehevi, Narmonee, Mow-Mow, Kolory, Warmoonoo, Kalow—running over, in their desire to make me comprehend their meaning, the names of all the principal chiefs.

Everything, in short, strengthened my suspicions with regard to the nature of the festival they were now celebrating; and which amounted almost to a certainty. While in Nukuheva I had frequently been informed that the whole tribe were never present at these cannibal banquets; but the chiefs and priests only, and everything I now observed agreed with the account.

The sound of the drums continued, without intermission, the whole day, and falling continually upon my ear, caused me a sensation of horror which I am unable to describe. On the following day, hearing none of those noisy indications of revelry, I concluded that the inhuman feast was terminated; and feeling a kind of morbid curiosity to discover whether the Ti might furnish any evidence of what had taken place there, I proposed to Kory-Kory to walk there. To this proposition he replied by pointing with his finger to the newly risen sun, and then up to the zenith, intimating that our visit must be deferred until noon. Shortly after that hour we accordingly proceeded to the Taboo Groves, and as soon as we entered their precincts, I looked fearfully round in quest of some memorial of the scenes which had so lately been acted there; but everything appeared as usual. On reaching the Ti, we found Mehevi and a few chiefs reclining on the mats, who gave me as friendly a reception as ever. No allusions of any kind were made by them to the recent events; and I refrained, for obvious reasons, from referring to them myself.

After staying a short time I took my leave. In passing along the piazza, previously to descending from the pi-pi, I observed a curiously carved vessel of wood, of considerable size, with a cover placed over it, of the same material, and which resembled in shape a small canoe. It was surrounded by a low railing of bamboos the top of which was scarcely a foot from the ground. As the vessel had been placed in its present position since my last visit, I at once concluded that it must have some connection with the recent festival; and, prompted by a curiosity I could not repress, in passing it I raised one end of the cover; at the same moment the chiefs, perceiving my design, loudly ejaculated, "Taboo! taboo!" But the slight glimpse sufficed; my eyes fell upon the disordered members of a human skeleton, the bones still fresh with moisture, and with particles of flesh clinging to them here and there!

Kory-Kory, who had been a little in advance of me, attracted by the exclamations of the chiefs, turned round in time to witness the expression of horror on my countenance. He now hurried towards me, pointing at the same time to the canoe, and exclaiming rapidly, "Puarkee! puarkee!" (Pig, pig). I pretended to yield to the deception, and repeated the words after him several times, as though acquiescing in what he said. The other savages, either deceived by my conduct or unwilling to manifest their displeasure at what could not now be remedied, took no further notice of the occurrence, and I immediately left the Ti.

All that night I lay awake, revolving in my mind the fearful situation in which I was placed. The last horrid revelation had now been made, and the full sense of my condition rushed upon my mind with a force I had never before experienced.

Where, thought I, desponding, is there the slightest prospect of escape? The only person who seemed to possess the ability to assist me was the stranger Marnoo; but would he ever return to the valley? And if he did, should I be permitted to hold any communication with him? It seemed as if I were cut off from every source of hope, and that nothing remained but passively to await whatever fate was in store for me. A thousand times I endeavored to account for the mysterious conduct of the natives. For what conceivable purpose did they thus retain me a captive? What could be their object in treating me with such apparent kindness, and did it not cover some treacherous scheme? Or, if they had no other design than to hold me a prisoner, how should I be able to pass away my days in this narrow valley, deprived of all intercourse with civilized beings, and for ever separated from friends and home?

One only hope remained to me. The French could not long defer a visit to the bay, and if they should permanently locate any of their troops in the valley, the savages could not for any length of time conceal my existence from them. But what reason had I to suppose that I should be spared until such an event occurred—an event which might be postponed by a hundred different contingencies?

XXXIII

"Marnoo, Marnoo pemi!" Such were the welcome sounds which fell upon my ear some ten days after the events related in the preceding chapter. Once more the approach of the stranger was heralded, and the intelligence operated upon me like magic. Again I should be able to converse with him in my own language; and I resolved at all hazards to concert with him some scheme, however desperate, to rescue me from a condition that had now become insupportable.

As he drew near, I remembered with many misgivings, the inauspicious termination of our former interview; and when he entered the house, I watched with intense anxiety the reception he met with from its inmates. To my joy, his appearance was hailed with the liveliest pleasure; and accosting me kindly, he seated himself by my side, and entered into conversation with the natives around him. It soon appeared, however, that on this occasion he had not any intelligence of importance to communicate. I inquired of him from whence he had last come? He replied from Pueearka, his native valley, and that he intended to return to it the same day.

At once it struck me that, could I but reach the valley under his protection, I might easily from thence reach Nukuheva by water; and animated by the prospect which this plan held out, I disclosed it in a few brief words to the stranger, and asked him how it could be best accomplished. My heart sunk within me when in his broken English he answered me that it could never be effected. "Kannaka no let you go no where," he said; "you taboo. Why you no like to stay? Plenty moee-moee (sleep)—plenty kiki (eat)—plenty whihe-nee (young girls)— Oh, very good place Typee? Suppose you no like this bay, why you come? You no hear about Typee? All white men afraid Typee, so no white men come."

These words distressed me beyond belief; and when I again related to him the circumstances under which I had descended into the valley, and sought to enlist his sympathies in my behalf by appealing to the bodily misery I endured, he listened to me with impatience and cut me short by exclaiming passionately, "Me no hear you talk any more; by by Kannaka get mad, kill you and me too. No you see he no want you to speak to me at all?—you see—ah! by by you no mind—you get well, he kill you, eat you, hang you head up there, like Happar Kannaka.—Now you listen—but no talk any more. By by I go;—you see way I go.—Ah! then some night Kannaka all moee-moee (sleep)—you run away, you come Pueearka. I speak Pueearka Kannaka— he no harm you—ah! then I take you my canoe Nuku-heva—and you no run away ship no more." With these words, enforced by a vehemence of gesture I cannot describe, Marnoo started from my side, and immediately engaged in conversation with some of the chiefs who had entered the house.

It would have been idle for me to have attempted resuming the interview so peremptorily terminated by Marnoo, who was evidently little disposed to compromise his own safety by any rash endeavors to ensure mine. But the plan he had suggested struck me as one which might possibly be accomplished, and I resolved to act upon it as speedily as possible.

Accordingly, when he rose to depart, I accompanied him with the natives outside of the house, with a view of carefully noting the path he would take in leaving the valley. Just before leaping from the pi-pi he clasped my hand, and looking significantly at me, exclaimed, "Now you see—you do what I tell you—ah! then you do good;—you no do so—ah! then you die." The next moment he waved his spear in adieu to the islanders, and following the route that conducted to a defile in the mountains lying opposite the Happar side, was soon out of sight.

A mode of escape was now presented to me, but how was I to avail myself of it? I was continually surrounded by the savages; I could not stir from one house to another without being attended by some of them; and even during the hours devoted to slumber the slightest movement which I made seemed to attract the notice of those who shared the mats with me. In spite of these obstacles, however, I determined forthwith to make the attempt. To do so with any prospect of success, it was necessary that I should have at least two hours' start before the islanders should discover my absence; for with such facility was any alarm spread through the valley, and so familiar, of course, were the inhabitants with the intricacies of the groves, that I could not hope, lame and feeble as I was, and ignorant of the route, to secure my escape unless I had this advantage. It was also by night alone that I could hope to accomplish my object, and then only by adopting the utmost precaution.

The entrance to Marheyo's habitation was through a low narrow opening in its wicker-work front. This passage, for no conceivable reason that I could devise, was always closed after the household had retired to rest, by drawing a heavy slide across it, composed of a dozen or more bits of wood, ingeniously fastened together by seizings of sinnate. When any of the inmates chose to go outside, the noise occasioned by the removing of this rude door awakened everybody else; and on more than one occasion I had remarked that the islanders were nearly as irritable as more civilized beings under similar circumstances.

The difficulty thus placed in my way I determined to obviate in the following manner. I would get up boldly in the course of the night, and drawing the slide, issue from the house, and pretend that my object was merely to procure a drink from the calabash, which always stood without the dwelling on the corner of the pi-pi.

On re-entering I would purposely omit closing the passage after me, and trusting that the indolence of the savages would prevent them from repairing my neglect, would return to my mat, and waiting patiently until all were again asleep, I would then steal forth, and at once take the route to Pueearka.

The very night which followed Marnoo's departure, I proceeded to put this project into execution. About midnight, as I imagined, I rose and drew the slide. The natives, just as I had expected, started up, while some of them asked, "Arware poo awa, Tommo?" (Where are you going, Tommo?) "Wai" (Water), I laconically answered, grasping the calabash. On hearing my reply they sank back again, and in a minute or two I returned to my mat, anxiously awaiting the result of the experiment.

One after another the savages, turning restlessly, appeared to resume their slumbers, and rejoicing at the stillness which prevailed, I was about to rise again from my couch, when I heard a slight rustling—a dark form was intercepted between me and the doorway—the slide was drawn across it, and the individual, whoever he was, returned to his mat. This was a sad blow to me; but as it might have roused the suspicions of the islanders to have made another attempt that night, I was reluctantly obliged to defer it until the next. Several times after I repeated the same maneuver but with as little success as before. As my pretense for withdrawing from the house was to allay my thirst, Kory-Kory, either suspecting some design on my part, or else prompted by a desire to please me, regularly every evening placed a calabash of water by my side.

Even under these inauspicious circumstances I again and again renewed the attempt; but when I did so my valet always rose with me, as if determined I should not remove myself from his observation. For the present, therefore, I was obliged to abandon the attempt; but I endeavored to console myself with the idea that by this mode I might yet effect my escape.

Shortly after Marnoo's visit I was reduced to such a state, that it was with extreme difficulty I could walk, even with the assistance of a spear, and Kory-Kory, as formerly, was obliged to carry me daily to the stream.

For hours and hours during the warmest part of the day I lay upon my mat, and while those around me were nearly all dozing away in careless ease, I remained awake gloomily pondering over the fate which it appeared now idle for me to resist, when I thought of the loved friends who were thousands and thousands of miles from the savage island in which I was held a captive, when I reflected that my dreadful fate would for ever be concealed from them, and that with hope deferred they might continue to await my return long after my inanimate form had blended with the dust of the valley—I could not repress a shudder of anguish.

How vividly is impressed upon my mind every minute feature of the scene which met my view during those long days of suffering and sorrow! At my request my mats were always spread directly facing the door, opposite which, and at a little distance, was the hut of boughs that Marheyo was building.

Whenever my gentle Fayaway and Kory-Kory, laying themselves down beside me, would leave me awhile to uninterrupted repose, I took a strange interest in the slightest movements of the eccentric old warrior. All alone during the stillness of the tropical mid-day, he would pursue his quiet work, sitting in the shade and weaving together the leaflets of his coco-nut branches, or rolling upon his knee the twisted fibers of bark to form the cords with which he tied together the thatching of his tiny house. Frequently suspending his employment, and noticing my melancholy eye fixed upon him, he would raise his hand with a gesture expressive of deep commiseration, and then moving towards me slowly would enter on tip-toes, fearful of disturbing the slumbering natives, and, taking the fan from my hand, would sit before me, swaying it gently to and fro, and gazing earnestly into my face.

Just beyond the pi-pi, and disposed in a triangle before the entrance of the house, were three magnificent breadfruit trees. At this moment I can recall to my mind their slender shafts, and the graceful inequalities of their bark, on which my eye was accustomed to dwell day after day in the midst of my solitary musings. It is strange how inanimate objects will twine themselves into our affections, especially in the hour of affliction. Even now, amidst all the bustle and stir of the proud and busy city in which I am dwelling, the image of those three trees seems to come as vividly before my eyes as if they were actually present, and I still feel the soothing quiet pleasure which I then had in watching hour after hour their topmost boughs waving gracefully in the breeze.

XXXIV

Nearly three weeks had elapsed since the second visit of Marnoo, and it must have been more than four months since I entered the valley, when one day about noon, and whilst everything was in profound silence, Mow-Mow, the one-eyed chief, suddenly appeared at the door, and leaning forward towards me as I lay directly facing him, said in a low tone, "Toby pemi ena." (Toby has arrived here.) Gracious heaven! What a tumult of emotions rushed upon me at this startling intelligence! Insensible to the pain that had before distracted me, I leaped to my feet, and called wildly to Kory-Kory, who was reposing by my side. The startled islanders sprang from their mats; the news was quickly communicated to them; and the next moment I was making my way to the Ti on the back of Kory-Kory, and surrounded by the excited savages.

All that I could comprehend of the particulars which Mow-Mow rehearsed to his auditors as we proceeded, was that my long-lost companion had arrived in a boat which had just entered the bay. These tidings made me most anxious to be carried at once to the sea, lest some untoward circumstance should prevent our meeting; but to this they would not consent, and continued their course towards the royal abode. As we approached it, Mehevi and several chiefs showed themselves from the piazza, and called upon us loudly to come to them.

As soon as we had approached, I endeavored to make them understand that I was going down to the sea to meet Toby. To this the king objected and motioned Kory-Kory to bring me into the house. It was in vain to resist; and in a few moments I found myself within the Ti, surrounded by a noisy group engaged in discussing the recent intelligence. Toby's name was frequently repeated, coupled with violent exclamations of astonishment. It seemed as if they yet remained in doubt with regard to the fact of his arrival, and at every fresh report that was brought from the shore they betrayed the liveliest emotions.

Almost frenzied at being held in this state of suspense, I passionately besought Mehevi to permit me to proceed. Whether my companion had arrived or not, I felt a presentiment that my own fate was about to be decided. Again and again I renewed my petition to Mehevi. He regarded me with a fixed and serious eye, but at length yielding to my importunity, reluctantly granted my request.

Accompanied by some fifty of the natives, I now rapidly continued my journey; every few moments being transferred from the back of one to another, and urging my bearer forward all the while with earnest entreaties. As I thus hurried forward no doubt as to the truth of the information I had received ever crossed my mind. I was alive only to the one overwhelming idea, that a chance of deliverance was now afforded me, if the jealous opposition of the savages could be overcome.

Having been prohibited from approaching the sea during the whole of my stay in the valley, I had always associated with it the idea of escape. Toby too—if indeed he had ever voluntarily deserted me—must have effected his flight by the sea; and now that I was drawing near to it myself, I indulged in hopes which I had never felt before. It was evident that a boat had entered the bay, and I saw little reason to doubt the truth of the report that it had brought my companion. Every time therefore that we gained an elevation, I looked eagerly around, hoping to behold him.

In the midst of an excited throng, who by their violent gestures and wild cries appeared to be under the influence of some excitement as strong as my own, I was now borne along at a rapid trot, frequently stooping my head to avoid the branches which crossed the path, and never ceasing to implore those who carried me to accelerate their already swift pace.

In this manner we had proceeded about four or five miles, when we were met by a party of some twenty islanders, between whom and those who accompanied me ensued an animated conference. Impatient of the delay occasioned by this interruption, I was beseeching the man who carried me to proceed without his loitering companions, when Kory-Kory, running to my side, informed me, in three fatal words, that the news had all proved false—that Toby had not arrived—"Toby owlee pemi." Heaven only knows how, in the state of mind and body I then was, I ever sustained the agony which this intelligence caused me: not that the news was altogether unexpected; but I had trusted that the fact might not have been made known until we should have arrived upon the beach. As it was, I at once foresaw the course the savages would pursue. They had only yielded thus far to my entreaties, that I might give a joyful welcome to my long-absent comrade; but now that it was known he had not arrived, they would at once oblige me to turn back.

My anticipations were but too correct. In spite of the resistance I made, they carried me into a house which was near the spot, and left me upon the mats. Shortly afterwards several of those who had accompanied me from the Ti, detaching themselves from the others, proceeded in the direction of the sea. Those who remained—among whom were Marheyo, Mow-Mow, Kory-Kory, and Tinor—gathered about the dwelling and appeared to be awaiting their return.

This convinced me that strangers—perhaps some of my own countrymen—had for some cause or other entered the bay. Distracted at the idea of their vicinity, and reckless of the pain which I suffered, I heeded not the assurances of the islanders, that there were no boats at the beach, but starting to my feet endeavored to gain the door. Instantly the passage was blocked up by several men, who commanded me to resume my seat.

The fierce looks of the irritated savages admonished me that I could gain nothing by force, and that it was by entreaty alone that I could hope to compass my object.

Guided by this consideration, I turned to Mow-Mow, the only chief present whom I had been much in the habit of seeing, and carefully concealing my real design, tried to make him comprehend that I still believed Toby to have arrived on the shore, and besought him to allow me to go forward to welcome him. To all his repeated assertions, that my companion had not been seen, I pretended to turn a deaf ear: while I urged my solicitations with an eloquence of gesture which the one-eyed chief appeared unable to resist. He seemed indeed to regard me as a froward child, to whose wishes he had not the heart to oppose force, and whom he must consequently humor. He spoke a few words to the natives, who at once retreated from the door, and I immediately passed out of the house.

Here I looked earnestly round for Kory-Kory; but that hitherto faithful servitor was nowhere to be seen. Unwilling to linger even for a single instant when every moment might be so important, I motioned to a muscular fellow near me to take me upon his back: to my surprise he angrily refused. I turned to another, but with a like result. A third attempt was as unsuccessful and I immediately perceived what had induced Mow-Mow to grant my request and why the other natives conducted themselves in so strange a manner. It was evident that the chief had only given me liberty to continue my progress towards the sea because he supposed that I was deprived of the means of reaching it.

Convinced by this of their determination to retain me a captive, I became desperate; and almost insensible to the pain which I suffered I seized a spear which was leaning against the projecting eaves of the house, and supporting myself with it, resumed the path that swept by the dwelling. To my surprise I was suffered to proceed alone, all the natives remaining in front of the house, and engaging in earnest conversation which every moment became more loud and vehement; and to my unspeakable delight I perceived that some difference of opinion had arisen between them; that two parties, in short, were formed, and consequently that in their divided counsels there was some chance of my deliverance.

Before I had proceeded a hundred yards I was again surrounded by the savages, who were still in all the heat of argument, and appeared every moment as if they would come to blows. In the midst of this tumult old Marheyo came to my side, and I shall never forget the benevolent expression of his countenance. He placed his arm upon my shoulder, and emphatically pronounced one expressive English word I had taught him—"Home." I at once understood what he meant, and eagerly expressed my thanks to him. Fayaway and Kory-Kory were by his side, both weeping violently; and it was not until the old man had twice repeated the command that his son could bring himself to obey him, and take me again upon his back. The one-eyed chief opposed his doing so, but he was overruled, and, as it seemed to me, by some of his own party.

We proceeded onwards, and never shall I forget the ecstasy I felt when I first heard the roar of the surf breaking upon the beach. Before long I saw the flashing billows themselves through the opening between the trees. Oh, glorious sight and sound of ocean! with what rapture did I hail you as familiar friends! By this time the shouts of the crowd upon the beach were distinctly audible, and in the blended confusion of sounds I almost fancied I could distinguish the voices of my own countrymen.

When we reached the open space which lay between the groves and the sea, the first object that met my view was an English whale-boat, lying with her bow pointed from the shore, and only a few fathoms distant from it. It was manned by five islanders, dressed in short tunics of calico. My first impression was that they were in the very act of pulling out from the bay; and that, after all my exertions, I had come too late. My soul sunk within me: but a second glance convinced me that the boat was only hanging off to keep out of the surf; and the next moment I heard my own name shouted out by a voice from the midst of the crowd.

Looking in the direction of the sound, I perceived, to my indescribable joy, the tall figure of Karakoee, an Oahu Kannaka, who had often been aboard the *Dolly*, while she lay in Nukuheva. He wore the green shooting-jacket with gilt buttons, which had been given to him by an officer of the *Reine Blanche*— the French flag-ship—and in which I had always seen him dressed. I now remembered the Kannaka had frequently told me that his person was tabooed in all the valleys of the island, and the sight of him at such a moment as this filled my heart with a tumult of delight.

Karakoee stood near the edge of the water with a large roll of cotton-cloth thrown over one arm, and holding two or three canvas bags of powder; while with the other hand he grasped a musket, which he appeared to be proffering to several of the chiefs around him. But they turned with disgust from his offers, and seemed to be impatient at his presence, with vehement gestures waving him off to his boat, and commanding him to depart.

The Kannaka, however, still maintained his ground, and I at once perceived that he was seeking to purchase my freedom. Animated by the idea, I called upon him loudly to come to me; but he replied, in broken English, that the islanders had threatened to pierce him with their spears, if he stirred a foot towards me. At this time I was still advancing, surrounded by a dense throng of the natives, several of whom had their hands upon me, and more than one javelin was threateningly pointed at me. Still I perceived clearly that many of those least friendly towards me looked irresolute and anxious.

I was still some thirty yards from Karakoee when my further progress was prevented by the natives, who compelled me to sit down upon the ground, while they still retained their hold upon my arms. The din and tumult now became tenfold, and I perceived that several of the priests were on the spot, all of whom were evidently urging Mow-Mow and the other chiefs to prevent my departure; and the detestable word "Roo-ne! Roo-ne!" which I had heard repeated a thousand times during the day, was now shouted out on every side of me. Still I saw that the Kannaka continued his exertions in my favor—that he was boldly debating the matter with the savages, and was striving to entice them by displaying his cloth and powder, and snapping the lock of his musket. But all he said or did appeared only to augment the clamors of those around him, who seemed bent upon driving him into the sea.

When I remembered the extravagant value placed by these people upon the articles which were offered to them in exchange for me, and which were so indignantly rejected, I saw a new proof of the same fixed determination of purpose they had all along manifested with regard to me, and in despair, and reckless of consequences, I exerted all my strength, and shaking myself free from the grasp of those who held me, I sprung upon my feet and rushed towards Karakoee.

The rash attempt nearly decided my fate; for, fearful that I might slip from them, several of the islanders now raised a simultaneous shout, and pressing upon Karakoee, they menaced him with furious gestures, and actually forced him into the sea. Appalled at their violence, the poor fellow, standing nearly to the waist in the surf, endeavored to pacify them; but at length, fearful that they would do him some fatal violence, he beckoned to his comrades to pull in at once, and take him into the boat.

It was at this agonizing moment, when I thought all hope was ended, that a new contest arose between the two parties who had accompanied me to the shore; blows were struck, wounds were given, and blood flowed. In the interest excited by the fray, every one had left me except Marheyo, Kory-Kory, and poor dear Fayaway, who clung to me, sobbing convulsively. I saw that now or never was the moment. Clasping my hands together, I looked imploringly at Marheyo, and moved towards the now almost deserted beach. The tears were in the old man's eyes, but neither he nor Kory-Kory attempted to hold me, and I soon reached the Kannaka who had been anxiously watching my movements; the rowers pulled in as near as they dared to the edge of the surf; I gave one parting embrace to Fayaway, who seemed speechless with sorrow, and the next instant I found myself safe in the boat, and Karakoee by my side, who told the rowers at once to give way. Marheyo and Kory-Kory, and a great many of the women, followed me into the water, and I was determined, as the only mark of gratitude I could show, to give them the articles which had been brought as my ransom. I handed the musket to Kory-Kory, with a rapid gesture which was equivalent to a "Deed of Gift" (in doing which he would fain have taken hold of me); threw the roll of cotton to old Marheyo, pointing as I did so to poor Fayaway, who had retired from the edge of the water and was sitting down disconsolate on the shingles; and tumbled the powder-bags out to the nearest young ladies, all of whom were vastly willing to take them. This distribution did not occupy ten seconds, and before it was over the boat was under full way; the Kannaka all the while exclaiming loudly against what he considered a useless throwing away of valuable property.

Although it was clear that my movements had been noticed by several of the natives, still they had not suspended the conflict in which they were engaged, and it was not until the boat was above fifty yards from the shore that Mow-Mow and some six or seven other warriors rushed into the sea and hurled their javelins at us. Some of the weapons passed quite as close to us as was desirable, but no one was wounded, and the men pulled away gallantly. But although soon out of the reach of the spears, our progress was extremely slow; it blew strong upon the shore, and the tide was against us; and I saw Karakoee, who was steering the boat, give many a look towards a jutting point of the bay round which we had to pass.

For a minute or two after our departure, the savages, who had formed into different groups, remained perfectly motionless and silent. All at once the enraged chief showed by his gestures that he had resolved what course he would take. Shouting loudly to his companions, and pointing with his tomahawk towards the headland, he set off at full speed in that direction, and was followed by about thirty of the natives, among whom were several of the priests, all yelling out "Roo-ne! Roo-ne!" at the very top of their voices. Their intention was evidently to swim off from the headland and intercept us in our course. The wind was freshening every minute, and was right in our teeth, and it was one of those chopping angry seas in which it is so difficult to row. Still the chances seemed in our favor, but when we came within a hundred yards of the point, the active savages were already dashing into the water, and we all feared that within five minutes' time we should have a score of the infuriated wretches around us. If so, our doom was sealed, for these savages, unlike the feeble swimmers of civilized countries, are, if anything, more formidable antagonists in the water than when on the land. It was all a trial of strength; our natives pulled till their oars bent again, and the crowd of swimmers shot through the water despite its roughness, with fearful rapidity.

By the time we had reached the headland, the savages were spread right across our course. Our rowers got out their knives and held them ready between their teeth, and I seized the boat-hook. We were well aware that if they succeeded in intercepting us they would practice upon us the maneuver which has proved so fatal to many a boat's crew in these seas. They would grapple the oars, and seizing hold of the gunwale, capsize the boat, and then we should be entirely at their mercy.

After a few breathless moments I discerned Mow-Mow. The athletic islander, with his tomahawk between his teeth, was dashing the water before him till it foamed again. He was the nearest to us, and in another instant he would have seized one of the oars. Even at the moment I felt horror at the act I was about to commit; but it was no time for pity or compunction, and with a true aim, and exerting all my strength, I dashed the boat-hook at him. It struck him just below the throat, and forced him downwards. I had no time to repeat my blow, but I saw him rise to the surface in the wake of the boat, and never shall I forget the ferocious expression of his countenance.

Only one other of the savages reached the boat. He seized the gunwale, but the knives of our rowers so mauled his wrists, that he was forced to quit his hold, and the next minute we were past them all, and in safety. The strong excitement which had thus far kept me up, now left me, and I fell back fainting into the arms of Karakoee.

.   .   .   .   .   .

The circumstances connected with my most unexpected escape may be very briefly stated. The captain of an Australian vessel, being in distress for men in these remote seas, had put into Nukuheva in order to recruit his ship's company; but not a single man was to be obtained; and the barque was about to get under weigh, when she was boarded by Karakoee, who informed the disappointed Englishman that an American sailor was detained by the savages in the neighboring bay of Typee; and he offered, if supplied with suitable articles of traffic, to undertake his release. The Kannaka had gained his intelligence from Marnoo, to whom, after all, I was indebted for my escape. The proposition was acceded to; and Karakoee, taking with him five tabooed natives of Nukuheva, again repaired aboard the barque, which in a few hours sailed to that part of the island, and threw her main-topsail aback right off the entrance to the Typee Bay. The whale-boat, manned by the tabooed crew, pulled towards the head of the inlet, while the ship lay "off and on" awaiting its return.

The events which ensued have already been detailed, and little more remains to be related. On reaching the *Julia* I was lifted over the side, and my strange appearance and remarkable adventure occasioned the liveliest interest. Every attention was bestowed upon me that humanity could suggest. But to such a state was I reduced, that three months elapsed before I recovered my health.

The mystery which hung over the fate of my friend and companion Toby has never been cleared up. I still remain ignorant whether he succeeded in leaving the valley, or perished at the hands of the islanders.

❖❖❖

On February 27, 1846, John Murray published the first part of *Typee,* its title revised to the more sober *Narrative of a Four Months' Residence among the Natives of a Valley of the Marquesas Islands.* The British press seemed just as intoxicated by the book's mixture of paganism and sophistication as was the American press when it appeared here in mid-March as *Typee.* The career of Herman Melville was well enough launched to have lasted him a lifetime if he had been content to repeat the sensational success of *Typee.*

As engineer of the new career Gansevoort Melville had suggestions to make on the continuation of this pleasing success, but before he could oversee this next step or enjoy the glamour that his brother's adventure and fame brought to the Secretary of the United States Legation, he was dead of a brain disease on May 12. On the following day President Polk proclaimed that a state of war existed between the United States and Mexico, and when Herman wrote to his brother in London on May 29, his letter was full of the war and his own buoyant mood; the mails bringing word of his brother's death had not yet arrived.

◇◇◇

To Gansevoort Melville

Lansingburgh
Friday, June [May] 29th 1846

My Dear Gansevoort—I look forward to three weeks from now, & think I see you opening this letter in [one] of those pleasant hamlets roundabout London, of which we read in novels. At any rate I pray Heaven that such may be the case & that you are mending rapidly. Remember that composure of mind is every thing. You should give no thought to matters here, until you are well enough to think about them. As far as I know they are in good train.

Mr Boyd's second letter announcing your still continued illness was a sad disappointment to us. Yet he seemed to think, that after all you were in a fair way for recovery—& that a removal to the country (then it appears intended shortly) would be attended with the happiest effects. I can not but think it must be;—& I look for good tidings by the next arrival.—Many anxious enquiries have been made after you by numerous friends here.—

The family here are quite well—tho' very busy dressmaking. Augusta is one of the bridesmaids to Miss C. Van R. & her preparations are now forwarding.

People here are all in a state of delirium about the Mexican War. A military order pervades all ranks—Militia Colonels wax red in their coat facings—and 'prenticeboys are running off to the wars by scores.—Nothing is talked of but the "Halls of the Montezumas."

And to hear folks prate about the purely figurative apartments one would suppose that they were another Versailles where our democratic rabble meant to "make a night of it" ere long.—The redoubtable General Viele "went off" in a violent war paroxysm to Washington the other day. His object is to get a commission for raising volunteers about here & taking the feild at their head next fall.—But seriously something great is impending. The Mexican War (tho' our troops have behaved right well) is nothing of itself—but "a little spark kindleth a great fire" as the well known author of the Proverbs very justly remarks—and who knows what all this may lead to— Will it provoke a war with England? Or any other great power?—Prithee, are there any notable battles in store—any Yankee Waterloos?—or think once of a mighty Yankee fleet coming to the war shock in the middle of the A[t]lantic with an English one.—Lord, the day is at hand, when we will be able to talk of our killed & wounded like some of the old Eastern conquerors reckoning them up by thousands;—when the Battle of Monmouth will be thought child's play—& canes made out of the Constitution's timbers be thought no more of than bamboos.—I am at the end of my sheet— God bless you My Dear Gansevoort & bring you to your feet again.

Herman Melville

Typee is coming on bravely—a second edition is nearly out,—I need not ask you to send me *every notice of any kind* that you see or hear of.

❖❖❖

The arrival of Gansevoort's body and the resultant emotional and financial upset did not long interrupt the tide of success-ful authorship—as the new head of the family Melville now had to write to feed them all. Even when he came to New

York to take his brother's body back to the Albany cemetery, he discussed his affairs with Evert Duyckinck (editor at Wiley and Putnam), and in particular the two threats to *Typee's* continued success in both countries: the resentment of the influential missionary societies and the growing suspicion that Melville's adventure was fictitious. John Wiley proposed that the first threat be countered by a drastic cleansing of the book's most heated passages, and a near-miracle occurred to support Melville's claim of truth: after reading a skeptical review in the *New York Evangelist* Richard Tobias Greene wrote to the editor of the Buffalo *Commercial Advertiser* that he, Toby, was very much alive.

◇◇◇

To Evert Duyckinck

Lansingburgh July 3ᵈ 1846

There was a spice of civil scepticism in your manner, my dear Sir, when we were conversing together the other day about "Typee"——What will the politely incredulous Mʳ Duyckinck now say to the true Toby's having turned up in Buffalo, and written a letter to the Commercial Advertiser of that place, vouching for the truth of all that part (what has been considered the most extraordinary part) of the narrative, where he is made to figure.——

Give ear then, oh ye of little faith—especially thou man of the Evangelist—and hear what Toby has to say for himself.——

Seriously, My Dear Sir, this resurection of Toby from the dead—this strange bringing together of two such places as Typee & Buffalo, is really very curious.—It can not but settle the question of the book's genuineness. The article in the C. A. with the letter of Toby can not possibly be gainsaid in any conceivable way—therefore I think it ought to be pushed into circulation. I doubt not but that many papers will copy it—Mr Duyckinck might say a word or two on the subject which would tell.—The paper I allude to is of the 1st Inst.

I have written Toby a letter & expect to see him soon & hear the sequel of the book I have written (How strangely that sounds!)

Bye the bye, since people have always manifested so much concern for "poor Toby," what do you think of writing an account of what befell him in escaping from the island—should the adventure prove to be of sufficient interest?——I should value your opinion very highly on this subject.—

I began with the intention of tracing a short note—I come near writing a long letter.

> Believe me, My Dear Sir
> Very Truly Yours
> Herman Melville

Pardon me, if I have unintentionally translated your patronymick into the Sancrit or some other tongue— "What's in a name?" says Juliet—a strange combination of vowels & consonants, at least in Mr Duyckinck's, Miss, is my reply.

> H M

P.S. No 2. Possibly the letter of Toby *might* by some silly ones be regarded as a hoax—to set you right on that point, altho' I only saw the letter last night for the first—I will tell you that it alludes to things that no human being could ever have heard of except Toby. Besides the Editor seems to have seen him.

❖❖❖

But doubts of *Typee's* truth were not all stilled, especially in England, where the suspicion was often expressed that there was no such person as Herman Melville, and John Murray was unsatisfied with the evidence. He abhorred the taint of fiction.

◇◇◇

To John Murray

Lansingburgh Sept. 2ᵈ 1846

. . . ——Concerning the book [*Omoo*] on the stocks (which bye the by must'nt fall to peices there, since I have not done much to it lately) I will forward you enough of it to enable you to judge thereof.—(Perhaps the whole)—However, you must not Dear Sir expect another Typee—The fates must send me adrift again ere I write another adventure like that exactly.——You ask for "documentary evidences" of my having been at the Marquesas—in Typee.—Dear Sir, how indescribably vexatious, when one really feels in his very bones that he has been there, to have a parcel of blockheads question it!—Not (let me hurry to tell you) that Mʳ John Murray comes under that category—Oh no—Mʳ Murray I am ready to swear stands fast by the faith, beleiving "Typee" from Preface to Sequel—He only wants something to stop the mouths of the senseless sceptics —men who go straight from their cradles to their graves & never dream of the queer things going on at the antipodes.——

I know not how to set about getting the evidence— How under Heaven am I to subpoena the skipper of the Dolly who by this time is the Lord only knows where, or Kory-Kory who I'll be bound is this blessed day taking his noon nap somewhere in the flowery vale of Typee, some leagues too from the Monument.

Seriously on the receipt of your welcome favor, Dear

Sir, I addressed a note to the owners of the ship, asking if they could procure for me, a copy of that part of the ship's log which makes mention of two rascals running away at Nukuheva—to wit Herman Melville and Richard T Greene. As yet I have nothing in reply—If I think of any other kind of evidence I will send it, if it can be had & despatched.—Typee however must at last be beleived on its own account—they beleive it here now—a little touched up they say but *true*.

◇◇◇

Murray took *Omoo*, too, but never stopped worrying. The attacks on Melville, inspired by his own attacks on the motives of the Pacific missionaries, were redoubled by *Omoo's* more circumstantial account of the missionary failure in Tahiti. His "evil tidings" did indeed bring their bearer "a losing office."

All this had only a challenging, stimulating effect on Melville, however; 1847 was for him a year of decision and bolder enterprise. A third book was begun. He accepted Duyckinck's invitation to contribute book reviews to *The Literary World* and satires on the hero of Palo Alto, General Zachary Taylor, to *Yankee Doodle*. And in August he married Elizabeth, daughter of Massachusetts' Chief Justice Lemuel Shaw. In this atmosphere of change, the new book did not remain the quasi-autobiographical sequel to *Typee* and *Omoo* that it had started out to be. He gave John Murray a last chance at this new phase of his work before turning to another English publisher.

◇◇◇

To John Murray

New York March 25th 1848

My Dear Sir—Nothing but a sad failing of mine—procrastination—has prevented me from replying ere this

to yours of the 17 Jany last, which I have just read over.
—Will you still continue, Mr Murray, to break seals
from the Land of Shadows—persisting in carrying on
this mysterious correspondence with an imposter shade,
that under the fanciful appellation of Herman Melvill
still practices upon your honest credulity?——Have a
care, I pray, lest while thus parleying with a ghost you
fall upon some horrible evel, peradventure sell your soul
ere you are aware.——But in tragic phrase "no more!"
—only glancing at the closing sentence of your letter,
I read there your desire to test the corporeality of H——
M—— by clapping eyes upon him in London.——I beleive that a letter I wrote you some time ago—I think
my last but one—gave you to understand, or implied,
that the work I then had in view was a bona-fide narrative of my adventures in the Pacific, continued from
"Omoo"——My object in now writing you—I should
have done so ere this—is to inform you of a change in
my determinations. To be blunt: the work I shall next
publish will be downright & out a "Romance of Polynesian Adventure"——But why this? The truth is, Sir,
that the reiterated imputation of being a romancer in
disguise has at last pricked me into a resolution to show
those who may take any interest in the matter, that a
real romance of mine is no Typee or Omoo, & is made
of different stuff altogether. This I confess has been the
main inducement in altering my plans—but others have
operated. I have long thought that Polynesia furnished
a great deal of rich poetical material that has never
been empl[o]yed hitherto in works of fancy; and which
to bring out suitably, required only that play of freedom
& invention accorded only to the Romancer & poet.——
However, I thought, that I would postpone trying my
hand at any thing fanciful of this sort, till some future

day; tho' at times when in the mood I threw off occasional sketches applicable to such a work.——Well: proceeding in my narrative of *facts* I began to feel an incurable distaste for the same; & a longing to plume my powers for a flight, & felt irked, cramped & fettered by plodding along with dull common places,—So suddenly abandoning the thing alltogether, I went to work heart & soul at a romance which is now in fair progress, since I hard worked at it under an earnest ardor.——Shout not, nor exclaim "Pshaw! Puh!"—My romance I assure you is no dish water nor its model borrowed from the Circulating Library. It is something new I assure you, & original if nothing more. But I can give you no adequate idea of it. You must see it for yourself.—Only forbear to prejudge it.——It opens like a true narrative —like Omoo for example, on ship board—the romance & poetry of the thing thence grow continuously, till it becomes a story wild enough I assure you & with a meaning too.——As for the policy of putting forth an acknowledged *romance* upon the heel of two books of travel which in some quarters have been received with no small incredulity—that, Sir, is a question for which I care little, really.—My *instinct* is to out with the Romance, & let me say that instincts are prophetic, & better than acquired wisdom—which alludes unnobely to your experience in literature as an eminent publisher. —Yet upon the whole if you consider the thing, I think you will unite with me in the opinion, that it is possible for me to write such a romance. That it shall afford the strongest presumptive evidence of the truth of Typee & Omoo by the sheer force of contrast—not that the Romance is to sink in the comparison, but shall be better—I mean as a literary achievement, & so essentially different from those two books. . . .

——By the way, you ask again for "documentary evidence" of my having been in the South Seas, where-withall to convince the unbeleivers——Bless my soul, Sir, will you Britons not credit that an American can be a gentleman, & have read the Waverly Novels, tho every digit may have been in the tar-bucket?——You make miracles of what are commonplaces to us.——I will give no evidence——Truth is mighty & will prevail——& shall & must.

> In all sincerity Yours
> Herman Melville

From Mardi and a Voyage Thither

Dreams

DREAMS! dreams! golden dreams: endless, and golden, as the flowery prairies, that stretch away from the Rio Sacramento, in whose waters Danæ's shower was woven;—prairies like rounded eternities: jonquil leaves beaten out; and my dreams herd like buffaloes, browsing on to the horizon, and browsing on round the world; and among them, I dash with my lance, to spear one, ere they all flee.

Dreams! dreams! passing and repassing, like Oriental empires in history; and scepters wave thick as Bruce's pikes at Bannockburn; and crowns are plenty as marigolds in June. And far in the background, hazy and blue, their steeps let down from the sky, loom Andes on Andes, rooted on Alps; and all round me, long rushing oceans, roll Amazons and Oronocos; waves, mounted Parthians; and, to and fro, toss the wide woodlands: all the world an elk, and the forests its antlers.

But far to the South, past my Sicily suns and my vineyards, stretches the Antarctic barrier of ice: a China wall, built up from the sea, and nodding its frosted towers in the dun, clouded sky. Do Tartary and Siberia lie beyond? Deathful, desolate dominions those; bleak and wild the ocean, beating at that barrier's base, hovering 'twixt freezing and foaming, and freighted with navies of ice-bergs—warring worlds crossing orbits, their long icicles projecting like spears to the charge. Wide away stream the floes of drift ice, frozen cemeteries of skeletons and bones. White bears howl as they drift from their cubs; and the grinding islands crush the skulls of the peering seals.

But beneath me, at the Equator, the earth pulses and beats like a warrior's heart; till I know not, whether it be not myself. And my soul sinks down to the depths, and soars to the skies; and cometlike reels on through such boundless expanses, that methinks all the worlds are my kin, and I invoke them to stay in their course. Yet, like a mighty three-decker, towing argosies by scores, I tremble, gasp, and strain in my flight, and fain would cast off the cables that hamper.

And like a frigate, I am full with a thousand souls; and as on, on, on, I scud before the wind, many mariners rush up from the orlop below, like miners from caves, running shouting across my decks; opposite braces are pulled; and this way and that, the great yards swing round on their axes; and boisterous speaking-trumpets are heard, and contending orders, to save the good ship from the shoals. Shoals, like nebulous vapors, shoring the white reef of the Milky Way, against which the wrecked worlds are dashed; strowing all the strand with their Himmaleh keels and ribs.

Aye: many, many souls are in me. In my tropical calms, when my ship lies tranced on Eternity's main, speaking one at a time, then all with one voice: an orchestra of many French bugles and horns, rising, and falling, and swaying, in golden calls and responses.

Sometimes, when these Atlantics and Pacifics thus undulate round me, I lie stretched out in their midst: a land-locked Mediterranean, knowing no ebb, nor flow. Then again, I am dashed in the spray of these sounds: an eagle at the world's end, tossed skyward, on the horns of the tempest.

Yet, again, I descend, and list to the concert.

Like a grand ground swell, Homer's old organ rolls its vast volumes under the light frothy wave-crests of Anacreon and Hafiz; and high over my ocean, sweet Shakespeare soars, like all the larks of the spring. Throned on my seaside, like Canute, bearded Ossian smites his hoar harp, wreathed with wild-flowers, in which warble my Wallers; blind Milton sings bass to my Petrarchs and Priors, and laureates crown me with bays.

In me, many worthies recline, and converse. I list to St. Paul who argues the doubts of Montaigne; Julian the Apostate cross-questions Augustine; and Thomas a Kempis unrolls his old black letters for all to decipher. Zeno murmurs maxims beneath the hoarse shout of Democritus; and though Democritus laugh loud and long, and the sneer of Pyrrho be seen, yet divine Plato, and Proclus, and Verulam are of my counsel, and Zoroaster whispered me before I was born. I walk a world that is mine; and enter many nations, as Mungo Park rested in African cots; I am served like Bajazet: Bacchus my butler, Virgil my minstrel, Philip Sidney my page. My memory is a life beyond birth; my memory, my library of the Vatican, its alcoves all endless perspectives, eve-tinted by cross-lights from Middle-Age oriels.

And as the great Mississippi musters his watery nations: Ohio, with all his leagued streams; Missouri, bringing down in torrents the clans from the highlands; Arkansas, his Tartar rivers from the plain; so, with all the past and present pouring in me, I roll down my billow from afar.

Yet not I, but another: God is my Lord; and though many satellites revolve around me, I and all mine revolve round the great central Truth, sun-like, fixed and luminous forever in the foundationless firmament.

Fire flames on my tongue; and though of old the Bactrian prophets were stoned, yet the stoners in oblivion sleep. But whoso stones me shall be as Erostratus, who put torch to the temple; though Genghis Khan with Cambyses combine to obliterate him, his name shall be extant in the mouth of the last man that lives. And if so be, down unto death, whence I came, will I go, like Xenophone retreating on Greece, all Persia brandishing her spears in his rear.

My cheek blanches white while I write; I start at the scratch of my pen; my own mad brood of eagles devours me; fain would I unsay this audacity; but an iron-mailed hand clenches mine in a vise, and prints down every letter in my spite. Fain would I hurl off this Dionysius that rides me; my thoughts crush me down till I groan; in far fields I hear the song of the reaper, while I slave and faint in this cell. The fever runs through me like lava; my hot brain burns like a coal; and like many a monarch, I am less to be envied than the veriest hind in the land.

(Chapter CXIX)

They Hearken unto a Voice from the Gods

Next day we retraced our voyage northward, to visit that section of Vivenza.

In due time we landed.

To look round was refreshing. Of all the lands we had seen, none looked more promising. The groves stood tall and green; the fields spread flush and broad; the dew of the first morning seemed hardly vanished from the grass. On all sides was heard the fall of waters, the swarming of bees, and the rejoicing hum of a thriving population. . . .

Rambling on, we espied a clamorous crowd gathered about a conspicuous palm, against which a scroll was fixed.

The people were violently agitated, storming out maledictions against the insolent knave, who, over night, must have fixed there that scandalous document. But whoever he may have been, certain it was he had contrived to hood himself effectually.

After much vehement discussion, during which sundry inflammatory harangues were made from the stumps of trees near by, it was proposed that the scroll should be read aloud, so that all might give ear.

Seizing it, a fiery youth mounted upon the bowed shoulders of an old man, his sire, and with a shrill voice, ever and anon interrupted by outcries, read as follows:

Sovereign-Kings of Vivenza! it is fit you should hearken to wisdom. But well aware that you give ear to little wisdom except of your own, and that as freemen, you are free to hunt down him who dissents from your majesties, I deem it proper to address you anonymously.

And if it please you, you may ascribe this voice to the gods: for never will you trace it to man.

It is not unknown, sovereign-kings! that in these boisterous days the lessons of history are almost discarded, as superseded by present experiences. And that while all Mardi's Present has grown out of its Past, it is becoming obsolete to refer to what has been. Yet, per-adventure, the Past is an apostle.

The grand error of this age, sovereign-kings! is the general supposition, that the very special Diabolus is abroad; whereas, the very special Diabolus has been abroad ever since Mardi began.

And the grand error of your nation, sovereign-kings! seems this: The conceit that Mardi is now in the last scene of the last act of her drama; and that all preceding events were ordained to bring about the catastrophe you believe to be at hand—a universal and permanent Republic.

May it please you, those who hold to these things are fools, and not wise.

Time is made up of various ages; and each thinks its own a novelty. But imbedded in the walls of the pyramids, which outrun all chronologies, sculptured stones are found, belonging to yet older fabrics. And as in the mound-building period of yore, so every age thinks its erections will forever endure. But as your forests grow apace, sovereign-kings! overrunning the tumuli in your western vales, so, while deriving their substance from the past, succeeding generations overgrow it, but in time themselves decay.

Oro decrees these vicissitudes.

In chronicles of old, you read, sovereign-kings! that an eagle from the clouds presaged royalty to the fugitive Taquinoo; and, a king, Taquinoo reigned. No end to my dynasty, thought he.

But another omen descended, foreshadowing the fall of Zooperbi, his son; and Zooperbi returning from his camp found his country a fortress against him. No more kings would she have. And for five hundred twelve-moons the Regifugium, or King's-flight, was annually celebrated like your own jubilee day. And rampant *young orators stormed out detestation of kings; and augurs swore that their birds presaged immortality to freedom.*

Then, Romara's free eagles flew over all Mardi, and perched on the topmost diadems of the East.

Ever thus must it be.

For, mostly, monarchs are as gemmed bridles upon the world, checking the plungings of a steed from the pampas. And republics are as vast reservoirs, draining down all streams to one level; and so breeding a fullness which cannot remain full without overflowing. And thus, Romara flooded all Mardi, till scarce an Ararat was left of the lofty kingdoms which had been.

Thus, also, did Franko, fifty twelve-moons ago. Thus may she do again. And though not yet have you, sovereign-kings! in any large degree done likewise, it is because you overflow your redundancies within your own mighty borders; having a wild western waste, which many shepherds with their flocks could not overrun in a day. Yet overrun at last it will be; and then the recoil must come.

And, may it please you, that thus far your chronicles had narrated a very different story, had your population been pressed and packed, like that of your old sire-land Dominora. Then, your great experiment might have proved an explosion, like the chemist's, who, stirring his mixture, was blown by it into the air.

For though crossed and recrossed by many brave quarterings, and boasting the great Bull in your pedigree, yet, sovereign-kings! you are not meditative philosophers like the people of a small republic of old; nor enduring stoics like their neighbors. Pent up, like them, may it please you, your thirteen original tribes had proved more turbulent than so many mutinous legions. Free horses need wide prairies; and fortunate for you, sovereign-kings! that you have room enough, wherein to be free.

And, may it please you, you are free, partly, because you are young. Your nation is like a fine, florid youth, full of fiery impulses, and hard to restrain; his strong hand nobly championing his heart. On all sides, freely he gives, and still seeks to acquire. The breath of his nostrils is like smoke in spring air; every tendon is electric with generous resolves. The oppressor he defies to his beard; the high walls of old opinions he scales with a bound. In the future he sees all the domes of the East.

But years elapse, and this bold boy is transformed. His eyes open not as of yore; his heart is shut up as a vise. He yields not a groat; and seeking no more acquisitions, is only bent on preserving his hoard. The maxims once trampled under foot are now printed on his front; and he who hated oppressors is become an oppressor himself.

Thus, often, with men; thus, often, with nations. Then marvel not, sovereign-kings! that old states are different from yours; and think not your own must forever remain liberal as now.

Each age thinks its own is eternal. But though for five hundred twelve-moons, all Romara, by courtesy of history, was republican; yet, at last, her terrible king-tigers came, and spotted themselves with gore.

And time was, when Dominora was republican, down to her sturdy backbone. The son of an absolute monarch became the man Karolus; and his crown and head both rolled in the dust. And Dominora had her patriots by thousands; and lusty Defenses, and glorious Areopagiticas were written, not since surpassed; and no turban was doffed save in homage of Oro.

Yet, may it please you, to the sound of pipe and

tabor, the second King Karolus returned in good time, and was hailed gracious majesty by high and low.

Throughout all eternity, the parts of the past are but parts of the future reversed. In the old footprints, up and down, you mortals go, eternally traveling your Sierras. And not more infallible the ponderings of the Calculating Machine than the deductions from the decimals of history.

In nations, sovereign-kings! there is a transmigration of souls; in you is a marvelous destiny. The eagle of Romara revives in your own mountain bird, and once more is plumed for her flight. Her screams are answered by the vauntful cries of a hawk, his red comb yet reeking with slaughter. And one East, one West, those bold birds may fly, till they lock pinions in the midmost beyond.

But, soaring in the sky over the nations that shall gather their broods under their wings, that bloody hawk may hereafter be taken for the eagle.

And though crimson republics may rise in constellations, like fiery Aldebarans, speeding to their culminations; yet down must they sink at last, and leave the old sultan-sun in the sky; in time, again to be deposed.

For little longer, may it please you, can republics subsist now than in days gone by. For, assuming that Mardi is wiser than of old; nevertheless, though all men approached sages in intelligence, some would yet be more wise than others, and so the old degrees be preserved. And no exemption would an equality of knowledge furnish from the inbred servility of mortal to mortal, from all the organic causes, which inevitably divide mankind into brigades and battalions, with captains at their head.

Civilization has not ever been the brother of equality. Freedom was born among the wild eyries in the moun-

tains; and barbarous tribes have sheltered under her wings, when the enlightened people of the plain have nestled under different pinions.

Though, thus far, for you, sovereign-kings! your republic has been fruitful of blessings, yet, in themselves, monarchies are not utterly evil. For many nations, they are better than republics; for many, they will ever so remain. And better, on all hands, that peace should rule with a scepter than that the tribunes of the people should brandish their broadswords. Better be the subject of a king, upright and just, than a freeman in Franko, with the executioner's axe at every corner.

It is not the prime end, and chief blessing, to be politically free. And freedom is only good as a means; is no end in itself. Nor, did man fight it out against his masters to the haft, not then would he uncollar his neck from the yoke. A born thrall to the last, yelping out his liberty, he still remains a slave unto Oro; and well is it for the universe that Oro's scepter is absolute.

World-old the saying, that it is easier to govern others than oneself. And that all men should govern themselves as nations needs that all men be better, and wiser, than the wisest of one-man rulers. But in no stable democracy do all men govern themselves. Though an army be all volunteers, martial law must prevail. Delegate your power, you leagued mortals must. The hazard you must stand. And though, unlike King Bello of Dominora, your great chieftain, sovereign-kings! may not declare war of himself, nevertheless has he done a still more imperial thing:—gone to war without declaring intentions. You yourselves were precipitated upon a neighboring nation, ere you knew your spears were in your hands.

But, as in stars you have written it on the welkin, sovereign-kings! you are a great and glorious people. And verily, yours is the best and happiest land under the sun. But not wholly because you, in your wisdom, decreed it: your origin and geography necessitated it. Nor, in their germ, are all your blessings to be ascribed to the noble sires who of yore fought in your behalf, sovereign-kings! Your nation enjoyed no little independence before your Declaration declared it. Your ancient pilgrims fathered your liberty; and your wild woods harbored the nursling. For the state that today is made up of slaves cannot tomorrow transmute her bond into free, though lawlessness may transform them into brutes. Freedom is the name for a thing that is not freedom; this, a lesson never learned in an hour or an age. By some tribes it will never be learned.

Yet, if it please you, there may be such a thing as being free under Cæsar. Ages ago, there were as many vital freemen as breathe vital air today.

Names make not distinctions; some despots rule without swaying scepters. Though King Bello's palace was not put together by yoked men, your federal temple of freedom, sovereign-kings! was the handiwork of slaves.

It is not gildings, and gold maces, and crown-jewels alone, that make a people servile. There is much bowing and cringing among you yourselves, sovereign-kings! Poverty is abased before riches, all Mardi over; anywhere, it is hard to be a debtor; anywhere, the wise will lord it over fools; everywhere, suffering is found.

Thus, freedom is more social than political. And its real felicity is not to be shared. That is of a man's own individual getting and holding. It is not, who rules the state, but who rules me. Better be secure under one king than exposed to violence from twenty millions of monarchs, though oneself be of the number.

But superstitious notions you harbor, sovereign-kings! Did you visit Dominora, you would not be marched straight into a dungeon. And though you would behold sundry sights displeasing, you would start to inhale such liberal breezes, and hear crowds boasting of their privileges, as you, of yours. Nor has the wine of Dominora a monarchical flavor.

Now, though far and wide, to keep equal pace with the times, great reforms, of a verity, be needed, nowhere are bloody revolutions required. Though it be the most certain of remedies, no prudent invalid opens his veins, to let out his disease with his life. And though all evils may be assuaged, all evils cannot be done away. For evil is the chronic malady of the universe; and checked in one place breaks forth in another.

Of late, on this head, some wild dreams have departed.

There are many who erewhile believed that the age of pikes and javelins was passed; that after a heady and blustering youth, old Mardi was at last settling down into a serene old age; and that the Indian summer, first discovered in your land, sovereign-kings! was the hazy vapor emitted from its tranquil pipe. But it has not so proved. Mardi's peaces are but truces. Long absent, at last the red comets have returned. And return they must, though their periods be ages. And should Mardi endure till mountain melt into mountain, and all the isles form one tableland, yet would it but expand the old battle-plain.

Students of history are horror-struck at the massacres of old; but in the shambles, men are being murdered today. Could time be reversed, and the future change places with the past, the past would cry out against us, and our future, full as loudly as we against the ages foregone. All the Ages are his children, calling each other names.

Hark ye, sovereign-kings! cheer not on the yelping pack too furiously. Hunters have been torn by their hounds. Be advised: wash your hands. Hold aloof. Oro has poured out an ocean for an everlasting barrier between you and the worst folly which other republics have perpetrated. That barrier hold sacred. And swear never to cross over to Porpheero, by manifesto or army, unless you traverse dry land.

And be not too grasping, nearer home. It is not freedom to filch. Expand not your area too widely, now. Seek you proselytes? Neighboring nations may be free, without coming under your banner. And if you cannot lay your ambition, know this: that it is best served by awaiting events.

Time, but Time only, may enable you to cross the equator, and give you the Arctic Circles for your boundaries.

So read the anonymous scroll, which straightway was torn into shreds.

"Old tory, and monarchist!" they shouted, "Preaching over his benighted sermons in these enlightened times! Fool! does he not know that all the Past and its graves are being dug over?"

(Chapter CLXI)

Sailing On

. . . And, as the sun, by influence divine, wheels through the Ecliptic, threading Cancer, Leo, Pisces, and Aquarius; so, by some mystic impulse am I moved to this fleet progress, through the groups in white-reefed Mardi's zone.

Oh, reader, list! I've chartless voyaged. With compass and the lead, we had not found these Mardian Isles. Those who boldly launch, cast off all cables; and turning from the common breeze, that's fair for all, with their own breath fill their own sails. Hug the shore, naught new is seen; and "Land ho!" at last was sung, when a new world was sought.

That voyager steered his bark through seas untracked before; ploughed his own path mid jeers; though with a heart that oft was heavy with the thought, that he might only be too bold, and grope where land was none.

So I.

And though essaying but a sportive sail, I was driven from my course, by a blast resistless; and ill-provided, young, and bowed to the brunt of things before my prime, still fly before the gale, hard have I striven to keep stout heart.

And if it harder be, than e'er before, to find new climes, when now our seas have oft been circled by ten thousand prows—much more the glory!

But this new world here sought is stranger far than his, who stretched his vans from Palos. It is the world of mind, wherein the wanderer may gaze round, with more of wonder than Balboa's band roving through the golden Aztec glades.

But fiery yearnings their own phantom-future make, and deem it present. So, if after all these fearful, fainting trances, the verdict be the golden haven was not gained—yet, in bold quest thereof, better to sink in boundless deeps than float on vulgar shoals; and give me, ye gods, an utter wreck, if wreck I do.

(Chapter CLXIX)

Some Pleasant, Shady Talk in the Groves, Between My Lords Abrazza and Media, Babbalanja, Mohi, and Yoomy

Abrazza had a cool retreat—a grove of dates, where we were used to lounge of noons, and mix our converse with the babble of the rills, and mix our punches in goblets chased with grapes. And, as ever, King Abrazza was the prince of hosts.

"Your crown," he said to Media, and with his own, he hung it on a bough.

"Be not ceremonious," and stretched his royal legs upon the turf.

"Wine!" and his pages poured it out.

So on the grass we lounged; and King Abrazza, who loved his antique ancestors, and loved old times, and would not talk of moderns, bade Yoomy sing old songs, bade Mohi rehearse old histories, bade Babbalanja tell of old ontologies, and commanded all, meanwhile, to drink his old, old wine.

So all round we quaffed and quoted.

At last, we talked of old Homeric bards: those who, ages back, harped, and begged, and groped their blinded way through all this charitable Mardi, receiving coppers then, and immortal glory now.

ABRAZZA. How came it, that they all were blind?

BABBALANJA. It was endemical, your highness. Few grand poets have good eyes; for they needs blind must be, who ever gaze upon the sun. Vavona himself was blind, when, in the silence of his secret bower, he said— "I will build another world. Therein, let there be kings and slaves, philosophers and wits, whose checkered actions, strange, grotesque, and merry-sad, will entertain my idle moods." So, my lord, Vavona played at kings and crowns, and men and manners, and loved that lonely game to play.

ABRAZZA. Vavona seemed a solitary Mardian, who seldom went abroad, had few friends, and, shunning others, was shunned by them.

BABBALANJA. But shunned not himself, my lord; like

gods, great poets dwell alone, while round them, roll the worlds they build.

MEDIA. You seem to know all authors: you must have heard of Lombardo, Babbalanja, he who flourished many ages since.

BABBALANJA. I have, and his grand Koztanza know by heart.

MEDIA (*to Abrazza*). A very curious work, that, my lord.

ABRAZZA. Yes, my dearest king. But, Babbalanja, if Lombardo had aught to tell to Mardi—why choose a vehicle so crazy?

BABBALANJA. It was his nature, I suppose.

ABRAZZA. But so it would not have been, to me.

BABBALANJA. Nor would it have been natural, for my noble lord Abrazza, to have worn Lombardo's head— every man has his own, thank Oro!

ABRAZZA. A curious work: a very curious work. Babbalanja, are you acquainted with the history of Lombardo?

BABBALANJA. None better. All his biographies have I read.

ABRAZZA. Then tell us how he came to write that work. For one, I cannot imagine how those poor devils contrive to roll such thunders through all Mardi.

MEDIA. Their thunder and lightning seem spontaneous combustibles, my lord.

ABRAZZA. With which they but consume themselves, my prince beloved.

BABBALANJA. In a measure, true, your highness. But pray you, listen; and I will try to tell the way in which Lombardo produced his great Koztanza.

MEDIA. But hark you, philosopher! this time no incoherencies; gag that devil, Azzageddi. And now, what was it that originally impelled Lombardo to the under-taking?

BABBALANJA. Primus and forever, a full heart: brim-ful, bubbling, sparkling, and running over like the flagon in your hand, my lord. Secundo, the necessity of bestirring himself to procure his yams.

ABRAZZA. Wanting the second motive, would the first have sufficed, philosopher?

BABBALANJA. Doubtful. More conduits than one to drain off the soul's overflowings. Besides, the greatest fullnesses overflow not spontaneously; and, even when decanted, like rich syrups, slowly ooze; whereas poor fluids glibly flow, wide-spreading. Hence, when great fullness weds great indolence, that man, to others, too often proves a cipher, though, to himself, his thoughts form an Infinite Series, indefinite, from its vastness; and incommunicable—not for lack of power, but for lack of an omnipotent volition, to move his strength. His own world is full before him; the fulcrum set; but lever there is none. To such a man, the giving of any boor's resolute-ness, with tendons braided, would be as hanging a clay-more to Valor's side, before unarmed. Our minds are cunning, compound mechanisms; and one spring, or wheel, or axle wanting, the movement lags, or halts. Cerebrum must not overbalance cerebellum; our brains should be round as globes, and planted on capacious chests, inhaling mighty morning-inspirations. We have had vast developments of parts of men, but none of many wholes. Before a full-developed man, Mardi would fall down and worship. We are idiot younger sons of gods, begotten in dotages divine; and our mothers all miscarry. Giants are in our germs; but we are dwarfs, staggering under heads overgrown. Heaped, our measures burst. We die of too much life.

MEDIA (to Abrazza). Be not impatient, my lord; he'll

recover presently. You were talking of Lombardo, Babbalanja.

BABBALANJA. I was, your Highness. Of all Mardians, by nature, he was the most inert. Hast ever seen a yellow lion, all day basking in the yellow sun: in reveries, rending droves of elephants, but his vast loins supine, and eyelids winking? Such, Lombardo; but fierce Want, the hunter, came and roused his roar. In hairy billows, his great mane tossed like the sea; his eye-balls flamed two hells; his paw had stopped a rolling world.

ABRAZZA. In other words, yams were indispensable, and, poor devil, he roared to get them.

BABBALANJA (*bowing*). Partly so, my literal lord. And as with your own golden scepter at times upon your royal teeth indolent tattooes you beat; then, potent, sway it o'er your isle; so, Lombardo. And ere Necessity plunged spur and rowel into him, he knew not his own paces. *That* churned him into consciousness, and brought ambition, ere then dormant, seething to the top, till he trembled at himself. No mailed hand lifted up against a traveler in woods can so appall as we ourselves. We are full of ghosts and spirits; we are as graveyards full of buried dead, that start to life before us. And all our dead sires, verily, are in us; *that* is their immortality. From sire to son, we go on multiplying corpses in ourselves; for all of which, are resurrections. Every thought's a soul of some past poet, hero, sage. We are fuller than a city. Woe it is that reveals these things. He knows himself, and all that's in him, who knows adversity. To scale great heights, we must come out of lowermost depths. The way to heaven is through hell. We need fiery baptisms in the fiercest flames of our own bosoms. We must feel our hearts hot—hissing in us. And ere their fire is revealed, it must burn its way out of us, though it consume us and itself. Oh, sleekcheeked Plenty! smiling at thine own dimples, vain for thee to reach out after greatness. Turn! turn! from all your tiers of cushions of eiderdown—turn! and be broken on the wheels of many woes. At white heat, brand thyself; and count the scars, like old war-worn veterans, over campfires. Soft poet! brushing tears from lilies—this way! and howl in sackcloth and in ashes! Know, thou, that the lines that live are turned out of a furrowed brow. Oh! there is a fierce, a cannibal delight, in the grief that shrieks to multiply itself. That grief is miserly of its own; it pities all the happy. Some damned spirits would not be otherwise, could they.

ABRAZZA (*to Media*). Pray, my lord, is this good gentleman a devil?

MEDIA. No, my lord; but he's possessed by one. His name is Azzageddi. You may hear more of him. But come, Babbalanja, hast forgotten all about Lombardo? How set he about that great undertaking, his Koztanza?

ABRAZZA (*to Media*). Oh, for all the ravings of your Babbalanja, Lombardo took no special pains; hence deserves small commendation. For, genius must be somewhat like us kings—calm, content, in consciousness of power. And to Lombardo, the scheme of his Koztanza must have come full-fledged, like an eagle from the sun.

BABBALANJA. No, your Highness; but like eagles, his thoughts were first callow, yet, born plumeless, they came to soar.

ABRAZZA. Very fine. I presume, Babbalanja, the first thing he did was to fast, and invoke the muses.

BABBALANJA. Pardon, my lord, on the contrary, he first procured a ream of vellum, and some sturdy quills: indispensable preliminaries, my worshipful lords, to the writing of the sublimest epics.

ABRAZZA. Ah! then the muses were afterward invoked.

BABBALANJA. Pardon again. Lombardo next sat down to a fine plantain pudding.

YOOMY. When the song-spell steals over me, I live upon olives.

BABBALANJA. Yoomy, Lombardo eschewed olives. Said he, "What fasting soldier can fight? and the fight of all fights is to write." In ten days Lombardo had written—

ABRAZZA. Dashed off, you mean.

BABBALANJA. He never dashed off aught.

ABRAZZA. As you will.

BABBALANJA. In ten days, Lombardo had written full fifty folios; he loved huge acres of vellum whereon to expatiate.

MEDIA. What then?

BABBALANJA. He read them over attentively, made a neat package of the whole, and put it into the fire.

ALL. How?

MEDIA. What! these great geniuses writing trash?

ABRAZZA. I thought as much.

BABBALANJA. My lords, they abound in it; more than any other men in Mardi. Genius is full of trash. But genius essays its best to keep it to itself; and giving away its ore, retains the earth; whence, the too frequent wisdom of its works and folly of its life.

ABRAZZA. Then genius is not inspired, after all. How they must slave in their mines! I weep to think of it.

BABBALANJA. My lord, all men are inspired; fools are inspired; your highness is inspired; for the essence of all ideas is infused. Of ourselves, and in ourselves, we originate nothing. When Lombardo set about his work, he knew not what it would become. He did not build himself in with plans; he wrote right on; and so doing, got deeper and deeper into himself; and like a resolute traveler, plunging through baffling woods, at last was rewarded for his toils. "In good time," saith he, in his autobiography, "I came out into a serene, sunny, ravishing region, full of sweet scents, singing birds, wild plaints, roguish laughs, prophetic voices. Here we are at last, then," he cried; "I have created the creative." And now the whole boundless landscape stretched away. Lombardo panted; the sweat was on his brow; he off mantle, braced himself, sat within view of the ocean, his face to a cool rushing breeze, placed flowers before him, and gave himself plenty of room. On one side was his ream of vellum—

ABRAZZA. And on the other, a brimmed beaker.

BABBALANJA. No, your highness; though he loved it, no wine for Lombardo while actually at work.

MOHI. Indeed? Why, I ever thought that it was to the superior quality of Lombardo's punches that Mardi was indebted for that abounding humor of his.

BABBALANJA. Not so; he had another way of keeping himself well braced.

YOOMY. Quick! tell us the secret.

BABBALANJA. He never wrote by rush-light. His lamp swung in heaven. He rose from his east, with the sun; he wrote when all nature was alive.

MOHI. Doubtless, then, he always wrote with a grin; and none laughed louder at his quips than Lombardo himself.

BABBALANJA. Hear you laughter at the birth of a man child, old man? The babe may have many dimples; not so, the parent. Lombardo was a hermit to behold.

MEDIA. What! did Lombardo laugh with a long face?

BABBALANJA. His merriment was not always merriment to him, your highness. For the most part, his meaning kept him serious. Then he was so intensely riveted to his work, he could not pause to laugh.

MOHI. My word for it, but he had a sly one, now and then.

BABBALANJA. For the nonce, he was not his own master; a mere amanuensis writing by dictation.

YOOMY. Inspiration, that!

BABBALANJA. Call it as you will, Yoomy, it was a sort of sleep-walking of the mind. Lombardo never threw down his pen: it dropped from him; and then, he sat disenchanted: rubbing his eyes, staring, and feeling faint—sometimes almost unto death.

MEDIA. But pray, Babbalanja, tell us how he made acquaintance with some of those rare worthies he introduces us to in his Koztanza.

BABBALANJA. He first met them in his reveries; they were walking about in him, sour and moody, and for a long time were shy of his advances; but still importuned, they at last grew ashamed of their reserve, stepped forward, and gave him their hands. After that, they were frank and friendly. Lombardo set places for them at his board; when he died, he left them something in his will.

MEDIA. What! those imaginary beings?

ABRAZZA. Wondrous witty! infernal fine!

MEDIA. But, Babbalanja, after all, the Koztanza found no favor in the eyes of some Mardians.

ABRAZZA. Aye: the arch-critics Verbi and Batho denounced it.

BABBALANJA. Yes; on good authority, Verbi is said to have detected a superfluous comma; and Batho declared that with the materials he could have constructed a far better world than Lombardo's. But didst ever hear of his laying his axis?

ABRAZZA. But the unities, Babbalanja, the unities! they are wholly wanting in the Koztanza.

BABBALANJA. Your highness, upon that point, Lombardo was frank. Saith he, in his autobiography: "For some time, I endeavored to keep in the good graces of those nymphs; but I found them so captious, and exacting; they threw me into such a violent passion with their fault-findings, that, at last, I renounced them."

ABRAZZA. Very rash!

BABBALANJA. No, your highness; for though Lombardo abandoned all monitors from without, he retained one autocrat within—his crowned and sceptered instinct. And what—if he pulled down one gross world, and ransacked the ethereal spheres, to build up something of his own—a composite—what then? matter and mind, though matching not, are mates; and sundered oft, in his Koztanza they unite: the airy waist, embraced by stalwart arms.

MEDIA. Incoherent again! I thought we were to have no more of this.

BABBALANJA. My lord Media, there are things infinite in the finite; and dualities in unities. Our eyes are pleased with the redness of the rose, but another sense lives upon its fragrance. Its redness you must approach, to view; its invisible fragrance pervades the field. So, with the Koztanza. Its mere beauty is restricted to its form: its expanding soul past Mardi does embalm. Modak is Modako; but fogle-foggle is not fugle-fi.

MEDIA (to Abrazza). My lord, you start again; but 'tis only another phase of Azzageddi; sometimes he's quite mad. But all this you must needs overlook.

ABRAZZA. I will, my dear prince; what one cannot see through, one must needs look over, as you say.

YOOMY. But trust me, your highness, some of those strange things fall far too melodiously upon the ear to be wholly deficient in meaning.

ABRAZZA. Your gentle minstrel, this must be, my lord.

But, Babbalanja, the Koztanza lacks cohesion; it is wild, unconnected, all episode.

BABBALANJA. And so is Mardi itself: nothing but episodes; valleys and hills; rivers, digressing from plains; vines, roving all over; boulders and diamonds; flowers and thistles; forests and thickets; and, here and there, fens and moors. And so, the world in the Koztanza.

ABRAZZA. Aye, plenty of dead-desert chapters there; horrible sands to wade through.

MEDIA. Now, Babbalanja, away with your tropes, and tell us of the work, directly it was done. What did Lombardo then? Did he show it to any one for an opinion?

BABBALANJA. Yes, to Zenzori; who asked him where he picked up so much trash; to Hanto, who bade him not be cast down, it was pretty good; to Lucree, who desired to know how much he was going to get for it; to Roddi, who offered a suggestion.

MEDIA. And what was that?

BABBALANJA. That he had best make a fagot of the whole, and try again.

ABRAZZA. Very encouraging.

MEDIA. Any one else?

BABBALANJA. To Pollo; who, conscious his opinon was sought, was thereby puffed up, and marking the faltering of Lombardo's voice, when the manuscript was handed him, straightway concluded that the man who stood thus trembling at the bar must needs be inferior to the judge. But his verdict was mild. After sitting up all night over the work, and diligently taking notes: "Lombardo, my friend! here, take your sheets. I have run through them loosely. You might have done better; but then you might have done worse. Take them, my friend; I have put in some good things for you."

MEDIA. And who was Pollo?

BABBALANJA. Probably some one who lived in Lombardo's time, and went by that name. He is incidentally mentioned and cursorily immortalized in one of the posthumous notes to the Koztanza.

MEDIA. What is said of him there?

BABBALANJA. Not much. In a very old transcript of the work—that of Aldina—the note alludes to a brave line in the text, and runs thus: "Diverting to tell, it was this passage that an old prosodist, one Pollo, claimed for his own. He maintained he made a free-will offering of it to Lombardo. Several things are yet extant of this Pollo, who died some weeks ago. He seems to have been one of those who would do great things if they could, but are content to compass the small. He imagined that the precedence of authors he had established in his library was their Mardi order of merit. He condemned the sublime poems of Vavona to his lowermost shelf. 'Ah,' thought he, 'how we library princes lord it over those beggarly authors!' Well-read in the history of their woes, Pollo pitied them all, particularly the famous, and wrote little essays of his own, which he read to himself."

MEDIA. Well, and what said Lombardo to those good friends of his—Zenzori, Hanto, and Roddi?

BABBALANJA. Nothing. Taking home his manuscript, he glanced it over, making three corrections.

ABRAZZA. And what then?

BABBALANJA. Then, your highness, he thought to try a conclave of professional critics, saying to himself, "Let them privately point out to me, now, all my blemishes, so that, what time they come to review me in public, all will be well." But curious to relate, those professional critics, for the most part, held their peace concerning a work yet unpublished; and, with some generous exceptions, in their vague, learned way, betrayed such base, beggarly notions of authorship that Lombardo could have wept, had tears been his. But in his very grief, he ground his teeth. Muttered he, "They are fools. In their eyes, bindings not brains make books. They criticize my tattered cloak, not my soul, caparisoned like a charger. He is the great author, think they, who drives the best bargain with his wares; and no bargainer am I. Because he is old, they worship some mediocrity of an ancient, and mock at the living prophet with the live coal on his lips. They are men who would not be men, had they no books. Their sires begat them not, but the authors they have read. Feelings they have none: and their opinions they borrow. They cannot say yea, nor nay, without first consulting all Mardi as an encyclopedia. And all the learning in them is as a dead corpse in a coffin. Were they worthy the dignity of being damned, I would damn them; but they are not. Critics? —Asses! rather mules!—so emasculated, from vanity, they cannot father a true thought. Like mules, too, from dunghills, they trample down gardens of roses: and deem that crushed fragrance their own. Oh! that all round the domains of genius should lie thus unhedged, for such cattle to uproot! Oh! that an eagle should be stabbed by a goose-quill! But at best, the greatest reviewers but prey on my leavings. For I am critic and creator; and, as critic, in cruelty surpass all critics merely as a tiger, jackals. For ere Mardi sees aught of mine, I scrutinize it myself, remorseless as a surgeon. I cut right and left; I probe, tear, and wrench; kill, burn, and destroy; and what's left after that, the jackals are welcome to. It is *I* that stab false thoughts, ere hatched; *I* that pull down wall and tower, rejecting materials which would make palaces for others. Oh! could Mardi but see how we work, it would marvel more at our primal chaos than at the round world thence emerging.

It would marvel at our scaffoldings, scaling heaven; marvel at the hills of earth, banked all round our fabrics ere completed.—How plain the pyramid! In this grand silence, so intense, pierced by that pointed mass, could ten thousand slaves have ever toiled? ten thousand hammers rung? There it stands, part of Mardi, claiming kin with mountains—was this thing piecemeal built?—It was. Piecemeal?—atom by atom it was laid. The world is built of mites."

YOOMY (*musing*). It is even so.

ABRAZZA. Lombardo was severe upon the critics; and they as much so upon him—of that, be sure.

BABBALANJA. Your Highness, Lombardo never presumed to criticize true critics, who are more rare than true poets. A great critic is a sultan among satraps; but pretenders are thick as ants, striving to scale a palm, after its aerial sweetness. And they fight among themselves. Essaying to pluck eagles, they themselves are geese, stuck full of quills, of which they rob each other.

ABRAZZA (*to Media*). Oro help the victim that falls in Babbalanja's hands!

MEDIA. Aye, my lord; at times, his every finger is a dagger: every thought a falling tower that whelms! But resume, philosopher—what of Lombardo now?

BABBALANJA. "For this thing," said he, "I have agonized over it enough. I can wait no more. It has faults—all mine; its merits all its own; but I can toil no longer. The beings knit to me implore; my heart is full; my brain is sick. Let it go—let it go—and Oro with it. Somewhere Mardi has a mighty heart—*that* struck, all the isles shall resound!"

ABRAZZA. Poor devil! he took the world too hard.

MEDIA. As most of these mortals do, my lord. That's the load, self-imposed, under which Babbalanja reels. But now, philosopher, ere Mardi saw it, what thought

Lombardo of his work, looking at it objectively, as a thing out of him, I mean?

ABRAZZA. No doubt, he hugged it.

BABBALANJA. Hard to answer. Sometimes, when by himself, he thought hugely of it, as my lord Abrazza says; but when abroad, among men, he almost despised it; but when he bethought him of those parts, written with full eyes, half blinded; temples throbbing; and pain at the heart—

ABRAZZA. Pooh! pooh!

BABBALANJA. He would say to himself, "Sure, it cannot be in vain!" Yet again, when he bethought him of the hurry and bustle of Mardi, dejection stole over him. "Who will heed it," thought he. "What care these fops and brawlers for me? But am I not myself an egregious coxcomb? Who will read me? Say one thousand pages —twenty-five lines each—each line ten words—every word ten letters. That's two million five hundred thousand *a's*, and *i's*, and *o's* to read! How many are superfluous? Am I not mad to saddle Mardi with such a task? Of all men, am I the wisest, to stand upon a pedestal, and teach the mob? Ah, my own Koztanza! child of many prayers! in whose earnest eyes, so fathomless, I see my own, and recall all past delights and silent agonies— thou may'st prove, as the child of some fond dotard: beauteous to me; hideous to Mardi! And methinks, that while so much slaving merits that thou should'st not die, it has not been intense, prolonged enough, for the high meed of immortality. Yet, things immortal have been written; and by men like me—men, who slept and waked, and ate, and talked with tongues like mine. Ah, Oro, how may we know or not, we are what we would be? Hath genius any stamp and imprint, obvious to possessors? Has it eyes to see itself, or is it blind? Or do we delude ourselves with being gods, and end in grubs?

Genius, genius?—a thousand years hence, to be a household word?—I?—Lombardo? but yesterday cut in the
marketplace by a spangled fool!—Lombardo immortal?
—Ha, ha, Lombardo! but thou art an ass, with vast ears
brushing the tops of palms! Ha, ha, ha! Methinks I see
thee immortal! 'Thus great Lombardo saith; and thus;
and thus; and thus:—thus saith he—illustrious Lombardo!—Lombardo, our great countryman! Lombardo,
prince of poets—Lombardo! great Lombardo!'—Ha, ha,
ha! go, go! dig thy grave, and bury thyself!"

ABRAZZA. He was very funny, then, at times.

BABBALANJA. Very funny, your highness—amazing
jolly! And from my nethermost soul, would to Oro thou
could'st but feel one touch of that jolly woe! It would
appall thee, my right worshipful lord Abrazza!

ABRAZZA (*to Media*). My dear lord, his teeth are
marvelously white and sharp; some sea-shark must have
been his dam: does he often grin thus? It was infernal!

MEDIA. Ah! that's Azzageddi. But, prithee, Babbalanja, proceed.

BABBALANJA. Your highness, even in his calmer critic
moods, Lombardo was far from fancying his work. He
confesses that it ever seemed to him but a poor scrawled
copy of something within, which, do what he would,
he could not completely transfer. "My canvas was
small," said he; "crowded out were hosts of things that
came last. But Fate is in it." And Fate it was, too, your
highness, which forced Lombardo, ere his work was
well done, to take it off his easel and send it to be
multiplied, "Oh, that I was not thus spurred!" cried he;
"but like many another, in its very childhood, this poor
child of mine must go out into Mardi, and get bread for
its sire."

ABRAZZA (*with a sigh*). Alas, the poor devil! But methinks 'twas wondrous arrogant in him to talk to all Mardi at that lofty rate. Did he think himself a god?

BABBALANJA. He himself best knew what he thought; but, like all others, he was created by Oro to some special end; doubtless partly answered in his Koztanza.

MEDIA. And now that Lombardo is long dead and gone—and his work, hooted during life, lives after him —what think the present company of it? Speak, my lord Abrazza! Babbalanja! Mohi! Yoomy!

ABRAZZA (*tapping his sandal with his scepter*). I never read it.

BABBALANJA (*looking upward*). It was written with a divine intent.

MOHI (*stroking his beard*). I never hugged it in a corner and ignored it before Mardi.

YOOMY (*musing*). It has bettered my heart.

MEDIA (*rising*). And I have read it through nine times.

BABBALANJA (*starting up*). Ah, Lombardo! this must make thy ghost glad!

(Chapter CLXXX)

◇◇◇

Prepared though he may have been for "an utter wreck," Melville experienced a natural excitement in awaiting *Mardi's* reception by critics and readers. Would its ideas reach and touch people? Would he be freed for more *Mardis?* Would the pains of the past two years' work be repaid in any currency of money or fame?

The lull before publication was filled with another waiting: Elizabeth was expecting their first child, and Melville had brought her back to her Boston for the birth. It was a season of new experience: he heard Emerson lecture; he bought an edition of Shakespeare printed in a type endurable "to my eyes which are tender as young sparrows." Even the news that his friend Charles Fenno Hoffman had committed himself to a hospital for the insane could not dim his exultation. The "uttermost" of *Mardi* was done. His first child, a promising boy, Malcolm, was born on February 16, 1849. Oro was generous.

◈◈◈

To Evert Duyckinck

Mount Vernon Street [Boston]
Saturday, 3ᵈ [March 1849]

Nay, I do not oscillate in Emerson's rainbow, but prefer rather to hang myself in mine own halter than swing in any other man's swing. Yet I think Emerson is more than a brilliant fellow. Be his stuff begged, borrowed, or stolen, or of his own domestic manufacture he is an uncommon man. Swear he is a humbug—then is he no common humbug. Lay it down that had not Sir Thomas Browne lived, Emerson would not have mystified—I will answer that had not Old Zack's father begot him, Old Zack would never have been the hero of Palo Alto. The truth is that we are all sons, grandsons, or nephews or great-nephews of those who go before us. No one is his own sire.——I was very agreeably disappointed in Mʳ Emerson. I had heard of him as full of transcendentalisms, myths & oracular gibberish; I had only glanced at a book of his once in Putnam's store—that was all I knew of him, till I heard him lecture.—To my surprise, I found him quite intelligible, tho' to say truth, they told me that that night he was unusually plain.——Now, there is a something about every man elevated above mediocrity, which is, for the most part, instinctively perceptible. This I see in Mʳ Emerson. And, frankly, for the sake of the argument, let us call him a fool;—then had I rather be a fool than a wise man.—I love all men who *dive*. Any fish can swim near the surface, but it takes a great whale to go down stairs five miles or more; & if he don't attain the bottom, why, all the lead in Galena can't fashion the plummet that will. I'm not talking of Mr Emerson now—but of the whole corps of thought-divers, that have been diving & coming up again with bloodshot eyes since the world began.

I could readily see in Emerson, notwithstanding his merit, a gaping flaw. It was the insinuation, that had he lived in those days when the world was made, he might have offered some valuable suggestions. These men are all cracked right across the brow. And never will the pullers-down be able to cope with the builders-up. And this pulling down is easy enough—a keg of powder blew up Block's Monument—but the man who applied the match, could not, alone, build such a pile to save his soul from the shark-maw of the Devil. But enough of this Plato who talks thro' his nose. To one of your habits of thought, I confess that in my last, I seemed, but only *seemed* irreverent. And do not think, my boy, that because I, impulsively broke forth in jubillations over Shakspeare, that, therefore, I am of the number of the *snobs* who burn their tuns of rancid fat at his shrine. No, I would stand afar off & alone, & burn some pure Palm oil, the product of some overtopping trunk.——I would to God Shakspeare had lived later, & promenaded in Broadway. Not that I might have had the pleasure of leaving my card for him at the Astor, or made merry with him over a bowl of the fine Duyckinck punch; but that the muzzle which all men wore on their souls in the Elizabethan day, might not have intercepted Shakspeare from articulation. Now I hold it a verity, that even Shakspeare, was not a frank man to the uttermost. And, indeed, who in this intolerant universe is, or can be? But the Declaration of Independence makes a difference.———There, I have driven my horse so hard that I have made my inn before sundown. I was going to say something more———It was this.——You complain that Emerson tho' a denizen of the land of gingerbread, is above munching a plain cake in company of jolly fellows, & swiging off his ale like you & me. Ah, my dear sir, that's his misfortune, not his fault. His belly, sir, is in his chest, & his brains descend down into his neck, & offer an obstacle to a draught of ale or a mouthful of cake. But here I am. Good bye—

                                                    H.M.

                                    Boston April 5th 1849

Dear Duyckinck—

Thank you for your note, & the paper which came duly to hand. By the way, that "Smoking Spiritualized" is not bad. Doubtless it has improved by age. The quaint old lines lie in coils like a sailor's pigtail in its keg.

———Ah this sovereign virtue of age—how can we living men attain unto it. We may spice up our dishes with all the condiments of the Spice Islands & Moluccas, & our dishes may be all venison & wild boar——yet how the deuce can we make them a century or two old? ———My dear Sir, the two great things yet to be discovered are these—The Art of rejuvenating old age in men, & oldageifying youth in books.——Who in the name of the trunk-makers would think of reading *Old Burton* were his book published for the first today? ———All ambitious authors should have ghosts capable of revisiting the world to snuff up the steam of adulation, which begins to rise straightway as the Sexton throws his last shovelfull on him.——Down goes his body & up flies his name.

Poor Hoffman—I remember the shock I had when I

first saw the mention of his madness.—But he was just
the man to go mad—imaginative, voluptuously inclined,
poor, unemployed, in the race of life distanced by his in-
feriors, unmarried—without a port or haven in the universe to make. His present misfortune—rather blessing
—is but the sequel to a long experience of unwhole
habits of thought.——This going mad of a friend or
acquaintance comes straight home to every man who
feels his soul in him,—which but few men do. For in
all of us lodges the same fuel to light the same fire. And
he who has never felt, momentarily, what madness
is has but a mouthful of brains. What sort of sensation
permanent madness is may be very well imagined—
just as we imagine how we felt when we were infants,
tho' we can not recall it. In both conditions we are
irresponsible & riot like gods without fear of fate.—It
is the climax of a mad night of revelry when the blood
has been transmuted into brandy.——But if we prate
much of this thing we shall be illustrating our own
proposition.——

I am glad you like that affair of mine [*Mardi*]. But
it seems so long now since I wrote it, & my mood has
so changed, that I dread to look into it, & have purposely abstained from so doing since I thanked God
it was off my hands.——Would that a man could do
something & then say—It is finished—not that one thing
only, but all others—that he has reached his uttermost,
& can never exceed it. But live & push—tho' we put one
leg forward ten miles—its no reason the other must lag
behind—no, *that* must again distance the other—& so
we go till we get the cramp & die.——I bought a set
of Bayle's Dictionary the other day, & on my return
to New York intend to lay the great old folios side by
side & go to sleep on them thro' the summer, with the
Phaedon in one hand & Tom Brown in the other—

Good bye I'm called.—I shall be in New York next week—early part.

H. Melville

❖❖❖

Melville claimed to take the attacks on *Mardi,* here and in England, as "matters of course," and derived some bolstering comfort from the thought "that there are goodly harvests which ripen late, especially when the grain is remarkably strong." There was, fortunately, no opportunity to succumb to his resentment—the lost time on *Mardi* and its unrealized fortunes had to be recouped in a hurry. Returning to his own past as base, he wrote what he always considered a pot-boiler—the experiences of a young American's trip to Liverpool as a deck-hand—and followed it, in such a rush that it is hard to figure out how all its words were actually written in so few weeks, with *White-Jacket,* Melville's "World in a Man-of-War," an allegory more subtle and successful than its parent *Mardi.* That harvest was ripening.

When Melville offered the unfinished *Redburn* to Bentley, the author's belief in unhappy *Mardi* had also to be maintained.

❖❖❖

To Richard Bentley

New York
June 5th 1849

Dear Sir—

The critics on your side of the water seem to have fired quite a broadside into "Mardi;" but it was not altogether unexpected. In fact the book is of a nature to attract compliments of that sort from some quarters; and as you may be aware yourself, it is judged only as a work meant to entertain. And I can not but think that its having been brought out in England in the ordinary novel form must have led to the disappointment of many readers, who would have been better pleased with it, perhaps, had they taken it up in the first place for what it really is.——Besides, the peculiar thoughts & fancies of a Yankee upon politics & other matters could hardly be presumed to delight that class of gentlemen who conduct your leading journals; while the metaphysical ingredients (for want of a better term) of the book, must of course repel some of those who read simply for amusement.——However, it will reach those for whom it is intended; and I have already received assurances that "Mardi," in its larger purposes, has not been written in vain.

You may think, in your own mind that a man is unwise,——indiscreet, to write a work of that kind, when he might have written one perhaps, calculated merely to please the general reader, not provoke attack, however masqued in an affectation of indifference or contempt. But some of us scribblers, my Dear Sir, always have a certain something unmanageable in us, that bids us to do this or that, and be done it must——hit or miss.

I have now in preparation a thing of a widely different cast from "Mardi":——a plain, straightforward, amusing narrative of personal experience—the son of a gentleman on his first voyage to sea as a sailor—no metaphysics, no conic-sections, nothing but cakes & ale. I have shifted my ground from the South Seas to a different quarter of the globe—nearer home—and what I write I have almost wholly picked up by my own observations under comical circumstances. In size the book will be perhaps a fraction smaller than "Typee"; will be printed here by the Harpers, & ready for them two or three months hence, or before. I value the English copyright at one hundred & fifty pounds, and think it would be wise to put it forth in a manner, admitting of a popular circulation.

Write me if you please at your earliest leisure; and as you have not yet sent me any copies of your edition of "Mardi"—(which of course I impute to the fact of the prodigious demand for the book with you)—I will thank you to forward me three copies. . . .

◇◇◇

The piracies of English books by American publishers and the increasingly severe copyright decisions rendered by English courts had created a delicate situation for every American book that sought English publication. Within weeks after Bentley's issuance of *Redburn,* English readers were offered a cheap piracy printed in Paris.

Melville believed that Bentley's hesitation in taking *White-Jacket* might be overcome by personal negotiation, but this was only the excuse, not the purpose, of his plans for a trip to England and the Continent. His ideas needed freshening and he looked forward to strange surroundings and new people. London was a natural focus for the trip, for he had in mind the enlargement of a narrative he had found—of the wanderings and misfortunes of Israel Potter, a soldier of the Revolution stranded in England. Potter had served on a whaler, too, and Melville was eager to make more use of his whaling years than had been necessary in *Mardi.*

◇◇◇

To Lemuel Shaw

New York. Oct. 6, 1849

My Dear Sir—

On Monday or Tuesday next the ship is to sail, and I must bid you the last good-bye. . . .

Lizzie is becoming more reconciled to the idea of

my departure, especially as she will have Malcolm for company during my absence. And I have no doubt, that when she finds herself surrounded by her old friends in Boston, she will bear the temporary separation with more philosophy than she has anticipated. At any rate, she will be ministered to by the best of friends.

It is uncertain, now, how long I may be absent; and, of course, my travels will have to be bounded by my purse & by prudential considerations. Economy, however, is my mottoe.

"Redburn" was published in London on the 25th of last month; & will come out here in the course of two weeks or so. The other book [*White-Jacket*] I have now in plate-proofs, all ready to go into my trunk.

For Redburn I anticipate no particular reception of any kind. It may be deemed a book of tolerable entertainment;—& may be accounted dull.—As for the other book, it will be sure to be attacked in some quarters. But no reputation that is gratifying to me, can possibly be achieved by either of these books. They are two *jobs,* which I have done for money—being forced to it, as other men are to sawing wood. And while I have felt obliged to refrain from writing the kind of book I would wish to; yet, in writing these two books, I have not repressed myself much—so far as *they* are concerned; but have spoken pretty much as I feel. —Being books, then, written in this way, my only desire for their "success" (as it is called) springs from my pocket, & not from my heart. So far as I am individually concerned, & independent of my pocket, it is my earnest desire to write those sort of books which are said to "fail"—pardon this egotism.

From Journal of a Voyage
from New York to London, 1849

Thursday Oct 11ᵗʰ

AFTER a detention of three or four days, owing to wind & weather, with the rest of the passengers I went on board the tug-boat Goliath about 12½ P.M. during a cold violent storm from the West. The "Southhampton" (a regular London liner) lay in the North river. We transferred ouselves aboard with some confusion, hove up our anchor, & were off. Our pilot, a large, beefy looking fellow resembled an oyster-man more than a sailor. We got outside the "Narrows" about 2 O'clock; shortly after, the "tug" left us & the Pilot. At half past 5. P.M. saw the last of the land, with our yards square, & in half a gale. As the ship dashed on, under double-reefed topsails, I walked the deck, thinking of what they might be doing at home, & of the last familiar faces I saw on the wharf—Allan was there, & George Duyckinck, and a Mʳ MᶜCurdy, a rich merchant of New York, who had seemed somewhat interested in the prospect of his son (a sickly youth of twenty bound for the grand tour) being my roommate. But to my great delight, the promise that the Captain had given me at an early day, he now made good; & I find myself in the undivided occupancy of a large state-room. It is as big almost as my own room at home; it has a spacious birth, a large wash-stand, a sofa, glass &c &c. I am the only person on board who is thus honored with a room to himself. I have plenty of light, & a little thick glass window in the side, which in fine weather I may open to the air. I have looked out upon the sea from it, often, tho not yet 24 hours on board.

Friday Oct 12th

Walked the deck last night till almost eight o'clock; then made up a whist party & played—till one of the number had to visit his room from sickness. Retired early & had a sound sleep. Was up betimes, & aloft, to recall the old emotions of being at the mast-head. Found that the ocean looked the same as ever. Have tried to read, but found it hard work. However, there are some very pleasant passengers on board, with whom to converse. Chief among these is a Mr Adler, a German scholar, to whom Duyckinck introduced me. He is author of a formidable lexicon, (German & English); in compiling which he almost ruined his health. He was almost crazy, he tells me, for a time. He is full of the German metaphysics, & discourses of Kant, Swedenborg &c. He has been my principal companion thus far. There is also a Mr Taylor among the passengers, cousin to James Bayard Taylor the pedestrian traveller. He is full of fun—or rather *was* full of it.—Just at this moment I hear his mysterious noises from the state-room next to mine. Poor fellow! he is sea-sick. As yet there have been but few thus troubled, owing to pleasant weather. There is a Scotch artist on board, a painter, with a most unpoetical looking only child, a young-one all cheecks & forehead, the former preponderating. Young McCurdy I find to be a lisping youth of genteel capacity, but quite disposed to be sociable. We have several Frenchmen & Englishmen. One of the latter has been hunting, & carries over with him two glorious pairs of antlers (moose) as trophies of his prowess in the woods of Maine. We have also, a middle-aged English woman, who sturdily walks the deck, & prides herself upon her sea-legs, & being an old tar.

Saturday Oct 13

Last evening was very pleasant. Walked the deck with the German, Mr Adler till a late hour, talking of "Fixed Fate, Free-will, fore-knowledge absolute" &c. His philosophy is *Colredgian:* he accepts the Scriptures as divine, & yet leaves himself free to inquire into Nature. He does not take it, that the Bible is absolutely infallible, & that anything opposed to it in Science must be wrong. He believes that there are things *out* of God and independent of him,—things that would have existed were there no God:—such as that two & two make four; for it is not that God so decrees mathematically, but that in the very nature of things, the fact is Thus.

———Rose early this morning, opened my bulls eye window, & looked out to the East. The sun was just rising, the horizon was red;—a familiar sight to me, reminding me of old times. Before breakfast went up to the mast-head, by way of gymnastics. About 10 o'clock A.M. the wind rose, the rain fell, & the deck looked dismally enough. By dinner time, it blew half a gale, & the passengers mostly retired to their rooms, sea sick. After dinner, the rain ceased, yet it still blew stiffly, & we were slowly forging along under close-reefed topsails—mainsail furled. I was walking the deck, when I perceived one of the steerage passengers looking over the side; I looked too, & saw a man in the water, his head completely lifted above the water,—about twelve feet from the ship, right abreast the gangway. For an instant, I thought I was dreaming; for no one seemed to see what I did. Next moment, I shouted

"Man overboard!" & turned to go aft. The Captain
ran forward, greatly confused. I dropped overboard the
tackle-fall of the quarter-boat, & swung it towards the
man, who was now drifting close to the ship. He did
not get hold of it, & I got over the side, within a foot
or two of the sea, & again swung the rope towards him.
He now got hold of it. By this time, a crowd of people
—sailors & others—were clustering about the bulwarks;
but none seemed very anxious to save him. They warned
me however, not to fall overboard. After holding on to
the rope, about a quarter of a minute the man let go
of it, & drifted astern under the mizzen chains. Four or
five of the seamen jumped over into the chains & swung
him more ropes. But his conduct was unaccountable; he
could have saved himself, had he been so minded. I
was struck by the expression of his face in the water.
It was merry. At last he drifted off under the ship's
counter, & all hands cried "He's gone!" Running to the
taffrail, we saw him again, floating off—saw a few
bubbles, & never saw him again. No boat was lowered,
no sail was shortened, hardly any noise was made. The
man drowned like a bullock. It afterwards turned out,
that he was crazy, & had jumped overboard. He had
declared he would do so several times; & just before he
did jump, he had tried to get possession of his child,
in order to jump into the sea, with the child in his arms.
His wife was miserably sick in her berth. The Captain
said that this was the fourth or fifth instance he had
known of people jumping overboard. He told a story
of a man who did so, with his wife on deck at the time.
As they were trying to save him, the wife said it was
no use; & when he was drowned, she said "there were
plenty more men to be had." Amiable creature!—By
night, it blew a terrific gale, & we hove to. Miserable
time! nearly every one sick, & the ship rolling & pitching

in an amazing manner. About midnight, I rose & went on deck. It was blowing horribly—pitch dark, & raining. The Captain was in the cuddy & directed my attention "to those fellows" as he called them,—meaning several "Corposant balls" on the yard arms & mast heads. They were the first I had ever seen, & resembled large, dim stars in the sky.

Sunday Oct 14

A regular blue devil day. A gale of wind, & every one sick. Saloons deserted, & all sorts of nausea noise heard from the state-rooms. Taylor, McCurdy, & Adler all in their berths—& I alone am left to tell the tale of their misery. Read a little in Miss Kirkland's European tour. Like it. She is a spirited, sensible, fine woman. Managed to get thro' the day somehow, by reading & walking the deck, tho' the last was almost as much as my neck was worth. I forgot to say that shortly after the loss of the crazy man (a Dutchman by the way) some of the steerage passengers came aft & told the Captain that there was another crazy man, an Englishman in the steerage. This morning, coming on deck, I saw a man leaning against the bulwarks, whom I immediately took for a steerage passenger. He stopped me, & told me to look off & *see the steamers*. So I looked for about five minutes,—straining my eyes very hard, but saw nothing. —I asked the 2^d Mate whether *he* could see the steamers; when he told me that my informant was the crazy Englishman. All the morning this poor fellow was on deck, crying out at steamers, boats, &c. &c. I thought that his mad feelings found something congenial in the riot of the raging sea. In the evening, he forced his way into the dining saloon, & struck the Steward, who knocked him down, & dragged him forward. We

have made no progress for the last 36 hours; wind
ahead, from the Eastward. The crazy man turns out
to be afflicted with delirium tremens, consequent upon
keeping drunk for the last two months. He is very
earnest in his enquiries after a certain Dr Dobbs. Saw
a lady with a copy of "Omoo" in her hand two days
ago. Now & then she would look up at me, as if comparing notes. She turns out to be the wife of a young
Scotchman, an artist, going out to Scotland to sketch
scenes for his patrons in Albany, including Dr Armsby.
He introduced himself to me by mentioning the name
of Mr Twitchell who painted my portrait gratis. He
is a very unpretending young man, & looks more like
a sailor than an artist. But appearances are &c. . . .

Thursday Nov 1st

Just three weeks from home, and made the land—
Start Point—about 3 P.M.—well up channel—passed the
Lizzard. Very fine day—great number of ships in sight.
Thro' these waters Blake's & Nelson's ships once sailed.
Taylor suggested that he & I should return McCurdy's
civilities. We did, and Captain Griswold joined and ordered a pitcher of his own. The Captain is a very intelligent & gentlemanly man—converses well & understands
himself. I never was more deceived in a person than I
was in him. Retired about midnight. Taylor played
a rare joke upon McCurdy this evening, passing himself off as Miss Wilbur, having borrowed her cloak &c.
They walked together. Shall see Portsmouth tomorrow
morning.

Friday Nov 2^d

Wind from the East—ahead. Clear & beautiful day
—but every one greivously disappointed. I think I

shall get off at Portsmouth, instead of going round. May be in to night, after all. Spoke a Portsmouth Pilot boat, but took no pilot. Made the Bill of Portland—from which the Portland stone is got. Melancholy looking voyage, White cliffs indeed! In the evening played chess, & talked metaphysics [with] my learned friend till midnight.

Saturday Nov 3d

Woke about 6 o'clock with an insane idea that we were going before the wind, & would be in Portsmouth in an hour's time. Soon found out my mistake. About eight o'clock took a pilot, who brought some papers two weeks old. Made the Isle of Wight about 10 A.M. High land—the Needles. Wind ahead &, tacking. Get in to night or to morrow—or next week or year. Devilish dull, & too bad altogether X X X X Continued tacking all day with a light wind from West. Isle of Wight in sight all day & numerous ships. One of our steerage passengers left in the Pilot Boat. Rum scene alongside with the boat. In the evening all hands in high spirits—Played chess in the ladies' saloon—another party at cards; good deal of singing in the gentlemen's cabin & drinking—very hilarious & noisy —Last night every one thought. Determined to go ashore at Portsmouth. Therefore prepared for it—arranged my trunk to be left behind—put up a shirt or two in Adler's carpet bag & retired pretty early.

Sunday Nov 4

Looked out of my window, first thing upon rising & saw the Isle of Wight again—very near—ploughed feilds &c. Light head wind—expected to be in a little after breakfast time. About 10 A.M. rounded the Eastern

end of the Isle, when it fell flat calm. The town in sight
by telescope. Were becalmed about three or four hours.
Foggy, drizzly; long faces at dinner—no porter bottles.
Wind came from the West at last. Squared the yards &
struck away for Dover—distant 60 miles. At 6 o'clock
(evening) passed Dungeness—then saw the Beachy
Head light. Close reefed the topsails so as not to run
too fast. Expect now to go ashore tomorrow morning
early at Dover—& get to London via Canterbury Cathedral. Mysterious hint dropped me about my green coat.
Talked with the Pilot about the perils of the Channel.
He told a story of running down a brig in a steamer &c.
—It is now eight o'clock in the evening. I am alone in
my state-room—lamp in tumbler. Spite of past disap-
pointments I *feel* that this is my last night aboard the
Southampton. This time tomorrow I shall be on land, &
press English earth after the lapse of ten years—*then*
a sailor, *now* H.M. author of "Peedee" "Hullabaloo" &
"Pog-Dog."—For the last time I lay aside my "log" to
add a line or two to Lizzie's letter—the last I shall write
aboard. ("Where dat old man?"—"Where books?")

❖❖❖

It was at Deal ("a person called Julius Caesar jumped ashore
about in this place, & took possession") that Melville was
beached with Adler and Taylor, and the London adventure
was begun. Homesickness and the copyright crisis were the
only flies in England's ointment. Returning to London from
an economical excursion to the Continent, Melville learned
that no satisfactory offer had been made for *White-Jacket*.
This meant the involuntary end of his tour and when he
wrote friends on December 14, his letters were full of complaint.

❖❖❖

To Nathaniel Parker Willis

[London, 14 December 1849]

. . . I very much doubt whether Gabriel enters the portals of Heaven without a fee to Peter the porter—so impossible is it to travel without money. Some people (999 in 1000) are very unaccountably shy about confessing to a want of money, as the reason why they do not do this or that; but, for my part, I think it such a capital clincher of a reason for not doing a thing, that I out with it, at once—for, who can gainsay it? And, what more satisfactory or unanswerable reason can a body give, I should like to know? Besides—tho' there are numbers of fine fellows, and hearts of blood, in the world, whom Providence hath blessed with purses furlongs in length—yet the class of wealthy people are, in the aggregate, such a mob of gilded dunces, that, not to be wealthy carries with it a certain distinction and nobility.

◇◇◇

Two days later Bentley accepted his terms for *White-Jacket*, and, though Melville's decision wavered a little, thoughts of Elizabeth and Malcolm brought him back. Before sailing, much of Bentley's payment was eaten into by the purchase of long-wanted books, and these, along with copies of the handsome Bentley editions of his own books, took up most of his luggage space in the *Independence*.

After his arrival in New York on February 1, 1850, one of his earliest gestures was to present the English copies to his relatives and friends. One *Mardi* went to Allan, to whom it was dedicated, and another copy of the three-volume edition was given to Duyckinck, with an explanation.

◇◇◇

To Evert Duyckinck

Saturday Evening, Feb 2ᵈ [1850]

My Dear Duyckinck—

Tho' somewhat unusual for a donor, I must beg to apologize for making you the accompanying present of "Mardi." But no one who knows your library can doubt, that such a choice conservatory of exotics & other rare things in literature, after being long enjoyed by yourself, must, to a late posterity, be preserved intact by your descendants. How natural then—tho' vain—in your friend to desire a place in it for a plant, which tho' now unblown (emblematically, the leaves, you perceive, are uncut) may possibly—by some miracle, that is— flower like the aloe, a hundred years hence—or not flower at all, which is more likely by far, for some aloes never flower.

Again: (as the divines say) political republics should be the asylum for the persecuted of all nations; so if Mardi be admitted to your shelves, your bibliographical Republic of Letters may find some contentment in the thought, that it has afforded refuge to a work, which almost everywhere else has been driven forth like a wild, mystic Mormon into shelterless exile.

——The leaves, I repeat, are uncut—let them remain so—and let me supplementaryly hint, that a bit of old parchment (from some old Arabic m.s.s. on Astrology) tied round each volume, & sealed on the back with a Sphynx, & never to be broken till the aloe flowers— would not be an unsuitable device for the bookbinder of "Mardi."—That book is a sort of dose, if you please— (tho', in the present case, charitably administered in three parts, instead of two) and by way of killing the flavor of it, I hurry to follow it up with a fine old spicy duodecimo mouthful in the shape of "Hudibras" which I got particularly for yourself at Stribbs's in the Strand. . . .

❖❖❖

White-Jacket's appearance was greeted by critics as a total atonement for the sins of *Mardi*, and was hailed with equal warmth by the legislators who needed support in their efforts to abolish flogging in the United States Navy.

Its author was hard at work on another book: Israel Potter had been laid aside, and whaling was Melville's whole subject now.

❖❖❖

To Richard Henry Dana, Jr.

New York May 1st 1850

My Dear Dana—I thank you very heartily for your friendly letter; and am more pleased than I can well tell, to think that any thing I have written about the sea has at all responded to your own impressions of it. Were I inclined to undue vanity, this one fact would be far more to me than acres & square miles of the superficial shallow praise of the publishing critics. And I am specially delighted at the thought, that those strange, congenial feelings, with which after my first voyage, I for the first time read "Two Years Before the Mast," and while so engaged was, as it were, tied & welded to you by a sort of Siamese link of affectionate sympathy—that these feelings should be reciprocated by you, in your turn, and be called out by any White Jackets or Redburns of mine—this is indeed delightful to me. In fact, My Dear Dana, did I not write these books of mine almost entirely for "lucre"—by the job, as a wood sawyer saws wood—I almost think, I should hereafter—in the case of a sea book—get my M.S.S. neatly & legibly copied by a scrivener—send you that one copy—& deem such a procedure the best publication.

You ask me about "the jacket." I answer it was a veritable garment—which I suppose is now somewhere at the bottom of Charles river. I was a great fool, or I should have brought such a remarkable fabric (as it really was, to behold) home with me. Will you excuse me from telling you—or rather from putting on pen-&-ink record over my name, the real names of the individuals who officered the frigate. I am very loath to do so, because I have never indulged in any ill-will or disrespect for them, personally; & shrink from any thing that approaches to a personal identification of them with characters that were only intended to furnish samples of a tribe—characters, also, which possess some not wholly complimentary traits. If you think it worth knowing,—I will tell you all, when I next have the pleasure of seeing you face to face.

Let me mention to you now my adventure with the letter you furnished me to Mr Moxon. Upon this, as upon some other similar occasions, I chose to waive cerimony; and so arranged it, that I saw Mr Moxon, immediately after his reception of the letter.—I was ushered into one of those jealous, guarded sanctums, in which those London publishers retreat from the vulgar gaze. It was a small, dim, religious looking room—a very chapel to enter. Upon the coldest day you would have taken off your hat in that room, tho' there were no fire, no occupant, & you a Quaker.—You have heard, I dare say, of that Greenland whaler discovered near the Pole, adrift & silent in a calm, with the frozen form of a man seated at a desk in the cabin before an ink-stand of

icy ink. Just so sat Mr Moxon in that tranced cabin of
his. I bowed to the spectre, & received such a galvanic
return, that I thought something of running out for
some officer of the Humane Society, & getting a supply
of hot water & blankets to resuscitate this melancholy
corpse. But knowing the nature of these foggy English,
& that they are not altogether impenetrable, I began a
sociable talk, and happening to make mention of Charles
Lamb, and alluding to the warmth of feeling with which
that charming punster is regarded in America, M^r
Moxon lighted up—grew cordial—hearty;—& going
into the heart of the matter—told me that he (Lamb)
was the best fellow in the world to "get drunk with" (I
use his own words) & that he had many a time put him
to bed. He concluded by offering to send me a copy of
his works (not Moxon's poetry, but Lambs prose) which
I have by me, now. It so happened, that on the passage
over, I had found a copy of Lamb in the ship's library—
& not having previously read him much, I dived into
him, & was delighted—as every one must be with such a
rare humorist & excellent hearted man. So I was very
sincere with Moxon, being fresh from Lamb. He inquired particularly concerning you—earnestly spoke in
admiration of "Two Years Before the Mast"—& told me
of the particular gratification it had afforded particular
persons of his acquaintance—including Mr Rogers, the
old Nestor, who poetically appreciated the scenic sea
passages, describing ice, storms, Cape Horn, & all that.

About the "whaling voyage"—I am half way in the
work, & am very glad that your suggestion so jumps with
mine. It will be a strange sort of a book, tho', I fear;
blubber is blubber you know; tho' you may get oil out
of it, the poetry runs as hard as sap from a frozen maple
tree;—& to cook the thing up, one must needs throw in

a little fancy, which from the nature of the thing, must be ungainly as the gambols of the whales themselves. Yet I mean to give the truth of the thing, spite of this.

Give my compliments to Mrs Dana, and remember me to your father.

Sincerely Yours

H Melville

❖❖❖

To continue work on his "strange sort of a book," and to protect Malcolm from the summer fevers of the city, Melville transferred his work and family to one of the happiest spots in the memory of his youth—the Melvill homestead outside Pittsfield, Massachusetts. Cousin Robert Melvill rented parts of its spaciousness to summer visitors, and through its windows the New York Melvilles were captured by the Berkshires.

A pleasant break in his work-schedule was provided by the visit of Evert Duyckinck, who, assisted by his fellow New Yorker, Cornelius Mathews, and the sociable couple vacationing nearby, Mr. and Mrs. John Morewood, at once set all the literati of the Berkshire Hills into whirling activity. Melville thus met his fellow writers of neighboring villages, making encounters that chance and convention might have delayed for months. So it is Evert Duyckinck whom we must thank for the meeting of Melville and Hawthorne (recently moved into a cottage between Lenox and Stockbridge) at such a critical moment in Melville's development.

Melville also met Hawthorne's writing that summer, when his Aunt Mary Melvill gave him a copy of *Mosses from an Old Manse,* and it must have been after hearing Melville speak enthusiastically about the man and his work that Duyckinck urged him to write an essay on Hawthorne for *The Literary World.* By the time the editor returned to New York he had the first installment of "Hawthorne and His Mosses" in his pocket.

❖❖❖

Hawthorne and His Mosses

By a Virginian Spending July in Vermont

A PAPERED chamber in a fine old farm-house—a mile from any other dwelling, and dipped to the eaves in foliage—surrounded by mountains, old woods, and Indian ponds—this, surely, is the place to write of Hawthorne. Some charm is in this northern air, for love and duty seem both impelling to the task. A man of a deep and noble nature has seized me in this seclusion. His wild, witch voice rings through me; or, in softer cadences, I seem to hear it in the songs of the hillside birds that sing in the larch trees at my window.

Would that all excellent books were foundlings, without father or mother, that so it might be, we could glorify them, without including their ostensible authors! Nor would any true man take exception to this—least of all, he who writes: "When the Artist rises high enough to achieve the Beautiful, the symbol by which he makes it perceptible to mortal senses becomes of little value in his eyes, while his spirit possesses itself in the enjoyment of the reality."

But more than this. I know not what would be the right name to put on the title page of an excellent book; but this I feel, that the names of all fine authors are fictitious ones, far more so than that of Junius—simply standing, as they do, for the mystical, ever-eluding Spirit of all Beauty, which ubiquitously possesses men of genius. Purely imaginative as this fancy may appear, it nevertheless seems to receive some warranty from the fact that on a personal interview no great author has ever come up to the idea of his reader. But that dust of which our bodies are composed, how can it fitly express the nobler intelligence among us? With reverence be it spoken, that not even in the case of one deemed more than man, not even in our Savior, did his visible frame betoken anything of the augustness of the nature within. Else, how could those Jewish eye-witnesses fail to see heaven in his glance?

It is curious, how a man may travel along a country road, and yet miss the grandest or sweetest of prospects, by reason of an intervening hedge so like all other hedges as in no way to hint of the wide landscape beyond. So has it been with me concerning the enchanting landscape in the soul of this Hawthorne, this most excellent Man of Mosses. His *Old Manse* has been written now four years, but I never read it till a day or two since. I had seen it in the bookstores—heard of it often —even had it recommended to me by a tasteful friend, as a rare, quiet book, perhaps too deserving of popularity to be popular. But there are so many books called "excellent," and so much unpopular merit, that amid the thick stir of other things, the hint of my tasteful friend was disregarded; and for four years the Mosses on the Old Manse never refreshed me with their perennial green. It may be, however, that all this while, the book, like wine, was only improving in flavor and body. At any rate, it so chanced that this long procrastination eventuated in a happy result. At breakfast the other day, a mountain girl, a cousin of mine, who for the last two weeks has every morning helped me to strawberries and raspberries—which, like the roses and pearls in the fairy-tale, seemed to fall into the saucer from those strawberry-beds, her cheeks—this delightful creature, this charming Cherry, says to me—"I see you spend

your mornings in the haymow; and yesterday I found
there Dwight's *Travels in New England.* Now I have
something far better than that—something more congenial to our summer on these hills. Take these raspberries, and then I will give you some moss."—"Moss!"
said I.—"Yes, and you must take it to the barn with
you, and good-by to 'Dwight.' "

With that she left me, and soon returned with a volume, verdantly bound, and garnished with a curious
frontispiece in green—nothing less than a fragment of
real moss cunningly pressed to a flyleaf.—"Why this,"
said I, spilling my raspberries, "this is the *Mosses from
an Old Manse.*" "Yes," said cousin Cherry, "yes, it is
that flowering Hawthorne."—"Hawthorne and Mosses,"
said I, "no more: it is morning: it is July in the country:
and I am off for the barn."

Stretched on that new-mown clover, the hillside
breeze blowing over me through the wide barn door,
and soothed by the hum of the bees in the meadows
around, how magically stole over me this Mossy Man!
And how amply, how bountifully, did he redeem that
delicious promise to his guests in the Old Manse, of
whom it is written: "Others could give them pleasure
and amusement, or instruction—these could be picked
up anywhere—but it was for me to give them rest. Rest,
in a life of trouble! What better could be done for those
weary and world-worn spirits? . . . what better could
be done for anybody, who came within our magic circle,
than to throw the spell of a magic spirit over him?"—
So all that day, half-buried in the new clover, I watched
this Hawthorne's "Assyrian dawn and Paphian sunset
and moonrise, from the summit of our eastern hill."

The soft ravishments of the man spun me round
about in a web of dreams, and when the book was
closed, when the spell was over, this wizard "dismissed

me, with but misty reminiscences, as if I had been dreaming of him."

What a wild moonlight of contemplative humor bathes that Old Manse!—the rich and rare distillment of a spicy and slowly oozing heart. No rollicking rudeness, no gross fun fed on fat dinners, and bred in the lees of wine— but a humor so spiritually gentle, so high, so deep, and yet so richly relishable, that it were hardly inappropriate in an angel. It is the very religion of mirth; for nothing so human but it may be advanced to that. The orchard of the Old Manse seems the visible type of the fine mind that has described it. Those twisted and contorted old trees that "stretch out their crooked branches, and take such hold of the imagination, that we remember them as humorists and odd fellows." And then, as surrounded by these grotesque forms, and hushed in the noon-day repose of this Hawthorne's spell, how aptly might the still fall of his ruddy thoughts into your soul be symbolized by "the thump of a great apple, in the stillest afternoon, falling without a breath of wind, from the mere necessity of perfect ripeness!" For no less ripe than ruddy are the apples of the thoughts and fancies in this sweet Man of Mosses.

"Buds and Bird-Voices"—What a delicious thing is that!—"Will the world ever be so decayed, that spring may not renew its greenness?"—And the "Fire-Worship." Was ever the hearth so glorified into an altar before? The mere title of that piece is better than any common work in fifty folio volumes. How exquisite is this:

Nor did it lessen the charm of his soft, familiar courtesy and helpfulness, that the mighty spirit, were opportunity offered him, would run riot through the peaceful house, wrap its inmates in his terrible embrace, and leave nothing of them save their whitened bones. This possibility of mad destruction only made his domestic kindness the more beautiful and touching. It was so sweet of him, being endowed with such power, to dwell, day after day, and one long, lonesome night after another, on the dusky hearth, only now and then betraying his wild nature, by thrusting his red tongue out of the chimney-top! True, he had done much mischief in the world, and was pretty certain to do more; but his warm heart atoned for all. He was kindly to the race of man. . . .

But he has still other apples, not quite so ruddy, though full as ripe—apples that have been left to wither on the tree, after the pleasant autumn gathering is past. The sketch of "The Old Apple-Dealer" is conceived in the subtlest spirit of sadness; he whose "subdued and nerveless boyhood prefigured his abortive prime, which, likewise, contained within itself the prophecy and image of his lean and torpid age." Such touches as are in this piece cannot proceed from any common heart. They argue such a depth of tenderness, such a boundless sympathy with all forms of being, such an omnipresent love, that we must needs say that this Hawthorne is here almost alone—in his generation at least—in the artistic manifestation of these things. Still more. Such touches as these—and many, very many similar ones, all through his chapters—furnish clues, whereby we enter a little way into the intricate, profound heart where they originated. And we see that suffering, some time or other and in some shape or other—this only can enable any man to depict it in others. All over him, Hawthorne's melancholy rests like an Indian summer, which, though bathing a whole country in one softness, still reveals the distinctive hue of every towering hill, and each far-winding vale.

But it is the least part of genius that attracts admiration. Where Hawthorne is known, he seems to be deemed a pleasant writer, with a pleasant style—a sequestered, harmless man, from whom any deep and weighty thing would hardly be anticipated: a man who means no meanings. But there is no man, in whom humor and love, like mountain peaks, soar to such a rapt height, as to receive the irradiations of the upper skies; there is no man in whom humor and love are developed in that high form called genius—no such man can exist without also possessing, as the indispensable complement of these, a great, deep intellect, which drops down into the universe like a plummet. Or, love and humor are only the eyes, through which such an intellect views this world. The great beauty in such a mind is but the product of its strength. What, to all readers, can be more charming than the piece entitled "Monsieur du Miroir"; and to a reader at all capable of fully fathoming it, what, at the same time, can possess more mystical depth of meaning?—Yes, there he sits, and looks at me—this "shape of mystery," this "identical Monsieur du Miroir."—"Methinks I should tremble now, were his wizard power, of gliding through all impediments in search of me, to place him suddenly before my eyes."

How profound, nay, appalling, is the moral evolved by the "Earth's Holocaust," where—beginning with the hollow follies and affectations of the world—all vanities and empty theories and forms are, one after another, and by an admirably graduated, growing comprehensiveness, thrown into the allegorical fire, till, at length, nothing is left but the all-engendering heart of man; which remaining still unconsumed, the great conflagration is naught.

Of a piece with this is "The Intelligence Office," a wondrous symbolizing of the secret workings in men's souls. There are other sketches, still more charged with ponderous import.

"The Christmas Banquet" and "The Bosom Serpent" would be fine subjects for a curious and elaborate analysis, touching the conjectural parts of the mind that produced them. For spite of all the Indian-summer sunlight on the hither side of Hawthorne's soul, the other side—like the dark half of the physical sphere—is shrouded in a blackness, ten times black. But this darkness but gives more effect to the ever-moving dawn, that forever advances through it, and circumnavigates his world. Whether Hawthorne has simply availed himself of this mystical blackness as a means to the wondrous effects he makes it to produce in his lights and shades; or whether there really lurks in him, perhaps unknown to himself, a touch of Puritanic gloom—this, I cannot altogether tell. Certain it is, however, that this great power of blackness in him derives its force from its appeals to that Calvinistic sense of Innate Depravity and Original Sin, from whose visitations, in some shape or other, no deeply thinking mind is always and wholly free. For, in certain moods, no man can weigh this world, without throwing in something, somehow like Original Sin, to strike the uneven balance. At all events, perhaps no writer has ever wielded this terrific thought with greater terror than this same harmless Hawthorne. Still more: this black conceit pervades him, through and through. You may be witched by his sunlight, transported by the bright gildings in the skies he builds over you, but there is the blackness of darkness beyond; and even his bright gildings but fringe and play upon the edges of thunder-clouds.—In one word, the world is mistaken in this Nathaniel Hawthorne. He himself must often have smiled at its absurd misconception of him. He is immeasurably deeper than the plummet of the mere critic. For it is not the brain that can test such a man; it is only the heart. You cannot come to know greatness by inspecting it; there is no glimpse to be caught of it, except by intuition; you need not ring it, you but touch it, and you find it is gold.

Now it is that blackness in Hawthorne, of which I have spoken, that so fixes and fascinates me. It may be, nevertheless, that it is too largely developed in him. Perhaps he does not give us a ray of his light for every shade of his dark. But however this may be, this blackness it is that furnishes the infinite obscure of his background—that background, against which Shakespeare plays his grandest conceits, the things that have made for Shakespeare his loftiest but most circumscribed renown, as the profoundest of thinkers. For by philosophers Shakespeare is not adored as the great man of tragedy and comedy.—"Off with his head! so much for Buckingham!" This sort of rant, interlined by another hand, brings down the house—those mistaken souls, who dream of Shakespeare as a mere man of Richard-the-Third humps, and Macbeth daggers. But it is those deep far-away things in him; those occasional flashings-forth of the intuitive Truth in him; those short, quick probings at the very axis of reality;—these are the things that make Shakespeare Shakespeare. Through the mouths of the dark characters of Hamlet, Timon, Lear, and Iago, he craftily says, or sometimes insinuates, the things which we feel to be so terrifically true that it were all but madness for any good man, in his own proper character, to utter, or even hint of them. Tormented into desperation, Lear the frantic king tears off the mask, and speaks the sane madness of vital truth. But, as I before said, it is the least part of genius that attracts admiration. And so, much of the blind, unbridled admiration that has been heaped upon Shakespeare has been lavished upon the least part of him. And few of his endless commentators and critics seem to have remembered, or even perceived, that the immediate products of a great mind are not so great as that undeveloped, and sometimes undevelopable yet dimly discernible greatness, to which these immediate products are but the infallible indices. In Shakespeare's tomb lies infinitely more than Shakespeare ever wrote. And if I magnify Shakespeare, it is not so much for what he did do, as for what he did not do, or refrained from doing. For in this world of lies, Truth is forced to fly like a scared white doe in the woodlands; and only by cunning glimpses will she reveal herself, as in Shakespeare and other masters of the great Art of Telling the Truth—even though it be covertly, and by snatches.

But if this view of the all-popular Shakespeare be seldom taken by his readers, and if very few who extol him have ever read him deeply, or, perhaps, only have seen him on the tricky stage (which alone made, and is still making, him his mere mob renown)—if few men have time, or patience, or palate, for the spiritual truth as it is in that great genius—it is, then, no matter of surprise that in a contemporaneous age, Nathaniel Hawthorne is a man as yet almost utterly mistaken among men. Here and there, in some quiet armchair in the noisy town, or some deep nook among the noiseless mountains, he may be appreciated for something of what he is. But unlike Shakespeare, who was forced to the contrary course by circumstances, Hawthorne (either from simple disinclination, or else from inaptitude) refrains from all the popularizing noise and show of broad farce, and blood-besmeared tragedy; content with the still, rich utterances of a great intellect in repose, and which sends few thoughts into circulation, except they be arterialized at his large warm lungs, and expanded in his honest heart.

Nor need you fix upon that blackness in him, if it

suit you not. Nor, indeed, will all readers discern it, for it is, mostly, insinuated to those who may best understand it, and account for it; it is not obtruded upon every one alike.

Some may start to read of Shakespeare and Hawthorne on the same page. They may say, that if an illustration were needed, a lesser light might have sufficed to elucidate this Hawthorne, this small man of yesterday. But I am not, willingly, one of those who, as touching Shakespeare at least, exemplify the maxim of Rochefoucauld, that "we exalt the reputation of some, in order to depress that of others"; who, to teach all noble-souled aspirants that there is no hope for them, pronounce Shakespeare absolutely unapproachable. But Shakespeare has been approached. There are minds that have gone as far as Shakespeare into the universe. And hardly a mortal man, who, at some time or other, has not felt as great thoughts in him as any you will find in *Hamlet*. We must not inferentially malign mankind for the sake of any one man, whoever he may be. This is too cheap a purchase of contentment for conscious mediocrity to make. Besides, this absolute and unconditional adoration of Shakespeare has grown to be a part of our Anglo-Saxon superstitions. The Thirty-Nine Articles are now Forty. Intolerance has come to exist in this matter. You must believe in Shakespeare's unapproachability, or quit the country. But what sort of a belief is this for an American, a man who is bound to carry republican progressiveness into Literature, as well as into Life? Believe me, my friends, that men not very much inferior to Shakespeare are this day being born on the banks of the Ohio. And the day will come when you shall say; who reads a book by an Englishman that is a modern? The great mistake seems to be that even with those Americans who look forward to the coming of a great literary genius among us, they somehow fancy he will come in the costume of Queen Elizabeth's day, be a writer of dramas founded upon old English history, or the tales of Boccaccio. Whereas great geniuses are parts of the times; they themselves are the times, and possess a correspondent coloring. It is of a piece with the Jews, who, while their Shiloh was meekly walking in their streets, were still praying for his magnificent coming; looking for him in a chariot, who was already among them on an ass. Nor must we forget that, in his own lifetime, Shakespeare was not Shakespeare, but only Master William Shakespeare of the shrewd, thriving business firm of Condell, Shakespeare & Co., proprietors of the Globe Theatre in London, and by a courtly author, of the name of Chettle, was looked at as an "upstart crow" beautified "with other birds' feathers." For, mark it well, imitation is often the first charge brought against real originality. Why this is so, there is not space to set forth here. You must have plenty of sea-room to tell the Truth in; especially when it seems to have an aspect of newness, as America did in 1492, though it was then just as old, and perhaps older than Asia, only those sagacious philosophers, the common sailors, had never seen it before, swearing it was all water and moonshine there.

Now, I do not say that Nathaniel of Salem is a greater than William of Avon, or as great. But the difference between the two men is by no means immeasurable. Not a very great deal more, and Nathaniel were verily William.

This, too, I mean—that if Shakespeare has not been equaled, give the world time, and he is sure to be surpassed, in one hemisphere or the other. [For it will never do for us who in most other things out-do as well as out-brag the world to fold our hands and say: In the highest department advance there is none.][1] Nor will it at all do to say that the world is getting gray and grizzled now, and has lost that fresh charm which she wore of old, and by virtue of which the great poets of past times made themselves what we esteem them to be. Not so. The world is as young today as when it was created and this Vermont morning dew is as wet to my feet as Eden's dew to Adam's. Nor has Nature been all over ransacked by our progenitors, so that no new charms and mysteries remain for this latter generation to find. Far from it. The trillionth part has not yet been said, and all that has been said but multiplies the avenues to what remains to be said. It is not so much paucity as superabundance of material that seems to incapacitate modern authors.

Let America then prize and cherish her writers; yea, let her glorify them. They are not so many in number as to exhaust her good will. And while she has good kith and kin of her own, to take to her bosom, let her not lavish her embraces upon the household of an alien. For believe it or not, England, after all, is, in many things, an alien to us. China has more bowels of real love for us than she. But even were there no strong literary individualities among us,[2] as there are some dozen at least, nevertheless, let America first praise mediocrity

---

[1] This and other bracketed passages and names indicate cancellations in the manuscript that seem too interesting to be omitted.—*J.L.*

[2] The manuscript shows an earlier, more specific version of this passage: "But even were there no Hawthorne, no Emerson, no Whittier, no Irving, no Bryant, no Dana, no Cooper, no Willis (not the author of the *Dashes* but the author of "The Belfry Pigeon")—were there none of these & others of like calibre among us . . ." The final version is in Duyckinck's hand.—*J.L.*

even, in her own children, before she praises (for everywhere, merit demands acknowledgment from every one) the best excellence in the children of any other land. Let her own authors, I say, have the priority of appreciation. I was much pleased with a hot-headed Carolina cousin of mine, who once said, "If there were no other American to stand by, in Literature—why, then, I would stand by Pop Emmons and his *Fredoniad*, and till a better epic came along, swear it was not very far behind the *Iliad*." Take away the words, and in spirit he was sound.

Not that American genius needs patronage in order to expand. For that explosive sort of stuff will expand though screwed up in a vise, and burst it, though it were triple steel. It is for the nation's sake, and not for her authors' sake, that I would have America be heedful of the increasing greatness among her writers. For how great the shame, if other nations should be before her, in crowning her heroes of the pen! But this is almost the case now. American authors have received more just and discriminating praise (however loftily and ridiculously given, in certain cases) even from some Englishmen, than from their own countrymen. There are hardly five critics in America; and several of them are asleep. As for patronage, it is the American author who now patronizes his country, and not his country him. And if at times some among them appeal to the people for more recognition, it is not always with selfish motives, but patriotic ones.

It is true that but few of them as yet have evinced that decided originality which merits great praise. But that graceful writer, who perhaps of all Americans has received the most plaudits from his own country for his productions—that very popular and amiable writer, however good, and self-reliant in many things, perhaps owes his chief reputation to the self-acknowledged imitation of a foreign model, and to the studied avoidance of all topics but smooth ones. But it is better to fail in originality than to succeed in imitation. He who has never failed somewhere, that man can not be great. Failure is the true test of greatness. And if it be said that continual success is a proof that a man wisely knows his powers, it is only to be added that, in that case, he knows them to be small. Let us believe it, then, once for all, that there is no hope for us in these smooth, pleasing writers that know their powers. Without malice, but to speak the plain fact, they but furnish an appendix to Goldsmith, and other English authors. And we want no American Goldsmiths; nay, we want no American Miltons. It were the vilest thing you could say of a true American author, that he were an American Tompkins. Call him an American, and have done; for you cannot say a nobler thing of him.—But it is not meant that all American writers should studiously cleave to nationality in their writings; only this, no American writer should write like an Englishman, or a Frenchman; let him write like a man, for then he will be sure to write like an American. Let us away with this [Bostonian] leaven of literary flunkyism towards England. If either must play the flunky in this thing, let England do it, not us. [And the time is not far off when circumstances may force her to it.] While we are rapidly preparing for that political supremacy among the nations, which prophetically awaits us at the close of the present century, in a literary point of view we are deplorably unprepared for it, and we seem studious to remain so. Hitherto, reasons might have existed why this should be; but no good reason exists now. And all that is requisite to amendment in this matter is simply this: that, while freely acknowledging all excellence, everywhere, we should refrain from unduly lauding foreign writers and, at the same time, duly recognize the meritorious writers that are our own; those writers who breathe that unshackled, democratic spirit of Christianity in all things, which now takes the practical lead in this world, though at the same time led by ourselves—us Americans. Let us boldly contemn all imitation, though it comes to us graceful and fragrant as the morning, and foster all originality, though, at first, it be crabbed and ugly as our own pine knots. And if any of our authors fail, or seem to fail, then, in the words of my enthusiastic Carolina cousin, let us clap him on the shoulder, and back him against all Europe for his second round. The truth is that, in our point of view, this matter of a national literature has come to such a pass with us that in some sense we must turn bullies, else the day is lost, or superiority so far beyond us, that we can hardly say it will ever be ours.

And now, my countrymen, as an excellent author, of your own flesh and blood—an unimitating, and, perhaps, in his way, an inimitable man—whom better can I commend to you, in the first place, than Nathaniel Hawthorne. He is one of the new and far better generation of your writers. The smell of your beeches and hemlocks is upon him; your own broad prairies are in his soul; and if you travel away inland into his deep and noble nature, you will hear the far roar of his Niagara. Give not over to future generations the glad duty of acknowledging him for what he is. Take that joy to yourself, in your own generation; and so shall he feel those grateful impulses in him that may possibly prompt him to the full flower of some still greater achievement in your eyes. And by confessing him, you thereby confess others; you brace the whole brotherhood. For genius, all over the world, stands hand in hand, and one shock of recognition runs the whole circle round.

In treating of Hawthorne, or rather of Hawthorne in his writings (for I never saw the man, and in the chances of a quiet plantation life, remote from his haunts, perhaps never shall); in treating of his works, I say, I have thus far omitted all mention of his *Twice-Told Tales*, and *The Scarlet Letter*. Both are excellent, but full of such manifold, strange, and diffusive beauties, that time would all but fail me to point the half of them out. But there are things in those two books which, had they been written in England a century ago, Nathaniel Hawthorne had utterly displaced [Oliver Goldsmith and] many of the bright names we now revere on authority. But I am content to leave Hawthorne to himself, and to the infallible finding of posterity; and however great may be the praise I have bestowed upon him, I feel, that in so doing, I have more served and honored myself than him. For, at bottom, great excellence is praise enough to itself; but the feeling of a sincere and appreciative love and admiration towards it—this is relieved by utterance; and warm, honest praise ever leaves a pleasant flavor in the mouth; and it is an honorable thing to confess to what is honorable in others.

But I cannot leave my subject yet. No man can read a fine author, and relish him to his very bones, while he reads, without subsequently fancying to himself some ideal image of the man and his mind. And if you rightly look for it, you will almost always find that the author himself has somewhere furnished you with his own picture. For poets (whether in prose or verse), being painters of Nature, are like their brethren of the pencil, the true portrait painters, who, in the multitude of likenesses to be sketched, do not invariably omit their own;

and in all high instances, they paint them without any vanity, though, at times, with a lurking something, that would take several pages to properly define.

I submit it, then, to those best acquainted with the man personally, whether the following is not Nathaniel Hawthorne; and to himself, whether something involved in it does not express the temper of his mind—that lasting temper of all true, candid men—a seeker, not a finder yet:

A man now entered, in neglected attire, with the aspect of a thinker, but somewhat too rough-hewn and brawny for a scholar. His face was full of sturdy vigor, with some finer and keener attribute beneath; though harsh at first, it was tempered with the glow of a large, warm heart, which had force enough to heat his powerful intellect through and through. He advanced to the Intelligencer, and looked at him with a glance of such stern sincerity, that perhaps few secrets were beyond its scope.

"I seek for Truth," said he.

Twenty-four hours have elapsed since writing the foregoing. I have just returned from the haymow, charged more and more with love and admiration of Hawthorne. For I have just been gleaning through the *Mosses*, picking up many things here and there that had previously escaped me. And I found that but to glean after this man is better than to be in at the harvest of others. To be frank (though, perhaps, rather foolish), notwithstanding what I wrote yesterday of these Mosses, I had not then culled them all; but had, nevertheless, been sufficiently sensible of the subtle essences in them as to write as I did. To what infinite height of loving wonder and admiration I may yet be borne, when by repeatedly banqueting on these Mosses, I shall have thoroughly incorporated their whole stuff into my being

—that, I can not tell. But already I feel that this Hawthorne has dropped germinous seeds into my soul. He expands and deepens down, the more I contemplate him; and further, and further, shoots his strong New England roots into the hot soil of my Southern soul.

By careful reference to the "Table of Contents," I now find that I have gone through all the sketches, but that when I yesterday wrote I had not at all read two particular pieces to which I now desire to call special attention—"A Select Party," and "Young Goodman Brown." Here be it said to all those whom this poor fugitive scrawl of mine may tempt to the perusal of the *Mosses* that they must on no account suffer themselves to be trifled with, disappointed, or deceived by the triviality of many of the titles to these Sketches. For in more than one instance the title utterly belies the piece. It is as if rustic demijohns containing the very best and costliest of Falernian and Tokay were labeled "Cider," "Perry," and "Elderberry Wine." The truth seems to be that, like many other geniuses, this Man of Mosses takes great delight in hoodwinking the world—at least with respect to himself. Personally, I doubt not that he rather prefers to be generally esteemed but a so-so sort of author; being willing to reserve the thorough and acute appreciation of what he is to that party most qualified to judge—that is, to himself. Besides, at the bottom of their natures, men like Hawthorne, in many things, deem the plaudits of the public such strong presumptive evidence of mediocrity in the object of them, that it would in some degree render them doubtful of their own powers, did they hear much and vociferous braying concerning them in the public pastures. True, I have been braying myself (if you please to be witty enough to have it so), but then I claim to be the first that has so brayed in this particular matter; and therefore, while pleading guilty to the charge, still claim all the merit due to originality.

But with whatever motive, playful or profound, Nathaniel Hawthorne has chosen to entitle his pieces in the manner he has, it is certain that some of them are directly calculated to deceive—egregiously deceive—the superficial skimmer of pages. To be downright and candid once more, let me cheerfully say that two of these titles did dolefully dupe no less an eagle-eyed reader than myself; and that, too, after I had been impressed with a sense of the great depth and breadth of this American man. "Who in the name of thunder" (as the country people say in this neighborhood), "who in the name of thunder," would anticipate any marvel in a piece entitled "Young Goodman Brown"? You would of course suppose that it was a simple little tale, intended as a supplement to "Goody Two-Shoes." Whereas it is deep as Dante; nor can you finish it, without addressing the author in his own words: "It is yours to penetrate, in every bosom, the deep mystery of sin." And with Young Goodman, too, in allegorical pursuit of his Puritan wife, you cry out in your anguish:

"Faith!" shouted Goodman Brown, in a voice of agony and desperation; and the echoes of the forest mocked him, crying—"Faith! Faith!" as if bewildered wretches were seeking her, all through the wilderness.

Now this same piece, entitled "Young Goodman Brown," is one of the two that I had not at all read yesterday; and I allude to it now, because it is, in itself, such a strong positive illustration of that blackness in Hawthorne which I had assumed from the mere occasional shadows of it, as revealed in several of the other sketches. But had I previously perused "Young Good-

man Brown,˙ I should have been at no pains to draw
the conclusion which I came to at a time when I was
ignorant that the book contained one such direct and
unqualified manifestation of it.

The other piece of the two referred to is entitled "A
Select Party," which, in my first simplicity upon originally taking hold of the book, I fancied must treat of
some pumpkin-pie party in Old Salem, or some chowder
party on Cape Cod. Whereas, by all the gods of Peedee!
it is the sweetest and sublimest thing that has been
written since Spenser wrote. Nay, there is nothing in
Spenser that surpasses it, perhaps, nothing that equals
it. And the test is this: read any canto in *The Faery
Queen,* and then read "A Select Party," and decide
which pleases you the most—that is, if you are qualified
to judge. Do not be frightened at this; for when Spenser
was alive, he was thought of very much as Hawthorne
is now, was generally accounted just such a "gentle"
harmless man. It may be that, to common eyes, the sub-
limity of Hawthorne seems lost in his sweetness—as
perhaps in this same "Select Party" of his, for whom he
has builded so august a dome of sunset clouds, and
served them on richer plate than Belshazzar's when he
banqueted his lords in Babylon.

But my chief business now is to point out a particular
page in this piece, having reference to an honored guest,
who, under the name of "The Master Genius" but in the
guise "of a young man of poor attire, with no insignia
of rank or acknowledged eminence," is introduced to the
Man of Fancy, who is the giver of the feast. Now the
page having reference to this "Master Genius" so happily expresses much of what I yesterday wrote, touching
the coming of the literary Shiloh of America, that I cannot but be charmed by the coincidence; especially,

when it shows such a parity of ideas, at least in this one point, between a man like Hawthorne and a man like me.

And here, let me throw out another conceit of mine touching this American Shiloh, or "Master Genius," as Hawthorne calls him. May it not be, that this commanding mind has not been, is not, and never will be, individually developed in any one man? And would it, indeed, appear so unreasonable to suppose that this great fullness and overflowing may be, or may be destined to be, shared by a plurality of men of genius? Surely, to take the very greatest example on record, Shakespeare cannot be regarded as in himself the concretion of all the genius of his time, nor as so immeasurably beyond Marlowe, Webster, Ford, Beaumont, Jonson, that those great men can be said to share none of his power? For one, I conceive that there were dramatists in Elizabeth's day, between whom and Shakespeare the distance was by no means great. Let anyone, hitherto little acquainted with those neglected old authors, for the first time read them thoroughly, or even read Charles Lamb's *Specimens* of them, and he will be amazed at the wondrous ability of those Anaks of men, and shocked at this renewed example of the fact that Fortune has more to do with fame than merit—though, without merit, lasting fame there can be none.

Nevertheless, it would argue too illy of my country were this maxim to hold good concerning Nathaniel Hawthorne, a man, who already, in some few minds, has shed "such a light as never illuminates the earth, save when a great heart burns as the household fire of a grand intellect."

The words are his—in "A Select Party"; and they are a magnificent setting to a coincident sentiment of my own, but ramblingly expressed yesterday, in reference to himself. Gainsay it who will, as I now write, I am Posterity speaking by proxy—and after times will make it more than good, when I declare that the American, who up to the present day, has evinced, in Literature, the largest brain with the largest heart—that man is Nathaniel Hawthorne. Moreover, that whatever Nathaniel Hawthorne may hereafter write, the *Mosses from an Old Manse* will be ultimately accounted his masterpiece. For there is a sure though a secret sign in some works which proves the culmination of the powers (only the developable ones, however) that produced them. But I am by no means desirous of the glory of a prophet. I pray Heaven that Hawthorne may *yet* prove me an impostor in this prediction. Especially, as I somehow cling to the strange fancy that, in all men, hiddenly reside certain wondrous, occult properties—as in some plants and minerals—which by some happy but very rare accident (as bronze was discovered by the melting of the iron and brass in the burning of Corinth) may chance to be called forth here on earth, not entirely waiting for their better discovery in the more congenial, blessed atmosphere of heaven.

Once more—for it is hard to be finite upon an infinite subject, and all subjects are infinite. By some people, this entire scrawl of mine may be esteemed altogether unnecessary, inasmuch, "as years ago" (they may say) "we found out the rich and rare stuff in this Hawthorne, whom you now parade forth as if only *yourself* were the discoverer of this Portuguese diamond in our [American] Literature."—But even granting all this—and adding to it, the assumption that the books of Hawthorne have sold by the five thousand—what does that signify? They should be sold by the hundred thousand, and read by the million, and admired by every one who is capable of admiration.

❖❖❖

When the time came to return to the New York house, crowded with Allan and his new family as well as with their mother and sisters, Herman and Elizabeth made up their minds to stay in the Berkshires. The Morewoods had bought the Melville house, and, with Judge Shaw's help, the Melvilles bought the adjacent estate with its firm old farmhouse, which Melville named "Arrowhead." The move was made in September, surprising their New York friends. Melville added to his schedule the career of farmer.

❖❖❖

To Evert Duyckinck

Sunday Evening [6 October] 1850
My Dear Duyckinck

I hardly thought that I should find time or even *table* to write you this long while. But it is Sunday at last, and after a day chiefly spent in *Jaquesizing* in the woods, I sit down to do what with me is an almost unexampled thing—inditing a letter at night. It has been a most glowing & Byzantine day—the heavens reflecting the hues of the October apples in the orchard—nay, the heavens themselves looking so ripe & ruddy, that it must be harvest-home with the angels, & Charle's Wain be heaped high as Saddle-Back with Autumn's sheaves.— You should see the maples—you should see the young perennial pines—the red blazings of the one contrasting with the painted green of the other, and the wide flushings of the autumn are harmonizing both. I tell you that sunrises and sunsets grow side by side in these woods, & momentarily moult in the falling leaves.———A hammer! yes a hammer is before me—the very one that so cruelly bruised the very finger that guides my pen. I can sentimentalise it no more.

Until today I have been as busy as man could be.

Every thing to be done, & scarcely any one to help me to do it. But I trust that before a great while we shall be all "to rights," and I shall take my ease on mine mountain. For a month to come, tho', I expect to be in the open air all day, except when assisting in lifting a bedstead or a bureau.

Thank you for your letter with the paper the other day. I am offering up devout jubilations for the abolition of the flogging law.

My love to Adler, & tell him I hope to have him behind a cigar one of these days & talk over old times. Remember me to your brother—& take this meagre letter for lack of a longer & a better one—and believe me to be what I am

Truly Yours

H Melville

❖❖❖

When Melville had offered the new book to Bentley, he told him that it would be ready this autumn; and in reporting Berkshire summer news to his brother George, Duyckinck had said that the book on the Whale Fishery was "mostly done." But the autumn passed and winter came without Harpers or Bentley receiving the finished manuscript. A new broader view, in whose shaping Hawthorne (then at work on his *House of the Seven Gables*) had played no small part, had compelled Melville to see his task newly, more deeply and daringly.

❖❖❖

To Evert Duyckinck

Friday Evening [13 December 1850]
Pittsfield

My Dear Duyckinck: If you overhaul your old diaries you will see that a long period ago you were acquainted with one Herman Melville; that he then resided in New York; but removing after a time into a remote region called Berkshire, and failing to answer what letters you sent him, you but reasonably supposed him dead; at any rate did not hear anything of him again, & so by degrees you thought no more about him.

I now write to inform you that this man has turned up—in short, My Dear Fellow in spite of my incivility I am alive & well, & would fain be remembered.

Before I go further let me say here that I am writing this by candle light—an uncommon thing with me—& therefore my writing wont be very legible, because I am keeping one eye shut & wink at the paper with the other.

If you expect a letter from a man who lives in the country you must make up your mind to receive an egotistical one—for he has no gossip nor news of any kind, unless his neighbor's cow has calved or the hen has laid a silver egg. . . .

I have a sort of sea-feeling here in the country, now that the ground is all covered with snow. I look out of my window in the morning when I rise as I would out of a port-hole of a ship in the Atlantic. My room seems a ship's cabin; & at nights when I wake up & hear the wind shrieking, I almost fancy there is too much sail on the house, & I had better go on the roof & rig in the chimney.

Do you want to know how I pass my time?—I rise at eight—thereabouts—& go to my barn—say good-morning to the horse, & give him his breakfast. (It goes to my heart to give him a cold one, but it can't be helped.) Then, pay a visit to my cow—cut up a pumpkin or two for her, & stand by to see her eat it—for its a pleasant sight to see a cow move her jaws—she does it so mildly & with such a sanctity.—My own breakfast over, I go to my work-room & light my fire—then spread my M.S.S. on the table—take one business squint at it, & fall to with a will. At 2½ P.M. I hear a preconcerted knock at my door, which (by request) continues till I rise and go to the door, which serves to wean me effectively from my writing, however interested I may be. My friends the horse & cow now demand their dinner—& I go & give it them. My own dinner over, I rig my sleigh & with my mother or sisters start off for the village—& if it be a Literary World day, great is the satisfaction thereof.—My evenings I spend in a sort of mesmeric state in my room—not being able to read—only now & then skimming over some large-printed book.—Can you send me about fifty fast-writing youths, with an easy style & not averse to polishing their labors? If you can, I wish you would, because since I have been here I have planned about that number of future works & cant find enough time to think about them separately. —But I dont know but a book in a man's brain is better off than a book bound in calf—at any rate it is safer from criticism. And taking a book off the brain is akin to the ticklish & dangerous business of taking an old painting off a panel—you have to scrape off the whole brain in order to get at it with due safety—& even then, the painting may not be worth the trouble.——I meant to have left more room for something else besides my own concerns. But I cant help it.—I see Adler is at work —or has already achieved a German translation. I am glad to hear it. Remember me to him.—In the country here, I begin to appreciate the Literary World. I read it as a sort of private letter from you to me. . . .

To Nathaniel Hawthorne

Pittsfield, Wednesday morning
[April 16(?), 1851]

My Dear Hawthorne, Concerning the young gentleman's shoes, I desire to say that a pair to fit him, of the
desired pattern cannot be had in all Pittsfield,—a fact
which sadly impairs that metropolitan pride I formerly
took in the capital of Berkshire. Henceforth Pittsfield
must hide its head. However, if a pair of *bootees* will at
all answer, Pittsfield will be very happy to provide them.
Pray mention all this to Mrs. Hawthorne, and command
me.

"The House of the Seven Gables: A Romance. By
Nathaniel Hawthorne. One vol. 16mo, pp. 344." The
contents of this book do not belie its rich, clustering,
romantic title. With great enjoyment we spent almost
an hour in each separate gable. This book is like a fine
old chamber, abundantly, but still judiciously, furnished
with precisely that sort of furniture best fitted to furnish
it. There are rich hangings, whereon are broidered
scenes from tragedies. There is old china with rare devices, set about on the carved buffet; there are long
and indolent lounges to throw yourself upon; there is
an admirable sideboard, plentifully stored with good
viands; there is a smell as of old wine in the pantry; and
finally, in one corner, there is a dark little black-letter
volume in golden clasps, entitled "Hawthorne: A Problem." It has delighted us; it has piqued a reperusal; it
has robbed us of a day, and made us a present of a
whole year of thoughtfulness; it has bred great exhila-
ration and exultation with the remembrance that the
architect of the Gables resides only six miles off, and

not three thousand miles away in England, say. We think the book, for pleasantness of running interest, surpasses the other works of the author. The curtains are now drawn; the sun comes in more; genialities peep out more. Were we to particularize what most struck us in the deeper passages, we would point out the scene where Clifford, for a moment, would fain throw himself forth from the window to join the procession; or the scene where the judge is left seated in his ancestral chair. Clifford is full of an awful truth throughout. He is conceived in the finest, truest spirit. He is no caricature. He is Clifford. And here we would say that, did circumstances permit, we should like nothing better than to devote an elaborate and careful paper to the full consideration and analysis of the purport and significance of what so strongly characterizes all of this author's writings. There is a certain tragic phase of humanity which, in our opinion, was never more powerfully embodied than by Hawthorne: we mean the tragicalness of human thought in its own unbiassed, native, and profounder workings. We think that into no recorded mind has the intense feeling of the visible truth ever entered more deeply than into this man's. By visible truth, we mean the apprehension of the absolute condition of present things as they strike the eye of the man who fears them not, though they do their worst to him,—the man who, like Russia or the British Empire, declares himself a sovereign nature (in himself) amid the powers of heaven, hell, and earth. He may perish; but so long as he exists he insists upon treating with all Powers upon an equal basis. If any of those other Powers choose to withhold certain secrets, let them; that does not impair my sovereignty in myself; that does not make me tributary. And perhaps, after all, there is *no* secret. We incline to think that the Problem of the

Universe is like the Freemason's mighty secret, so terrible to all children. It turns out, at last, to consist in a triangle, a mallet, and an apron,—nothing more! We incline to think that God cannot explain His own secrets, and that He would like a little information upon certain points Himself. We mortals astonish Him as much as He us. But it is this *Being* of the matter; there lies the knot with which we choke ourselves. As soon as you say *Me*, a *God*, a *Nature*, so soon you jump off from your stool and hang from the beam. Yes, that word is the hangman. Take God out of the dictionary, and you would have Him in the street.

There is the grand truth about Nathaniel Hawthorne. He says NO! in thunder; but the Devil himself cannot make him say *yes*. For all men who say *yes*, lie; and all men who say *no*,—why, they are in the happy condition of judicious, unincumbered travellers in Europe; they cross the frontiers into Eternity with nothing but a carpet-bag,—that is to say, the Ego. Whereas those *yes*-gentry, they travel with heaps of baggage, and, damn them! they will never get through the Custom House. What's the reason, Mr Hawthorne, that in the last stages of metaphysics a fellow always falls to *swearing* so? I could rip an hour. You see, I began with a little criticism extracted for your benefit from the "Pittsfield Secret Review," and here I have landed in Africa.

Walk down one of these mornings and see me. No nonsense; come. Remember me to Mrs. Hawthorne and the children.

H. Melville

P.S. The marriage of Phoebe with the daguerreotypist is a fine stroke, because of his turning out to be a *Maule*. If you pass Hepzibah's cent-shop, buy me a **Jim Crow** (fresh) and send it to me by Ned Higgins.

[June 1(?) 1851]

My Dear Hawthorne—I should have been rumbling down to you in my pine-board chariot a long time ago, were it not that for some weeks past I have been more busy than you can well imagine,—out of doors,—building and patching and tinkering away in all directions. Besides, I had my crops to get in,—corn and potatoes (I hope to show you some famous ones by and by),—and many other things to attend to, all accumulating upon this one particular season. I work myself; and at night my bodily sensations are akin to those I have so often felt before, when a hired man, doing my day's work from sun to sun. But I mean to continue visiting you until you tell me that my visits are both supererogatory and superfluous. With no son of man do I stand upon any etiquette or ceremony, except the Christian ones of charity and honesty. I am told, my fellow-man, that there is an aristocracy of the brain. Some men have boldly advocated and asserted it. Schiller seems to have done so, though I don't know much about him. At any rate, it is true that there have been those who, while earnest in behalf of political equality, still accept the intellectual estates. And I can well perceive, I think, how a man of superior mind can, by its intense cultivation, bring himself, as it were, into a certain spontaneous aristocracy of feeling,—exceedingly nice and fastidious, —similar to that which, in an English Howard, conveys a torpedo-fish thrill at the slightest contact with a social plebian. So, when you see or hear of my ruthless democracy on all sides, you may possibly feel a touch of a shrink, or something of that sort. It is but nature to be shy of a mortal who boldly declares that a thief in jail is as honorable a personage as Gen. George Washington.

This is ludicrous. But Truth is the silliest thing under the sun. Try to get a living by the Truth—and go to the Soup Societies. Heavens! Let any clergyman try to preach the Truth from its very stronghold, the pulpit, and they would ride him out of his church on his own pulpit bannister. It can hardly be doubted that all Reformers are bottomed upon the truth, more or less; and to the world at large are not reformers almost universally laughing-stocks? Why so? Truth is ridiculous to men. Thus easily in my room here do I, conceited and garrulous, reverse the test of my Lord Shaftesbury.

It seems an inconsistency to assert unconditional democracy in all things, and yet confess a dislike to all mankind—in the mass. But not so.—But it's an endless sermon,—no more of it. I began by saying that the reason I have not been to Lenox is this,—in the evening I feel completely done up, as the phrase is, and incapable of the long jolting to get to your house and back. In a week or so, I go to New York, to bury myself in a third-story room, and work and slave on my "Whale" while it is driving through the press. *That* is the only way I can finish it now,—I am so pulled hither and thither by circumstances. The calm, the coolness, the silent grass-growing mood in which a man *ought* always to compose,—that, I fear, can seldom be mine. Dollars damn me; and the malicious Devil is forever grinning in upon me, holding the door ajar. My dear Sir, a presentiment is on me,—I shall at last be worn out and perish, like an old nutmeg-grater, grated to pieces by the constant attrition of the wood, that is, the nutmeg. What I feel most moved to write, that is banned,—it will not pay. Yet, altogether, write the *other* way I cannot. So the product is a final hash, and all my books are botches. I'm rather sore, perhaps, in this letter; but see my hand! four blisters on this palm, made by hoes and hammers within the last few days. It is a rainy morning; so I am indoors, and all work suspended. I feel cheerfully disposed, and therefore I write a little bluely. Would the Gin were here! If ever, my dear Hawthorne, in the eternal times that are to come, you and I shall sit down in Paradise, in some little shady corner by ourselves; and if we shall by any means be able to smuggle a basket of champagne there (I won't believe in a Temperance Heaven), and if we shall then cross our celestial legs in the celestial grass that is forever tropical, and strike our glasses and our heads together, till both musically ring in concert,—then, O my dear fellow-mortal, how shall we pleasantly discourse of all the things manifold which now so distress us,—when all the earth shall be but a reminiscence, yea, its final dissolution an antiquity. Then shall songs be composed as when wars are over: humorous, comic songs,—"Oh, when I lived in that queer little hole called the world," or, "Oh, when I toiled and sweated below," or, "Oh, when I knocked and was knocked in the fight"—yes, let us look forward to such things. Let us swear that, though now we sweat, yet it is because of the dry heat which is indispensable to the nourishment of the vine which is to bear the grapes that are to give us the champagne hereafter.

But I was talking about the "Whale." As the fishermen say, "he's in his flurry" when I left him some three weeks ago. I'm going to take him by his jaw, however, before long, and finish him up in some fashion or other. What's the use of elaborating what, in its very essence, is so short-lived as a modern book? Though I wrote the Gospels in this century, I should die in the gutter.—I talk all about myself, and this is selfishness and egotism. Granted. But how help it? I am writing to you; I know little about you, but something about myself. So I write about myself,—at least to you. Don't trouble yourself, though, about writing; and don't trouble yourself about visiting; and when you *do* visit, don't trouble yourself about talking. I will do all the writing and visiting and talking myself.—By the way, in the last "Dollar Magazine" I read "The Unpardonable Sin." He was a sad fellow, that Ethan Brand. I have no doubt you are by this time responsible for many a shake and tremor of the tribe of "general readers." It is a frightful poetical creed that the cultivation of the brain eats out the heart. But it's my *prose* opinion that in most cases, in those men who have fine brains and work them well, the heart extends down to hams. And though you smoke them with the fire of tribulation, yet, like veritable hams, the head only gives the richer and the better flavor. I stand for the heart. To the dogs with the head! I had rather be a fool with a heart, than Jupiter Olympus with his head. The reason the mass of men fear God, and *at bottom dislike* Him, is because they rather distrust His Heart, and fancy Him all brain like a watch. (You perceive I employ a capital initial in the pronoun referring to the Deity; don't you think there is a slight dash of flunkeyism in that usage?) Another thing. I was in New York for four-and-twenty hours the other day, and saw a portrait of N.H. And I have seen and heard many flattering (in a publisher's point of view) allusions to the "Seven Gables." And I have seen "Tales" and "A New Volume" announced, by N.H. So upon the whole, I say to myself, this N.H. is in the ascendant. My dear Sir, they begin to patronize. All Fame is patronage. Let me be infamous; there is no patronage in *that*. What "reputation" H.M. has is horrible. Think of it! To go down to posterity is bad enough, any way; but to go down as a "man who lived among the cannibals"! When I speak of posterity, in reference to myself, I only mean the babies who will probably be born in the moment im-

mediately ensuing upon my giving up the ghost. I shall
go down to some of them, in all likelihood. "Typee" will
be given to them, perhaps, with their gingerbread. I
have come to regard this matter of Fame as the most
transparent of all vanities. I read Solomon more and
more, and every time see deeper and deeper and unspeakable meanings in him. I did not think of Fame,
a year ago, as I do now. My development has been all
within a few years past. I am like one of those seeds
taken out of the Egyptian Pyramids, which, after being
three thousand years a seed and nothing but a seed,
being planted in English soil, it developed itself, grew
to greenness, and then fell to mould. So I. Until I was
twenty-five, I had no development at all. From my
twenty-fifth year I date my life. Three weeks have
scarcely passed, at any time between then and now,
that I have not unfolded within myself. But I feel that I
am now come to the inmost leaf of the bulb, and that
shortly the flower must fall to the mould. It seems to
me now that Solomon was the truest man who ever
spoke, and yet that he a little *managed* the truth with a
view to popular conservatism; or else there have been
many corruptions and interpolations of the text.—In
reading some of Goethe's sayings, so worshipped by his
votaries, I came across this, *"Live in the all."* That is
to say, your separate identity is but a wretched one,—
good; but get out of yourself, spread and expand yourself, and bring to yourself the tinglings of life that are
felt in the flowers and the woods, that are felt in the
planets Saturn and Venus, and the Fixed Stars. What
nonsense! Here is a fellow with a raging toothache. "My
dear boy," Goethe says to him, "you are sorely afflicted
with that tooth; but you must *live in the all,* and then
you will be happy!" As with all great genius, there is an
immense deal of flummery in Goethe, and in proportion

to my own contact with him, a monstrous deal of it in me.

H Melville

P.S. "Amen!" saith Hawthorne.

N.B. This "all" feeling, though, there is some truth in. You must often have felt it, lying on the grass on a warm summer's day. Your legs seem to send out shoots into the earth. Your hair feels like leaves upon your head. This is the *all* feeling. But what plays the mischief with the truth is that men will insist upon the universal application of a temporary feeling or opinion.

P.S. You must not fail to admire my discretion in paying the postage on this letter.

Pittsfield, June 29, 1851.

My Dear Hawthorne—The clear air and open window invite me to write to you. For some time past I have been so busy with a thousand things that I have almost forgotten when I wrote you last, and whether I received an answer. This most persuasive season has now for weeks recalled me from certain crotchety and over-doleful chimeras, the like of which men like you and me, and some others, forming a chain of God's posts round the world, must be content to encounter now and then, and fight them the best way we can. But come they will, —for, in the boundless, trackless, but still glorious wild wilderness through which these outposts run, the Indians do sorely abound, as well as the insignificant but still stinging mosquitoes. Since you have been here, I have been building some shanties of houses (connected with the old one) and likewise some shanties of chapters and essays. I have been ploughing and sowing and raising and painting and printing and praying,—and now begin to come out upon a less bristling time, and to enjoy the calm prospect of things from a fair piazza at the north of the old farmhouse here.

Not entirely yet, tho', am I without something to be urgent with. The "Whale" is only half thro' the press; for, wearied with the long delays of the printers, and disgusted with the heat and dust of the Babylonish brick-kiln of New York, I came back to the country to feel the grass—and end the book reclining on it, if I may.—I am sure you will pardon this speaking all about myself; for if I *say* so much on that head, be sure all the rest of the world are thinking about themselves ten times as much. Let us speak, tho' we show all our faults and weaknesses,—for it is a sign of strength to be weak, to know it, and out with it,—not in set way and ostentatiously, tho', but incidentally and without premeditation.——But I am falling into my old foible,—preaching. I am busy, but shall not be very long. Come and spend a day here, if you can and want to; if not, stay in Lenox, and God give you long life. When I am quite free of my present engagements, I am going to treat myself to a ride and a visit to you. Have ready a bottle of brandy, because I always feel like drinking that heroic drink when we talk ontological heroics together. This is rather a crazy letter in some respects, I apprehend. If so, ascribe it to the intoxicating effects of the latter end of June operating upon a very susceptible and peradventure feeble temperament.

Shall I send you a fin of the "Whale" by way of a specimen mouthful? The tail is not yet cooked—tho' the hell-fire in which the whole book is broiled might not unreasonably have cooked it all ere this. This is the book's motto (the secret one), Ego non baptiso te in nomine—but make out the rest yourself.

H.M.

To Richard Bentley

Pittsfield, Berkshire County, Mass:
July 20th 1851.

My Dear Sir—I promptly received your note of the 3d
Inst: in reply to mine concerning the publication of my
new book.

I accept your offer for the work; but not without
strong hope that before long, we shall be able to treat
upon a firmer basis than now, & heretofore; & that with
the more assurance you will be disposed to make over-
tures for American books. And here let me say to you,
—since you are peculiarly interested in the matter—that
in all reasonable probability no International Copyright
will ever be obtained—in our time, at least—if you
Englishmen wait at all for the first step to be taken in
this country. Who have any motive in this country to
bestir themselves in this thing? Only the authors.—Who
are the authors?—A handful. And what influence have
they to bring to bear upon any question whose settle-
ment must necessarily assume a political form?——They
can bring scarcely any influence whatever. This country
& nearly all its affairs are governed by sturdy backs-
woodsmen—noble fellows enough, but not at all literary, & who care not a fig for any authors except those
who write those most saleable of all books nowadays
—i e—the newspapers, & magazines. And tho' the number of cultivated, Catholic men, who may be supposed
to feel an interest in a national literature, is large &
every day growing larger; yet they are nothing in com-
parison with the overwhelming majority who care nothing about it. This country is at present engaged in

furnishing material for future authors; not in encouraging its living ones.

Nevertheless, if this matter by any means comes to be made nationally conspicuous; and if you in England come out magnanimously, & protect a foreign author; then there is that sort of stuff in the people here, which will be sure to make them all eagerness in reciprocating. For, be assured, that my countrymen will never be outdone in generosity.——Therefore, if you desire an International Copyright—hoist your flag on your side of the water, & the signal will be answered; but look for no flag on this side till then.

I am now passing thro' the press, the closing sheets of my new work; so that I shall be able to forward it to you in the course of two or three weeks—perhaps a little longer. I shall forward it to you thro' the office of the Legation. And upon your receipt of it, I suppose you will immediately proceed to printing; as, of course, publication will not take place here, till you have made yourself safe.——You say you will give me your notes at three & six months; I infer that this means from the time of receiving the book.

Very Truly Yours
H Melville

From Moby Dick, or, The Whale

The Sermon

FATHER MAPPLE rose, and in a mild voice of unassuming authority ordered the scattered people to condense. "Starboard gangway, there! side away to larboard

—larboard gangway, to starboard! Midships! midships!"

There was a low rumbling of heavy sea-boots among the benches, and a still slighter shuffling of women's shoes, and all was quiet again, and every eye on the preacher.

He paused a little; then kneeling in the pulpit's bows, folded his large brown hands across his chest, uplifted his closed eyes, and offered a prayer so deeply devout that he seemed kneeling and praying at the bottom of the sea.

This ended, in prolonged solemn tones, like the continual tolling of a bell in a ship that is foundering at sea in a fog—in such tones he commenced reading the following hymn; but, changing his manner towards the concluding stanzas, burst forth with a pealing exultation and joy—

> The ribs and terrors in the whale
>   Arched over me a dismal gloom,
> While all God's sun-lit waves rolled by,
>   And left me deepening down to doom.
>
> I saw the opening maw of hell,
>   With endless pains and sorrows there;
> Which none but they that feel can tell—
>   Oh, I was plunging to despair.
>
> In black distress, I called my God,
>   When I could scarce believe him mine,
> He bowed his ear to my complaints—
>   No more the whale did me confine.
>
> With speed he flew to my relief,
>   As on a radiant dolphin borne;
> Awful, yet bright, as lightning shone
>   The face of my Deliverer God.
>
> My song for ever shall record
>   That terrible, that joyful hour;

I give the glory to my God,
His all the mercy and the power.

Nearly all joined in singing this hymn, which swelled high above the howling of the storm. A brief pause ensued; the preacher slowly turned over the leaves of the Bible, and at last, folding his hand down upon the proper page, said: "Beloved shipmates, clinch the last verse of the first chapter of Jonah—'And God had prepared a great fish to swallow up Jonah.'

"Shipmates, this book, containing only four chapters —four yarns—is one of the smallest strands in the mighty cable of the Scriptures. Yet what depths of the soul does Jonah's deep sea-line sound! what a pregnant lesson to us is this prophet! What a noble thing is that canticle in the fish's belly! How billow-like and boisterously grand! We feel the floods surging over us; we sound with him to the kelpy bottom of the waters; seaweed and all the slime of the sea is about us! But *what* is this lesson that the book of Jonah teaches? Shipmates, it is a two-stranded lesson; a lesson to us all as sinful men, and a lesson to me as a pilot of the living God. As sinful men, it is a lesson to us all, because it is a story of the sin, hard-heartedness, suddenly awakened fears, the swift punishment, repentance, prayers and finally the deliverance and joy of Jonah. As with all sinners among men, the sin of this son of Amittai was in his willful disobedience of the command of God—never mind now what that command was, or how conveyed— which he found a hard command. But all the things that God would have us do are hard for us to do—remember that—and hence he oftener commands us than endeavors to persuade. And if we obey God, we must disobey ourselves; and it is in this disobeying ourselves wherein the hardness of obeying God consists.

"With this sin of disobedience in him, Jonah still further flouts at God, by seeking to flee from Him. He thinks that a ship made by men will carry him into countries where God does not reign, but only the Captains of this earth. He skulks about the wharves of Joppa, and seeks a ship that's bound for Tarshish. There lurks, perhaps, a hitherto unheeded meaning here. By all accounts Tarshish could have been no other city than the modern Cadiz. That's the opinion of learned men. And where is Cadiz, shipmates? Cadiz is in Spain; as far by water, from Joppa, as Jonah could possibly have sailed in those ancient days, when the Atlantic was an almost unknown sea. Because Joppa, the modern Jaffa, shipmates, is on the most easterly coast of the Mediterranean, the Syrian; and Tarshish or Cadiz more than two thousand miles to the westward from that, just outside the Straits of Gibraltar. See ye not then, shipmates, that Jonah sought to flee world-wide from God? Miserable man! Oh! most contemptible and worthy of all scorn; with slouched hat and guilty eye, skulking from his God; prowling among the shipping like a vile burglar hastening to cross the seas. So disordered, self-condemning is his look that had there been policemen in those days, Jonah, on the mere suspicion of something wrong, had been arrested ere he touched a deck. How plainly he's a fugitive! no baggage, not a hat-box, valise, or carpet-bag, no friends accompany him to the wharf with their adieux. At last, after much dodging search, he finds the Tarshish ship receiving the last items of her cargo; and as he steps on board to see its Captain in the cabin, all the sailors for the moment desist from hoisting in the goods, to mark the stranger's evil eye. Jonah sees this; but in vain he tries to look all ease and confidence; in vain essays his wretched smile. Strong intuitions of the man assure the mariners he can be no innocent. In their gamesome but still serious way, one whispers to the other—'Jack, he's robbed a widow'; or, 'Joe, do you mark him; he's a bigamist'; or, 'Harry lad, I guess he's the adulterer that broke jail in old Gomorrah, or belike, one of the missing murderers from Sodom.' Another runs to read the bill that's stuck against the spile upon the wharf to which the ship is moored, offering five hundred gold coins for the apprehension of a parricide, and containing a description of his person. He reads, and looks from Jonah to the bill; while all his sympathetic shipmates now crowd round Jonah, prepared to lay their hands upon him. Frighted Jonah trembles, and summoning all his boldness to his face, only looks so much the more a coward. He will not confess himself suspected; but that itself is strong suspicion. So he makes the best of it; and when the sailors find him not to be the man that is advertised, they let him pass, and he descends into the cabin.

"'Who's there?' cries the Captain at his busy desk, hurriedly making out his papers for the Customs. 'Who's there?' Oh! how that harmless question mangles Jonah! For the instant he almost turns to flee again. But he rallies. 'I seek a passage in this ship to Tarshish; how soon sail ye, Sir?' Thus far the busy Captain had not looked up to Jonah, though the man now stands before him; but no sooner does he hear that hollow voice than he darts a scrutinizing glance. 'We sail with the next coming tide,' at last he slowly answered, still intently eyeing him. 'No sooner, Sir?'—'Soon enough for any honest man that goes a passenger.' Ha! Jonah, that's another stab. But he swiftly calls away the Captain from that scent. 'I'll sail with ye,' he says, 'the passage money, how much is that?—I'll pay now.' For it is particularly written, shipmates, as if it were a thing not to be overlooked in this history, 'that he paid the fare thereof' ere the craft did sail. And taken with the context, this is full of meaning.

"Now Jonah's Captain, shipmates, was one whose discernment detects crime in any, but whose cupidity exposes it only in the penniless. In this world, shipmates, Sin that pays its way can travel freely, and without a passport; whereas Virtue, if a pauper, is stopped at all frontiers. So Jonah's Captain prepares to test the length of Jonah's purse, ere he judge him openly. He charges him thrice the usual sum; and it's assented to. Then the Captain knows that Jonah is a fugitive; but at the same time resolves to help a flight that paves its rear with gold. Yet when Jonah fairly takes out his purse, prudent suspicions still molest the Captain. He rings every coin to find a counterfeit. Not a forger, anyway, he mutters; and Jonah is put down for his passage. 'Point out my stateroom, Sir,' says Jonah now, 'I'm travel-weary; I need sleep.' 'Thou look'st like it,' says the Captain, 'there's thy room.' Jonah enters, and would lock the door, but the lock contains no key. Hearing him foolishly fumbling there, the Captain laughs lowly to himself, and mutters something about the doors of convicts' cells being never allowed to be locked within. All dressed and dusty as he is, Jonah throws himself into his berth, and finds the little stateroom ceiling almost resting on his forehead. The air is close, and Jonah gasps. Then, in that contracted hole, sunk, too, beneath the ship's waterline, Jonah feels the heralding presentiment of that stifling hour when the whale shall hold him in the smallest of his bowels' wards.

"Screwed at its axis against the side, a swinging lamp slightly oscillates in Jonah's room; and the ship, heeling over towards the wharf with the weight of the last bales received, the lamp, flame and all, though in slight motion, still maintains a permanent obliquity with ref-

erence to the room; though, in truth, infallibly straight
itself, it but made obvious the false, lying levels among
which it hung. The lamp alarms and frightens Jonah, as
lying in his berth his tormented eyes roll round the
place, and this thus far successful fugitive finds no
refuge for his restless glance. But that contradiction in
the lamp more and more appals him. The floor, the
ceiling, and the side, are all awry. 'Oh! so my conscience hangs in me!' he groans, 'straight upward, so it
burns; but the chambers of my soul are all in crookedness!'

"Like one who after a night of drunken revelry hies
to his bed, still reeling, but with conscience yet pricking him; as the plungings of the Roman racehorse but
so much the more strike his steel tags into him, as one
who in that miserable plight still turns and turns in
giddy anguish, praying God for annihilation until the
fit be passed, and at last amid the whirl of woe he feels,
a deep stupor steals over him, as over the man who
bleeds to death, for conscience is the wound, and there's
naught to staunch it—so, after sore wrestlings in his
berth, Jonah's prodigy of ponderous misery drags him
drowning down to sleep.

"And now the time of tide has come; the ship casts off
her cables; and from the deserted wharf the uncheered
ship for Tarshish, all careening, glides to sea. That ship,
my friends, was the first of recorded smugglers! the
contraband was Jonah. But the sea rebels; he will not
bear the wicked burden. A dreadful storm comes on; the
ship is like to break. But now when the boatswain calls
all hands to lighten her, when boxes, bales, and jars
are clattering overboard, when the wind is shrieking,
and the men are yelling, and every plank thunders with
trampling feet right over Jonah's head—in all this raging
tumult, Jonah sleeps his hideous sleep. He sees no black

sky and raging sea, feels not the reeling timbers, and little hears he or heeds he the far rush of the mighty whale, which even now with open mouth is cleaving the seas after him. Aye, shipmates, Jonah was gone down into the sides of the ship—a berth in the cabin as I have taken it, and was fast asleep. But the frightened master comes to him, and shrieks in his dead ear, 'What meanest thou, O sleeper! arise!' Startled from his lethargy by that direful cry, Jonah staggers to his feet, and stumbling to the deck, grasps a shroud, to look out upon the sea. But at that moment he is sprung upon by a panther billow leaping over the bulwarks. Wave after wave thus leaps into the ship, and finding no speedy vent runs roaring fore and aft, till the mariners come nigh to drowning while yet afloat. And ever, as the white moon shows her affrighted face from the steep gullies in the blackness overhead, aghast Jonah sees the rearing bowsprit pointing high upward, but soon beat downward again towards the tormented deep.

"Terrors upon terrors run shouting through his soul. In all his cringing attitudes, the God-fugitive is now too plainly known. The sailors mark him; more and more certain grow their suspicions of him, and at last, fully to test the truth, by referring the whole matter to high Heaven, they fall to casting lots, to see for whose cause this great tempest was upon them. The lot is Jonah's; that discovered, then how furiously they mob him with their questions. 'What is thine occupation? Whence comest thou? Thy country? What people?' But mark now, my shipmates, the behavior of poor Jonah. The eager mariners but ask him who he is, and where from; whereas, they not only receive an answer to those questions, but likewise another answer to a question not put by them, but the unsolicited answer is forced from Jonah by the hard hand of God that is upon him.

" 'I am a Hebrew,' he cries—and then—'I fear the Lord the God of Heaven who hath made the sea and the dry land!' Fear Him, O Jonah? Aye, well mightest thou fear the Lord God *then!* Straightway, he nows goes on to make a full confession; whereupon the mariners become more and more appalled, but still are pitiful. For when Jonah, not yet supplicating God for mercy, since he but too well knew the darkness of his deserts, when wretched Jonah cries out to them to take him and cast him forth into the sea, for he knew that for *his* sake this great tempest was upon them, they mercifully turn from him, and seek by other means to save the ship. But all in vain; the indignant gale howls louder; then, with one hand raised invokingly to God, with the other they not unreluctantly lay hold of Jonah.

"And now behold Jonah taken up as an anchor and dropped into the sea; when instantly an oily calmness floats out from the east, and the sea is still, as Jonah carries down the gale with him, leaving smooth water behind. He goes down in the whirling heart of such a masterless commotion that he scarce heeds the moment when he drops seething into the yawning jaws awaiting him; and the whale shoots-to all his ivory teeth, like so many white bolts, upon his prison. Then Jonah prayed unto the Lord out of the fish's belly. But observe his prayer, and learn a weighty lesson. For sinful as he is, Jonah does not weep and wail for direct deliverance. He feels that his dreadful punishment is just. He leaves all his deliverance to God, contenting himself with this, that spite of all his pains and pangs, he will still look towards His holy temple. And here, shipmates, is true and faithful repentance; not clamorous for pardon, but grateful for punishment. And how pleasing to God was this conduct in Jonah, is shown in the eventual deliverance of him from the sea and the whale. Shipmates, I do not place Jonah before you to be copied for his sin but I do place him before you as a model for repentance. Sin not; but if you do, take heed to repent of it like Jonah."

While he was speaking these words, the howling of the shrieking, slanting storm without seemed to add new power to the preacher, who, when describing Jonah's sea storm, seemed tossed by a storm himself. His deep chest heaved as with a ground swell; his tossed arms seemed the warring elements at work; and the thunders that rolled away from off his swarthy brow, and the light leaping from his eye, made all his simple hearers look on him with a quick fear that was strange to them.

There now came a lull in his look, as he silently turned over the leaves of the Book once more; and, at last, standing motionless, with closed eyes, for the moment, seemed communing with God and himself.

But again he leaned over towards the people, and bowing his head lowly, with an aspect of the deepest yet manliest humility, he spake these words:

"Shipmates, God has laid but one hand upon you; both his hands press upon me. I have read ye by what murky light may be mine the lesson that Jonah teaches to all sinners; and therefore to ye, and still more to me, for I am a greater sinner than ye. And now how gladly would I come down from this mast-head and sit on the hatches there where you sit, and listen as you listen, while some one of you reads *me* that other and more awful lesson which Jonah teaches to *me*, as a pilot of the living God. How being an anointed pilot-prophet, or speaker of true things, and bidden by the Lord to sound those unwelcome truths in the ears of a wicked Nineveh, Jonah, appalled at the hostility he should raise, fled from his mission, and sought to escape his duty and his God by taking ship at Joppa. But God is everywhere; Tarshish he never reached. As we have seen, God came upon him in the whale, and swallowed him down to living gulfs of doom, and with swift slantings tore him along 'into the midst of the seas,' where the eddying depths sucked him ten thousand fathoms down, and 'the weeds were wrapped about his head,' and all the watery world of woe bowled over him. Yet even then beyond the reach of any plummet—'out of the belly of hell' —when the whale grounded upon the ocean's utmost bones, even then, God heard the engulfed, repenting prophet when he cried. Then God spake unto the fish; and from the shuddering cold and backness of the sea, the whale came breaching up toward the warm and pleasant sun, and all the delights of air and earth; and 'vomited out Jonah upon the dry land'; when the word of the Lord came a second time; and Jonah, bruised and beaten—his ears, like two seashells, still multitudinously murmuring of the ocean—Jonah did the Almighty's bidding. And what was that, shipmates? To preach the Truth to the face of Falsehood! That was it!

"This, shipmates, this is that other lesson; and woe to that pilot of the living God who slights it. Woe to him whom this world charms from Gospel duty! Woe to him who seeks to pour oil upon the waters when God has brewed them into a gale! Woe to him who seeks to please rather than to appal! Woe to him whose good name is more to him than goodness! Woe to him who, in this world, courts not dishonor! Woe to him who would not be true, even though to be false were salvation! Yea, woe to him who, as the great Pilot Paul has it, while preaching to others is himself a castaway!"

He drooped and fell away from himself for a moment; then lifting his face to them again, showed a deep joy in his eyes, as he cried out with a heavenly enthusiasm, "But oh! shipmates! on the starboard hand of every woe, there is a sure delight; and higher the top of that delight than the bottom of the woe is deep. Is not the maintruck higher than the kelson is low? Delight is to him—a far, far upward, and inward delight—who against the proud gods and commodores of this earth ever stands forth his own inexorable self. Delight is to him whose strong arms yet support him, when the ship of this base treacherous world has gone down beneath him. Delight is to him who gives no quarter in the truth, and kills, burns, and destroys all sin though he pluck it out from under the robes of Senators and Judges. Delight—top-gallant delight is to him who acknowledges no law or lord, but the Lord his God, and is only a patriot to heaven. Delight is to him, whom all the waves of the billows of the seas of the boisterous mob can never shake from this sure Keel of the Ages. And eternal delight and deliciousness will be his, who coming to lay him down, can say with his final breath—O Father! chiefly known to me by Thy rod—mortal or immortal, here I die. I have striven to be Thine, more than to be this world's, or mine own. Yet this is nothing; I leave eternity to Thee; for what is man that he should live out the lifetime of his God?"

He said no more, but slowly waving a benediction, covered his face with his hands, and so remained kneeling, till all the people had departed, and he was left alone in the place.

(Chapter IX)

To Sarah Morewood

Pittsfield, Friday Morning [September (?) 1851]
If to receive some thoughtful kindness from one, upon
whom self-delusion whispers we have some claims, if
this be so agreeable to us; then how far more delightful, to be the recipient of amiable offices from one who
has claims upon ourselves, not we upon them. This
indeed is to sow the true seed of Christianity among
all the asperities of mankind; this converts infidels, &
gives misanthropy no foot to stand on.

Most considerate of all the delicate roses that diffuse
their blessed perfume among men, is Mrs: Morewood;
(I say it not in "bitterness"—I appeal to all the Sweet-
Briars, if I do;) for the little box contained nourishment
for both body & soul; and the two flasks of Cologne—
why, I have not done smelling of them yet.

The "Hour & the Man" is exceedingly acceptable to
me. "Zanoni" is a very fine book in very fine print—
but I shall endeavor to surmount that difficulty. At
present, however, the Fates have plunged me into certain silly thoughts and wayward speculations, which
will prevent me, for a time, from falling into the reveries
of these books—for a fine book is a sort of revery to
us—is it not?—So I shall regard them as my Paradise
in store, & Mrs Morewood the goddess from whom it
comes.

Concerning my own forthcoming book—it is off my
hands, but must cross the sea before publication here.
Dont you buy it—dont you read it, when it does come
out, because it is by no means the sort of book for you.
It is not a peice of fine feminine Spitalfields silk—but
is of the horrible texture of a fabric that should be

woven of ships' cables & hawsers. A Polar wind blows through it, & birds of prey hover over it. Warn all gentle fastidious people from so much as peeping into the book —on risk of a lumbago & sciatics.

My best remembrances and sympathies to Mrs Pollock, who, I trust, is convalescent now. Fail not to remind Miss Henderson also, that I desire she will not entirely forget me; and present my regards to Mr: Morewood.

H Melville

❖❖❖

On October 18 *The Whale* (the changed title had arrived too late for Bentley's edition) was published in London, and at Arrowhead Melville's second son Stanwix was born four days later. By mid-November American readers were offered *Moby Dick* by Harpers. As editor of *The Literary World,* Duyckinck had been sent prepublication sheets of the new work. He was startled to find in it a final catastrophe strangely like one described in a newly arrived news item from Panama, which he passed on at once to Melville—a whale had attacked and sunk the whale ship *Ann Alexander.*

❖❖❖

To Evert Duyckinck

Pittsfield, Friday afternoon [7 November 1851] Dear Duyckinck—Your letter received last night had a sort of stunning effect on me. For some days past busy engaged in the woods with axe, wedge, & beetle, the Whale had almost completely slipped me for a time (& I was the merrier for it) when Crash! comes Moby Dick himself (as you justly say) & reminds me of what I have been about for part of the last year or two. It is really & truly a surprising coincidence—to say the least. I make no doubt it *is* Moby Dick himself, for there is no account of his capture after the sad fate of the Pequod about fourteen years ago.——Ye Gods! what a Commentator is this Ann Alexander whale. What he has to say is short & pithy & very much to the point. I wonder if my evil art has raised this monster.

The Behrings Straits Disaster, too, & the cording along the New Foundland coast of those scores & scores of fishermen, and the inland gales on the Lakes. Verily the pot boileth inside & out. And woe unto us, we but live in the days that have been. Not even then they found time to be jolly.

Why didn't you send me that inestimable item of "Norman de Wardt" before? Oh had I but had that pie to cut into! But that & many other fine things doubtless are omitted. All one can do is to pick up what chips he can hug round him. They have no Vatican (as you have) in Pittsfield here.

The boy you inquire about is well. His name will probably be "Stanwix" for some account of which, vide *Stone's Life of Brandt*, where mention is made of how this lad's great grandfather spent his summers in the Revolutionary War before Saratoga came into being— I mean Saratoga Springs & Ballston.

And now what is the news with you? I suppose the Knights of the Round Table still assemble over their cigars & punch, & I know that once every week the "Literary World" revolves upon its axis. I should like to hear again the old tinkle of glasses in your basement, & may do so, before many months.

For us here, winter is coming. The hills & the noses begin to look blue, & the trees have stripped themselves for the December tussle. I have had my dressing-gown patched up, & got some wood in the wood-house,

&—by the way,—have in full blast our great dining-room fire-place, which swallows down cords of wood as a whale does boats.

To Nathaniel Hawthorne

Pittsfield, Monday afternoon
[November 17(?), 1851]

My Dear Hawthorne—People think that if a man has undergone any hardship, he should have a reward; but for my part, if I have done the hardest possible day's work, and then come to sit down in a corner and eat my supper comfortably—why, then I don't think I deserve any reward for my hard day's work—for am I not now at peace? Is not my supper good? My peace and my supper are my reward, my dear Hawthorne. So your joy-giving and exultation-breeding letter is not my reward for my ditcher's work with that book, but is the good goddess's bonus over and above what was stipulated for—for not one man in five cycles, who is wise, will expect appreciative recognition from his fellows, or any one of them. Appreciation! Recognition! Is love appreciated? Why, ever since Adam, who has got to the meaning of his great allegory—the world? Then we pygmies must be content to have our paper allegories but ill comprehended. I say your appreciation is my glorious gratuity. In my proud, humble way, —a shepherd-king,—I was lord of a little vale in the solitary Crimea; but you have now given me the crown of India. But on trying it on my head, I found it fell down on my ears, notwithstanding their asinine length— for it's only such ears that sustain such crowns.

Your letter was handed me last night on the road going to Mr Morewood's, and I read it there. Had I been at home, I would have sat down at once and answered it. In me divine magnanimities are spontaneous and instantaneous—catch them while you can. The world goes round, and the other side comes up. So now I can't write what I felt. But I felt pantheistic then—your heart beat in my ribs and mine in yours, and both in God's. A sense of unspeakable security is in me this moment, on account of your having understood the book. I have written a wicked book, and feel spotless as the lamb. Ineffable socialities are in me. I would sit down and dine with you and all the gods in old Rome's Pantheon. It is a strange feeling—no hopefulness is in it, no despair. Content—that is it; and irresponsibility; but without licentious inclination. I speak now of my profoundest sense of being, not of an incidental feeling.

Whence come you, Hawthorne? By what right do you drink from my flagon of life? And when I put it to my lips—lo, they are yours and not mine. I feel that the Godhead is broken up like the bread at the Supper, and that we are the pieces. Hence this infinite fraternity of feeling. Now, sympathizing with the paper, my angel turns over another page. You did not care a penny for the book. But, now and then as you read, you understood the pervading thought that impelled the book—and that you praised. Was it not so? You were archangel enough to despise the imperfect body, and embrace the soul. Once you hugged the ugly Socrates because you saw the flame in the mouth, and heard the rushing of the demon,—the familiar,—and recognized the sound; for you have heard it in your own solitudes.

My dear Hawthorne, the atmospheric skepticisms steal into me now, and make me doubtful of my sanity in writing you thus. But, believe me, I am not mad, most noble Festus! But truth is ever incoherent, and when the big hearts strike together, the concussion is a little stunning. Farewell. Don't write a word about the book. That would be robbing me of my miserly delight. I am heartily sorry I ever wrote anything about you—it was paltry. Lord, when shall we be done growing? As long as we have anything more to do, we have done nothing. So, now, let us add Moby Dick to our blessing, and step from that. Leviathan is not the biggest fish;—I have heard of Krakens.

This is a long letter, but you are not at all bound to answer it. Possibly, if you do answer it, and direct it to Herman Melville, you will missend it—for the very fingers that now guide this pen are not precisely the same that just took it up and put it on this paper. Lord, when shall we be done changing? Ah! it's a long stage, and no inn in sight, and night coming, and the body cold. But with you for a passenger, I am content and can be happy. I shall leave the world, I feel, with more satisfaction for having come to know you. Knowing you persuades me more than the Bible of our immortality.

What a pity, that, for your plain, bluff letter, you should get such gibberish! Mention me to Mrs. Hawthorne and to the children, and so, good-by to you, with my blessing.

Herman

P.S. I can't stop yet. If the world was entirely made up of Magians, I'll tell you what I should do. I should have a paper-mill established at one end of the house, and so have an endless riband of foolscap rolling in upon my desk; and upon that endless riband I should write a thousand—a million—billion thoughts, all under the form of a letter to you. The divine magnet is on you, and my magnet responds. Which is the biggest? A foolish question—they are *One*.

P.P.S. Don't think that by writing me a letter, you shall always be bored with an immediate reply to it—and so keep both of us delving over a writing-desk eternally. No such thing! I sha'n't always answer your letters, and you may do just as you please.

To Sophia Hawthorne

New York Jan: 8th 1852

My Dear Mrs Hawthorne

I have hunted up the finest Bath I could find, gilt-edged and stamped, whereon to inscribe my humble acknowledgment of your highly flattering letter of the 29th Dec:——It really amazed me that you should find any satisfaction in that book. It is true that some *men* have said they were pleased with it, but you are the only woman—for as a general thing, women have small taste for the sea. But, then, since you, with your spiritualizing nature, see more things than other people, and by the same process, refine all you see, so that they are not the same things that other people see, but things which while you think you but humbly discover them, you do in fact create them for yourself—therefore, upon the whole, I do not so much marvel at your expressions concerning Moby Dick. At any rate, your allusion for example to the "Spirit Spout" first showed to me that there was a subtle significance in that thing —but I did not, in that case, *mean* it. I had some vague idea while writing it, that the whole book was susceptible of an allegoric construction, & also that *parts* of it were—but the speciality of many of the particular subordinate allegories, were first revealed to me, after reading Mr Hawthorne's letter, which, without citing any particular examples, yet intimated the part-&-parcel allegoricalness of the whole.——But, My Dear Lady, I shall not again send you a bowl of salt water. The next chalice I shall commend, will be a rural bowl of milk.

And now, how are you in West Newton? Are all domestic affairs regulated? Is Miss Una content? And Master Julian satisfied with the landscape in general? And does Mr Hawthorne continue his series of calls upon all his neighbors within a radius of ten miles? Shall I send him ten packs of visiting cards? And a box of kid gloves? and the latest style of Parisian handkerchief?—He goes into society too much altogether—seven evenings out a week should content any reasonable man.

Now, Madam, had you not said anything about Moby Dick, & had Mr Hawthorne been equally silent, then had I said perhaps, something to both of you about another Wonder-(-full) Book. But as it is, I must be silent. How is it, that while all of us human beings are so entirely disembarrassed in censuring a person; that so soon as we would praise, then we begin to feel awkward? I never blush after denouncing a man; but I grow scarlet, after eulogizing him. And yet this is all wrong; and yet we can't help it; and so we see how true was that musical sentence of the poet when he sang—

"We can't help ourselves"

For tho' we know what we ought to be; & what it would be very sweet & beautiful to be; yet we can't be it. That is most sad, too. Life is a long Dardenelles,

My Dear Madam, the shores whereof are bright with
flowers, which we want to pluck, but the bank is too
high; & so we float on & on, hoping to come to a landing-
place at last—but swoop! we launch into the great sea!
Yet the geographers say, even then we must not despair,
because across the great sea, however desolate & vacant it may look, lie all Persia & the delicious lands
roundabout Damascus.

So wishing you a pleasant voyage at last to that sweet
& far countree—

> Believe Me
> Earnestly Thine
> Herman Melville

❖❖❖

As a description of *Pierre*, "a rural bowl of milk" is not necessarily a Melvillian irony, for by January he could not have
been far enough into its writing to be beyond the idyllic
pastorale (which modern readers find the most distasteful
part of *Pierre*), and into the "certain silly thoughts and wayward speculations" that he confessed to Sarah Morewood
(and which his contemporaries found so offensive). When
he completed the book in March he tried to sell it to Bentley
as "a regular romance, with a mysterious plot to it, &
stirring passions at work, and withall, representing a new
& elevated aspect of American life"—terms that may be
thought more salesmanlike than analytic.

Within the same period Hawthorne had written *The
Blithedale Romance*, and the two men exchanged copies of
their new books this summer, a summer brightened for Melville by Lemuel Shaw's attempt to show him new material
on an excursion to Nantucket and the Elizabeths.

❖❖❖

To Nathaniel Hawthorne

Pittsfield, July 17th [1852]

My Dear Hawthorne: This name of *"Hawthorne"* seems to be ubiquitous. I have been on something of a tour lately, and it has saluted me vocally & typographically in all sorts of places & in all sorts of ways.—I was at the solitary Crusoisth island of Naushon (one of the Elisabeth group) and there, on a stately piazza, I saw it gilded on the back of a very new book, and in the hand of a clergyman.—I went to meet a gentleman in Brooklyne, and as we were sitting at our wine, in came the lady of the house, holding a beaming volume in her hand, from the city—"My Dear," to her husband, "I have brought your *Hawthorne's* new book." I entered the cars at Boston for this place. In came a lively boy— *"Hawthorne's* new book!"—In good time I arrived home. Said my lady-wife, "There is Mr *Hawthorne's* new book, come by mail." And this morning, lo! on my table a little note, subscribed *Hawthorne* again.—Well, the Hawthorne is a sweet flower; may it flourish in every hedge.

I am sorry, but I can not at present come to see you at Concord as you propose.—I am but just returned from a two weeks' absence; and for the last three months & more I have been an utter idler and a savage—out of doors all the time. So, the hour has come for me to sit down again.

Do send me a specimen of your sand-hill, and a sunbeam from the countenance of Mrs: Hawthorne, and a vine from the curly arbor of Master Julian.

As I am only just home, I have not yet got far into

the book but enough to see that you have most admirably employed materials which are richer than I had fancied them. Especially at this day, the volume is welcome, as an antidote to the mooniness of some dreamers —who are merely dreamers——Yet who the devil aint a dreamer?

H Melville

My remembrances to Miss Una & Master Julian—& the "compliments" & perfumes of the season to the "Rose-Bud."

[note at top, beside an embossed crown and laurel wreath, to which Melville has added a penned plume:]

By the way, here's a crown. Significant this. Pray, allow me to place it on your head in victorious token of your "Blithedale" success. Tho' not in strict keeping, I have embellished it with a plume.

Pittsfield Aug 13th 1852

[Salutation torn away]

—While visiting Nantucket some four weeks ago, I made the acquaintance of a gentleman from New Bedford, a lawyer, who gave me considerable information upon several matters concerning which I was curious. —One night we were talking, I think, of the great patience, & endurance, & resignedness of the women of the island in submitting so uncomplainingly to the long, long absences of their sailor husbands, when, by way of anecdote, this lawyer gave me a leaf from his professional experience. Altho' his memory was a little confused with regard to some of the items of the story, yet he told me enough to awaken the most lively interest in me; and I begged him to be sure and send me a more full account so soon as he arrived home—he having previously told me that at the time of the affair he had

made a record in his books.——I heard nothing more,
till a few days after arriving here at Pittsfield I received
thro' the Post Office the enclosed document.——You
will perceive by the gentleman's note to me that he assumed that I had purposed making literary use of the
story; but I had not hinted anything of the kind to him,
& my first spontaneous interest in it arose from very different considerations. I confess, however, that since then
I have a little turned the subject over in my mind with
a view to a regular story to be founded on these striking incidents. But, thinking again, it has occurred to
me that this thing lies very much in a vein, with which
you are peculiarly familiar. To be plump, I think that in
this matter you would make a better hand at it than I
would.——Besides the thing seems naturally to gravi-
tate towards you (to speak [*half a line torn*] should of
right belong to you. I could [*half a line torn*] the
Steward to deliver it to you.——

The very great interest I felt in this story while nar-
rating to me, was heightened by the emotion of the
gentleman who told it, who evinced the most unaffected
sympathy in it, tho' now a matter of his past.——But
perhaps this great interest of mine may have been
largely helped by some accidental circumstance or
other; so that, possibly, to you the story may not seem
to possess so much of pathos, & so much of depth. But
you will see how it is.——

In estimating the character of Robinson Charity
should be allowed a liberal play. I take exception to that
passage from the Diary which says that *"he must have
received a portion of his punishment in this life"*—thus
hinting of a future supplemental castigation.——I do
not at all suppose that his desertion of his wife was a
premeditated thing. If it had been so, he would have
changed his name, probably, after quitting her.——No:

he was a weak man, & his temptations (tho' we know little of them) were strong. The whole sin stole upon him insensibly—so that it would perhaps have been hard for him to settle upon the exact *day* when he could say to himself, *"Now* I have deserted my wife;" unless, indeed upon the day he wedded the Alexandria lady.——And here I am reminded of your *London husband:* tho' the cases so widely contrast.——Many more things might be mentioned; but I forbear; you will find out the suggestiveness for yourself; & all the better perhaps, for my not intermeddling.——

If you should be sufficiently interested, to engage upon a regular story founded on this narration; then I consider you but fairly entitled to the following tributary items, collected by me, by chance, during my strolls thro the islands; & which—as you will perceive—seem legitimately to belong to the story, in its rounded & beautified & thoroughly developed state;—but of all this you must of course be your own judge—I but submit matter to you—I dont decide.

Supposing the story to open with the wreck—then there must be a storm; & it were well if some faint shadow of the preceding *calm* were thrown forth to lead the whole.——Now imagine a high cliff overhanging the sea & crowned with a pasture for sheep; a little way off—higher up,—a light-house, where resides the father of the future Mrs Robinson the First. The afternoon is mild & warm. The sea with an air of solemn deliberation, with an elaborate deliberation, ceremoniously rolls upon the beach. The air is suppressedly charged with the sound of long lines of surf. There is no land over against this cliff short of Europe & the West Indies. Young Agatha (but you must give her some other name) comes wandering along the cliff. She marks how the continual assaults of the sea have undermined it; so that the fences fall over, & have need of many shiftings inland. The sea has encroached also upon that part where their dwelling-house stands near the light-house.——Filled with meditations, she reclines along the edge of the cliff & gazes out seaward. She marks a handful of cloud on the horizon, presaging a storm thro' all this quietude. (Of a maritime family & always dwelling on the coast, she is learned in these matters) This again gives food for thought. Suddenly she catches the long shadow of the cliff cast upon the beach 100 feet beneath her; and now she notes a shadow moving along the shadow. It is cast by a sheep from the pasture. It has advanced to the very edge of the water. There, in strange & beautiful contrast, we have the innocence of the lamb placidly eyeing the malignity of the sea, (All this having poetic reference to Agatha & her sea-lover, who is coming in the storm: the storm carries her lover to her; she catches a dim distant glimpse of his ship ere quitting the cliff)——P.S. It were well, if from her knowledge of the deep miseries produced to wives by marrying seafaring men, Agatha should have formed a young determination never to marry a sailor; which resolve in her, however, is afterwards overborne by the omnipotence of love.——P.S. No 2. Agatha should be active during the wreck, and should, in some way, be made the saviour of young Robinson. He should be the only survivor. He should be ministered to by Agatha at the house during the illness ensuing upon his injuries from the wreck.——Now this wrecked ship has driven over the shoals, & driven upon the beach where she goes to pieces, all but her stem-part. This in course of time becomes embedded in the sand—after the lapse of some years showing nothing but the sturdy stem (or, prow-bone) projecting some two feet at low water. All the rest is filled & packed down with the sand.——So that after her husband has disappeared the sad Agatha every day sees this melancholy monument, with all its remindings.——

After a sufficient lapse of time——when Agatha has become alarmed about the protracted absence of her young husband & is feverishly expecting a letter from ——then we must introduce the mail-post——no, that phrase wont do, but here is the *thing*.——Owing to the remoteness of the lighthouse from any settled place no regular mail reaches it. But some mile or so distant there is a road leading between two post-towns. And at the junction of what we shall call the Light-House road with this Post Road, there stands a post surmounted with a little rude wood box with a lid to it & a leather hinge. Into this box the Post boy drops all letters for the people of the light house & that vicinity of fishermen. To this post they must come for their letters. And, of course, young Agatha goes——for seventeen years she goes thither daily. As her hopes gradually decay in her, so does the post itself, & the little box decay. The post rots in the ground at last. Owing to its being little used—— hardly used at all——grass grows rankly about it. At last a little bird nests in it. At last the post falls.

The father of Agatha must be an old widower——a man of the sea, but early driven away from it by repeated disasters. Hence, is he subdued & quiet & wise in his life. And now he tends a light house, to warn people from those very perils, from which he himself has suffered.

Some few other items occur to me——but nothing material——and I fear to weary you, if not, make you smile at my strange impertinent officiousness.——And it would be so, were it not that these things do, in my mind, seem legitimately to belong to the story; for they were visibly suggested to me by scenes I actually beheld while on the very coast where the story of Agatha occurred.——I do not therefore, My Dear Hawthorne, at all imagine that you will think that I am so silly as to flatter myself I am giving you anything of my own. I am but restoring to you your own property—which you would quickly enough have identified for yourself— had you but been on the spot as I happened to be.

Let me conclude by saying that it seems to me that with your great power in these things, you can construct a story of remarkable interest out of this material furnished by the New Bedford lawyer.——You have a skeleton of actual reality to build about with fulness & veins & beauty. And if I thought I could do it as well as you, why, I should not let you have it.——The narrative from the Diary is instinct with significance.—— Consider the mention of the *shawls*—& the inference derived from it. Ponder the conduct of this Robinson throughout.——Mark his trepidation & suspicion when anyone called upon him.——But why prate so—you will mark it all & mark it deeper than I would, perhaps.

I have written all this in a great hurry; so you must spell it out the best way you may.

◇◇◇

Attached to this letter was a document headed "The Lawyer's Story," a transcript from the journal of the New Bedford lawyer (presumably, John Clifford) of May 28, 1842, written on his return from "one of the most interesting and romantic cases I ever expect to be engaged in." The step-son and administrator of a recently deceased business-man named James Robertson (Melville's "Robinson") had asked his assistance in investigating other claimants of Robertson's estate that had appeared. These claimed to be a wife and daughter, whom Robertson's family had not known existed. "It appeared that Robertson was wrecked on the coast of Pembroke where this girl, then Miss Agatha Hatch, was living—that he was hospitably entertained and cared for, and that within a year after, he married her, in due form of law. . . . About two years after the marriage, leaving his wife *enceinte* he started off in search of employment and from that time until *Seventeen* years afterwards she never heard from him in any way whatsoever. . . . In the meantime Robertson had gone to Alexandria, D. C., where he had entered into a successful and profitable business and married a second wife." Seventeen years after his departure, he reappeared to give Agatha and her daughter gifts and money, but told them nothing of his present circumstances. He remained in communication with them and later (after the death of his second wife) asked the family to go with him to Missouri. "The offer was not accepted." It was after the death of Robertson and his third wife that his past (he was an Englishman, really named Shinn) was inquired into.

It was logical for Melville to think of Hawthorne as the poet of Agatha's weary, faithful waiting, but in Melville's frame of mind he too was the right writer of Agatha's story. So when Hawthorne eventually returned these materials and suggestions to him, Melville worked on this story through the winter of 1852/53, in a period of the deepest hopelessness, caused by the unanimous hostility to *Pierre*. It was apparently added one day to a bonfire of unsuccessful work, but much that he had wanted to say of Agatha found its way into the characters of his first contributions to *Putnam's Monthly*—the afflictive Bartleby, and afflicted Hunilla, that "heart of earthly yearning, frozen by the frost which falleth from the sky."

❖❖❖

Bartleby

I AM a rather elderly man. The nature of my avocations, for the last thirty years, has brought me into more than ordinary contact with what would seem an interesting and somewhat singular set of men, of whom, as yet, nothing, that I know of, has ever been written—I mean the law-copyists, or scriveners. I have known very many of them, professionally and privately, and, if I pleased, could relate divers histories, at which good-natured gentlemen might smile, and sentimental souls might weep. But I waive the biographies of all other scriveners, for a few passages in the life of Bartleby, who was a scrivener, the strangest I ever saw, or heard of. While, of other law-copyists, I might write the complete life, of Bartleby nothing of that sort can be done. I believe that no materials exist for a full and satisfactory biography of this man. It is an irreparable loss to literature. Bartleby was one of those beings of whom nothing is ascertainable, except from the original sources, and, in his case, those are very small. What my own astonished eyes saw of Bartleby, that is all I know of him, except, indeed, one vague report, which will appear in the sequel.

Ere introducing the scrivener, as he first appeared to me, it is fit I make some mention of myself, my employees, my business, my chambers, and general surroundings, because some such description is indispensable to an adequate understanding of the chief character about to be presented. Imprimis: I am a man who, from his youth upward, has been filled with a profound conviction that the easiest way of life is the best. Hence, though I belong to a profession proverbially energetic and nervous, even to turbulence, at times, yet nothing of that sort have I ever suffered to invade my peace. I am one of those unambitious lawyers who never address a jury, or in any way draw down public applause; but, in the cool tranquillity of a snug retreat, do a snug business among rich men's bonds, and mortgages, and title-deeds. All who know me consider me an eminently

safe man. The late John Jacob Astor, a personage little
given to poetic enthusiasm, had no hesitation in pronouncing my first grand point to be prudence; my next,
method. I do not speak it in vanity, but simply record
the fact, that I was not unemployed in my profession
by the late John Jacob Astor; a name which, I admit,
I love to repeat; for it hath a rounded and orbicular
sound to it, and rings like unto bullion. I will freely add
that I was not insensible to the late John Jacob Astor's
good opinion.

Some time prior to the period at which this little history begins, my avocations had been largely increased.
The good old office, now extinct in the State of New
York, of a Master in Chancery had been conferred upon
me. It was not a very arduous office, but very pleasantly remunerative. I seldom lose my temper; much
more seldom indulge in dangerous indignation at wrongs
and outrages; but I must be permitted to be rash here
and declare that I consider the sudden and violent abrogation of the office of Master in Chancery, by the new
Constitution, as a —— premature act; inasmuch as I had
counted upon a life-lease of the profits, whereas I only
received those of a few short years. But this is by the
way.

My chambers were up stairs, at No. —— Wall Street.
At one end, they looked upon the white wall of the
interior of a spacious skylight shaft, penetrating the
building from top to bottom.

This view might have been considered rather tame
than otherwise, deficient in what landscape painters
call "life." But, if so, the view from the other end of my
chambers offered, at least, a contrast, if nothing more.
In that direction, my windows commanded an unobstructed view of a lofty brick wall, black by age and
everlasting shade; which wall required no spy-glass

to bring out its lurking beauties, but, for the benefit of all near-sighted spectators, was pushed up to within ten feet of my window-panes. Owing to the great height of the surrounding buildings, and my chambers being on the second floor, the interval between this wall and mine not a little resembled a huge square cistern.

At the period just preceding the advent of Bartleby, I had two persons as copyists in my employment, and a promising lad as an office-boy. First, Turkey; second, Nippers; third, Ginger Nut. These may seem names the like of which are not usually found in the Directory. In truth, they were nicknames, mutually conferred upon each other by my three clerks, and were deemed expressive of their respective persons or characters. Turkey was a short, pursy Englishman, of about my own age— that is, somewhere not far from sixty. In the morning, one might say, his face was of a fine florid hue, but after twelve o'clock, meridian—his dinner hour—it blazed like a grate full of Christmas coals, and continued blazing—but, as it were, with a gradual wane—till six o'clock, P.M., or thereabouts; after which, I saw no more of the proprietor of the face, which, gaining its meridian with the sun, seemed to set with it, to rise, culminate, and decline the following day, with the like regularity and undiminished glory. There are many singular coincidences I have known in the course of my life, not the least among which was the fact, that, exactly when Turkey displayed his fullest beams from his red and radiant countenance, just then, too, at that critical moment, began the daily period when I considered his business capacities as seriously disturbed for the remainder of the twenty-four hours. Not that he was absolutely idle, or averse to business then; far from it. The difficulty was, he was apt to be altogether too energetic. There was a strange, inflamed, flurried, flighty recklessness of activity about him. He would be incautious in dipping his pen into his inkstand. All his blots upon my documents were dropped there after twelve o'clock, meridian. Indeed, not only would he be reckless and sadly given to making blots in the afternoon, but, some days, he went further, and was rather noisy. At such times, too, his face flamed with augmented blazonry, as if cannel coal had been heaped on anthracite. He made an unpleasant racket with his chair, spilled his sand-box; in mending his pens, impatiently split them all to pieces, and threw them on the floor in a sudden passion; stood up, and leaned over his table, boxing his papers about in a most indecorous manner, very sad to behold in an elderly man like him. Nevertheless, as he was in many ways a most valuable person to me, and all the time before twelve o'clock, meridian, was the quickest, steadiest creature, too, accomplishing a great deal of work in a style not easily to be matched— for these reasons, I was willing to overlook his eccentricities, though, indeed, occasionally, I remonstrated with him. I did this very gently, however, because, though the civilest, nay, the blandest and most reverential of men in the morning, yet, in the afternoon, he was disposed, upon provocation, to be slightly rash with his tongue—in fact, insolent. Now, valuing his morning services as I did, and resolved not to lose them—yet, at the same time, made uncomfortable by his inflamed ways after twelve o'clock—and being a man of peace, unwilling by my admonitions to call forth unseemly retorts from him, I took upon me, one Saturday noon (he was always worse on Saturdays) to hint to him, very kindly, that, perhaps, now that he was growing old, it might be well to abridge his labors; in short, he need not come to my chambers after twelve o'clock, but, dinner over, had best go home to his lodgings, and rest

himself till tea-time. But no; he insisted upon his afternoon devotions. His countenance became intolerably
fervid, as he oratorically assured me—gesticulating
with a long ruler at the other end of the room—that if
his services in the morning were useful, how indispensable, then, in the afternoon?

"With submission, sir," said Turkey, on this occasion,
"I consider myself your right-hand man. In the morning I but marshal and deploy my columns; but in the
afternoon I put myself at their head, and gallantly
charge the foe, thus"—and he made a violent thrust with
the ruler.

"But the blots, Turkey," intimated I.

"True; but, with submission, sir, behold these hairs!
I am getting old. Surely, sir, a blot or two of a warm
afternoon is not to be severely urged against gray hairs.
Old age—even if it blot the page—is honorable. With
submission, sir, we both are getting old."

This appeal to my fellow-feeling was hardly to be resisted. At all events, I saw that go he would not. So
I made up my mind to let him stay, resolving, nevertheless, to see to it that, during the afternoon, he had to do
with my less important papers.

Nippers, the second on my list, was a whiskered,
sallow, and, upon the whole, rather piratical-looking
young man, of about five-and-twenty. I always deemed
him the victim of two evil powers—ambition and indigestion. The ambition was evinced by a certain impatience of the duties of a mere copyist, an unwarrant-
able usurpation of strictly professional affairs, such as
the original drawing up of legal documents. The indigestion seemed betokened in an occasional nervous testiness
and grinning irritability, causing the teeth to audibly
grind together over mistakes committed in copying; unnecessary maledictions, hissed, rather than spoken, in

the heat of business; and especially by a continual discontent with the height of the table where he worked.
Though of a very ingenious mechanical turn, Nippers
could never get this table to suit him. He put chips
under it, blocks of various sorts, bits of pasteboard, and
at last went so far as to attempt an exquisite adjustment, by final pieces of folded blotting-paper. But no
invention would answer. If, for the sake of easing his
back, he brought the table-lid at a sharp angle well up
toward his chin, and wrote there like a man using the
steep roof of a Dutch house for his desk, then he declared that it stopped the circulation in his arms. If
now he lowered the table to his waistbands, and stooped
over it in writing, then there was a sore aching in his
back. In short, the truth of the matter was, Nippers
knew not what he wanted. Or, if he wanted anything,
it was to be rid of a scrivener's table altogether. Among
the manifestations of his diseased ambition was a fond-
ness he had for receiving visits from certain ambiguous-
looking fellows in seedy coats, whom he called his
clients. Indeed, I was aware that not only was he, at
times, considerable of a ward-politician, but he occasionally did a little business at the Justices' courts, and
was not unknown on the steps of the Tombs. I have
good reason to believe, however, that one individual
who called upon him at my chambers, and who, with a
grand air, he insisted was his client, was no other than
a dun, and the alleged title-deed, a bill. But, with all
his failings, and the annoyances he caused me, Nippers,
like his compatriot Turkey, was a very useful man to
me; wrote a neat, swift hand; and, when he chose, was
not deficient in a gentlemanly sort of deportment. Added
to this, he always dressed in a gentlemanly sort of way;
and so, incidentally, reflected credit upon my chambers.
Whereas, with respect to Turkey, I had much ado to

keep him from being a reproach to me. His clothes were apt to look oily, and smell of eating-houses. He wore his pantaloons very loose and baggy in summer. His coats were execrable; his hat not to be handled. But while the hat was a thing of indifference to me, inasmuch as his natural civility and deference, as a dependent Englishman, always led him to doff it the moment he entered the room, yet his coat was another matter. Concerning his coats, I reasoned with him, but with no effect. The truth was, I suppose, that a man with so small an income could not afford to sport such a lustrous face and a lustrous coat at one and the same time. As Nippers once observed, Turkey's money went chiefly for red ink. One winter day, I presented Turkey with a highly respectable-looking coat of my own—a padded gray coat, of a most comfortable warmth, and which buttoned straight up from the knee to the neck. I thought Turkey would appreciate the favor, and abate his rashness and obstreperousness of afternoons. But no; I verily believe that buttoning himself up in so downy and blanket-like a coat had a pernicious effect upon him—upon the same principle that too much oats are bad for horses. In fact, precisely as a rash, restive horse is said to feel his oats, so Turkey felt his coat. It made him insolent. He was a man whom prosperity harmed.

Though, concerning the self-indulgent habits of Turkey, I had my own private surmises, yet, touching Nippers, I was well persuaded that, whatever might be his faults in other respects, he was, at least, a temperate young man. But, indeed, Nature herself seemed to have been his vintner, and, at his birth, charged him so thoroughly with an irritable, brandy-like disposition, that all subsequent potations were needless. When I consider how, amid the stillness of my chambers, Nippers would sometimes impatiently rise from his seat, and stooping over his table, spread his arms wide apart, seize the whole desk, and move it, and jerk it, with a grim, grinding motion on the floor, as if the table were a perverse voluntary agent, intent on thwarting and vexing him, I plainly perceive that, for Nippers, brandy-and-water were altogether superfluous.

It was fortunate for me that, owing to its peculiar cause—indigestion—the irritability and consequent nervousness of Nippers were mainly observable in the morning, while in the afternoon he was comparatively mild. So that, Turkey's paroxysms only coming on about twelve o'clock, I never had to do with their eccentricities at one time. Their fits relieved each other, like guards. When Nippers's was on, Turkey's was off; and vice versa. This was a good natural arrangement, under the circumstances.

Ginger Nut, the third on my list, was a lad, some twelve years old. His father was a car-man, ambitious of seeing his son on the bench instead of a cart, before he died. So he sent him to my office, as student at law, errand-boy, cleaner, and sweeper, at the rate of one dollar a week. He had a little desk to himself, but he did not use it much. Upon inspection, the drawer exhibited a great array of the shells of various sorts of nuts. Indeed, to this quick-witted youth, the whole noble science of the law was contained in a nutshell. Not the least among the employments of Ginger Nut, as well as one which he discharged with the most alacrity, was his duty as cake and apple purveyor for Turkey and Nippers. Copying law papers being proverbially a dry, husky sort of business, my two scriveners were fain to moisten their mouths very often with Spitzenbergs, to be had at the numerous stalls nigh the Custom House and Post Office. Also, they sent Ginger Nut very frequently for that peculiar cake—small, flat, round, and very spicy—after which he had been named by them. Of a cold morning, when business was but dull, Turkey would gobble up scores of these cakes, as if they were mere wafers—indeed, they sell them at the rate of six or eight for a penny—the scrape of his pen blending with the crunching of the crisp particles in his mouth. Of all the fiery afternoon blunders and flurried rashnesses of Turkey, was his once moistening a ginger-cake between his lips, and clapping it on to a mortgage, for a seal. I came within an ace of dismissing him then. But he mollified me by making an Oriental bow, and saying—

"With submission, sir, it was generous of me to find you in stationery on my own account."

Now my original business—that of a conveyancer and title hunter, and drawer-up of recondite documents of all sorts—was considerably increased by receiving the Master's office. There was now great work for scriveners. Not only must I push the clerks already with me, but I must have additional help.

In answer to my advertisement, a motionless young man one morning stood upon my office threshold, the door being open, for it was summer. I can see that figure now—pallidly neat, pitiably respectable, incurably forlorn! It was Bartleby.

After a few words touching his qualifications, I engaged him, glad to have among my corps of copyists a man of so singularly sedate an aspect, which I thought might operate beneficially upon the flighty temper of Turkey and the fiery one of Nippers.

I should have stated before that ground glass folding-doors divided my premises into two parts, one of which was occupied by my scriveners, the other by myself. According to my humor, I threw open these doors, or closed them. I resolved to assign Bartleby a corner by the folding-doors, but on my side of them, so as to have this quiet man within easy call, in case any trifling thing was to be done. I placed his desk close up to a small side window in that part of the room, a window which originally had afforded a lateral view of certain grimy backyards and bricks, but which owing to subsequent erections commanded at present no view at all, though it gave some light. Within three feet of the panes was a wall, and the light came down from far above, between two lofty buildings, as from a very small opening in a dome. Still further to a satisfactory arrangement, I procured a high green folding screen, which might entirely isolate Bartleby from my sight, though not remove him from my voice. And thus, in a manner, privacy and society were conjoined.

At first, Bartleby did an extraordinary quantity of writing. As if long famishing for something to copy, he seemed to gorge himself on my documents. There was no pause for digestion. He ran a day and night line, copying by sun-light and by candle-light. I should have been quite delighted with his application, had he been cheerfully industrious. But he wrote on silently, palely, mechanically.

It is, of course, an indispensable part of a scrivener's business to verify the accuracy of his copy, word by word. Where there are two or more scriveners in an office, they assist each other in this examination, one reading from the copy, the other holding the original. It is a very dull, wearisome, and lethargic affair. I can readily imagine that, to some sanguine temperaments, it would be altogether intolerable. For example, I cannot credit that the mettlesome poet, Byron, would have contentedly sat down with Bartleby to examine a law document of, say, five hundred pages, closely written in a crimpy hand.

Now and then, in the haste of business, it had been

my habit to assist in comparing some brief document myself, calling Turkey or Nippers for this purpose. One object I had, in placing Bartleby so handy to me behind the screen, was to avail myself of his services on such trivial occasions. It was on the third day, I think, of his being with me, and before any necessity had arisen for having his own writing examined, that, being much hurried to complete a small affair I had in hand, I abruptly called to Bartleby. In my haste and natural expectancy of instant compliance, I sat with my head bent over the original on my desk, and my right hand sideways, and somewhat nervously extended with the copy, so that, immediately upon emerging from his retreat, Bartleby might snatch it and proceed to business without the least delay.

In this very attitude did I sit when I called to him, rapidly stating what it was I wanted him to do—namely, to examine a small paper with me. Imagine my surprise, nay, my consternation, when, without moving from his privacy, Bartleby, in a singularly mild, firm voice, replied, "I would prefer not to."

I sat awhile in perfect silence rallying my stunned faculties. Immediately it occurred to me that my ears had deceived me, or Bartleby had entirely misunderstood my meaning. I repeated my request in the clearest tone I could assume; but in quite as clear a one came the previous reply, "I would prefer not to."

"Prefer not to," echoed I, rising in high excitement, and crossing the room with a stride. "What do you mean? Are you moon-struck? I want you to help me compare this sheet here—take it," and I thrust it towards him.

"I would prefer not to," said he.

I looked at him steadfastly. His face was leanly composed; his gray eye dimly calm. Not a wrinkle of agitation rippled him. Had there been the least uneasiness, anger, impatience or impertinence in his manner; in other words, had there been anything ordinarily human about him, doubtless I should have violently dismissed him from the premises. But as it was, I should have as soon thought of turning my pale plaster-of-Paris bust of Cicero out of doors. I stood gazing at him awhile, as he went on with his own writing, and then reseated myself at my desk. This is very strange, thought I. What had one best do? But my business hurried me. I concluded to forget the matter for the present, reserving it for my future leisure. So, calling Nippers from the other room, the paper was speedily examined.

A few days after this, Bartleby concluded four lengthy documents, being quadruplicates of a week's testimony taken before me in my High Court of Chancery. It became necessary to examine them. It was an important suit, and great accuracy was imperative. Having all things arranged, I called Turkey, Nippers, and Ginger Nut from the next room, meaning to place the four copies in the hands of my four clerks, while I should read from the original. Accordingly, Turkey, Nippers, and Ginger Nut had taken their seats in a row, each with his document in his hand, when I called to Bartleby to join this interesting group.

"Bartleby! quick, I am waiting."

I heard a slow scrape of his chair legs on the uncarpeted floor, and soon he appeared standing at the entrance of his hermitage.

"What is wanted?" said he, mildly.

"The copies, the copies," said I, hurriedly. "We are going to examine them. There"—and I held toward him the fourth quadruplicate.

"I would prefer not to," he said, and gently disappeared behind the screen.

For a few moments I was turned into a pillar of salt, standing at the head of my seated column of clerks. Recovering myself, I advanced toward the screen, and demanded the reason for such extraordinary conduct.

"*Why* do you refuse?"

"I would prefer not to."

With any other man I should have flown outright into a dreadful passion, scorned all further words, and thrust him ignominiously from my presence. But there was something about Bartleby that not only strangely disarmed me, but, in a wonderful manner, touched and disconcerted me. I began to reason with him.

"These are your own copies we are about to examine. It is labor saving to you, because one examination will answer for your four papers. It is common usage. Every copyist is bound to help examine his copy. Is it not so? Will you not speak? Answer!"

"I prefer not to," he replied in a flute-like tone. It seemed to me that, while I had been addressing him, he carefully revolved every statement that I made; fully comprehended the meaning; could not gainsay the irresistible conclusion; but, at the same time, some paramount consideration prevailed with him to reply as he did.

"You are decided, then, not to comply with my request—a request made according to common usage and common sense?"

He briefly gave me to understand that on that point my judgment was sound. Yes: his decision was irreversible.

It is not seldom the case that, when a man is browbeaten in some unprecedented and violently unreasonable way, he begins to stagger in his own plainest faith.

He begins, as it were, vaguely to surmise that, wonderful as it may be, all the justice and all the reason is on the other side. Accordingly, if any disinterested persons are present, he turns to them for some reinforcement for his own faltering mind.

"Turkey," said I, "what do you think of this? Am I not right?"

"With submission, sir," said Turkey, in his blandest tone, "I think that you are."

"Nippers," said I, "what do *you* think of it?"

"I think I should kick him out of the office."

(The reader of nice perceptions will here perceive that, it being morning, Turkey's answer is couched in polite and tranquil terms, but Nippers replies in ill-tempered ones. Or, to repeat a previous sentence, Nippers's ugly mood was on duty, and Turkey's off.)

"Ginger Nut," said I, willing to enlist the smallest suffrage in my behalf, "what do *you* think of it?"

"I think, sir, he's a little *luny*," replied Ginger Nut, with a grin.

"You hear what they say," said I, turning towards the screen. "Come forth and do your duty."

But he vouchsafed no reply. I pondered a moment in sore perplexity. But once more business hurried me. I determined again to postpone the consideration of this dilemma to my future leisure. With a little trouble we made out to examine the papers without Bartleby, though at every page or two Turkey deferentially dropped his opinion, that this proceeding was quite out of the common; while Nippers, twitching in his chair with a dyspeptic nervousness, ground out, between his set teeth, occasional hissing maledictions against the stubborn oaf behind the screen. And for his (Nippers's) part, this was the first and the last time he would do another man's business without pay.

Meanwhile Bartleby sat in his hermitage, oblivious to everything but his own peculiar business there.

Some days passed, the scrivener being employed upon another lengthy work. His late remarkable conduct led me to regard his ways narrowly. I observed that he never went to dinner; indeed, that he never went anywhere. As yet I had never, of my personal knowledge, known him to be outside of my office. He was a perpetual sentry in the corner. At about eleven o'clock though, in the morning, I noticed that Ginger Nut would advance toward the opening in Bartleby's screen, as if silently beckoned thither by a gesture invisible to me where I sat. The boy would then leave the office, jingling a few pence, and reappear with a handful of ginger-nuts, which he delivered in the hermitage, receiving two of the cakes for his trouble.

He lives, then, on ginger-nuts, thought I; never eats a dinner, properly speaking; he must be a vegetarian, then; but no; he never eats even vegetables, he eats nothing but ginger-nuts. My mind then ran on in reveries concerning the probable effects upon the human constitution of living entirely on ginger-nuts. Ginger-nuts are so called, because they contain ginger as one of their peculiar constituents, and the final flavoring one. Now, what was ginger? A hot, spicy thing. Was Bartleby hot and spicy? Not at all. Ginger, then, had no effect upon Bartleby. Probably he preferred it should have none.

Nothing so aggravates an earnest person as a passive resistance. If the individual so resisted be of a not inhumane temper, and the resisting one perfectly harmless in his passivity, then, in the better moods of the former, he will endeavor charitably to construe to his imagination what proves impossible to be solved by his judgment. Even so, for the most part, I regarded

Bartleby and his ways. Poor fellow! thought I, he means
no mischief; it is plain he intends no insolence; his
aspect sufficiently evinces that his eccentricities are involuntary. He is useful to me. I can get along with him.
If I turn him away, the chances are he will fall in with
some less indulgent employer, and then he will be
rudely treated, and perhaps driven forth miserably to
starve. Yes. Here I can cheaply purchase a delicious
self-approval. To befriend Bartleby; to humor him in
his strange willfulness, will cost me little or nothing,
while I lay up in my soul what will eventually prove a
sweet morsel for my conscience. But this mood was not
invariable with me. The passiveness of Bartleby sometimes irritated me. I felt strangely goaded on to encounter him in new opposition—to elicit some angry
spark from him answerable to my own. But, indeed, I
might as well have essayed to strike fire with my
knuckles against a bit of Windsor soap. But one afternoon the evil impulse in me mastered me, and the following little scene ensued:

"Bartleby," said I, "when those papers are all copied,
I will compare them with you."

"I would prefer not to."

"How? Surely you do not mean to persist in that
mulish vagary?"

No answer.

I threw open the folding-doors near by, and, turning upon Turkey and Nippers, exclaimed: "Bartleby a
second time says he won't examine his papers. What
do you think of it, Turkey?"

It was afternoon, be it remembered. Turkey sat glowing like a brass boiler, his bald head steaming, his
hands reeling among his blotted papers.

"Think of it?" roared Turkey. "I think I'll just step
behind his screen, and black his eyes for him!"

So saying, Turkey rose to his feet and threw his arms into a pugilistic position. He was hurrying away to make good his promise, when I detained him, alarmed at the effect of incautiously rousing Turkey's combativeness after dinner.

"Sit down, Turkey," said I, "and hear what Nippers has to say. What do you think of it, Nippers? Would I not be justified in immediately dismissing Bartleby?"

"Excuse me, that is for you to decide, sir. I think his conduct quite unusual, and, indeed, unjust, as regards Turkey and myself. But it may only be a passing whim."

"Ah," exclaimed I, "you have strangely changed your mind, then—you speak very gently of him now."

"All beer," cried Turkey; "gentleness is effects of beer —Nippers and I dined together to-day. You see how gentle *I* am, sir. Shall I go and black his eyes?"

"You refer to Bartleby, I suppose. No, not to-day, Turkey," I replied. "Pray, put up your fists."

I closed the doors, and again advanced toward Bartleby. I felt additional incentives tempting me to my fate. I burned to be rebelled against again. I remembered that Bartleby never left the office.

"Bartleby," said I, "Ginger Nut is away; just step around to the postoffice, won't you? (it was but a three minutes' walk) and see if there is anything for me."

"I would prefer not to."

"You *will* not?"

"I *prefer* not."

I staggered to my desk and sat there in a deep study. My blind inveteracy returned. Was there any other thing in which I could procure myself to be ignominiously repulsed by this lean, penniless wight?—my hired clerk? What added thing is there, perfectly reasonable, that he will be sure to refuse to do?

"Bartleby!"

No answer.

"Bartleby," in a louder tone.

No answer.

"Bartleby," I roared.

Like a very ghost, agreeably to the laws of magical invocation, at the third summons, he appeared at the entrance of his hermitage.

"Go to the next room, and tell Nippers to come to me."

"I prefer not to," he respectfully and slowly said, and mildly disappeared.

"Very good, Bartleby," said I, in a quiet sort of serenely severe self-possessed tone, intimating the unalterable purpose of some terrible retribution very close at hand. At the moment I half intended something of the kind. But upon the whole, as it was drawing towards my dinner hour, I thought it best to put on my hat and walk home for the day, suffering much from perplexity and distress of mind.

Shall I acknowledge it? The conclusion of this whole business was that it soon became a fixed fact of my chambers, that a pale young scrivener, by the name of Bartleby, had a desk there; that he copied for me at the usual rate of four cents a folio (one hundred words); but he was permanently exempt from examining the work done by him, the duty being transferred to Turkey and Nippers, out of compliment, doubtless, to their superior acuteness; moreover, said Bartleby was never, on any account, to be dispatched on the most trivial errand of any sort; and that, even if entreated to take upon him such a matter, it was generally understood that he would "prefer not to"—in other words, that he would refuse point-blank.

As days passed on, I became considerably reconciled

to Bartleby. His steadiness, his freedom from all dissipation, his incessant industry (except when he chose to throw himself into a standing reverie behind his screen), his great stillness, his unalterableness of demeanor under all circumstances, made him a valuable acquisition. One prime thing was this—he was always there—first in the morning, continually through the day, and the last at night. I had a singular confidence in his honesty. I felt my most precious papers perfectly safe in his hands. Sometimes, to be sure, I could not, for the very soul of me, avoid falling into sudden spasmodic passions with him. For it was exceeding difficult to bear in mind all the time those strange peculiarities, privileges, and unheard-of exemptions, forming the tacit stipulations on Bartleby's part under which he remained in my office. Now and then, in the eagerness of dispatching pressing business, I would inadvertently summon Bartleby, in a short, rapid tone, to put his finger, say, on the incipient tie of a bit of red tape with which I was about compressing some papers. Of course, from behind the screen the usual answer, "I prefer not to," was sure to come; and then how could a human creature, with the common infirmities of our nature, refrain from bitterly exclaiming upon such perverseness—such unreasonableness? However, every added repulse of this sort which I received only tended to lessen the probability of my repeating the inadvertence.

Here it must be said that, according to the custom of most legal gentlemen occupying chambers in densely populated law buildings, there were several keys to my door. One was kept by a woman residing in the attic, which person weekly scrubbed and daily swept and dusted my apartments. Another was kept by Turkey for convenience' sake. The third I sometimes carried in my own pocket. The fourth I knew not who had.

Now, one Sunday morning I happened to go to Trinity Church, to hear a celebrated preacher, and finding myself rather early on the ground I thought I would walk round to my chambers for a while. Luckily I had my key with me; but upon applying it to the lock, I found it resisted by something inserted from the inside. Quite surprised, I called out; when to my consternation a key was turned from within; and thrusting his lean visage at me, and holding the door ajar, the apparition of Bartleby appeared, in his shirt-sleeves, and otherwise in a strangely tattered deshabille, saying quietly that he was sorry, but he was deeply engaged just then, and— preferred not admitting me at present. In a brief word or two, he moreover added, that perhaps I had better walk round the block two or three times, and by that time he would probably have concluded his affairs.

Now, the utterly unsurmised appearance of Bartleby, tenanting my law-chambers of a Sunday morning, with his cadaverously gentlemanly *nonchalance,* yet withal firm and self-possessed, had such a strange effect upon me, that incontinently I slunk away from my own door, and did as desired. But not without sundry twinges of impotent rebellion against the mild effrontery of this unaccountable scrivener. Indeed, it was his wonderful mildness chiefly which not only disarmed me, but unmanned me, as it were. For I consider that one, for the time, is a sort of unmanned when he tranquilly permits his hired clerk to dictate to him, and order him away from his own premises. Furthermore, I was full of uneasiness as to what Bartleby could possibly be doing in my office in his shirt-sleeves, and in an otherwise dismantled condition, of a Sunday morning. Was anything amiss going on? Nay, that was out of the question. It was not to be thought of for a moment that Bartleby was an immoral person. But what could he be doing there?—copying? Nay again, whatever might be his eccentricities, Bartleby was an eminently decorous person. He would be the last man to sit down to his desk in any state approaching to nudity. Besides, it was Sunday; and there was something about Bartleby that forbade the supposition that he would by any secular occupation violate the proprieties of the day.

Nevertheless, my mind was not pacified; and full of a restless curiosity, at last I returned to the door. Without hindrance I inserted my key, opened it, and entered. Bartleby was not to be seen. I looked round anxiously, peeped behind his screen; but it was very plain that he was gone. Upon more closely examining the place, I surmised that for an indefinite period Bartleby must have ate, dressed, and slept in my office, and that too without plate, mirror, or bed. The cushioned seat of a rickety old sofa in one corner bore the faint impress of a lean, reclining form. Rolled away under his desk, I found a blanket; under the empty grate, a blacking box and brush; on a chair, a tin basin, with soap and a ragged towel; in a newspaper a few crumbs of gingernuts and a morsel of cheese. Yes, thought I, it is evident enough that Bartleby has been making his home here, keeping Bachelor's Hall all by himself. Immediately then the thought came sweeping across me, what miserable friendlessness and loneliness are here revealed! His poverty is great; but his solitude, how horrible! Think of it. Of a Sunday, Wall Street is deserted as Petra; and every night of every day it is an emptiness. This building, too, which of week-days hums with industry and life, at nightfall echoes with sheer vacancy, and all through Sunday is forlorn. And here Bartleby makes his home; sole spectator of a solitude which he has seen all populous—a sort of innocent and transformed Marius brooding among the ruins of Carthage!

For the first time in my life a feeling of overpowering stinging melancholy seized me. Before, I had never experienced aught but a not unpleasing sadness. The bond of a common humanity now drew me irresistibly to gloom. A fraternal melancholy! For both I and Bartleby were sons of Adam. I remembered the bright silks and sparkling faces I had seen that day, in gala trim, swan-like sailing down the Mississippi of Broadway; and I contrasted them with the pallid copyist, and thought to myself, Ah, happiness courts the light, so we deem the world is gay; but misery hides aloof, so we deem that misery there is none. These sad fancyings—chimeras, doubtless, of a sick and silly brain—led on to other and more special thoughts, concerning the eccentricities of Bartleby. Presentiments of strange discoveries hovered round me. The scrivener's pale form appeared to me laid out, among uncaring strangers, in its shivering winding-sheet.

Suddenly I was attracted by Bartleby's closed desk, the key in open sight left in the lock.

I mean no mischief, seek the gratification of no heartless curiosity, thought I; besides, the desk is mine, and its contents, too, so I will make bold to look within. Everything was methodically arranged, the papers smoothly placed. The pigeon-holes were deep, and removing the files of documents, I groped into their recesses. Presently I felt something there, and dragged it out. It was an old bandanna handkerchief, heavy and knotted. I opened it, and saw it was a savings bank.

I now recalled all the quiet mysteries which I had noted in the man. I remembered that he never spoke but to answer; that, though at intervals he had considerable time to himself, yet I had never seen him reading—no, not even a newspaper; that for long periods he would stand looking out, at his pale window behind the screen, upon the dead brick wall; I was quite sure he never visited any refectory or eating-house; while his pale face clearly indicated that he never drank beer like Turkey, or tea and coffee even, like other men; that he never went anywhere in particular that I could learn; never went out for a walk, unless, indeed, that was the case at present; that he had declined telling who he was, or whence he came, or whether he had any relatives in the world; that though so thin and pale, he never complained of ill-health. And more than all, I remembered a certain unconscious air of pallid—how shall I call it?—of pallid haughtiness, say, or rather an austere reserve about him, which had positively awed me into my tame compliance with his eccentricities, when I had feared to ask him to do the slightest inciden-tal thing for me, even though I might know, from his long-continued motionlessness, that behind his screen he must be standing in one of those dead-wall reveries of his.

Revolving all these things, and coupling them with the recently discovered fact that he made my office his constant abiding place and home, and not forgetful of his morbid moodiness; revolving all these things, a prudential feeling began to steal over me. My first emo-tions had been those of pure melancholy and sincerest pity; but just in proportion as the forlornness of Bartleby grew and grew to my imagination, did that same mel-ancholy merge into fear, that pity into repulsion. So true it is, and so terrible, too, that up to a certain point the thought or sight of misery enlists our best affections; but, in certain special cases, beyond that point it does not. They err who would assert that invariably this is owing to the inherent selfishness of the human heart. It rather proceeds from a certain hopelessness of rem-edying excessive and organic ill. To a sensitive being, pity is not seldom pain. And when at last it is perceived that such pity cannot lead to effectual succor, common sense bids the soul be rid of it. What I saw that morning persuaded me that the scrivener was the victim of innate and incurable disorder. I might give alms to his body; but his body did not pain him; it was his soul that suffered, and his soul I could not reach.

I did not accomplish the purpose of going to Trinity Church that morning. Somehow, the things I had seen disqualified me for the time from church-going. I walked homeward, thinking what I would do with Bartleby. Finally, I resolved upon this—I would put certain calm questions to him the next morning, touching his history, etc., and if he declined to answer them openly and unreservedly (and I supposed he would prefer not), then to give him a twenty dollar bill over and above whatever I might owe him, and tell him his services were no longer required; but that if in any other way I could assist him, I would be happy to do so, especially if he desired to return to his native place, wherever that might be, I would willingly help to defray the expenses. Moreover, if, after reaching home, he found himself at any time in want of aid, a letter from him would be sure of a reply.

The next morning came.

"Bartleby," said I, gently calling to him behind his screen.

No reply.

"Bartleby," said I, in a still gentler tone, "come here; I am not going to ask you to do anything you would prefer not to do—I simply wish to speak to you."

Upon this he noiselessly slid into view.

"Will you tell me, Bartleby, where you were born?"

"I would prefer not to."

"Will you tell me *anything* about yourself?"

"I would prefer not to."

"But what reasonable objection can you have to speak to me? I feel friendly towards you."

He did not look at me while I spoke, but kept his glance fixed upon my bust of Cicero, which, as I then sat, was directly behind me, some six inches above my head.

"What is your answer, Bartleby?" said I, after waiting a considerable time for a reply, during which his countenance remained immovable, only there was the faintest conceivable tremor of the white attenuated mouth.

"At present I prefer to give no answer," he said, and retired into his hermitage.

It was rather weak in me, I confess, but his manner, on this occasion, nettled me. Not only did there seem to lurk in it a certain calm disdain, but his perverseness seemed ungrateful, considering the undeniable good usage and indulgence he had received from me.

Again I sat ruminating what I should do. Mortified as I was at his behavior, and resolved as I had been to dismiss him when I entered my office, nevertheless I strangely felt something superstitious knocking at my heart, and forbidding me to carry out my purpose, and denouncing me for a villain if I dared to breathe one bitter word against this forlornest of mankind. At last, familiarly drawing my chair behind his screen, I sat down and said: "Bartleby, never mind, then, about revealing your history; but let me entreat you, as a friend, to comply as far as may be with the usages of this office. Say now, you will help to examine papers to-morrow or next day: in short, say now, that in a day or two you will begin to be a little reasonable:—say so, Bartleby."

"At present I would prefer not to be a little reasonable," was his mildly cadaverous reply.

Just then the folding-doors opened, and Nippers approached. He seemed suffering from an unusually bad night's rest, induced by severer indigestion than common. He overheard those final words of Bartleby.

"*Prefer not*, eh?" gritted Nippers—"I'd *prefer* him, if I were you, sir," addressing me—"I'd *prefer* him; I'd give him preferences, the stubborn mule! What is it, sir, pray, that he *prefers* not to do now?"

Bartleby moved not a limb.

"Mr. Nippers," said I, "I'd prefer that you would withdraw for the present."

Somehow, of late, I had got into the way of involuntarily using this word "prefer" upon all sorts of not exactly suitable occasions. And I trembled to think that my contact with the scrivener had already and seriously affected me in a mental way. And what further and deeper aberration might it not yet produce? This apprehension had not been without efficacy in determining me to summary measures.

As Nippers, looking very sour and sulky, was departing, Turkey blandly and deferentially approached.

"With submission, sir," said he, "yesterday I was thinking about Bartleby here, and I think that if he would but prefer to take a quart of good ale every day, it would do much towards mending him, and enabling him to assist in examining his papers."

"So you have got the word, too," said I, slightly excited.

"With submission, what word, sir?" asked Turkey, respectfully crowding himself into the contracted space behind the screen, and by so doing, making me jostle the scrivener. "What word, sir?"

"I would prefer to be left alone here," said Bartleby, as if offended at being mobbed in his privacy.

"*That's* the word, Turkey," said I, "*that's* it."

"Oh, *prefer?* oh yes—queer word. I never use it myself. But, sir, as I was saying, if he would but prefer—"

"Turkey," interrupted I, "you will please withdraw."

"Oh certainly, sir, if you prefer that I should."

As he opened the folding-door to retire, Nippers at his desk caught a glimpse of me, and asked whether I would prefer to have a certain paper copied on blue paper or white. He did not in the least roguishly accent the word "prefer." It was plain that it involuntarily rolled from his tongue. I thought to myself, surely I must get rid of a demented man, who already has in some degree turned the tongues, if not the heads, of myself and clerks. But I thought it prudent not to break the dismission at once.

The next day I noticed that Bartleby did nothing but stand at his window in his dead-wall reverie. Upon asking him why he did not write, he said that he had decided upon doing no more writing.

"Why, how now? what next?" exclaimed I, "do no more writing?"

"No more."

"And what is the reason?"

"Do you not see the reason for yourself?" he indifferently replied.

I looked steadfastly at him, and perceived that his eyes looked dull and glazed. Instantly it occurred to me, that his unexampled diligence in copying by his dim window for the first few weeks of his stay with me might have temporarily impaired his vision.

I was touched. I said something in condolence with him. I hinted that of course he did wisely in abstaining from writing for a while, and urged him to embrace that opportunity of taking wholesome exercise in the open air. This, however, he did not do. A few days after this, my other clerks being absent, and being in a great hurry to dispatch certain letters by the mail, I thought that, having nothing else earthly to do, Bartleby would surely be less inflexible than usual, and carry these letters to the postoffice. But he blankly declined. So, much to my inconvenience, I went myself.

Still added days went by. Whether Bartleby's eyes improved or not, I could not say. To all appearance, I thought they did. But when I asked him if they did, he vouchsafed no answer. At all events, he would do no copying. At last, in reply to my urgings, he informed me that he had permanently given up copying.

"What!" exclaimed I; "suppose your eyes should get entirely well—better than ever before—would you not copy then?"

"I have given up copying," he answered, and slid aside.

He remained as ever, a fixture in my chamber. Nay —if that were possible—he became still more of a fixture than before. What was to be done? He would do nothing in the office; why should he stay there? In plain fact, he had now become a millstone to me, not only useless as a necklace, but afflictive to bear. Yet I was sorry for him. I speak less than truth when I say that, on his own account, he occasioned me uneasiness. If he would but have named a single relative or friend, I would instantly have written, and urged their taking the poor fellow away to some convenient retreat. But he seemed alone, absolutely alone in the universe. A bit of wreck in the mid-Atlantic. At length, necessities connected with my business tyrannized over all other considerations. Decently as I could, I told Bartleby that in six days' time he must unconditionally leave the office. I warned him to take measures, in the interval, for procuring some other abode. I offered to assist him in this endeavor, if he himself would but take the first step towards a removal. "And when you finally quit me, Bartleby," added I, "I shall see that you go not away entirely unprovided. Six days from this hour, remember."

At the expiration of that period, I peeped behind the screen, and lo! Bartleby was there.

I buttoned up my coat, balanced myself, advanced slowly towards him, touched his shoulder, and said, "The time has come; you must quit this place; I am sorry for you; here is money; but you must go."

"I would prefer not," he replied, with his back still towards me.

"You *must*."

He remained silent.

Now I had an unbounded confidence in this man's common honesty. He had frequently restored to me sixpences and shillings carelessly dropped upon the floor, for I am apt to be very reckless in such shirt-button affairs. The proceeding, then, which followed will not be deemed extraordinary.

"Bartleby," said I, "I owe you twelve dollars on account; here are thirty-two; the odd twenty are yours —Will you take it?" and I handed the bills towards him.

But he made no motion.

"I will leave them here, then," putting them under a weight on the table. Then taking my hat and cane and going to the door, I tranquilly turned and added, "After you have removed your things from these offices, Bartleby, you will of course lock the door—since every one is now gone for the day but you—and if you please, slip your key underneath the mat, so that I may have it in the morning. I shall not see you again; so good-by to you. If, hereafter, in your new place of abode, I can be of any service to you, do not fail to advise me by letter. Good-by, Bartleby, and fare you well."

But he answered not a word; like the last column of some ruined temple, he remained standing mute and solitary in the middle of the otherwise deserted room.

As I walked home in a pensive mood, my vanity got the better of my pity. I could not but highly plume myself on my masterly management in getting rid of Bartleby. Masterly I call it, and such it must appear to any dispassionate thinker. The beauty of my procedure seemed to consist in its perfect quietness. There was no vulgar bullying, no bravado of any sort, no choleric hectoring, and striding to and fro across the apartment, jerking out vehement commands for Bartleby to bundle himself off with his beggarly traps. Nothing of the kind. Without loudly bidding Bartleby depart—as an inferior genius might have done—I *assumed* the ground that depart he must; and upon that assumption built all I had to say. The more I thought over my procedure, the more I was charmed with it. Nevertheless, next morning, upon awakening, I had my doubts—I had somehow slept off the fumes of vanity. One of the coolest and wisest hours a man has is just after he awakes in the morning. My procedure seemed as sagacious as ever— but only in theory. How it would prove in practice— there was the rub. It was truly a beautiful thought to have assumed Bartleby's departure; but, after all, that assumption was simply my own, and none of Bartleby's. The great point was, not whether I had assumed that he would quit me, but whether he would prefer so to do. He was more a man of preferences than assumptions.

After breakfast, I walked down town, arguing the probabilities *pro* and *con*. One moment I thought it would prove a miserable failure, and Bartleby would be found all alive at my office as usual; the next moment it seemed certain that I should find his chair empty. And so I kept veering about. At the corner of Broadway and Canal Street, I saw quite an excited group of people standing in earnest conversation.

"I'll take odds he doesn't," said a voice as I passed.

"Doesn't go?—done!" said I, "put up your money."

I was instinctively putting my hand in my pocket to produce my own, when I remembered that this was an election day. The words I had overheard bore no reference to Bartleby, but to the success or non-success of some candidate for the mayoralty. In my intent frame of mind, I had, as it were, imagined that all Broadway shared in my excitement, and were debating the same question with me. I passed on, very thankful that the uproar of the street screened my momentary absentmindedness.

As I had intended, I was earlier than usual at my office door. I stood listening for a moment. All was still. He must be gone. I tried the knob. The door was locked. Yes, my procedure had worked to a charm; he indeed must be vanished. Yet a certain melancholy mixed with this: I was almost sorry for my brilliant success. I was fumbling under the door mat for the key, which Bartleby was to have left there for me, when accidentally my knee knocked against a panel, producing a summoning sound, and in response a voice came to me from within—"Not yet; I am occupied."

It was Bartleby.

I was thunderstruck. For an instant I stood like the man who, pipe in mouth, was killed one cloudless afternoon long ago in Virginia, by summer lightning; at his own warm open window he was killed, and remained leaning out there upon the dreamy afternoon, till some one touched him, when he fell.

"Not gone!" I murmured at last. But again obeying that wondrous ascendancy which the inscrutable scrivener had over me, and from which ascendancy, for all my chafing, I could not completely escape, I slowly went down stairs and out into the street, and while walking round the block, considered what I should next do in this unheard-of perplexity. Turn the man out by an actual thrusting I could not; to drive him away by calling him hard names would not do; calling in the police was an unpleasant idea; and yet, permit him to enjoy his cadaverous triumph over me—this, too, I could not think of. What was to be done? or, if nothing could be done, was there anything further that I could *assume* in the matter? Yes, as before I had prospectively assumed that Bartleby would depart, so now I might retrospectively assume that departed he was. In the legitimate carrying out of this assumption, I might enter my office in a great hurry, and pretending not to see Bartleby at all, walk straight against him as if he were air. Such a proceeding would in a singular degree have the appearance of a home-thrust. It was hardly possible that Bartleby could withstand such an application of the doctrine of assumptions. But upon second thoughts the success of the plan seemed rather dubious. I resolved to argue the matter over with him again.

"Bartleby," said I, entering the office, with a quietly severe expression, "I am seriously displeased. I am pained, Bartleby. I had thought better of you. I had imagined you of such a gentlemanly organization that in any delicate dilemma a slight hint would suffice—in short, an assumption. But it appears I am deceived. Why," I added, unaffectedly starting, "you have not

even touched that money yet," pointing to it, just where
I had left it the evening previous.

He answered nothing.

"Will you, or will you not, quit me?" I now demanded
in a sudden passion, advancing close to him.

"I would prefer *not* to quit you," he replied, gently
emphasizing the *not*.

"What earthly right have you to stay here? Do you
pay any rent? Do you pay my taxes? Or is this property
yours?"

He answered nothing.

"Are you ready to go on and write now? Are your
eyes recovered? Could you copy a small paper for me
this morning? or help examine a few lines? or step round
to the postoffice? In a word, will you do anything at
all, to give a coloring to your refusal to depart the
premises?"

He silently retired into his hermitage.

I was now in such a state of nervous resentment that
I thought it but prudent to check myself at present from
further demonstrations. Bartleby and I were alone. I
remembered the tragedy of the unfortunate Adams and
the still more unfortunate Colt in the solitary office of
the latter; and how poor Colt, being dreadfully incensed
by Adams, and imprudently permitting himself to get
wildly excited, was at unawares hurried into his fatal
act—an act which certainly no man could possibly
deplore more than the actor himself. Often it had occurred to me in my ponderings upon the subject that
had altercation taken place in the public street, or at a
private residence, it would not have terminated as it
did. It was the circumstance of being alone in a solitary
office, up stairs, of a building entirely unhallowed by
humanizing domestic associations—an uncarpeted office,
doubtless, of a dusty, haggard sort of appearance—this

it must have been, which greatly helped to enhance the irritable desperation of the hapless Colt.

But when this old Adam of resentment rose in me and tempted me concerning Bartleby, I grappled him and threw him. How? Why, simply by recalling the divine injunction: "A new commandment give I unto you, that ye love one another." Yes, this it was that saved me. Aside from higher considerations, charity often operates as a vastly wise and prudent principle— a great safeguard to its possessor. Men have committed murder for jealousy's sake, and anger's sake, and hatred's sake, and selfishness' sake, and spiritual pride's sake; but no man that ever I heard of ever committed a diabolical murder for sweet charity's sake. Mere self-interest, then, if no better motive can be enlisted, should, especially with high-tempered men, prompt all beings to charity and philanthropy. At any rate, upon the occasion in question, I strove to drown my exasperated feelings towards the scrivener by benevolently construing his conduct. Poor fellow, poor fellow! thought I, he don't mean anything; and besides, he has seen hard times, and ought to be indulged.

I endeavored, also, immediately to occupy myself, and at the same time to comfort my despondency. I tried to fancy, that in the course of the morning, at such time as might prove agreeable to him, Bartleby, of his own free accord, would emerge from his hermitage and take up some decided line of march in the direction of the door. But no. Half-past twelve o'clock came; Turkey began to glow in the face, overturn his inkstand, and become generally obstreperous; Nippers abated down into quietude and courtesy; Ginger Nut munched his noon apple; and Bartleby remained standing at his window in one of his profoundest dead-wall reveries. Will it be credited? Ought I to acknowledge it? That afternoon I left the office without saying one further word to him.

Some days now passed, during which, at leisure intervals I looked a little into *Edwards on the Will,* and *Priestley on Necessity.* Under the circumstances, those books induced a salutary feeling. Gradually I slid into the persuasion that these troubles of mine, touching the scrivener, had been all predestinated from eternity, and Bartleby was billeted upon me for some mysterious purpose of an all-wise Providence, which it was not for a mere mortal like me to fathom. Yes, Bartleby, stay there behind your screen, thought I; I shall persecute you no more; you are harmless and noiseless as any of these old chairs; in short, I never feel so private as when I know you are here. At last I see it, I feel it; I penetrate to the predestinated purpose of my life. I am content. Others may have loftier parts to enact; but my mission in this world, Bartleby, is to furnish you with office room for such period as you may see fit to remain.

I believe that this wise and blessed frame of mind would have continued with me, had it not been for the unsolicited and uncharitable remarks obtruded upon me by my professional friends who visited the rooms. But thus it often is, that the constant friction of illiberal minds wears out at last the best resolves of the more generous. Though to be sure, when I reflected upon it, it was not strange that people entering my office should be struck by the peculiar aspect of the unaccountable Bartleby, and so be tempted to throw out some sinister observations concerning him. Sometimes an attorney, having business with me, and calling at my office, and finding no one but the scrivener there, would undertake to obtain some sort of precise information from him touching my whereabouts; but without heeding his idle talk, Bartleby would remain standing immovable in the middle of the room. So after contemplating him in that position for a time, the attorney would depart, no wiser than he came.

Also, when a reference was going on, and the room full of lawyers and witnesses, and business driving fast, some deeply occupied legal gentleman present, seeing Bartleby wholly unemployed, would request him to run round to his (the legal gentleman's) office and fetch some papers for him. Thereupon, Bartleby would tranquilly decline, and yet remain idle as before. Then the lawyer would give a great stare, and turn to me. And what could I say? At last I was made aware that all through the circle of my professional acquaintance, a whisper of wonder was running round, having reference to the strange creature I kept at my office. This worried me very much. And as the idea came upon me of his possibly turning out a long-lived man, and keep occupying my chambers, and denying my authority, and perplexing my visitors, and scandalizing my professional reputation, and casting a general gloom over the premises; keeping soul and body together to the last upon his savings (for doubtless he spent but half a dime a day), and in the end perhaps outlive me, and claim possession of my office by right of his perpetual occupancy: as all these dark anticipations crowded upon me more and more, and my friends continually intruded their relentless remarks upon the apparition in my room, a great change was wrought in me. I resolved to gather all my faculties together, and forever rid me of this intolerable incubus.

Ere revolving any complicated project, however, adapted to this end, I first simply suggested to Bartleby the propriety of his permanent departure. In a calm and serious tone, I commended the idea to his careful and mature consideration. But, having taken three days to meditate upon it, he apprised me that his original determination remained the same; in short, that he still preferred to abide with me.

What shall I do? I now said to myself, buttoning up my coat to the last button. What shall I do? what ought I to do? what does conscience say I *should* do with this man, or, rather, ghost. Rid myself of him, I must; go, he shall. But how? You will not thrust him, the poor, pale, passive mortal—you will not thrust such a helpless creature out of your door? you will not dishonor yourself by such cruelty? No, I will not, I cannot do that. Rather would I let him live and die here, and then mason up his remains in the wall. What, then, will you do? For all your coaxing, he will not budge. Bribes he leaves under your own paper-weight on your table; in short, it is quite plain that he prefers to cling to you.

Then something severe, something unusual must be done. What! surely you will not have him collared by a constable, and commit his innocent pallor to the common jail? And upon what ground could you procure such a thing to be done?—a vagrant, is he? What! he a vagrant, a wanderer, who refuses to budge? It is because he will *not* be a vagrant, then, that you seek to count him *as* a vagrant. That is too absurd. No visible means of support: there I have him. Wrong again: for indubitably he *does* support himself, and that is the only unanswerable proof that any man can show of his possessing the means so to do. No more, then. Since he will not quit me, I must quit him. I will change my offices; I will move elsewhere, and give him fair notice that if I find him on my new premises I will then proceed against him as a common trespasser.

Acting accordingly, next day I thus addressed him: "I find these chambers too far from the City Hall; the air is unwholesome. In a word, I propose to remove my offices next week, and shall no longer require your services. I tell you this now, in order that you may seek another place."

He made no reply, and nothing more was said.

On the appointed day I engaged carts and men, proceeded to my chambers, and, having but little furniture, everything was removed in a few hours. Throughout, the scrivener remained standing behind the screen, which I directed to be removed the last thing. It was withdrawn, and, being folded up like a huge folio, left him the motionless occupant of a naked room. I stood in the entry watching him a moment, while something from within me upbraided me.

I re-entered, with my hand in my pocket—and—and my heart in my mouth.

"Good-by, Bartleby; I am going—good-by, and God some way bless you; and take that," slipping something in his hand. But it dropped upon the floor, and then—strange to say—I tore myself from him whom I had so longed to be rid of.

Established in my new quarters, for a day or two I kept the door locked, and started at every footfall in the passages. When I returned to my rooms, after any little absence, I would pause at the threshold for an instant, and attentively listen, ere applying my key. But these fears were needless. Bartleby never came nigh me.

I thought all was going well, when a perturbed-looking stranger visited me, inquiring whether I was the person who had recently occupied rooms at No. ⸺ Wall Street.

Full of forebodings, I replied that I was.

"Then, sir," said the stranger, who proved a lawyer, "you are responsible for the man you left there. He refuses to do any copying; he refuses to do anything;

he says he prefers not to; and he refuses to quit the premises."

"I am very sorry, sir," said I, with assumed tranquillity, but an inward tremor, "but, really, the man you allude to is nothing to me—he is no relation or apprentice of mine, that you should hold me responsible for him."

"In mercy's name, who is he?"

"I certainly cannot inform you. I know nothing about him. Formerly I employed him as a copyist; but he has done nothing for me now for some time past."

"I shall settle him, then—good morning, sir."

Several days passed, and I heard nothing more; and, though I often felt a charitable prompting to call at the place and see poor Bartleby, yet a certain squeamishness, of I know not what, withheld me.

All is over with him, by this time, thought I, at last, when, through another week, no further intelligence reached me. But, coming to my room the day after, I found several persons waiting at my door in a high state of nervous excitement.

"That's the man—here he comes," cried the foremost one, whom I recognized as the lawyer who had previously called upon me alone.

"You must take him away, sir, at once," cried a portly person among them, advancing upon me, and whom I knew to be the landlord of No. — Wall Street. "These gentlemen, my tenants, cannot stand it any longer; Mr. B——," pointing to the lawyer, "has turned him out of his room, and he now persists in haunting the building generally, sitting upon the banisters of the stairs by day, and sleeping in the entry by night. Everybody is concerned; clients are leaving the offices; some fears are entertained of a mob; something you must do, and that without delay."

Aghast at this torrent, I fell back before it, and would fain have locked myself in my new quarters. In vain I persisted that Bartleby was nothing to me— no more than to any one else. In vain—I was the last person known to have anything to do with him, and they held me to the terrible account. Fearful, then, of being exposed in the papers (as one person present obscurely threatened), I considered the matter, and, at length, said, that if the lawyer would give me a confidential interview with the scrivener, in his (the lawyer's) own room, I would, that afternoon, strive my best to rid them of the nuisance they complained of.

Going up stairs to my old haunt, there was Bartleby silently sitting upon the banister at the landing.

"What are you doing here, Bartleby?" said I.

"Sitting upon the banister," he mildly replied.

I motioned him into the lawyer's room, who then left us.

"Bartleby," said I, "are you aware that you are the cause of great tribulation to me, by persisting in occupying the entry after being dismissed from the office?"

No answer.

"Now one of two things must take place. Either you must do something, or something must be done to you. Now what sort of business would you like to engage in? Would you like to re-engage in copying for some one?"

"No; I would prefer not to make any change."

"Would you like a clerkship in a dry-goods store?"

"There is too much confinement about that. No, I would not like a clerkship; but I am not particular."

"Too much confinement," I cried, "why, you keep yourself confined all the time!"

"I would prefer not to take a clerkship," he rejoined, as if to settle that little item at once.

"How would a bar-tender's business suit you? There is no trying of the eyesight in that."

"I would not like it at all; though, as I said before, I am not particular."

His unwonted wordiness inspirited me. I returned to the charge.

"Well, then, would you like to travel through the country collecting bills for the merchants? That would improve your health."

"No, I would prefer to be doing something else."

"How, then, would going as a companion to Europe, to entertain some young gentleman with your conversation—how would that suit you?"

"Not at all. It does not strike me that there is anything definite about that. I like to be stationary. But I am not particular."

"Stationary you shall be, then," I cried, now losing all patience, and, for the first time in all my exasperating connection with him, fairly flying into a passion. "If you do not go away from these premises before night, I shall feel bound—indeed, I *am* bound—to—to—to quit the premises myself!" I rather absurdly concluded, knowing not with what possible threat to try to frighten his immobility into compliance. Despairing of all further efforts, I was precipitately leaving him, when a final thought occurred to me—one which had not been wholly unindulged before.

"Bartleby," said I, in the kindest tone I could assume under such exciting circumstances, "will you go home with me now—not to my office, but my dwelling—and remain there till we can conclude upon some convenient arrangement for you at our leisure? Come, let us start now, right away."

"No, at present I would prefer not to make any change at all."

I answered nothing; but, effectually dodging every one by the suddenness and rapidity of my flight, rushed from the building, ran up Wall Street towards Broadway, and, jumping into the first omnibus, was soon removed from pursuit. As soon as tranquillity returned, I distinctly perceived that I had now done all that I possibly could, both in respect to the demands of the landlord and his tenants, and with regard to my own desire and sense of duty, to benefit Bartleby, and shield him from rude persecution. I now strove to be entirely carefree and quiescent; and my conscience justified me in attempt; though, indeed, it was not so successful as I could have wished. So fearful was I of being again hunted out by the incensed landlord and his exasperated tenants, that, surrendering my business to Nippers for a few days, I drove about the upper part of the town and through the suburbs, in my rockaway, crossed over to Jersey City and Hoboken, and paid fugitive visits to Manhattanville and Astoria. In fact, I almost lived in my rockaway for the time.

When again I entered my office, lo, a note from the landlord lay upon the desk. I opened it with trembling hands. It informed me that the writer had sent to the police, and had Bartleby removed to the Tombs as a vagrant. Moreover, since I knew more about him than any one else, he wished me to appear at that place, and make a suitable statement of the facts. These tidings had a conflicting effect upon me. At first I was indignant, but, at last, almost approved. The landlord's energetic, summary disposition had led him to adopt a procedure which I do not think I would have decided upon myself; and yet, as a last resort, under such peculiar circumstances, it seemed the only plan.

As I afterwards learned, the poor scrivener, when told that he must be conducted to the Tombs, offered not the slightest obstacle, but, in his pale, unmoving way, silently acquiesced.

Some of the compassionate and curious bystanders joined the party; and headed by one of the constables arm-in-arm with Bartleby, the silent procession filed its way through all the noise, and heat, and joy of the roaring thoroughfares at noon.

The same day I received the note, I went to the Tombs, or, to speak more properly, the Halls of Justice. Seeking the right officer, I stated the purpose of my call, and was informed that the individual I described was, indeed, within. I then assured the functionary that Bartleby was a perfectly honest man, and greatly to be compassionated, however unaccountably eccentric. I narrated all I knew, and closed by suggesting the idea of letting him remain in as indulgent confinement as possible, till something less harsh might be done— though, indeed, I hardly knew what. At all events, if nothing else could be decided upon, the almshouse must receive him. I then begged to have an interview.

Being under no disgraceful charge, and quite serene and harmless in all his ways, they had permitted him freely to wander about the prison, and, especially, in the inclosed grass-platted yards thereof. And so I found him there, standing all alone in the quietest of the yards, his face towards a high wall, while all around, from the narrow slits of the jail windows, I thought I saw peering out upon him the eyes of murderers and thieves.

"Bartleby!"

"I know you," he said, without looking round, "and I want nothing to say to you."

"It was not I that brought you here, Bartleby," said I, keenly pained at his implied suspicion. "And to you, this should not be so vile a place. Nothing reproachful attaches to you by being here. And see, it is not so sad a place as one might think. Look, there is the sky, and here is the grass."

"I know where I am," he replied, but would say nothing more, and so I left him.

As I entered the corridor again, a broad meat-like man, in an apron, accosted me, and, jerking his thumb over his shoulder, said, "Is that your friend?"

"Yes."

"Does he want to starve? If he does, let him live on the prison fare, that's all."

"Who are you?" asked I, not knowing what to make of such an unofficially speaking person in such a place.

"I am the grub-man. Such gentlemen as have friends here hire me to provide them with something good to eat."

"Is this so?" said I, turning to the turnkey.

He said it was.

"Well, then," said I, slipping some silver into the grub-man's hands (for so they called him), "I want you to give particular attention to my friend there; let him have the best dinner you can get. And you must be as polite to him as possible."

"Introduce me, will you?" said the grub-man, looking at me with an expression which seemed to say he was all impatience for an opportunity to give a specimen of his breeding.

Thinking it would prove of benefit to the scrivener, I acquiesced, and, asking the grub-man his name, went up with him to Bartleby.

"Bartleby, this is a friend; you will find him very useful to you."

"Your sarvant, sir, your sarvant," said the grub-man, making a low salutation behind his apron. "Hope you find it pleasant here, sir; nice grounds—cool apartments—hope you'll stay with us some time—try to make it agreeable. What will you have for dinner to-day?"

"I prefer not to dine to-day," said Bartleby, turning away. "It would disagree with me; I am unused to dinners." So saying, he slowly moved to the other side of the inclosure, and took up a position fronting the dead-wall.

"How's this?" said the grub-man, addressing me with a stare of astonishment. "He's odd, ain't he?"

"I think he is a little deranged," said I, sadly.

"Deranged? deranged is it? Well, now, upon my word, I thought that friend of yourn was a gentleman forger; they are always pale and genteel-like, them forgers. I can't help pity 'em—can't help it, sir. Did you know Monroe Edwards?" he added, touchingly, and paused, then, laying his hand piteously on my shoulder, sighed, "He died of consumption at Sing-Sing. So you weren't acquainted with Monroe?"

"No, I was never socially acquainted with any forgers. But I cannot stop longer. Look to my friend yonder. You will not lose by it. I will see you again."

Some few days after this, I again obtained admission to the Tombs, and went through the corridors in quest of Bartleby, but without finding him.

"I saw him coming from his cell not long ago," said a turnkey, "may be he's gone to loiter in the yards."

So I went in that direction.

"Are you looking for the silent man?" said another turnkey, passing me. "Yonder he lies—sleeping in the yard there. 'Tis not twenty minutes since I saw him lie down."

The yard was entirely quiet. It was not accessible to the common prisoners. The surrounding walls, of amazing thickness, kept off all sounds behind them. The

Egyptian character of the masonry weighed upoﾠ ﾠﾮﾠﾮﾠe
with its gloom. But a soft imprisoned turf grew under
foot. The heart of the eternal pyramids, it seemed,
wherein, by some strange magic, through the clefts,
grass seed, dropped by birds, had sprung.

Strangely huddled at the base of the wall, his knees
drawn up, and lying on his side, his head touching the
cold stones, I saw the wasted Bartleby. But nothing
stirred. I paused; then went close up to him; stooped
over, and saw that his dim eyes were open; otherwise
he seemed profoundly sleeping. Something prompted
me to touch him. I felt his hand, when a tingling shiver
ran up my arm and down my spine to my feet.

The round face of the grub-man peered upon me
now. "His dinner is ready. Won't he dine today, either?
Or does he live without dining?"

"Lives without dining," said I, and closed the eyes.

"Eh!—He's asleep, ain't he?"

"With kings and counselors," murmured I.

There would seem little need for proceeding further
in this history. Imagination will readily supply the
meager recital of poor Bartleby's interment. But, ere
parting with the reader, let me say that if this little
narrative has sufficiently interested him to awaken curiosity as to who Bartleby was, and what manner of
life he led prior to the present narrator's making his
acquaintance, I can only reply that in such curiosity
I fully share, but am wholly unable to gratify it. Yet
here I hardly know whether I should divulge one little
item of rumor, which came to my ear a few months
after the scrivener's decease. Upon what basis it rested,
I could never ascertain, and hence how true it is I
cannot tell. But, inasmuch as this vague report has not
been without a certain suggestive interest to me, how-

ever sad, it may prove the same with some others; and so I will briefly mention it. The report was this: that Bartleby had been a subordinate clerk in the Dead Letter Office at Washington, from which he had been suddenly removed by a change in the administration. When I think over this rumor, hardly can I express the emotions which seize me. Dead letters! does it not sound like dead men? Conceive a man by nature and misfortune prone to a pallid hopelessness, can any business seem more fitted to heighten it than that of continually handling these dead letters, and assorting them for the flames? For by the cart-load they are annually burned. Sometimes from out the folded paper the pale clerk takes a ring—the finger it was meant for, perhaps, moulders in the grave; a bank-note sent in swiftest charity—he whom it would relieve nor eats nor hungers any more; pardon for those who died despairing; hope for those who died unhoping; good tidings for those who died stifled by unrelieved calamities. On errands of life, these letters speed to death.

Ah, Bartleby! Ah, humanity!

(From *The Piazza Tales*)

From The Encantadas, or Enchanted Isles

Norfolk Isle and the Chola Widow

FAR TO the northeast of Charles's Isle, sequestered from the rest, lies Norfolk Isle; and, however insignificant to most voyagers, to me, through sympathy, that lone island has become a spot made sacred by the strangest trials of humanity.

It was my first visit to the Encantadas. Two days had been spent ashore in hunting tortoises. There was not time to capture many; so on the third afternoon we loosed our sails. We were just in the act of getting under way, the uprooted anchor yet suspended and invisibly swaying beneath the wave, as the good ship gradually turned her heel to leave the isle behind, when the seaman who heaved with me at the windlass paused suddenly, and directed my attention to something moving on the land, not along the beach, but somewhat back, fluttering from a height.

In view of the sequel of this little story, be it here narrated how it came to pass that an object, which, partly from its being so small, was quite lost to every other man on board still caught the eye of my handspike companion. The rest of the crew, myself included, merely stood up to our spikes in heaving, whereas, unwontedly exhilarated, at every turn of the ponderous windlass, my belted comrade leaped atop of it, with might and main giving a downward, thewy, perpendicular heave, his raised eye bent in cheery animation upon the slowly receding shore. Being high lifted above all others was the reason he perceived the object, otherwise unperceivable; and this elevation of his eye was owing to the elevation of his spirits; and this again— for truth must out—to a dram of Peruvian pisco, in guerdon for some kindness done, secretly administered to him that morning by our mulatto steward. Now, certainly, pisco does a deal of mischief in the world; yet seeing that, in the present case, it was the means, though indirect, of rescuing a human being from the most dreadful fate, must we not also needs admit that sometimes pisco does a deal of good?

Glancing across the water in the direction pointed out, I saw some white thing hanging from an inland rock, perhaps half a mile from the sea.

"It is a bird; a white-winged bird; perhaps a—no; it is—it is a handkerchief!"

"Aye, a handkerchief!" echoed my comrade, and with a louder shout apprised the captain.

Quickly now—like the running out and training of a great gun—the long cabin spy-glass was thrust through the mizzen-rigging from the high platform of the poop; whereupon a human figure was plainly seen upon the inland rock, eagerly waving towards us what seemed to be the handkerchief.

Our captain was a prompt, good fellow. Dropping the glass, he lustily ran forward, ordering the anchor to be dropped again; hands to stand by a boat, and lower away.

In a half-hour's time the swift boat returned. It went with six and came with seven; and the seventh was a woman.

It is not artistic heartlessness, but I wish I could but draw in crayons; for this woman was a most touching sight; and crayons, tracing softly melancholy lines, would best depict the mournful image of the dark-damasked Chola widow.

Her story was soon told, and though given in her own strange language was as quickly understood; for our captain, from long trading on the Chilean coast, was well versed in the Spanish. A Cholo, or half-breed Indian woman, of Payta in Peru, three years gone by, with her young new-wedded husband Felipe, of pure Castilian blood, and her one only Indian brother, Truxill, Hunilla had taken passage on the main in a French whaler, commanded by a joyous man; which vessel, bound to the cruising grounds beyond the Enchanted Isles, proposed passing close by their vicinity. The object of the little party was to procure tortoise oil, a fluid which for its great purity and delicacy is held in high estimation wherever known; and it is well known all along this part of the Pacific coast. With a chest of clothes, tools, cooking utensils, a rude apparatus for trying out the oil, some casks of biscuit, and other things, not omitting two favorite dogs, of which faithful animal all the Cholos are very fond, Hunilla and her companions were safely landed at their chosen place; the Frenchman, according to the contract made ere sailing, engaged to take them off upon returning from a four months' cruise in the westward seas; which interval the three adventurers deemed quite sufficient for their purposes.

On the isle's lone beach they paid him in silver for their passage out, the stranger having declined to carry them at all except upon that condition; though willing to take every means to insure the due fulfillment of his promise. Felipe had striven hard to have this payment put off to the period of the ship's return. But in vain. Still they thought they had, in another way, ample pledge of the good faith of the Frenchman. It was arranged that the expenses of the passage home should not be payable in silver, but in tortoises; one hundred tortoises ready captured to the returning captain's hand. These the Cholos meant to secure after their own work was done, against the probable time of the Frenchman's coming back; and no doubt in prospect already felt, that in those hundred tortoises—now somewhere ranging the isle's interior—they possessed one hundred hostages. Enough: the vessel sailed; the gazing three on shore answered the loud glee of the singing crew;

and ere evening, the French craft was hull down in the distant sea, its masts three faintest lines which quickly faded from Hunilla's eye.

The stranger had given a blithesome promise, and anchored it with oaths; but oaths and anchors equally will drag; naught else abides on fickle earth but unkept promises of joy. Contrary winds from out unstable skies, or contrary moods of his more varying mind, or shipwreck and sudden death in solitary waves; whatever was the cause, the blithe stranger never was seen again.

Yet, however dire a calamity was here in store, misgivings of it ere due time never disturbed the Cholos' busy minds, now all intent upon the toilsome matter which had brought them hither. Nay, by swift doom coming like the thief at night, ere seven weeks went by, two of the little party were removed from all anxieties of land or sea. No more they sought to gaze with feverish fear, or still more feverish hope, beyond the present's horizon line; but into the furthest future their own silent spirits sailed. By persevering labor beneath that burning sun, Felipe and Truxill had brought down to their hut many scores of tortoises, and tried out the oil, when, elated with their good success, and to reward themselves for such hard work, they, too hastily, made a catamaran, or Indian raft, much used on the Spanish Main, and merrily started on a fishing trip, just without a long reef with many jagged gaps, running parallel with the shore, about half a mile from it. By some bad tide or hap, or natural negligence of joyfulness (for though they could not be heard, yet by their gestures they seemed singing at the time), forced in deep water against that iron bar, the ill-made catamaran was overset, and came all to pieces; when dashed by broadchested swells between their broken logs and the sharp teeth of the reef, both adventurers perished before Hunilla's eyes.

Before Hunilla's eyes they sank. The real woe of this event passed before her sight as some sham tragedy on the stage. She was seated in a rude bower among the withered thickets, crowning a lofty cliff, a little back from the beach. The thickets were so disposed that in looking upon the sea at large she peered out from among the branches as from the lattice of a high balcony. But upon the day we speak of here, the better to watch the adventure of those two hearts she loved, Hunilla had withdrawn the branches to one side, and held them so. They formed an oval frame, through which the bluely boundless sea rolled like a painted one. And there, the invisible painter painted to her view the wave-tossed and disjointed raft, its once-level logs slantingly upheaved, as raking masts, and the four struggling arms undistinguishable among them, and then all subsided into smooth-flowing creamy waters, slowly drifting the splintered wreck, while first and last, no sound of any sort was heard. Death in a silent picture; a dream of the eye; such vanishing shapes as the mirage shows.

So instant was the scene, so trance-like its mild pictorial effect, so distant from her blasted bower and her common sense of things, that Hunilla gazed and gazed, nor raised a finger or a wail. But as good to sit thus dumb, in stupor staring on that dumb show, for all that otherwise might be done. With half a mile of sea between, how could her two enchanted arms aid those four fated ones? The distance long, the time one sand. After the lightning is beheld, what fool shall stay the thunder-bolt? Felipe's body was washed ashore, but Truxill's never came; only his gay, braided hat of golden straw—that same sunflower thing he waved to her, pushing from the strand—and now, to the last gallant, it still saluted her. But Felipe's body floated to the marge, with one arm encirclingly outstretched. Lock-jawed in grim death, the lover-husband softly clasped his bride, true to her even in death's dream. Ah, Heaven, when man thus keeps his faith, wilt Thou be faithless who created the faithful one? But they cannot break faith who never plighted it.

It needs not to be said what nameless misery now wrapped the lonely widow. In telling her own story she passed this almost entirely over, simply recounting the event. Construe the comment of her features as you might, from her mere words little would you have weened that Hunilla was herself the heroine of her tale. But not thus did she defraud us of our tears. All hearts bled that grief could be so brave.

She but showed us her soul's lid, and the strange ciphers thereon engraved; all within, with pride's timid-ity, was withheld. Yet was there one exception. Holding out her small olive hand before her Captain, she said in mild and slowest Spanish, "Señor, I buried him," then paused, struggled as against the writhed coilings of a snake, and cringing suddenly, leaped up, repeating in impassioned pain, "I buried him, my life, my soul!"

Doubtless, it was by half-unconscious, automatic mo-tions of her hands that this heavy-hearted one per-formed the final office for Felipe, and planted a rude cross of withered sticks—no green ones might be had—at the head of that lonely grave, where rested now in lasting uncomplaint and quiet haven he whom untran-quil seas had overthrown.

But some dull sense of another body that should be interred, of another cross that should hallow another grave—unmade as yet, some dull anxiety and pain touching her undiscovered brother, now haunted the oppressed Hunilla. Her hands fresh from the burial earth, she slowly went back to the beach, with unshaped purposes wandering there, her spell-bound eye bent upon the incessant waves. But they bore nothing to her but a dirge, which maddened her to think that murderers should mourn. As time went by, and these things came less dreamingly to her mind, the strong persuasions of her Romish faith, which sets peculiar store by consecrated urns, prompted her to resume in waking earnest that pious search which had but been begun as in somnambulism. Day after day, week after week, she trod the cindery beach, till at length a double motive edged every eager glance. With equal longing she now looked for the living and the dead; the brother and the captain; alike vanished, never to return. Little accurate note of time had Hunilla taken under such emotions as were hers, and little, outside herself, served for calendar or dial. As to poor Crusoe in the self-same sea, no saint's bell pealed forth the lapse of week or month; each day went by unchallenged; no chanticleer announced those sultry dawns, no lowing herds those poisonous nights. Of all wonted and steadily recurring sounds, human, or humanized by sweet fellowship with man, but one stirred that torrid trance—the cry of dogs; save which naught but the rolling sea invaded it, an all-pervading monotone; and to the widow that was the least loved voice she could have heard.

No wonder that as her thoughts now wandered to the unreturning ship, and were beaten back again, the hope against hope so struggled in her soul, that at length she desperately said, "Not yet, not yet; my foolish heart runs on too fast." So she forced patience for some further weeks. But to those whom earth's sure indraft draws, patience or impatience is still the same.

Hunilla now sought to settle precisely in her mind, to

ən hour, how long it was since the ship had sailed; and then, with the same precision, how long a space remained to pass. But this proved impossible. What present day or month it was she could not say. Time was her labyrinth, in which Hunilla was entirely lost.

And now follows ——

Against my own purposes a pause descends upon me here. One knows not whether nature doth not impose some secrecy upon him who has been privy to certain things. At least, it is to be doubted whether it be good to blazon such. If some books are deemed most baneful and their sale forbid, how, then, with deadlier facts, not dreams of doting men? Those whom books will hurt will not be proof against events. Events, not books, should be forbid. But in all things man sows upon the wind, which bloweth just there whither it listeth; for ill or good, man cannot know. Often ill comes from the good, as good from ill.

When Hunilla ——

Dire sight it is to see some silken beast long dally with a golden lizard ere she devour. More terrible, to see how feline Fate will sometimes dally with a human soul, and by a nameless magic make it repulse a sane despair with a hope which is but mad. Unwittingly I imp this cat-like thing, sporting with the heart of him who reads; for if he feel not he reads in vain.

"The ship sails this day, to-day," at last said Hunilla to herself; "this gives me certain time to stand on; without certainty I go mad. In loose ignorance I have hoped and hoped; now in firm knowledge I will but wait. Now I live and no longer perish in bewilderings. Holy Virgin, aid me! Thou wilt waft back the ship. Oh, past length of weary weeks—all to be dragged over—to buy the certainty of to-day, I freely give ye, though I tear ye from me!"

As mariners tost in tempest on some desolate ledge patch them a boat out of the remnants of their vessel's wreck, and launch it in the selfsame waves, see here Hunilla, this lone shipwrecked soul, out of treachery invoking trust. Humanity, thou strong thing, I worship thee, not in the laureled victor, but in this vanquished one.

Truly Hunilla leaned upon a reed, a real one; no metaphor: a real Eastern reed. A piece of hollow cane, drifted from unknown isles, and found upon the beach, its once jagged ends rubbed smoothly even as by sandpaper; its golden glazing gone. Long ground between the sea and land, upper and nether stone, the unvarnished substance was filed bare, and wore another polish now, one with itself, the polish of its agony. Circular lines at intervals cut all round this surface, divided it into six panels of unequal length. In the first were scored the days, each tenth one marked by a longer and deeper notch; the second was scored for the number of sea-fowl eggs for sustenance, picked out from the rocky nests; the third, how many fish had been caught from the shore; the fourth, how many small tortoises found inland; the fifth, how many days of sun; the sixth, of clouds; which last, of the two, was the greater one. Long night of busy numbering, misery's mathematics, to weary her too-wakeful soul to sleep; yet sleep for that was none.

The panel of the days was deeply worn—the long tenth notches half-effaced, as alphabets of the blind. Ten thousand times the longing widow had traced her finger over the bamboo—dull flute, which, played on, gave no sound—as if counting birds flown by in air would hasten tortoises creeping through the woods.

After the one hundred and eightieth day no further mark was seen; that last one was the faintest, as the first the deepest.

"There were more days," said our Captain; "many, many more; why did you not go on and notch them, too, Hunilla?"

"Señor, ask me not."

"And meantime did no other vessel pass the isle?"

"Nay, Señor; but—"

"You do not speak; but what, Hunilla?"

"Ask me not, Señor."

"You saw ships pass, far away; you waved to them; they passed on—was that it, Hunilla?"

"Señor, be it as you say."

Braced against her woe, Hunilla would not, durst not, trust the weakness of her tongue. Then when our Captain asked whether any whale-boats had ——

But no, I will not file this thing complete for scoffing souls to quote, and call it firm proof upon their side. The half shall here remain untold. Those two unnamed events which befell Hunilla on this isle, let them abide between her and her God. In nature, as in law, it may be libelous to speak some truths.

Still, how it was that, although our vessel had lain three days anchored nigh the isle, its one human tenant should not have discovered us till just upon the point of sailing, never to revisit so lone and far a spot, this needs explaining ere the sequel come.

The place where the French captain had landed the little party was on the further and opposite end of the isle. There, too, it was that they had afterward built their hut. Nor did the widow in her solitude desert the spot where her loved ones had dwelt with her, and where the dearest of the twain now slept his last long sleep, and all her plaints awaked him not, and he of husbands the most faithful during life.

Now, high broken land rises between the opposite

extremities of the isle. A ship anchored at one side is invisible from the other. Neither is the isle so small but a considerable company might wander for days through the wilderness of one side, and never be seen, or their halloos heard, by any stranger holding aloof on the other. Hence Hunilla, who naturally associated the possible coming of ships with her own part of the isle, might to the end have remained quite ignorant of the presence of our vessel, were it not for a mysterious presentiment, borne to her, so our mariners averred, by this isle's enchanted air. Nor did the widow's answer undo the thought.

"How did you come to cross the isle this morning, then, Hunilla?" said our Captain.

"Señor, something came flitting by me. It touched my cheek, my heart, Señor."

"What do you say, Hunilla?"

"I have said, Señor, something came through the air."

It was a narrow chance. For when in crossing the isle Hunilla gained the high land in the center, she must then for the first have perceived our masts, and also marked that their sails were being loosed, perhaps even heard the echoing chorus of the windlass song. The strange ship was about to sail, and she behind. With all haste she now descends the height on the hither side, but soon loses sight of the ship among the sunken jungles at the mountain's base. She struggles on through the withered branches, which seek at every step to bar her path, till she comes to the isolated rock, still some way from the water. This she climbs, to reassure herself. The ship is still in plainest sight. But now, worn out with over-tension, Hunilla all but faints; she fears to step down from her giddy perch; she is fain to pause, there where she is, and as a last resort catches the turban from her head, unfurls and waves it over the jungles towards us.

During the telling of her story the mariners formed a voiceless circle round Hunilla and the Captain; and when at length the word was given to man the fastest boat, and pull round to the isle's thither side, to bring away Hunilla's chest and the tortoise oil, such alacrity of both cheery and sad obedience seldom before was seen. Little ado was made. Already the anchor had been recommitted to the bottom, and the ship swung calmly to it.

But Hunilla insisted upon accompanying the boat as indispensable pilot to her hidden hut. So being refreshed with the best the steward could supply, she started with us. Nor did ever any wife of the most famous admiral, in her husband's barge, receive more silent reverence of respect than poor Hunilla from this boat's crew.

Rounding many a vitreous cape and bluff, in two hours' time we shot inside the fatal reef; wound into a secret cove, looked up along a green many-gabled lava wall, and saw the island's solitary dwelling.

It hung upon an impending cliff, sheltered on two sides by tangled thickets, and half-screened from view in front by juttings of the rude stairway, which climbed the precipice from the sea. Built of canes, it was thatched with long, mildewed grass. It seemed an abandoned hayrick, whose haymakers were now no more. The roof inclined but one way, the eaves coming to within two feet of the ground. And here was a simple apparatus to collect the dews, or rather doubly distilled and finest winnowed rains, which, in mercy or in mockery, the night-skies sometimes drop upon these blighted Encantadas. All along beneath the eaves, a spotted sheet, quite weather-stained, was spread, pinned to short, upright stakes, set in the shallow sand. A small clinker, thrown into the cloth, weighed its middle down, thereby straining all moisture into a calabash placed below. This vessel supplied each drop of water ever drunk upon the isle by the Cholos. Hunilla told us the calabash would sometimes, but not often, be half-filled overnight. It held six quarts, perhaps. "But," said she, "we were used to thirst. At sandy Payta, where I live, no shower from heaven ever fell; all the water there is brought on mules from the inland vales."

Tied among the thickets were some twenty moaning tortoises, supplying Hunilla's lonely larder; while hundreds of vast tableted black bucklers, like displaced, shattered tombstones of dark slate, were also scattered round. These were the skeleton backs of those great tortoises from which Felipe and Truxill had made their precious oil. Several large calabashes and two goodly kegs were filled with it. In a pot near by were the caked crusts of a quantity which had been permitted to evaporate. "They meant to have strained it off next day," said Hunilla, as she turned aside.

I forgot to mention the most singular sight of all, though the first that greeted us after landing.

Some ten small, soft-haired, ringleted dogs, of a beautiful breed, peculiar to Peru, set up a concert of glad welcomings when we gained the beach, which was responded to by Hunilla. Some of these dogs had, since her widowhood, been born upon the isle, the progeny of the two brought from Payta. Owing to the jagged steeps and pitfalls, tortuous thickets, sunken clefts and perilous intricacies of all sorts in the interior, Hunilla, admonished by the loss of one favorite among them, never allowed these delicate creatures to follow her in her occasional birds' nests climbs and other wanderings, so that, through long habituation, they offered not to follow, when that morning she crossed the

land, and her own soul was then too full of other things
to heed their lingering behind. Yet, all along she had so
clung to them, that, besides what moisture they lapped
up at early daybreak from the small scoop-holes among
the adjacent rocks, she had shared the dew of her calabash among them, never laying by any considerable
store against those prolonged and utter droughts which,
in some disastrous seasons, warp these isles.

Having pointed out, at our desire, what few things
she would like transported to the ship—her chest, the
oil, not omitting the live tortoises which she intended
for a grateful present to our Captain—we immediately
set to work, carrying them to the boat down the long,
sloping stair of deeply shadowed rock. While my comrades were thus employed, I looked and Hunilla had
disappeared.

It was not curiosity alone, but, it seems to me, something different mingled with it, which prompted me to
drop my tortoise, and once more gaze slowly around.
I remembered the husband buried by Hunilla's hands.
A narrow pathway led into a dense part of the thickets.
Following it through many mazes, I came out upon a
small, round, open space, deeply chambered there.

The mound rose in the middle; a bear heap of finest
sand, like that unverdured heap found at the bottom of
an hour-glass run out. At its head stood the cross of
withered sticks, the dry, peeled bark still fraying from
it, its transverse limb tied up with rope, and forlornly
adroop in the silent air.

Hunilla was partly prostrate upon the grave; her
dark head bowed, and lost in her long, loosened Indian
hair; her hands extended to the cross foot, with a little
brass crucifix clasped between, a crucifix worn feature-
less, like an ancient graven knocker long plied in vain.

She did not see me, and I made no noise, but slid aside, and left the spot.

A few moments ere all was ready for our going, she reappeared among us. I looked into her eyes, but saw no tear. There was something which seemed strangely haughty in her air, and yet it was the air of woe. A Spanish and an Indian grief, which would not visibly lament. Pride's height in vain abased to proneness on the rack; nature's pride subduing nature's torture.

Like pages the small and silken dogs surrounded her, as she slowly descended towards the beach. She caught the two most eager creatures in her arms—*"Tita mia! Tomotita mia!"* and fondling them, inquired how many could we take on board.

The mate commanded the boat's crew; not a hardhearted man, but his way of life had been such that in most things, even in the smallest, simple utlilty was his leading motive.

"We cannot take them all, Hunilla; our supplies are short; the winds are unreliable; we may be a good many days going to Tumbez. So take those you have, Hunilla, but no more."

She was in the boat; the oarsmen, too, were seated; all save one, who stood ready to push off and then spring himself. With the sagacity of their race, the dogs now seemed aware that they were in the very instant of being deserted upon a barren strand. The gunwales of the boat were high; its prow—presented inland—was lifted; so owing to the water, which they seemed instinctively to shun, the dogs could not well leap into the little craft. But their busy paws hard scraped the prow, as it had been some farmer's door shutting them out from shelter in a winter storm. A clamorous agony of alarm. They did not howl, or whine; they all but spoke.

"Push off! Give way!" cried the mate. The boat gave one heavy drag and lurch, and next moment shot swiftly from the beach, turned on her heel, and sped. The dogs ran howling along the water's marge, now pausing to gaze at the flying boat, then motioning as if to leap in chase, but mysteriously withheld themselves, and again ran howling along the beach. Had they been human beings, hardly would they have more vividly inspired the sense of desolation. The oars were plied as confederate feathers of two wings. No one spoke. I looked back upon the beach, and then upon Hunilla, but her face was set in a stern dusky calm. The dogs crouching in her lap vainly licked her rigid hands. She never looked behind her, but sat motionless, till we turned a promontory of the coast and lost all sights and sounds astern. She seemed as one who, having experienced the sharpest of mortal pangs, was henceforth content to have all lesser heart-strings riven, one by one. To Hunilla, pain seemed so necessary that pain in other beings, though by love and sympathy made her own, was unrepiningly to be borne. A heart of yearning in a frame of steel. A heart of earthly yearning, frozen by the frost which falleth from the sky.

The sequel is soon told. After a long passage, vexed by calms and baffling winds, we made the little port of Tumbez in Peru, there to recruit the ship. Payta was not very distant. Our captain sold the tortoise oil to a Tumbez merchant, and, adding to the silver a contribution from all hands, gave it to our silent passenger, who knew not what the mariners had done.

The last seen of lone Hunilla she was passing into Payta town, riding upon a small gray ass; and before her cn the ass's shoulders, she eyed the jointed workings of the beast's armorial cross.

(Sketch Eighth; from *The Piazza Tales*)

❖❖❖

Melville needed the fortitude of Hunilla, as the downward fortunes of his career had not yet reached bottom. In December 1853, a ruinous fire at Harper & Brothers destroyed most of their stock of Melville's books, though the stereotyped plates were preserved for later printings that were little help to the writer's finances. This catastrophe, coming so soon upon the *Pierre* disaster, temporarily severed Melville's connection with this firm.

For his next novel Melville "served up" his long-shelved ideas for "the Revolutionary narrative of the beggar," and his single historical novel was published serially in *Putnam's*, attracting many contemporary readers who expressed surprise that the author of *Moby Dick* and *Pierre* could have written such a simple, direct story, called by Melville an "adventure." Modern readers will not be so deceived by the easy style and surface of *Israel Potter*. Even in the selected three portraits of Americans (all, like Israel, in some sort of exile from America) there is more to be found about Melville than his historical skepticisms and admirations.

❖❖❖

From Israel Potter: His Fifty Years of Exile

[PORTRAITS OF THREE AMERICANS]

Israel Enters the Presence of the Renowned Sage, Dr. Franklin, Whom He Finds Right Learnedly and Multifariously Employed

UPON hearing the name of Doctor Franklin mentioned, the old woman, all alacrity, hurried out of her den and with much courtesy showed Israel across the court, up three flights of stairs to a door in the rear of the spacious building. There she left him while Israel knocked.

"Come in," said a voice.

And immediately Israel stood in the presence of the venerable Doctor Franklin.

Wrapped in a rich dressing-gown, a fanciful present from an admiring Marchesa, curiously embroidered with algebraic figures like a conjuror's robe, and with a skull-cap of black satin on his hive of a head, the man of gravity was seated at a huge claw-footed old table, round at the zodiac. It was covered with printed papers, files of documents, rolls of manuscripts, stray bits of strange models in wood and metal, odd-looking pamphlets in various languages, and all sorts of books, including many presentation copies, embracing history, mechanics, diplomacy, agriculture, political economy, metaphysics, meteorology, and geometry. The walls had a necromantic look, hung round with barometers of different kinds; drawings of surprising inventions; wide maps of far countries in the New World, containing vast empty spaces in the middle, with the word D E S E R T diffusely printed there, so as to span five-and-twenty degrees of longitude with only two syllables, which printed word, however, bore a vigorous pen-mark, in the Doctor's hand, drawn straight through it, as if in summary repeal of it; crowded topographical and trigonometrical charts of various parts of Europe; with geometrical diagrams, and endless other surprising hangings and upholstery of science.

The chamber itself bore evident marks of antiquity. One part of the rough-finished wall was sadly cracked and, covered with dust, looked dim and dark. But the aged inmate, though wrinkled as well, looked neat and hale. Both wall and sage were compounded of like materials—lime and dust; both, too, were old; but while the rude earth of the wall had no painted luster to shed off all fadings and tarnish and still keep fresh without, though with long eld its core decayed, the living lime and dust of the sage was frescoed with defensive bloom of his soul.

The weather was warm; like some old West India hogshead on the wharf, the whole chamber buzzed with flies. But the sapient inmate sat still and cool in the midst. Absorbed in some other world of his occupations and thoughts, these insects, like daily cark and care, did not seem one whit to annoy him. It was a goodly sight to see this serene, cool, and ripe old philosopher, who by sharp inquisition of man in the street and then long meditating upon him, surrounded by all those queer old implements, charts, and books, had grown at last so wondrous wise. There he sat, quite motionless among those restless flies, and, with a sound like the low noon murmur of foliage in the woods, turning over the leaves of some ancient and tattered folio, with a binding dark and shaggy as the bark of any old oak. It seemed as if supernatural lore must needs pertain to this gravely ruddy personage; at least far foresight, pleasant wit, and working wisdom. Old age seemed in no wise to have dulled him but to have sharpened; just as old dinner-knives—so they be of good steel— wax keen, spear-pointed, and elastic as whale-bone with long usage. Yet though he was thus lively and vigorous to behold, spite of his seventy-two years (his exact date at that time), somehow the incredible seniority of an antediluvian seemed his. Not the years of the calendar wholly, but also the years of sapience. His white hairs and mild brow spoke of the future as well as the past. He seemed to be seven score years old; that is, three score and ten of prescience added to three score and ten of remembrance makes just seven score years in all.

But when Israel stepped within the chamber, he lost the complete effect of all this; for the sage's back, not his face, was turned to him.

So, intent on his errand, hurried and heated with his recent run, our courier entered the room, inadequately impressed, for the time, by either it or its occupant.

"Bon jour, bon jour, monsieur," said the man of wisdom, in a cheerful voice, but too busy to turn round just then.

"How do you do, Doctor Franklin," said Israel.

"Ah! I smell Indian corn," said the Doctor, turning round quickly on his chair. "A countryman; sit down, my good sir. Well, what news? Special?"

"Wait a minute, sir," said Israel, stepping across the room towards a chair.

Now there was no carpet on the floor, which was of dark-colored wood, set in lozenges, and slippery with wax, after the usual French style. As Israel walked this slippery floor, his unaccustomed feet slid about very strangely as if walking on ice, so that he came very near falling.

"'Pears to me you have rather high heels to your boots," said the grave man of utility, looking sharply down through his spectacles. "Don't you know that it's both wasting leather and endangering your limbs, to wear such high heels? I have thought, at my first leisure, to write a little pamphlet against that very abuse. But pray, what are you doing now? Do your boots pinch you, my friend, that you lift one foot from the floor that way?"

At this moment Israel, having seated himself, was just putting his right foot across his left knee.

"How foolish," continued the wise man, "for a rational creature to wear tight boots. Had nature in-

tended rational creatures should do so, she would have
made the foot of solid bone, or perhaps of solid iron,
instead of bone, muscle, and flesh. But—I see. Hold!"

And springing to his own slippered feet, the venerable sage hurried to the door and shot-to the bolt. Then
drawing the curtain carefully across the window looking out across the court to various windows on the
opposite side, bade Israel proceed with his operations.

"I was mistaken this time," added the Doctor, smiling, as Israel produced his documents from their curious recesses—"your high heels, instead of being idle
vanities, seem to be full of meaning."

"Pretty full, Doctor," said Israel, now handing over
the papers. "I had a narrow escape with them just now."

"How? How's that?" said the sage, fumbling the
papers eagerly.

"Why, crossing the stone bridge over the Seen—"

"*Seine*," interrupted the Doctor, giving the French
pronunciation. "Always get a new word right in the
first place, my friend, and you will never get it wrong
afterwards."

"Well, I was crossing the bridge there, and who
should hail me, but a suspicious-looking man, who,
under pretense of seeking to polish my boots, wanted
slyly to unscrew their heels, and so steal all these precious papers I've brought you."

"My good friend," said the man of gravity, glancing
scrutinizingly upon his guest, "have you not in your
time undergone what they call hard times? Been set
upon, and persecuted, and very illy entreated by some
of your fellow-creatures?"

"That I have, Doctor; yes, indeed."

"I thought so. Sad usage has made you sadly suspicious, my honest friend. An indiscriminate distrust of
human nature is the worst consequence of a miserable

condition, whether brought about by innocence or guilt. And though want of suspicion, more than want of sense, sometimes leads a man into harm, yet too much suspicion is as bad as too little sense. The man you met, my friend, most probably had no artful intention; he knew just nothing about you or your heels; he simply wanted to earn two sous by brushing your boots. Those blacking-men regularly station themselves on the bridge."

"How sorry I am then that I knocked over his box, and then ran away. But he didn't catch me."

"How? Surely, my honest friend, you—appointed to the conveyance of important secret dispatches—did not act so imprudently as to kick over an innocent man's box in the public streets of the capital, to which you had been especially sent?"

"Yes, I did, Doctor."

"Never act so unwisely again. If the police had got hold of you, think of what might have ensued."

"Well, it was not very wise of me, that's a fact, Doctor. But, you see, I thought he meant mischief."

"And because you only thought he *meant* mischief, *you* must straightway proceed to *do* mischief. That's poor logic. But think over what I have told you now, while I look over these papers."

In half an hour's time, the Doctor, laying down the documents, again turned towards Israel and, removing his spectacles very placidly, proceeded in the kindest and most familiar manner to read him a paternal detailed lesson upon the ill-advised act he had been guilty of upon the Pont Neuf, concluding by taking out his purse, and putting three small silver coins into Israel's hands, charging him to seek out the man that very day, and make both apology and restitution for his unlucky mistake.

"All of us, my honest friend," continued the Doctor, "are subject to making mistakes; so that the chief art of life is to learn how best to remedy mistakes. Now one remedy for mistakes is honesty. So pay the man for the damage done to his box. And now, who are you, my friend? My correspondents here mention your name— Israel Potter—and say you are an American, an escaped prisoner of war, but nothing further. I want to hear your story from your own lips."

Israel immediately began, and related to the Doctor all his adventures up to the present time.

"I suppose," said the Doctor, upon Israel's concluding, "that you desire to return to your friends across the sea?"

"That I do, Doctor," said Israel.

"Well, I think I shall be able to procure you a passage."

Israel's eyes sparkled with delight. The mild sage noticed it, and added: "But events in these times are uncertain. At the prospect of pleasure never be elated; but, without depression, respect the omens of ill. So much my life has taught me, my honest friend."

Israel felt as though a plum-pudding had been thrust under his nostrils, and then as rapidly withdrawn.

"I think it is probable that in two or three days I shall want you to return with some papers to the persons who sent you to me. In that case you will have to come here once more, and then, my good friend, we will see what can be done towards getting you safely home again."

Israel was pouring out torrents of thanks when the Doctor interrupted him.

"Gratitude, my friend, cannot be too much towards God, but towards man, it should be limited. No man can possibly so serve his fellow, as to merit unbounded gratitude. Over-gratitude in the helped person is apt to breed vanity or arrogance in the helping one. Now in assisting you to get home—if indeed I shall prove able to do so—I shall be simply doing part of my official duty as agent of our common country. So you owe me just nothing at all, but the sum of these coins I put in your hand just now. But that, instead of repaying to me hereafter, you can, when you get home, give it to the first soldier's widow you meet. Don't forget it, for it is a debt, a pecuniary liability, owing to me. It will be about a quarter of a dollar, in the Yankee currency. A quarter of a dollar, mind. My honest friend, in pecuniary matters always be exact as a second hand; never mind with whom it is, father or stranger, peasant or king, be exact to a tick of your honor."

"Well, Doctor," said Israel, "since exactness in these matters is so necessary, let me pay back my debt in the very coins in which it was loaned. There will be no chance of mistake then. Thanks to my Brentford friends, I have enough to spare of my own to settle damages with the boot-black of the bridge. I only took the money from you, because I thought it would not look well to push it back after being so kindly offered."

"My honest friend," said the Doctor, "I like your straightforward dealing. I will receive back the money."

"No interest, Doctor, I hope," said Israel.

The sage looked mildly over his spectacles upon Israel and replied: "My good friend, never permit yourself to be jocose upon pecuniary matters. Never joke at funerals, or during business transactions. The affair between us two you perhaps deem very trivial, but trifles may involve momentous principles. But no more at present. You had better go immediately and find the boot-black. Having settled with him, return hither, and you will find a room ready for you near this, where you will stay during your sojourn in Paris."

"But I thought I would like to have a little look round the town, before I go back to England," said Israel.

"Business before pleasure, my friend. You must absolutely remain in your room, just as if you were my prisoner, until you quit Paris for Calais. Not knowing now at what instant I shall want you to start, your keeping to your room is indispensable. But when you come back from Brentford again, then, if nothing happens, you will have a chance to survey this celebrated capital ere taking ship for America. Now go directly, and pay the boot-black. Stop, have you the exact change ready? Don't be taking out all your money in the open street."

"Doctor," said Israel, "I am not so simple."

"But you knocked over the box."

"That, Doctor, was bravery."

"Bravery in a poor cause is the height of simplicity, my friend. Count out your change. It must be French coin, not English, that you are to pay the man with. Ah, that will do—those three coins will be enough. Put them in a pocket separate from your other cash. Now go, and hasten to the bridge."

"Shall I stop to take a meal anywhere, Doctor, as I return? I saw several cookshops as I came hither."

"Cafés and restaurants, they are called here, my honest friend. Tell me, are you the possessor of a liberal fortune?"

"Not very liberal," said Israel.

"I thought as much. Where little wine is drunk, it is good to dine out occasionally at a friend's; but where a poor man dines out at his own charge, it is bad policy.

Never dine out that way, when you can dine in. Do not stop on the way at all, my honest friend, but come directly back hither, and you shall dine at home, free of cost, with me."

"Thank you very kindly, Doctor."

•

The first, both in point of time and merit, of American envoys was famous not less for the pastoral simplicity of his manners than for the politic grace of his mind. Viewed from a certain point, there was a touch of primeval orientalness in Benjamin Franklin. Neither is there wanting something like his Scriptural parallel. The history of the patriarch Jacob is interesting not less from the unselfish devotion which we are bound to ascribe to him than from the deep worldly wisdom and polished Italian tact, gleaming under an air of Arcadian unaffectedness. The diplomatist and the shepherd are blended; a union not without warrant; the apostolic serpent and dove. A tanned Machiavelli in tents.

Doubtless, too, notwithstanding his eminence as lord of the moving manor, Jacob's raiment was of homespun; the economic envoy's plain coat and hose, who has not heard of?

Franklin all over is of a piece. He dressed his person as his periods: neat, trim, nothing superfluous, nothing deficient. In some of his works his style is only surpassed by the unimprovable sentences of Hobbes of Malmsbury, the paragon of perspicuity. The mental habits of Hobbes and Franklin in several points, especially in one of some moment, assimilated. Indeed, making due allowance for soil and era, history presents few trios more akin, upon the whole, than Jacob, Hobbes, and Franklin; three labyrinth-minded but plain-spoken Broadbrims, at once politicians and philosophers; keen observers of the main chance; prudent courtiers; practical magians in linsey-woolsey.

In keeping with his general habitudes, Doctor Franklin while at the French Court did not reside in the aristocratical faubourgs. He deemed his worsted hose and scientific tastes more adapted in a domestic way to the other side of the Seine, where the Latin Quarter, at once the haunt of erudition and economy, seemed peculiarly to invite the philosophical Poor Richard to its venerable retreats. Here, of gray, chilly, drizzly November mornings, in the dark-stoned quadrangle of the time-honored Sorbonne, walked the lean and slippered metaphysician—oblivious for the moment that his sublime thoughts and tattered wardrobe were famous throughout Europe—meditating on the theme of his next lecture. . . .

In this congenial vicinity of the Latin Quarter, and in an ancient building something like those alluded to, at a point midway between the Palais des Beaux Arts and the College of the Sorbonne, the venerable American envoy pitched his tent when not passing his time at his country retreat at Passy. The frugality of his manner of life did not lose him the good opinion even of the voluptuaries of the showiest of capitals, whose very iron railings are not free from gilt. Franklin was not less a lady's man, than a man's man, a wise man, and an old man. Not only did he enjoy the homage of the choicest Parisian literati, but at the age of seventy-two he was the caressed favorite of the highest-born beauties of the Court, who, through blind fashion having been originally attracted to him as a famous *savant,* were permanently retained as his admirers by his Plato-like graciousness of good humor. Having carefully weighed the world, Franklin could act any part in it. By nature turned to knowledge, his mind was often grave, but never serious. At times he had seriousness—extreme seriousness—for others, but never for himself. Tranquillity was to him instead of it. This philosophical levity of tranquillity, so to speak, is shown in his easy variety of pursuits. Printer, postmaster, almanac-maker, essayist, chemist, orator, tinker, statesman, humorist, philosopher, parlor-man, political economist, professor of housewifery, ambassador, projector, maxim-monger, herb-doctor, wit—Jack of all trades, master of each and mastered by none—the type and genius of his land. Franklin was everything but a poet. But since a soul with many qualities, forming of itself a sort of handy index and pocket congress of all humanity, needs the contact of just as many different men, or subjects, in order to the exhibition of its totality; hence very little indeed of the sage's multifariousness will be portrayed in a simple narrative like the present. This casual private intercourse with Israel but served to manifest him in his far lesser lights: thrifty, domestic, dietarian, and, it may be, didactically waggish. There was much benevolent irony, innocent mischievousness, in the wise man. Seeking here to depict him in his less exalted habitudes, the narrator feels more as if he were playing with one of the sage's worsted hose, than reverentially handling the honored hat which once oracularly sat upon his brow.

(Chapters VII-VIII)

Paul Jones in a Reverie

Complying with what seemed as much a command as a request, Israel, though in bed, could not fall into slumber for thinking of the little circumstance that this strange swarthy man, flaming with wild enterprises, sat

in full suit in the chair. He felt an uneasy misgiving
sensation, as if he had retired, not only without covering up the fire but leaving it fiercely burning with spit-
ting fagots of hemlock.

But his natural complaisance induced him at least
to feign himself asleep; whereupon Paul, laying down
Poor Richard, rose from his chair, and, withdrawing his
boots, began walking rapidly but noiselessly to and fro,
in his stockings, in the spacious room, wrapped in
Indian meditations. Israel furtively eyed him from beneath the coverlid, and was anew struck by his aspect,
now that Paul thought himself unwatched. Stern relentless purposes, to be pursued to the points of adverse bayonets and the muzzles of hostile cannon, were
expressed in the now rigid lines of his brow. His ruffled right hand was clutched by his side, as if grasping
a cutlass. He paced the room as if advancing upon a
fortification. Meantime a confused buzz of discussion
came from the neighboring chamber. All else was profound midnight tranquillity. Presently, passing the large
mirror over the mantel, Paul caught a glimpse of his
person. He paused, grimly regarding it, while a dash of
pleased coxcombry seemed to mingle with the otherwise
savage satisfaction expressed in his face. But the latter
predominated. Soon, rolling up his sleeve, with a queer
wild smile, Paul lifted his right arm, and stood thus for
an interval, eyeing its image in the glass. From where
he lay, Israel could not see that side of the arm presented to the mirror, but he saw its reflection, and
started at perceiving there, framed in the carved and
gilded wood, certain large intertwisted ciphers covering
the whole inside of the arm, so far as exposed, with
mysterious tattooings. The design was wholly unlike
the fanciful figures of anchors, hearts, and cables, sometimes decorating small portions of seamen's bodies. It

was a sort of tattooing such as is seen only on thorough-bred savages—deep blue, elaborate, labyrinthine, caba-listic. Israel remembered having beheld, on one of his early voyages, something similar on the arm of a New Zealand warrior, once met, fresh from battle, in his native village. He concluded that on some similar early voyage Paul must have undergone the manipulations of some pagan artist.

Covering the arm again with his laced coatsleeve, Paul glanced ironically at the hand of the same arm, now again half muffled in ruffles, and ornamented with several Parisian rings. He then resumed his walking with a prowling air, like one haunting an ambuscade; while a gleam of the consciousness of possessing a char-acter as yet unfathomed, and hidden power to back unsuspected projects, irradiated his cold white brow, which, owing to the shade of his hat in equatorial climates, had been left surmounting his swarthy face, like the snow topping the Andes.

So at midnight, the heart of the metropolis of mod-ern civilization was secretly trod by this jaunty bar-barian in broadcloth; a sort of prophetical ghost, glim-mering in anticipation upon the advent of those tragic scenes of the French Revolution which leveled the ex-quisite refinement of Paris with the bloodthirsty feroc-ity of Borneo; showing that brooches and finger-rings, not less than nose-rings and tattooing, are tokens of the primeval savageness which ever slumbers in human kind, civilized or uncivilized.

Israel slept not a wink that night. The troubled spirit of Paul paced the chamber till morning; when, copi-ously bathing himself at the washstand, Paul looked carefree and fresh as a daybreak hawk. After a closeted consultation with Doctor Franklin, he left the place with a light and dandified air, switching his gold-headed

cane, and throwing a passing arm round all the pretty
chambermaids he encountered, kissing them resound-
ingly, as if saluting a frigate. All barbarians are rakes.

(Chapter XI)

Samson among the Philistines

At length, as the ship, gliding on past three or four
vessels at anchor in the roadstead—one a man-of-war
just furling her sails—came nigh Falmouth town, Israel,
from his perch, saw crowds in violent commotion on the
shore, while the adjacent roofs were covered with sight-
seers. A large man-of-war cutter was just landing its
occupants, among whom were a corporal's guard and
three officers, besides the naval lieutenant and boat's
crew. Some of this company having landed, and formed
a sort of lane among the mob, two trim soldiers, armed
to the teeth, rose in the stern-sheets, and between them,
a martial man of Patagonian stature, their ragged and
handcuffed captive, whose defiant head overshadowed
theirs, as St. Paul's dome its inferior steeples. Immediately the mob raised a shout, pressing in curiosity
towards the colossal stranger; so that, drawing their
swords, four of the soldiers had to force a passage for
their comrades, who followed on, conducting the giant.

As the letter-of-marque drew still nigher, Israel heard
the officer in command of the party ashore shouting,
"To the castle! to the castle!" and so, surrounded by
shouting throngs, the company moved on, preceded by
the three drawn swords, ever and anon flourished at the
rioters, towards a large grim pile on a cliff about a
mile from the landing. Long as they were in sight, the
bulky form of the captive was seen at times swayingly
towering over the flashing bayonets and cutlasses, like

a great whale breaching amid a hostile retinue of sword-fish. Now and then, too, with barbaric scorn, he taunted them with cramped gestures of his manacled hands.

When at last the vessel had gained her anchorage, opposite a distant detached warehouse, all was still; and the work of breaking out in the hold immediately commencing, and continuing till nightfall, absorbed all further attention for the present.

Next day was Sunday; and about noon Israel, with others, was allowed to go ashore for a stroll. The town was quiet. Seeing nothing very interesting there, he passed out, alone, into the fields alongshore, and presently found himself climbing the cliff whereon stood the grim pile before spoken of.

"What place is yon?" he asked of a rustic passing.

"Pendennis Castle."

As he stepped upon the short crisp sward under its walls, he started at a violent sound from within, as of the roar of some tormented lion. Soon the sound became articulate, and he heard the following words bayed out with an amazing vigor:

"Brag no more, Old England; consider you are but an island! Order back your broken battalions! Home, and repent in ashes! Long enough have your hired tories across the sea forgotten the Lord their God, and bowed down to Howe and Knyphausen—the Hessian! Hands off, red-skinned jackal! Wearing the king's plate,[1] as I do, I have treasures of wrath against you British."

Then came a clanking, as of a chain; many vengeful sounds, all confusedly together; with strugglings. Then again the voice:

"Ye brought me out here, from my dungeon to this green—affronting yon Sabbath sun—to see how a rebel looks. But I show ye how a true gentleman and Chris-

[1] Meaning, probably, certain manacles.—H.M.

tian can conduct in adversity. Back, dogs! Respect a
gentleman and a Christian, though he *be* in rags and
smell of bilge-water."

Filled with astonishment at these words, which came
from over a massive wall, enclosing what seemed an
open parade-space, Israel pressed forward, and soon
came to a black archway, leading far within, underneath, to a grassy tract, through a tower. Like two
boar's tusks, two sentries stood on guard at either side
of the open jaws of the arch. Scrutinizing our adven-
turer a moment, they signed him permission to enter.

Arrived at the end of the arched way, where the
sun shone, Israel stood transfixed at the scene.

Like some baited bull in the ring, crouched the Pata-
gonian-looking captive, handcuffed as before; the grass
of the green trampled, and gored up all about him,
both by his own movements and those of the people
around. Except some soldiers and sailors, these seemed
mostly townspeople, collected here out of curiosity. The
stranger was outlandishly arrayed in the sorry remains
of a half-Indian, half-Canadian sort of a dress, consisting of a fawn-skin jacket—the fur outside and hanging
in ragged tufts—a half-rotten, bark-like belt of wam-
pum; aged breeches of sagathy; bedarned worsted
stockings to the knee; old moccasins riddled with holes,
their metal tags yellow with salt-water rust; a faded
red woolen bonnet, not unlike a Russian night-cap, or
a portentous, ensanguined full moon, all soiled, and
stuck about with bits of half-rotted straw. He seemed
just broken from the dead leaves in David's outlawed
cave of Adullam. Unshaven, beard and hair matted
and profuse as a corn-field beaten down by hailstorms,
his whole marred aspect was that of some wild beast,
but of a royal sort, and unsubdued by the cage.

"Aye, stare, stare! Though but last night dragged

out of a ship's hold, like a smutty tierce; and this morning out of your littered barracks here, like a murderer; for all that, you may well stare at Ethan Ticonderoga Allen, the unconquered soldier, by ——! You Turks never saw a Christian before. Stare on! I am he, who, when your Lord Howe wanted to bribe a patriot to fall down and worship him by an offer of a major-generalship and five thousand acres of choice land in old Vermont (Ha! three-times-three for glorious old Vermont, and my Green Mountain boys! Hurrah! Hurrah! Hurrah!)—I am he, I say, who answered your Lord Howe, 'You, *you* offer *our* land? You are like the devil in Scripture, offering all the kingdoms in the world, when the d——d soul had not a corner-lot on earth!' Stare on!"

"Look you, rebel, you had best heed how you talk against General Lord Howe," here said a thin, wasp-waisted, epauletted officer of the castle, coming near and flourishing his sword like a schoolmaster's ferule.

"General Lord Howe? Heed how I talk of that toad-hearted king's lick-spittle of a scarlet poltroon, the vilest wriggler in God's worm-hole below? I tell you that herds of red-haired devils are impatiently snorting to ladle Lord Howe with all his gang (you included) into the seethingest syrups of Tophet's flames!"

At this blast, the wasp-waisted officer was blown backwards as from before the suddenly burst head of a steam-boiler.

Staggering away, with a snapped spine, he muttered something about its being beneath his dignity to bandy further words with a low-lived rebel.

"Come, come, Colonel Allen," here said a mild-looking man in a sort of clerical undress, "respect the day better than to talk thus of what lies beyond. Were you to die this hour, or what is more probable, be hung next week at Tower-wharf, you know not what might become, in eternity, of yourself."

"Reverend Sir," with a mocking bow, "when not better employed braiding my beard, I have a little dabbled in your theologies. And let me tell you, Reverend Sir," lowering and intensifying his voice, "that as to the world of spirits, of which you hint, though I know nothing of the mode or manner of that world, no more than do you, yet I expect when I shall arrive there to be treated as well as any other gentleman of my merit. That is to say, far better than you British know how to treat an American officer and meek-hearted Christian captured in honorable war, by ——! Every one tells me, as you yourself just breathed, and as, crossing the sea, every billow dinned into my ear, that I, Ethan Allen, am to be hung like a thief. If I am, the great Jehovah and the Continental Congress shall avenge me; while I, for my part, shall show you, even on the tree, how a Christian gentleman can die. Meantime, sir, if you are the clergyman you look, act out your consolatory function, by getting an unfortunate Christian gentleman about to die a bowl of punch."

The good-natured stranger, not to have his religious courtesy appealed to in vain, immediately dispatched his servant, who stood by, to procure the beverage.

At this juncture, a faint rustling sound, as of the advance of an army with banners, was heard. Silks, scarfs, and ribbons fluttered in the background. Presently, a bright squadron of fair ladies drew nigh, escorted by certain outriding gallants of Falmouth.

"Ah," sighed a soft voice, "what a strange sash, and furred vest, and what leopard-like teeth, and what flaxen hair, but all mildewed;—is that he?"

"Yea, is it, lovely charmer," said Allen, like an Ottoman, bowing over his broad, bovine forehead, and breathing the words out like a lute, "it is he—Ethan Allen, the soldier; now, since ladies' eyes visit him, made trebly a captive."

"Why, he talks like a beau in a parlor, this wild, mossed American from the woods," sighed another fair lady to her mate; "but can this be he we came to see? I must have a lock of his hair."

"It is he, adorable Delilah; and fear not, even though incited by the foe, by clipping my locks, to dwindle my strength. Give me your sword, man," turning to an officer. "Ah! I'm fettered. Clip it yourself, lady."

"No, no—I am—"

"Afraid, would you say? Afraid of the vowed friend and champion of all ladies all round the world? Nay, nay, come hither."

The lady advanced; and soon, overcoming her timidity, her white hand shone like whipped foam amid the matted waves of flaxen hair.

"Ah, this is like clipping tangled tags of gold-lace," cried she; "but see, it is half straw."

"But the wearer is no man-of-straw, lady; were I free, and you had ten thousand foes—horse, foot, and dragoons—how like a friend I could fight for you! Come, you have robbed me of my hair; let me rob your dainty hand of its price. What, afraid again?"

"No, not that; but—"

"I see, lady; I may do it, by your leave, but not by your word: the wonted way of ladies. There, it is done. Sweeter that kiss, than the bitter heart of a cherry."

•

Among the episodes of the Revolutionary War, none is stranger than that of Ethan Allen in England; the event and the man being equally uncommon.

Allen seems to have been a curious combination of
a Hercules, a Joe Miller, a Bayard, and a Tom Hyer;
had a person like the Belgian giants; mountain music
in him like a Swiss; a heart plump as Cœur de Lion's.
Though born in New England, he exhibited no trace
of her character. He was frank, bluff, companionable
as a pagan, convivial as a Roman, hearty as a harvest.
His spirit was essentially Western; and herein is his peculiar Americanism; for the Western spirit is, or will yet
be (for no other is, or can be), the true American one.

For the most part, Allen's manner while in England
was scornful and ferocious in the last degree; however,
qualified by that wild, heroic sort of levity, which in
the hour of oppression or peril seems inseparable from
a nature like his; the mode whereby such a temper
best evinces its barbaric disdain of adversity, and how
cheaply and waggishly it holds the malice, even though
triumphant, of its foes! Aside from that inevitable
egotism relatively pertaining to pine trees, spires, and
giants, there were, perhaps, two special incidental reasons for the Titanic Vermonter's singular demeanor
abroad. Taken captive while heading a forlorn hope
before Montreal, he was treated with inexcusable cruelty and indignity, something as if he had fallen into
the hands of the Dyaks. Immediately upon his capture
he would have been deliberately suffered to have been
butchered by the Indian allies in cold blood on the spot,
had he not, with desperate intrepidity, availed himself
of his enormous physical strength, by twitching a British officer to him, and using him for a living target,
whirling him round and round against the murderous
tomahawks of the savages. Shortly afterwards, led into
the town, fenced about by bayonets of the guard, the
commander of the enemy, one Colonel McCloud,[2] flourished his cane over the captive's head, with brutal in-

sults promising him a rebel's halter at Tyburn. During his passage to England in the same ship wherein went passenger Colonel Guy Johnson, the implacable tory, he was kept heavily ironed in the hold, and in all ways treated as a common mutineer; or, it may be, rather as a lion of Asia, which, though caged, was still too dreadful to behold without fear and trembling, and consequent cruelty. And no wonder, at least for the fear; for on one occasion, when chained hand and foot, he was insulted on shipboard by an officer; with his teeth he twisted off the nail that went through the mortise of his handcuffs, and so, having his arms at liberty, challenged his insulter to combat. Often, as at Pendennis Castle, when no other avengement was at hand, he would hurl on his foes such howling tempests of anathema as fairly to shock them into retreat. Prompted by somewhat similar motives, both on shipboard and in England, he would often make the most vociferous allusions to Ticonderoga, and the part he played in its capture, well knowing, that of all American names, Ticonderoga was, at that period, by far the most famous and galling to Englishmen.

Parlor-men, dancing-masters, the graduates of the Abbé Bellegarde, may shrug their laced shoulders at the boisterousness of Allen in England. True, he stood upon no punctilios with his jailers; for where modest gentlemanhood is all on one side, it is a losing affair; as if my Lord Chesterfield should take off his hat, and smile, and bow, to a mad bull, in hopes of a recipro-

---

[2] In actuality, it was General Robert Prescott who behaved so vindictively towards Allen; Melville unwittingly gave this role to a Captain McLeod (M'Cloud in Allen's *Narrative*) who had appealed for a more honorable treatment of the prisoner.—*J.L.*

cation of politeness. When among wild beasts, if they menace you, be a wild beast. Neither is it unlikely that this was the view taken by Allen. For, besides the exasperating tendency to self-assertion which such treatment as his must have bred on a man like him, his experience must have taught him that by assuming the part of a jocular, reckless, and even braggart barbarian, he would better sustain himself against bullying turnkeys, than by submissive quietude. Nor should it be forgotten that, besides the petty details of personal malice, the enemy violated every international usage of right and decency in treating a distinguished prisoner of war as if he had been a Botany Bay convict. If, at the present day, in any similar case between the same States, the repetition of such outrages would be more than unlikely, it is only because it is among nations as among individuals: imputed indigence provokes oppression and scorn, but that same indigence being risen to opulence receives a politic consideration even from its former insulters.

(Chapters XXI-XXII)

Marginalia

IN *Don Quixote de la Mancha* (Philadelphia, 1853)

VOLUME II, PAGE 216
". . . a knight-errant without a mistress is like a tree without leaves, a building without cement, a shadow without a body that causes it."

Or as Confucius said, 'a dog without a master,' or to drop both Cervantes & Confucius parables—a god-like mind without a God.

◇◇◇

It is possible that *The Confidence-Man* was also intended for serial publication, but its bitter voice was perhaps considered too disturbing for magazine readers. A deeply anxious writer needed more than a cap and bells to entertain American readers on the edge of a financial depression—the just but not the propitious moment for a satire on "confidence."

◇◇◇

From The Confidence-Man: His Masquerade

A Mute Goes Aboard a Boat on the Mississippi

A T SUNRISE on a first of April, there appeared, suddenly as Manco Capac at the lake Titicaca, a man in cream-colors, at the waterside in the city of St. Louis.

His cheek was fair, his chin downy, his hair flaxen, his hat a white fur one, with a long fleecy nap. He had neither trunk, valise, carpet-bag, nor parcel. No porter followed him. He was unaccompanied by friends. From the shrugged shoulders, titters, whispers, wonderings of the crowd, it was plain that he was, in the extremest sense of the word, a stranger.

In the same moment with his advent, he stepped aboard the favorite steamer *Fidèle*, on the point of starting for New Orleans. Stared at, but unsaluted, with the air of one neither courting nor shunning regard, but evenly pursuing the path of duty, lead it through solitudes or cities, he held on his way along the lower deck until he chanced to come to a placard nigh the captain's office, offering a reward for the capture of a mysterious impostor, supposed to have recently arrived from the East; quite an original genius in his vocation, as would appear, though wherein his originality consisted was not clearly given; but what purported to be a careful description of his person followed.

As if it had been a theater-bill, crowds were gathered about the announcement, and among them certain chevaliers, whose eyes, it was plain, were on the capitals, or, at least, earnestly seeking sight of them from behind intervening coats; but as for their fingers, they were enveloped in some myth; though, during a chance interval, one of these chevaliers somewhat showed his hand in purchasing from another chevalier, ex-officio a peddler of money-belts, one of his popular safeguards, while another peddler, who was still another versatile chevalier, hawked, in the thick of the throng, the lives of Measan, the bandit of Ohio; Murrel, the pirate of the Mississippi; and the brothers Harpe, the Thugs of the Green River country in Kentucky—creatures, with others of the sort, one and all exterminated at the time, and for the most part, like the hunted generations of wolves in the same regions, leaving comparatively few successors; which would seem cause for unalloyed gratulation, and is such to all except those who think that in new countries, where the wolves are killed off, the foxes increase.

Pausing at this spot, the stranger so far succeeded in threading his way, as at last to plant himself just beside the placard, when, producing a small slate and tracing some words upon it, he held it up before him on a level with the placard, so that they who read the one might read the other. The words were these:

Charity thinketh no evil

As, in gaining his place, some little perseverance, not to say persistence, of a mildly inoffensive sort, had been unavoidable, it was not with the best relish that the crowd regarded his apparent intrusion; and upon a more attentive survey, perceiving no badge of authority about him, but rather something quite the contrary —he being of an aspect so singularly innocent; an aspect, too, which they took to be somehow inappropriate to the time and place, and inclining to the notion that his writing was of much the same sort: in short, taking him for some strange kind of simpleton, harmless enough, would he keep to himself, but not wholly unobnoxious as an intruder—they made no scruple to jostle him aside; while one, less kind than the rest, or more of a wag, by an unobserved stroke, dexterously flattened down his fleecy hat upon his head. Without readjusting it, the stranger quietly turned, and writing anew upon the slate, again held it up:

Charity suffereth long, and is kind

Illy pleased with his pertinacity, as they thought it, the crowd a second time thrust him aside, and not without epithets and some buffets, all of which were unresented. But, as if at last despairing of so difficult an adventure, wherein one, apparently a non-resistant, sought to impose his presence upon fighting characters, the stranger now moved slowly away, yet not before altering his writing to this:

Charity endureth all things

Shield-like bearing his slate before him, amid stares and jeers he moved slowly up and down, at his turning points again changing his inscription to:

Charity believeth all things

and then:

Charity never faileth

The word "Charity," as originally traced, remained throughout uneffaced, not unlike the left-hand numeral of a printed date otherwise left for convenience in blank.

To some observers, the singularity, if not lunacy, of the stranger was heightened by his muteness, and, perhaps also, by the contrast to his proceedings afforded in the actions—quite in the wonted and sensible order of things—of the barber of the boat, whose quarters, under a smoking-saloon, and over against a bar-room, were next door but two to the captain's office. As if the long, wide, covered deck, hereabouts built up on both sides with shop-like windowed spaces, were some Constantinople arcade or bazaar, where more than one trade is plied, this river barber, aproned and slippered, but rather crusty-looking for the moment, it may be from being newly out of bed, was throwing open his premises for the day, and suitably arranging the exterior. With business-like dispatch, having rattled down his shutters, and at a palm-tree angle set out in the iron fixture his little ornamental pole, and this without overmuch tenderness for the elbows and toes of the crowd, he concluded his operations by bidding people stand still more aside, when, jumping on a stool, he hung over his door, on the customary nail, a gaudy sort of illuminated pasteboard sign, skillfully executed by himself, gilt with the likeness of a razor elbowed in readiness to shave, and also, for the public benefit, with two words not unfrequently seen ashore gracing other shops besides barbers':

NO TRUST

an inscription which, though in a sense not less intrusive than the contrasted ones of the stranger, did not, as it seemed, provoke any corresponding derision or surprise, much less indignation; and still less, to all appearances, did it gain for the inscriber the repute of being a simpleton.

Meanwhile, he with the slate continued moving slowly up and down, not without causing some stares to change into jeers, and some jeers into pushes, and some pushes into punches; when suddenly, in one of his turns, he was hailed from behind by two porters carrying a large trunk; but as the summons, though loud, was without effect, they accidentally or otherwise swung their burden against him, nearly overthrowing him; when, by a quick start, a peculiar inarticulate moan, and a pathetic telegraphing of his fingers, he involuntarily betrayed that he was not alone dumb, but also deaf.

Presently, as if not wholly unaffected by his reception thus far, he went forward, seating himself in a retired spot on the forecastle, nigh the foot of a ladder there leading to a deck above, up and down which ladder some of the boatmen, in discharge of their duties, were occasionally going.

From his betaking himself to this humble quarter, it was evident that, as a deck-passenger, the stranger, simple though he seemed, was not entirely ignorant of his place, though his taking a deck-passage might have been partly for convenience; as, from his having no luggage, it was probable that his destination was one of the small wayside landings within a few hours' sail. But, though he might not have a long way to go, yet he seemed already to have come from a very long distance.

Though neither soiled nor slovenly, his cream-colored suit had a tossed look, almost linty, as if, traveling night and day from some far country beyond the prairies, he had long been without the solace of a bed. His aspect was at once gentle and jaded, and, from the moment of seating himself, increasing in tired abstraction and dreaminess. Gradually overtaken by slumber, his flaxen head drooped, his whole lamb-like figure relaxed, and, half reclining against the ladder's foot, lay motionless, as some sugar-snow in March, which, softly stealing down over night, with its white placidity startles the brown farmer peering out from his threshold at daybreak.

(Chapter I)

Showing That Many Men Have Many Minds

"Odd fish!"

"Poor fellow!"

"Who can he be?"

"Caspar Hauser."

"Bless my soul!"

"Uncommon countenance."

"Green prophet from Utah."

"Humbug!"

"Singular innocence."

"Means something."

"Spirit-rapper."

"Moon-calf."

"Piteous."

"Trying to enlist interest."

"Beware of him."

"Fast asleep here, and, doubtless, pickpockets on board."

"Kind of daylight Endymion."

"Escaped convict, worn out with dodging."

"Jacob dreaming at Luz."

Such the epitaphic comments, conflictingly spoken or thought, of a miscellaneous company who, assembled on the overlooking crosswise balcony at the forward end of the upper deck near by, had not witnessed preceding occurrences.

Meantime, like some enchanted man in his grave, happily oblivious of all gossip, whether chiseled or chatted, the deaf and dumb stranger still tranquilly slept, while now the boat started on her voyage.

The great ship-canal of Ving-King-Ching, in the Flowery Kingdom, seems the Mississippi in parts, where, amply flowing between low, vine-tangled banks, flat as tow-paths, it bears the huge toppling steamers, bedizened and lacquered within like imperial junks.

Pierced along its great white bulk with two tiers of small embrasure-like windows, well above the water-line, the *Fidèle*, though, might at distance have been taken by strangers for some whitewashed fort on a floating isle.

Merchants on 'change seem the passengers that buzz on her decks, while, from quarters unseen, comes a murmur as of bees in the comb. Fine promenades, domed saloons, long galleries, sunny balconies, confidential passages, bridal chambers, staterooms plenty as pigeon-holes, and out-of-the-way retreats like secret drawers in an escritoire, present like facilities for publicity or privacy. Auctioneer or coiner, with equal ease, might somewhere here drive his trade.

Though her voyage of twelve hundred miles extends from apple to orange, from clime to clime, yet, like any small ferry-boat, to right and left, at every landing, the huge *Fidèle* still receives additional passengers in exchange for those that disembark; so that, though always full of strangers, she continually, in some degree, adds to, or replaces them with strangers still more strange; like Rio Janeiro fountain, fed from the Corcovado mountains, which is ever overflowing with strange waters, but never with the same strange particles in every part.

Though hitherto, as has been seen, the man in creamcolors had by no means passed unobserved, yet by stealing into retirement, and there going asleep and continuing so, he seemed to have courted oblivion, a boon not often withheld from so humble an applicant as he. Those staring crowds on the shore were now left far behind, seen dimly clustering like swallows on eaves; while the passengers' attention was soon drawn away to the rapidly shooting high bluffs and shot-towers on the Missouri shore, or the bluff-looking Missourians and towering Kentuckians among the throngs on the decks.

By and by—two or three random stoppages having been made, and the last transient memory of the slumberer vanished, and he himself, not unlikely, waked up and landed ere now—the crowd, as is usual, began in all parts to break up from a concourse into various clusters or squads, which in some cases disintegrated again into quartettes, trios, and couples, or even solitaires, involuntarily submitting to that natural law which ordains dissolution equally to the mass, as in time to the member.

As among Chaucer's Canterbury pilgrims, or those Oriental ones crossing the Red Sea towards Mecca in the festival month, there was no lack of variety. Natives of all sorts, and foreigners; men of business and men of pleasure; parlor-men and backwoodsmen; farm-hunters and fame-hunters; heiress-hunters, gold-hunters, buffalo-hunters, bee-hunters, happiness-hunters, truth-hunters, and still keener hunters after all these hunters. Fine ladies in slippers, and moccasined squaws; Northern speculators and Eastern philosophers; English, Irish, German, Scotch, Danes; Santa Fé traders in striped blankets, and Broadway bucks in cravats of cloth of gold; fine-looking Kentucky boatmen, and Japanese-looking Mississippi cotton-planters; Quakers in full drab, and United States soldiers in full regimentals; slaves, black, mulatto, quadroon; modish young Spanish Creoles, and old-fashioned French Jews; Mormons and Papists; Dives and Lazarus; jesters and mourners, teetotalers and convivialists; deacons and blacklegs; hardshell Baptists and clay-eaters; grinning Negroes, and Sioux chiefs solemn as high-priests. In short, a piebald parliament, an Anacharsis Clootz congress of all kinds of that multiform pilgrim species, man.

As pine, beech, birch, ash, hackmatack, hemlock, spruce, basswood, maple, interweave their foliage in the natural wood, so these varieties of mortals blended their varieties of visage and garb. A Tartar-like picturesqueness; a sort of pagan abandonment and assurance. Here reigned the dashing and all-fusing spirit of the West, whose type is the Mississippi itself, which, uniting the streams of the most distant and opposite zones, pours them along, helter-skelter, in one cosmopolitan and confident tide.

(Chapter II)

["Quite an Original"]

"Quite an original": a phrase, we fancy, rather oftener used by the young, or the unlearned, or the untraveled,

than by the old, or the well-read, or the man who has made the grand tour. Certainly, the sense of originality exists at its highest in an infant, and probably at its lowest in him who has completed the circle of the sciences.

As for original characters in fiction, a grateful reader will, on meeting with one, keep the anniversary of that day. True, we sometimes hear of an author who, at one creation, produces some two or three score such characters; it may be possible. But they can hardly be original in the sense that Hamlet is, or Don Quixote, or Milton's Satan. That is to say, they are not, in a thorough sense, original at all. They are novel, or singular, or striking, or captivating, or all four at once.

More likely, they are what are called odd characters; but for that, are no more original than what is called an odd genius, in his way, is. But, if original, whence came they? Or where did the novelist pick them up?

Where does any novelist pick up any character? For the most part, in town, to be sure. Every great town is a kind of man-show, where the novelist goes for his stock, just as the agriculturist goes to the cattle-show for his. But in the one fair new species of quadrupeds are hardly more rare than in the other are new species of characters—that is, original ones. Their rarity may still the more appear from this, that, while characters, merely singular, imply but singular forms, so to speak, original ones, truly so, imply original instincts.

In short, a due conception of what is to be held for this sort of personage in fiction would make him almost as much of a prodigy there as in real history is a new law-giver, a revolutionizing philosopher, or the founder of a new religion.

In nearly all the original characters loosely accounted

such in works of invention, there is discernible something prevailingly local, or of the age; which circumstance, of itself, would seem to invalidate the claim, judged by the principles here suggested.

Furthermore, if we consider, what is popularly held to entitle characters in fiction to be deemed original is but something personal—confined to itself. The character sheds not its characteristic on its surroundings, whereas, the original character, essentially such, is like a revolving Drummond light, raying away from itself all round it—everything is lit by it, everything starts up to it (mark how it is with Hamlet), so that, in certain minds, there follows upon the adequate conception of such a character, an effect, in its way, akin to that which in Genesis attends upon the beginning of things.

For much the same reason that there is but one planet to one orbit, so can there be but one such original character to one work of invention. Two would conflict to chaos. In this view, to say that there are more than one to a book is good presumption there is none at all. But for new, singular, striking, odd, eccentric, and all sorts of entertaining and instructive characters, a good fiction may be full of them. To produce such characters, an author, beside other things, must have seen much, and seen through much: to produce but one original character, he must have had much luck.

There would seem but one point in common between this sort of phenomenon in fiction and all other sorts: it cannot be born in the author's imagination—it being as true in literature as in zoology, that all life is from the egg.

In the endeavor to show, if possible, the impropriety of the phrase, "Quite an original," as applied by the barber's friends, we have, at unawares, been led into a dissertation bordering upon the prosy, perhaps upon the smoky. If so, the best use the smoke can be turned to will be by retiring under cover of it, in good trim as may be, to the story.

(Chapter XXIV)

❖❖❖

"Travel to a large and generous nature is as a new birth. Its legitimate tendency is to teach profound personal humility. At the same time it enlarges the sphere of comprehensive benevolence till it includes the whole human race. . . . The sight of novel objects, the acquirement of novel ideas, the breaking up of old prejudices, the enlargement of heart and mind—are the proper fruit of rightly undertaken travel." Something of these large and positive purposes (pronounced in a lecture after his return) sent Melville up the Straits in 1856, but the bitter wit of *The Confidence-Man* was not all left behind in its pages. The traveler "must not anticipate unalloyed pleasure. . . . The minute discomforts, the afflictions of Egypt and Italy, in the shape of fleas and other insects, we shall pass over lightly. Though they by no means pass lightly over the traveler. . . . The persecutions and extortions of guides, not only the rough and robber-like, but those who combine the most finished politeness with the most delicate knavery, are another serious drawback on your pleasure. . . . Honest and humane men are also to be found, but not in the overwhelming majority." No wonder he planned a sequel to his *Masquerade*, not realizing that he had written the last novel that he was to see published. It was to appear before he got back to the United States and Arrowhead. The characters he "picked up" in Egypt, Asia Minor, and Europe were to remain as notes in his journal.

❖❖❖

From Journal up the Straits, 1856–1857

Egypt

Jan 3ᵈ [1857].

Steamer for Jaffa will not sail till tomorrow, so that I am wearied to death with two days in Alexandria which might have been delightfully spent in Cairo. But travellers must expect these things.—I will now without any order jot down my impressions of Cairo, ere they grow dim.—It seems one booth and Bartholemew Fair—a grand masquerade of mortality.—Several of the thoroughfares covered at vast height with old planks & matting, so that the street has the light of a closed verandah. In one case this matting extends from mosque to mosque, where they are opposite. The houses seem a collection of old orchestras, organs, proscenium boxes, —or like masses of old furniture (grotesque) lumbering a garret & covered with dust. Lattice-work of the projecting windows. With little square holes, just large enough to contain the head. Curious aspect of women's faces peeping out. Most of the houses built of stone of a brownish white. Some of the streets of private houses are like tunnels from meeting overhead of projecting windows &c. Like night at noon. Sometimes high blank walls—mysterious passages,—dim peeps at courts & wells in shadow. Great numbers of uninhabited houses in the lonelier parts of the city. Their dusty, cadaverous ogerish look. Ghostly, & suggestive of all that is weird. Haunted houses & Cock Lanes. Ruined mosques, domes knocked in like stoven boats. Others, upper part empty & desolate with broken rafters & dismantled windows; (rubbish) below, the dirty rites of religion. Aspect of the thoroughfares like London streets on Saturday night. All the world gossiping & marketing,—but in picturesque costumes. Crookedness of the streets—multitudes of blind men—worst city in the world for them. Flies on the eyes at noon. Nature feeding on man. Contiguity of desert & verdure, splendor & squalor, gloom & gayety; numerous blind men going about led. Children opthalmic. Too much light & no defence against it.—The antiquity of Egypt stamped upon individuals.—Appearance of the women. Thing for the face. Black crape hanging like trunk of elephant. Profusion of jewelry. Brass on face. Staining the eyes (black) & fingernails (yellow)—Some in fine silks & on donkeys. Animated appearance of the population. Turks in carriages, with Osmanli drivers & footmen; sitting back proudly & gazing round on the people still with the air of conquerors. Footmen running ahead with silver tipped bamboos. Rapid driving, shouts of the driver. . . .

Pyramids. Scamper to them with officers on donkeys. Rapid passing of crowds upon the road; following of the donkey-boys &c. In heyday holyday spirits arrived at the eternal sorrows of the pyramids. Cross Nile in boats. Isle Roda, pavilions & kiosks & gardens. Donkeys crossing, rapid current, muddy banks. Pyramids from distance purple like mountains. Seem high & pointed, but flatten & depress as you approach. Vapors below summits. Kites sweeping & soaring around, hovering right over apex. At angles, like broken cliffs. Table-rock overhanging, adhering solely by mortar. Sidelong look when midway up. Pyramids on a great ridge of sand.

You leave the angle, and ascend hillock of sand & ashes & broken mortar & pottery to a point, & then go along a ledge to a path &c. Zig-zag routes, As many routes as to cross the Alps—The Simplon, Great St: Bernard &c. Mules on Andes. Caves—platforms. Looks larger midway than from top or bottom. Precipice on precipice, cliff on cliff. Nothing in Nature gives such an idea of vastness. A balloon to ascend them. View of persons ascending, Arab guides in flowing white mantles. Conducted as by angels up to heaven. Guides so tender. Resting. Pain in the chest. Exhaustion. Must hurry. None but the phlegmatic go deliberately. Old man with the spirits of youth—long looked for this chance—tried the ascent, half way—failed—brought down. Tried to go into the interior—fainted—brought out—leaned against the pyramid by the entrance—pale as death. Nothing so pathetic. Too much for him; oppressed by the massiveness & mystery of the pyramids. I myself too. A feeling of awe & terror came over me. Dread of the Arabs. Offering to lead me into a side-hole. The Dust. Long arched way,—then down as in a coal shaft. Then as in mines, under the sea. The stooping & doubling. I shudder at idea of ancient Egyptians. It was in these pyramids that was conceived the idea of Jehovah. Terrible mixture of the cunning and awful. Moses learned in all the lore of the Egyptians. The idea of Jehovah born here.—When I was at top, thought it not so high—sat down on edge. Looked below—gradual nervousness & final giddiness & terror. Entrance of pyramids like shoot for coal or timber. Horrible place for assassination. As long as earth endures some vestige will remain of the pyramids. Nought but earthquake or geological revolution can obliterate them. Only people who made their mark, both in their masonry & their religion (through Moses). *Color of Pyramids same as desert.*

Some of the stone (but few) friable; most of them hard as ever. The climate favors them. Pyramids not in line. Between, like Notch of White Mountains. *No vestige of moss upon them. Not the least. Other ruins ivied. Dry as tinder. No speck of green.* Arabs climb them like goats, or any other animal. Down one & up the other. Pyramids still loom before me—something vast, indefinite, incomprehensible, and awful. Line of desert & verdure, plain as line between good & evil. An instant collision of alien elements. A long billow of desert forever hovers as in act of breaking, upon the verdure of Egypt. Grass near the pyramids, but will not touch them—as if in fear or awe of them. Desert more fearful to look at than ocean. Theory of design of pyramids. Defense against desert. A Line of them. Absurd. Might have been created with the creation. . . .

The lines of stone look less like courses of masonry, than like strata of rocks. The long slope of crags & precipices. The vast plane. No wall, no roof. In other buildings, however vast, the eye is gradually innured to the sense of magnitude, by passing from part to part. But here there is no stay or stage. It is all or nothing. It is not the sense of heigh or breadth or length or depth, but the sense of immensity, that is stirred. After seeing the pyramid, all other architecture seems but pastry. Though I had but so short a time to view the pyramid, yet I doubt whether any time spent upon it, would tend to a more precise impression of it. As with the ocean, you learn as much of its vastness by the first five minutes glance as you would in a month, so with the pyramid. Its simplicity confounds you. Finding it vain to take in its vastness man has taken to sounding it & weighing its density; so with the pyramid, he measures the base, & computes the size of individual stones. It refuses to be studied or adequately comprehended.

It still looms in my imagination, dim & indefinite. The tearing away of the casing, though it removed enough stone to build a walled-town, has not one whit subtracted from the apparent magnitude of the pyramid. It has had just the contrary effect. When the pyramid presented a smooth plane, it must have lost as much in impressiveness as the ocean does when unfurrowed. A dead calm of masonry. But now the ridges majestically diversify it. It has been said in panegyric of some extraordinary works of man, that they affect the imagination like the works of Nature. But the pyramid affects one in neither way exactly. Man seems to have had as little to do with it as Nature. It was that supernatural creature, the priest. They must needs have been terrible inventors, those Egyptian wise men. And one seems to see that as out of the crude forms of the natural earth they could evoke by art the transcendent mass & symetry & voids of the pyramid so out of the rude elements of the insignificant thoughts that are in all men, they could rear the transcendent conception of a God. But for no holy purpose was the pyramid founded.

Palestine

From Jerusalem to Dead Sea &c [Mid-January 1857.]

Over Olivet by St: Stephens Gate to Bethany—on a hill—wretched Arab village—fine view—tomb of Lazarus, a mere cave or cell—On down into vallies & over hills—all barren—Brook Kedron—immense depth—black & funereal—Valley of Jehosophat, grows more diabolical as approaches Dead Sea—Plain of Jericho —looks green, (part of it) an orchard, but only trees of apple of Sodom—P. of J. corresponds to P. of S. on other side of mountains. Mount of Temptation—a black, arid mount—nought to be seen but Dead Sea, mouth of Kedron—very tempting—foolish fiend—but it was a display in vision—Then why take him up to Mount?—the *thing itself* was in vision.—Where Kedron opens into Plain of Jericho looks like Gate of Hell.—Tower with sheiks smoking & huts on top—thick walls—village of Jericho—ruins on hill-side—tent—fine dinner—jolly time—sitting at door of tent looking at mountains of Moab.—tent the charmed circle, keeping off the curse. Marsaba.—Rain at night—Thunder in mountains of Moab—Lightning—cry of jackall & wolf.—Broke up camp—rain—wet—rode out on *mouldy* plain—nought grows but wiry, prickly bush—muddy—every creature *in human form* seen ahead—escort alarmed & galloped on to learn something—salutes—every man understands it—shows native dignity—worthy of salute—Arabs on hills over Jordan—alarm—scampering ahead of escort —after rain, turbid & yellow stream—foliaged banks— beyond, arid hills.—Arabs crossing the river—lance— old crusaders—pistols—menacing cries—tobacco.— Robbers—rob Jericho annually—&c—Ride over mouldy plain to Dead Sea—Mountains on both sides—Lake George—all but verdure.—foam on beach & pebbles like slaver of mad dog—smarting bitter of the water,— carried the bitter in my mouth all day—bitterness of life—thought of all bitter things—Bitter is it to be poor & bitter, to be reviled, & Oh bitter are these waters of Death, thought I.—Old boughs tossed up by water— relics of pick-nick—nought to eat but bitumen & ashes with desert of Sodom apples washed down with water of Dead Sea.—Must bring your own provisions, as well, too, for mind as body—for all is barren. Drank of brook, but brackish.—Ascended among the mountains again— barren.—

Barrenness of Judea

Whitish mildew pervading whole tracts of landscape—
bleached—leprosy—encrustation of curses—old cheese
—bones of rocks,—crunched, knawed, & mumbled—
mere refuse & rubbish of creation—like that laying
outside of Jaffa Gate—all Judea seems to have been
accumulations of this rubbish.—So rubbishy, that no
chiffonier could find any thing all over it.—*No moss
as in other ruins—no grace of decay—no ivy—the
unleavened nakedness of desolation*—whitish ashes—
lime-kilns—You see the anatomy—compares with ordinary regions as skeleton with living & rosy man.— . . .

Stones of Judea. We read a good deal about stones
in Scriptures. Monuments & memorials are set up of
stones; men are stoned to death; the figurative seed falls
in stony places; And no wonder that stones should so
largely figure in the Bible. Judea is one accumulation of
stones—Stony mountains & stony plains; stony torrents
& stony roads; stony vales & stony fields, stony homes &
stony tombs; stony eyes & stony hearts. Before you, &
behind you are stones. Stones to right & stones to left.
In many places laborious attempts have been made, to
clear the surface of these stones. You see heaps of stones
here & there; and stone walls of immense thickness are
thrown together, less for boundaries than to get them
out of the way. But in vain; The removal of one stone
only serves to reveal there stones still larger, below it.
It is like mending an old barn; the more you uncover,
the more it grows.—The toes of every ones shoes are
all stubbed to pieces with the stones. They are seldom
as round as our stones; but sharp, flinty & scratchy. But
in the roads, such as that to Jaffa, they have been worn
smooth by continuous travel.—To account for this abundance of stones, many theories have been started; *My*

theory is that long ago, some whimsical king of the country took it into his head to pave all Judea, and entered into contracts to that effect; but the contractor becoming bankrupt mid-way in his business, the stones were only dumped on the ground, & there they lie to this day. . . .

Jerusalem

. . . In Jehosophat, Jew grave stones lie as if indiscriminately flung abroad by a blast in a quarry. So thick, a warren of the dead—so old, the Hebrew inscriptions can hardly be distinguished from the wrinkles formed by Time. Shapeless stones &c.—Side by side here tombs of Absalom, Zachariah & St James. Cut out of live rock in Petra style. St: James a stone verandah overlooking the gorge—pillars.—Jehosophat, shows seams of natural rock—capitals of pilasters rubbed off by Time.—Large hole in front—full of stones inside, heap of stones (cart loads) before it—The maledictory contribution of the pilgrims, one of the melancholy amenities of Jerusalem. To be stoned is his memorial.—The grave stones project *out* from the side-hill, as if already in act of resurrection . . .

The Beautiful, or Golden, Gate—two arches, highly ornamental sculpture, undoubtedly old, Herod's time—the gate from which Christ would go to Bethany & Olivet—& also that in which he made his entry (with palms) into the city. Turks walled it up because of tradition that through this Gate the city would be taken.—One of the most interesting things in Jerusalem—seems expressive of the finality of Christianity, as if this was the last religion of the world,—no other, possible.

In pursuance of my object, the saturation of my mind with the atmosphere of Jerusalem, offering myself up a passive subject, and no unwilling one, to its weird impressions, I always rose at dawn & walked without the walls. Nor so far as escaping the pent-up air within was concerned was I singular here . . .

The Holy Sepulchre—ruined dome—confused & half-ruinous pile.—Labyrinths & terraces of mouldy grottos, tombs, & shrines. Smells like a dead-house. Dingy light. —At the entrance, in a sort of grotto in the wall a divan for Turkish policemen, where they sit crosslegged & smoking, scornfully observing the continuous troops of pilgrims entering & prostrating themselves before the anointing-stone of Christ, which veined with streaks of a mouldy red looks like a butcher's slab.—Near by is a blind stair of worn marble, ascending to the reputed Calvary where among other things they show you by the smoky light of old pawnbrokers lamps of dirty gold, the hole in which the cross was fixed and through a narrow grating as over a coal cellar, point out the rent in the rock! On the same level, near by is a kind of gallery, railed with marble, overlooking the entrance of the church; And here almost every day I would hang, looking down upon the spectacle of the scornful Turks on the divan, & the scorned pilgrims kissing the stone of the anointing.—The door of the church is like that of a jail —a grated window in it.—The main body of the church is overhung by the lofty & ruinous dome whose fallen plastering reveals the meagre skeleton of beams & laths. A sort of plague-stricken splendor reigns in the painted & mildewed walls around. In the midst of all, stands the Sepulchre: a church in a church. It is of marble, richly sculptured in parts & bearing the faded aspect of age. From its porch, issues a garish stream of light upon the faces of the pilgrims who crowd for admittance into a space which will hold but four or five at a time. First passing a wee vestibule where is shown the stone on which the angel sat, you enter the tomb. It is like entering a lighted lanthorn. Wedged & half-dazzled, you stare for a moment on the ineloquence of the bedizened slab, and glad to come out, wipe your brow glad to escape as from the heat & jam of a show-box. All is glitter & nothing is gold. A sickening cheat. The countenances of the poorest & most ignorant pilgrims would seem tacitly to confess it as well as your own. . . .

Talk of the guides. "There is the stone Christ leaned against, & here is the English Hotel." Yonder is the arch where Christ was shown to the people, & just by that open window is sold the best coffee in Jerusalem. &c &c &c.

Had Jerusalem no peculiar historic associations, still would it, by its physical aspect evoke peculiar emotion in the traveller. As the sight of haunted Haddon Hall suggested to Mrs. Radcliffe her curdling romances, so I have little doubt, the diabolical landscape of Judea must have suggested to the Jewish prophets, their ghastly theology. . . .

The olive tree much resembles in its grotesque contortions the apple tree—only it is much more gnarled & less lovely in its green. It is generally planted in orchards, which helps the resemblance. It is a haunted melancholy looking tree (sober & penitent), quite in keeping with Jerusalem & its associations. There are many olives on the plain north of the walls. The Cave of Jeremiah is in this part. In its lamentable recesses he composed his lamentable Lamentations. . . .

The color of the whole city is grey & looks at you like a cold grey eye in a cold old man.—its strange aspect in the pale olive light of the morning. . . .

Is the desolation of the land the result of the fatal embrace of the Deity? Hapless are the favorites of heaven.

Oxford

May 2ᵈ [1857]

Left London by R.R. for Oxford. Clear day. Rich country . . . At 11½ arrived at Oxford.—Most interesting spot I have seen in England. Made tour of all colleges. It was here I first confessed with gratitude my mother land, & hailed her with pride. Oxford to Americans as well worth visiting as Paris, tho' in a very different way. —Pulpit in corner of quadrangle. Deer. Garden girdled by river.—Meadows beyond. Oxen & sheep. Pastoral & collegiate life blended.—Christ Church Meadow. Avenue of trees.—Old reef washed by waves & showing detached parts—so Oxford. Ivy branch over portal of St. John intertwining with sculpture. Amity of art & nature. Accord. Grotesque figures. Catching rheumatism in Oxford cloisters different from catching it in Rome. Contagion in Pamfili Doria but wholesome beauty in Oxford. Learning lodged like a faun. Garden to every college. Lands for centuries never molested by labor. Sacred to beauty & tranquility. Fell's avenue. Has beheld unstirred all the violence of revolutions, &c. —Ship roof. Spanish chestnut. Dining halls. Dormer window derived from gable, as spire from elevating & sharpening roof in snowy climates—final result of gradual process.—Stair case of Christ Church. Single pillar as on Paris chapel. Each college has dining room & chapel—on a par—large windows. Soul & body equally cared for.—Grass smooth as green baize of billiard table.—The picturesque never goes beyond this.—I know nothing more fitted by mild & beautiful rebuke to chastise the presumptuous ranting of Yankees.—In such a retreat old Burton sedately smiled at men.

◇◇◇

"The pleasure of leaving home, care-free, with no concern but to enjoy, has also as a pendant the pleasure of coming back to the old hearthstone, the home to which the heart, however traveled, still fondly turns, ignoring the burden of its anxieties and cares." This pleasure of travel, too, was not unalloyed, for, waiting alongside his wife and four children, were the burdens of an estate he could no longer care for and a career that hampered his earning capacity. One suggestion was that he should exploit his latest journey on the popular lecture circuits.

Melville's debut as lecturer was made on November 23, 1857, in Lawrence, Massachusetts, where his brother-in-law and best friend, John C. Hoadley, lived. The subject was "Statues in Rome," a topic to which lecture audiences showed the clearest antipathy. A second lecture in a more promising field, "The South Seas," was written and introduced later in the season. When he read this in Baltimore on February 8, 1859, there was a "phonographist" present from the *Baltimore American*.

◇◇◇

The South Seas

Mr. M. began by saying:

The subject of our lecture this evening, "the South Seas" may be thought perhaps a theme if not ambitious, at least somewhat expansive, covering, according to the authorities, I am afraid to say how much of the earth's surface—in short, more than one-half. We have, therefore, a rather spacious field before us, and I hardly think we shall be able, in a thorough way, to go over the whole of it to-night.

And here (to do away with any erroneous anticipations as to our topic) I hope you do not expect me to repeat what has long been in print touching my own casual adventures in Polynesia. I propose to treat of matters of more general interest, and, in a random way, discuss the South Seas at large and under various aspects, introducing, as occasion may serve, any little incident, personal or other, fitted to illustrate the point in hand.

South Seas is simply an equivalent term for Pacific Ocean. Then why not say Pacific Ocean at once?— Because one may have a lingering regard for certain old associations, linking the South Seas as a name with many pleasant and venerable books of voyages, full of well-remembered engravings.

To be sure those time-worn tomes are pretty nearly obsolete, but none the less are they, with the old name they enshrine, dear to the memory of their reader; in much the same way too that the old South Sea House in London was dear to the heart of Charles Lamb.— Who that has read it can forget that quaint sketch, the introductory essay of Elia, where he speaks of the Balclutha-like desolation of those haunted old offices of the once famous South Sea Company—the old oaken wainscots hung with the dusty maps of Mexico and soundings of the Bay of Panama—the vast cellarages under the whole pile where Mexican dollars and doubloons once lay heaped in huge bins for Mammon to solace his solitary heart withal?

But besides summoning up the memory of brave old books, Elia's fine sketch, and the great South Sea Bubble, originating in the institution there celebrated—the words South Seas are otherwise suggestive, yielding to the fancy an indefinable odor of sandalwood and cinnamon. In the adventures of Captain Dampier (that eminent and excellent buccaneer) you read only of South Seas. In Harris' old voyages, and many others, the title is the same, and even as late as 1803 we find that Admiral Burney prefers the old title to the new, Pacific, which appellation has in the present century only become the popular one—notwithstanding which we occasionally find the good old name first bestowed still employed by writers of repute.

But since these famous waters lie on both sides of the Equator and wash the far northern shores of Kamchatka as well as the far southern ones of Tierra del Fuego, how did they ever come to be christened with such a misnomer as *South* Seas? The way it happened was this: The Isthmus of Darien runs not very far from east and west; if you stand upon its further shore the ocean will appear to the *south* of you, and were you ignorant of the general direction of the coastline you would infer that it rolled away wholly toward that quarter. Now Balboa, the first white man who laid eyes upon these waters, stood in just this position; drew just this inference and bestowed its name accordingly.

The circumstances of Balboa's discovery are not uninteresting. In the earliest days of the Spanish dominion on this continent, he commanded a petty post on the northern shore of the Isthmus, and hearing it rumored that there was a vast sea on the other side of the land —its beach not distant, but of difficult approach, owing to a range of steep mountain wall and other obstruction, he resolved to explore in that direction. His hardships may be imagined by recalling the narrative a few years since of the adventures of Lieut. Strain and party who in like manner with the Spaniard, undertook [in 1854] to cross from sea to sea, through the primeval wilderness.

A party of buccaneers also likewise crossed the Isthmus under suffering, the utmost that nature is capable of sustaining. Balboa and the buccaneers, though not more courageous, were certainly more hardy or more fortunate than the American officer, since, after all they underwent, their efforts were at last successful.

The thronging Indians opposed Balboa's passage, demanding who he was, what he wanted, and whither he was going. The reply is a model of Spartan directness. "I am a Christian, my errand is to spread true religion and to seek gold, and I am going in search of the sea."

Coming at last to the foot of a mountain, he was told that from its summit he could see the object of his search. He ordered a halt, and, like Moses, the devout Spaniard "went up into the mountain alone." When he beheld the sea he fell upon his knees and thanked God for the sight. The next day with sword and target, wading up to his waist in its waters, he called upon his troop and the assembled Indians to bear witness that he took possession of that whole ocean with all the lands and kingdoms pertaining to it for his soverign master the King of Castile and Leon. A large-minded gentleman, of great latitude of sentiment, was Vasco Nuñez de Balboa, commander of that petty post of Darien.

The tempests off Cape Horn were here described by the lecturer, with allusion to the rapid run often made up the west coast of South America, sometimes leaving but a few days between the latitudes of icebergs and oranges.

The European who first sailed upon those waters had this experience intensified. True, Magellan passed not round the yet undiscovered Horn, but through the straits which bear his name. But this only made the matter worse. For, in these straits, narrow, tortuous, and rock-bound, dense fogs prevail and antarctic squalls, and the navigation is peculiarly dangerous. Magellan worked through, however, and when he beheld ahead a fine open ocean, by good fortune smooth and serene, in his excess of emotion he burst into tears, stout sailor as he was, and this was the man who gave to this sea its second name—Pacific. The great sea then was in a happy humor, and hence received a name which will forever be called Pacific, even by the sailor destined to perish in one of its terrible typhoons.

Although the Pacific covers half the surface of the planet, yet with all its dotted isles and people it remained almost unknown to even a recent period. Captain Cook's account of his visit to Tahiti could produce, as late as 1780, upon the English people almost the full thrill of novelty. Indeed, but little was known of the whole region till Cook's time. It was California that first brought the Pacific home to the great body of Anglo-Saxons.

The world of water here is so broad and its living races so various, that one is puzzled where to choose his matter for a lecture.

We might tell of tribes of sharks that populate some parts of the Pacific as thickly as the celestials do the Chinese Empire, or we might introduce that gallant chevalier, the swordfish—the Hector of the seas—and tell of his martial exploits; the tilts he runs at the great ships; the duels he fights with them—sometimes leaving his weapon in their ribs, or by withdrawing it, leaving an open wound, to the great peril of the craft and crew, as in the case of the English ship *Foxhound*. We might tell of the devil-fish, which sailors say, dives to the profoundest abyss and comes up roaring with mouths as many and as wide open as the Mississippi.

The pelican, with his pouch stuffed with game like a sportsman's bag; the melancholy penguin standing on one spot all day with a fit of the blues; the man-of-war hawk, that fierce black bandit; and the storied albatross, with white and arching wing like an archangel's, his haughty beak curved like a scimetar. Yes, a whole hour might be spent in telling about either the fishes or the birds.

Furthermore, there are exceptional phenomena, such as the peculiar phosphoric aspect of the water sometimes. I have been in a whale-boat at midnight when, having lost the ship, we would keep steering through the lonely night for her, while the sea that weltered by us would present the pallid look of the face of a corpse, and lit by its spectral gleam we men in the boat showed to each other like so many weather-beaten ghosts. Then to mark Leviathan come wallowing along, dashing the pale sea into sparkling cascades of fire, showering it all over him till the monster would look like Milton's Satan, riding the flame billows of the infernal world. We might fill night after night with that fertile theme, the whaling voyage. The adventurous sailors, either on the blank face of the waters, where often for months together their ship floats lonely as the ark of Noah, or in their intercourse with the natives of coasts reached by few or none but themselves. The islands, too, are an endless theme; thick as the stars in the milky way. The name bestowed upon their swarming clusters—Polynesia— not inaptly hints at their numberlessness.

The most noted of these are the Sandwich and Society groups; the Friendly, Navigator, and Feejee clusters; the Pelew, Ladrone, Mulgrave, Kingsmills, and Radack chains—but there are more than Briareus could number on all his finger ends.

The popular notion, from the early vague accounts, imagines them to hold enameled plains, with groves of shadowing palms, watered by purling brooks and the country but little elevated. The reverse of this is true: bold rock-bound coasts—a beating surf—lofty and craggy cliffs, split here and there into deep inlets opening to the view deeper valleys parted by masses of emerald mountains sweeping seaward from an interior of lofty peaks.[1]

But, would you get the best water view of a Polynesian island, select one with a natural breakwater of surf-beaten coral all around it, leaving within a smooth, circular canal, broad and deep, entrance to which is had through natural sea-gates. Lounging in a canoe, there is nothing more pleasant than to float along—especially where Boraborra, and Otaha, the glorious twins of the Society group, rear their lofty masses to the ever vernal heights, belted about by the same zone of reef—the reef itself being dotted with small islets perpetually thick and green with grass.

The virgin freshness of these unviolated wastes, the exemption of those far-off archipelagoes from the heat and dust of civilization, acts sometimes as the last provocative to those jaded tourists to whom even Europe has become hackneyed, and who look upon the Parthenon and the Pyramids with a yawn.

Why don't the English yachters give up the prosy Mediterranean and sail out here? Any one who treats the natives fairly is just as safe as if he were on the Nile or Danube. But I am sorry to say we whites have a sad reputation among many of the Polynesians. They esteem us, with rare exceptions, such as *some* of the

[1] Despite his introductory warning to his audience "not [to] expect me to repeat what has long been in print touching my own casual adventures in Polynesia," Melville had consulted his earlier works in composing this lecture; *Mardi* had colored its fishes, "The Encantadas" its birds, and if the reader will turn to page 22, he will find in *Typee* the model for the above paragraph.—*J.L.*

missionaries, the most barbarous, treacherous, irreligious, and devilish creatures on the earth. It may be a mere prejudice of these unlettered savages, for have not our traders always treated them with brotherly affection? Who has ever heard of a vessel sustaining the honor of a Christian flag and the spirit of the Christian Gospel by opening its batteries in indiscriminate massacre upon some poor little village on the seaside—splattering the torn bamboo huts with blood and brains of women and children, defenceless and innocent?

We have not space to follow the speaker fully in the remainder of his lecture, in which he graphically described the boundless expanse of the Pacific and its myriad islands as a hiding place as far removed from the life of the great world as though its people dwelt upon another planet. This mantle of mystery long hid the Buccaneers, who plundered the Spanish commerce; and covered for years Christian, the mutineer of the *Bounty,* who, after a life of exile and immunity from European law, was found, bent with age, amid a thriving colony of half-breed children and grand-children, whom his savage wives had reared for him amid ever-green woods, under ever-healthful skies, and through the plenty of perpetual harvests. *There is no such hiding place on earth, said the lecturer, except the solitude of London.*

The lecturer then spoke of the projects of some reformers who, despairing of civilizing Europe or America according to their rule, projected establishments in the Pacific where they hoped to find a fitting place for the good time coming. The Polynesians themselves, he said, were not without their dream, their ideal, their Utopia. As Ponce de Leon hoped to find in Florida the fountain of perpetual youth, so the mystic Kamapuhai left the western shore of the island where he suffered with his restless philosophy and, hoping to find the joy-giving fountain and the people like to the Gods, sailed after the sinking sun, and has not yet returned to cheer mankind with his discoveries.

Another strange quest was that of Alvaro, a bold Spanish captain, who stirred up such enthusiasm among the courtly Dons and Donnas of his time that many of them joined his expedition, in which he was sure he would find the Phœnician Ophir of King Hiram and bring from it more than the treasure stores with which Solomon had beautified his temple. After months and months of voyaging with hope deferred, the mines of Mammon were not found, and the poor Captain, dying, was buried in the solitude of an unfathomed sea.

Graphic descriptions were given of the graceful forms of the Polynesian women, and the splendid figures of the men, with their symmetrical and columnar legs.

The rapid advance, in the externals only, of civilized life was then spoken of, and the prospect of annexing the Sandwich Islands to the American Union commented on, with the remark that the whalemen of Nantucket and the Westward ho! of California were every day getting them more and more annexed.

The lecturer closed with an earnest wish that adventurers from our soil and from the lands of Europe would abstain from those brutal and cruel vices which disgust even savages with our manners, while they turn an earthly paradise into a pandemonium. And as for annexation he begged, as a general philanthropist, to offer up an earnest prayer, and he entreated all present to join him in it, that the banns of that union should be forbidden until we had found for ourselves a civilization moral, mental, and physical, higher than one which has culminated in almshouses, prisons, and hospitals.

❖❖❖

Kept secret from all but his wife, his sisters, his closest
friends, and his hopes was a new career in an unfamiliar
medium—poetry. Yet when his brother Thomas, captain
of the clipper ship *Meteor,* returned to Boston Harbor at the
end of April 1860 and suggested that Melville round Cape
Horn again with him, Herman accepted the invitation with
an alacrity surprising in a poet preparing his first volume of
verse for peddling. Leaving all the problems of the volume
in the hands of Elizabeth as copyist and Allan as agent,
Melville asked Evert Duyckinck to help with publishers and
"to lend something of an overseeing eye to the launching of
this craft—the committing of it to the elements."

❖❖❖

To Allan Melville

[May 22ᵈ 1860]

Memoranda for Allan
concerning the publication of my verses

1—Don't stand on terms much with the publisher—
half profits after expenses are paid will content me
—not that I expect much "profits"—but that will be
a fair nomical arrangement—They should also give
me 1 doz. copies of the book—

2—Don't have the Harpers.—I should like the Apple-
tons or Scribner—But Duyckinck's advice will be
good here.

3—The sooner the thing is printed and published, the
better. The "season" will make little or no difference,
I fancy, in this case.

4—After printing, don't let the book hang back—but
publish & have done.

5—For God's sake don't have *By the author of "Typee" "Piddledee" &c* on the title-page.

6—Let the title-page be simply,

Poems

by

Herman Melville

7—Don't have any clap-trap announcements and "sensation" puffs—nor any extracts published previous to publication of book—Have a decent publisher, in short.

8—Don't take any measures, or make inquiries as to expediency of an English edition simultaneous with the American—as in case of "Confidence-Man."

9—In the M.S.S. each piece is on a page by itself, however small the piece. This was done merely for convenience in the final classification; and should be no guide for the printer—of course in printing two or more pieces will sometimes appear on the same page —according to length of pieces &c. you understand—

10—The poems are divided into books as you will see; but the divisions are not *called* books—they are only numbered—Thus it is in the M.S.S., and should be the same in print. There should be a page with the number between every division.

11—Anything not perfectly plain in the M.S.S. can be referred to Lizzie—also have the M.S.S. returned to her after printing.

12—Lizzie should by all means see the printed sheets *before* being bound, in order to detect any gross errors consequent upon misconstruing the M.S.S.—

These are the thoughts which hurriedly occur to me at this moment. Pardon the abruptness of their expression, but time is precious.—Of all human events, perhaps, the publication of a first volume of verses is the most insignificant; but though a matter of no moment to the world, it is still of some concern to the author, —as these *Mem.* show—Pray therefore, don't laugh at my *Mem.* but give heed to them, and so oblige

Your brother
Herman

To Evert Duyckinck

Boston, May 29th [28] 1860
On board ship "Meteor"

My Dear Duyckinck: I am glad that the postponement of the ship's day of sailing gives me a chance to answer your letter, received, in reply to mine, on the eve of my leaving Pittsfield. It was a very welcome one—quite a wind from the fields of old times.

My wife will send you the parcel [of poems] in the course of a week or so—there remaining something to be finished in copying the M.S.S.

As my wife has interested herself a good deal in this matter, and in fact seems to know more about it than I do—at least about the *merits* of the performance—I must therefore refer you to her in case of any exigency requiring information further than you are in possession of.

If your brother George is not better employed, I hope he will associate himself with you in looking over my scribblings.

That is enough in the egotistic way. Now for something else.

I anticipate as much pleasure as, at the age of forty, one temperately can, in the voyage I am going. I go under very happy auspices so far as ship & Captain is concerned. A noble ship and a nobler captain—& he my brother. We have the breadth of the tropics before us, to sail over twice; & shall round the world. Our first port is San Francisco, which we shall probably make in 110 days from Boston. Thence we go to Manilla— & thence, I hardly know where.—I wish devoutly you were going along. I think it would agree with you. The prime requisite for enjoyment in sea voyages, for passengers, is 1st health—2d good-nature. Both first-rate things, but not universally to be found.—At sea a fellow comes out. Salt water is like wine, in that respect.

I have a good lot of books with me—such as they are;—plenty of old periodicals—lazy reading for lazy latitudes.—

Now I am called away & must close.

Good bye to you & God bless you

H Melville

Journal on the Clipper Ship *Meteor*, 1860

Thomas Melville, Commander
Herman Melville, Passenger

[Boston] Wednesday May 30th

At 10½ A.M. Tom, Fanny, George Griggs, and I went off to ship in the stream. Beautiful day, and pleasant sail down the harbor. Mr Peabody was on board, and lunched in the cabin. We bade Fanny good bye, and I assisted her into the tug-boat, preparatory to its going ahead to tow. At ¼ past one P.M. pilot and tug-boat left us. Waved our handkerchiefs to Fanny, and the voyage began.——Quite sea-sick at night.

June 8th Friday

During the past days, cloudy, foggy rainy weather, with good breeze generally, and sailing Eastward, or little south of East.—Gulf Stream disagreeable. But this [day] there is a change. Clear & bright—light breeze. Wind still from the South. Sent up skysail yard. Crew busy in rigging &c

June 11th[9?] Saturday

The same bright, clear weather, growing warmer each day. Feel very sensibly improving in appetite &c, after seasick qualmishness. Have seen flying-fish, weed, Portuguese men-of-war, and several sail lately. This afternoon had a collision with an English brig [*Elizabeth Baxter*] from Pernambuco bound for Liverpool. She blundered down across our bow, & was locked with us for a time; ripping & tearing her sails. We also were damaged in fore-yard & main. At the moment of collision the Steward of the brig being in jeopardy, leaped aboard of us, and, the vessels separating, remained aboard, till taken off by boat sent from the brig. He told me that the Captain was asleep in his berth when we came together, and added the Mate was half-blind &c. It was altogether an instance of the grossest heedlessness possible on the part of the brig—quite unaccountable.—When it was plain that she purposed crossing our bow, and that it was out of the question for her to do so, Tom at once put his helm up, and by so doing, we came off with less damage than could have been anticipated.

June 12th[10?] Sunday

Came out to day in light clothes.

June 20th[18?] Monday

During the past week took the Trades—crossed the Northern Tropic—and last night saw the Southern Cross—the North Star sensibly sinking. Unvarying fine weather. Went out to flying-jib-boom end this morning. Glorious view of the ship. Spend the day dipping into the "Quarterlies,"—Find methodical reading out of the question. Not yet completely settled in my stomach. Head all right, tho'.

Monday June 27th[25?]

For four days past have been in the Doleful Doldrums.—The whole ship's crew given up to melancholly, and meditating darkly on the mysteries of Providence. But this morning, we have a wind, and feel better.

Friday June 29th

Crossed the Line last evening. Saw bonetoes under the bow.

Sunday July 8th

For the last five or six days—Calm—profound at times. Few or no fish seen. A comet made its appearance to the N.W. the other night, & was still visible last night. At 4½ P.M. yesterday the Calcutta sow commenced delivering her pigs, and about 6½ P.M. concluded. Eleven were born, but two were dead; Thus, nine "souls" have been added to our company. Some ten days since the Carpenter made a set of chessmen;

and Tom and I have played a game or two every evening. This morning sprang up a breeze—I hope it will continue.

Sunday July 21[22?]

Clear fine mild day. Speckled haglets & other birds about. Since writing last, have had two hard blows. Have a stove up in the cabin. Play chess every evening. Put up cabin-stove yesterday—started it this morning. Quite comfortable & domestic in the cabin now.

Monday Aug 8[6?]

Since last date have had several gales, with snow, rain, hail, sleet, mist, fog, squalls, head-winds, refractory stove, smoky cabin, drunken ship &c &c &c.—In one gale, several men washed off the t'gallant forecastle, and the boy Charlie was sent flying into the pigpen which was stove, & the sow & little pigs came, with the deluge, aft. One (pigling) drowned, poor fellow. —A man hurt by a sea; assisted his chum in getting him into his berth, the crew being engaged taking in sail. —One of the gales lasted three days. In one we split the mainsail all to pieces, & the mizzen topsail, and a staysail—Days short—but not sweet. Winter.

Tuesday Aug 7th

At daylight made the land—Fair wind & pleasant. —Made Staten Land & N.W. Coast of Terra del Fuego. Two sail in sight. Entered the Strait of Le Maire, & through the short day had a fine view of the land on both sides—Horrible snowy mountains—black, thundercloud woods—gorges—hell-landscape. Signalled ship "Black Prince" from New York.—There are three on the Sick List. The man hurt by the sea—one with a fever —the third, a boy with general debility.—

Wednesday Aug 8th

Moderate breeze & fair, but thick. Could not see the land, tho' to be wished. Just before sunset, in a squall, the mist lifted & showed, within 12 or fifteen miles the horrid sight of Cape Horn—(the Cape proper)—a black, bare steep cliff, the face of it facing the South Pole;—with[in] some miles were other awful islands & rocks—an infernal group. Tried to weather Cape Horn, as sloops weather Castle Garden Point N.Y.—but were headed off. Tacked ship to the southward.

Thursday Aug. 9th

A gale of wind, with snow & hail & sleet.—

[Benjamin] Ray, a Nantucketer, about 25 years old, a good honest fellow (to judge from his face & demeanor during the passage) fell this morning about day-break from the Main topsail yard to the deck, & striking head foremost upon one of the spars was instantly killed. His chum, Macey (Fisher) of Nantucket, I found alone in the upper cabin sitting over the body —a harrowing spectacle. "I have lost my best friend," said he; and then "His mother will go crazy—she did not want to let him go, she feared something might happen." ——it was in vain to wash the blood from the head—the body bled incessantly & up to the moment of burying; which was about one o'clock, and from the poop, in the interval between blinding squalls of sharp sleet. Tom read some lines from the prayer-book—the plank was sloped, and——God help his mother.—During the brief ceremony, made still the more trying from being under the lee of the reefed spanker where the wind eddies so—all stood covered with Sou-Westers or Russia caps & comforters, except Macey—who stood bareheaded.——The Chief Mate imputes the fall to the excess of clothing worn.—excess, not as regards comfort—but activity aloft.—The ship's motion very violent to day.

Friday Aug 10th

——Calm: blue sky, sun out, dry deck. Calm lasting all day—almost pleasant enough to atone for the gales, but not for Ray's fate, which belongs to that order of human events, which staggers those whom the Primal Philosophy hath not confirmed.—But little sorrow to the crew—all goes on as usual—I, too, read & think, & walk & eat & talk, as if nothing had happened—as if I did not know that death is indeed the King of Terrors—when thus happening; when thus heart-breaking to a fond mother—the King of Terrors, not to the dying or the dead, but to the mourner—the mother. —Not so easily will his fate be washed out of her heart, as his blood from the deck.

Marginalia

IN *The New Testament of Our Lord and Saviour Jesus Christ* (New York, 1844)

Romans 14: 22
Hast thou faith? have it to thyself before God.

The only kind of Faith—one's own.

◇◇◇

Neither Melville nor the *Meteor* rounded the world. They didn't even get to Manila, for cargo plans were altered in San Francisco, and after eight days there, Melville turned back to New York and "Arrowhead," not visibly benefited by the voyage.

The future was not brightened by the discovery that his poems had not found a publisher. Nevertheless, poetry had become his chief concern and central activity, "nursing through night the ethereal spark."

◇◇◇

Early Verse

(Probably composed before 1865)

A Reasonable Constitution[1]

What though Reason forged your scheme?
'Twas Reason dreamed the Utopia's dream:
'Tis dream to think that Reason can
Govern the reasoning creature, man.

Monody

To have known him, to have loved him
    After loneness long;
And then to be estranged in life,
    And neither in the wrong;
And now for death to set his seal—
    Ease me, a little ease, my song!

[1] Observable in Sir Thomas More's *Utopia* are, First, its almost entire reasonableness; Second, its almost entire impracticability. The remark applies more or less to the Utopia's prototype, Plato's *Republic*.—*H.M.*

By wintry hills his hermit-mound
　The sheeted snow-drifts drape,
And houseless there the snow-bird flits
　Beneath the fir-trees' crape:
Glazed now with ice the cloistral vine
　That hid the shyest grape.

The Lake

Pontoosuc

Crowning a bluff where gleams the lake below,
Some pillared pines in well-spaced order stand
And like an open temple show.
And here in best of seasons bland,
Autumnal noon-tide, I look out
From dusk arcades on sunshine all about.

Beyond the Lake, in upland cheer,
Fields, pastoral fields, and barns appear,
They skirt the hills where lonely roads
Revealed in links thro' tiers of woods
Wind up to indistinct abodes
And faery-peopled neighborhoods;
While further fainter mountains keep
Hazed in romance impenetrably deep.

Look, corn in stacks, on many a farm,
And orchards ripe in languorous charm,
As dreamy Nature, feeling sure
Of all her genial labor done,
And the last mellow fruitage won,
Would idle out her term mature;
Reposing like a thing reclined
In kinship with man's meditative mind.

For me, within the brown arcade—
Rich life, methought; sweet here in shade
And pleasant abroad in air!—But, nay,
A counter thought intrusive played,
A thought as old as thought itself,
And who shall lay it on the shelf!—
I felt the beauty bless the day
In opulence of autumn's dower;
But evanescence will not stay!
A year ago was such an hour,
As this, which but foreruns the blast
Shall sweep these live leaves to the dead leaves past.

All dies!—

    I stood in reverie long.
Then, to forget death's ancient wrong,
I turned me in the deep arcade,
And there by chance in lateral glade
I saw low tawny mounds in lines,
Relics of trunks of stately pines
Ranked erst in colonnades where, lo!
Erect succeeding pillars show!

    All dies! and not alone
The aspiring trees and men and grass;
The poet's forms of beauty pass,
And noblest deeds they are undone;
Even truth itself decays, and lo,
From truth's sad ashes fraud and falsehood grow.

All dies!

The workman dies, and after him, the work;
Like to these pines whose graves I trace,

Statue and statuary fall upon their face:
In very amaranths the worm doth lurk,
Even stars, Chaldæans say, have left their place.
Andes and Appalachee tell
Of havoc ere our Adam fell,
And present Nature as a moss doth show
On the ruins of the Nature of the æons of long ago.

But look—and hark!

　　　　　Adown the glade,
Where light and shadow sport at will,
Who cometh vocal, and arrayed
As in the first pale tints of morn—
So pure, rose-clear, and fresh and chill!
Some ground-pine sprigs her brow adorn,
The earthy rootlets tangled clinging.
Over tufts of moss which dead things made,
Under vital twigs which danced or swayed,
Along she floats, and lightly singing:

"Dies, all dies!
The grass it dies, but in vernal rain
Up it springs and it lives again;
Over and over, again and again,
It lives, it dies and it lives again.
Who sighs that all dies?
Summer and winter, and pleasure and pain,
And everything everywhere in God's reign,
They end, and anon they begin again:
Wane and wax, wax and wane:
Over and over and over amain,
End, ever end, and begin again—
End, ever end, and forever and ever begin again!"

She ceased, and nearer slid, and hung
In dewy guise; then softlier sung:
"Since light and shade are equal set
And all revolves, nor more ye know;
Ah, why should tears the pale cheek fret
For aught that waneth here below.
Let go, let go!"

With that, her warm lips thrilled me through,
She kissed me, while her chaplet cold
Its rootlets brushed against my brow,
With all their humid clinging mould.
She vanished, leaving fragrant breath
And warmth and chill of wedded life and death.

❖❖❖

The election victory of the Republicans and Lincoln gave
Melville's family new hopes of a consular post (with salary)
for him. He had published nothing for four years. His efforts
to earn something as a lecturer were not revived after his
return from San Francisco. His last income, if any, may have
come from Arrowhead's surplus. For a father of four children
poetry was out of the question—that is, food-wise. His
father-in-law and Allan urged him to try for the Florence
Consulate by going to Washington and appealing directly
for Charles Sumner's help.

When he reported on Washington to his wife (in his only
surviving letter to her), he said little of the horde of fellow
office-seekers, and nothing of the storm warnings in this last
month of peace.

❖❖❖

To Elizabeth Shaw Melville

[March 24, 1861]
Sunday afternoon
Washington

My dearest Lizzie:

I wrote you the other day from here, and now for another note. In the first place I must say that as yet I have been able to accomplish nothing in the matter of the counsul ship—have not in fact been able as yet so much as even to *see* any one on the subject. I called last night at Senator's Sumner's, but he was at a dinner somewhere. I shall call again to-morrow. After leaving Sumner's I went with Dr. Nourse to a little sort of a party given by the wife of a man connected with one of the Departments. Had quite a pleasant evening. Several Senators were there with wives, daughters, &c. The Vice President also & wife. Mrs. Hamlin is in appearance something like you—so she struck me at least. I need not add that she was very pleasing in her manner.—The night previous to this I was at the second levee at the White House. There was a great crowd, & a brilliant scene. Ladies in full dress by the hundred. A steady stream of two-&-twos wound thro' the apartments shaking hands with "Old Abe" and immediately passing on. This continued without cessation for an hour & a half. Of course I was one of the shakers. Old Abe is much better looking than I expected & younger looking. He shook hands like a good fellow—working hard at it like a man sawing wood at so much per cord. Mrs Lincoln is rather good-looking I thought. The scene was very fine altogether. Superb furniture—flood of light —magnificent flowers—full band of music &c.

I have attended the Senate twice; but nothing very interesting. The new wings of the Capitol are noble buildings, by far the richest in marble of any on the continent. I allude more particularly to the marble of the interior—staircases &c. They are in short palatial. The whole structure taken together is truly immense. It would astonish you to get lost among the labyrinths of halls, passages & splendid corridors.

This morning I spent in the park opposite the White House, sunning myself on a seat. The grass is bright & beautiful, & the shrubbery beginning to bud. It is just cool enough to make an overcoat comfortable sitting out of doors. The wind is high however, & except in the parks, all is dust. I am boarded in a plain home— plain fare plain people—in fact all plain but the road to Florence. But if nothing else comes of it, I will at least derive good from the trip at this season. Though, to tell the truth, I feel home-sick at times, strange as it may seem. How long I shall remain is uncertain. I am expecting letters every day, & can do little or nothing till they arrive.

This afternoon I visited the Washington Monument. Huge tower some 160 feet high of white marble. Could not get inside. Nothing been done to it for long time.

Dr. Nourse is as facetious as ever. I went with him to the White House at the levee. But he is the greater part of the time engaged prosecuting his application for office. I venture to say, he will not succeed, & he begins to think so himself, I judge, from what he tells me of his experiences thus far. He leaves here probably on Tuesday.

Monday Morning.

Dearest Lizzie: Felt rather overdone this morning— overwalked yesterday. But the trip will do me good.

Kisses to the children. Hope to get a letter from you today.

Thine, My Dearest Lizzie,
Herman

❖❖❖

The appointment went to a politician. When war came, Melville offered his services, which were unacceptable to the Navy. He watched the military careers of his cousins Henry and Guert Gansevoort, and went back to his job as poet, and to his education for this job.

He spent the winter and spring of 1862 away from Arrowhead, in New York, and made the most of the city's second-hand bookstore opportunities. When he returned to the Berkshires for his last year there, he was equipped for plenty of reading and thinking.

❖❖❖

Marginalia

IN *Essays* by R. W. Emerson; First Series (Boston, 1847)

"Spiritual Laws"
The good, compared to the evil which he sees, is as his own good to his own evil.

A Perfectly good being, therefore, would see no evil. —But what did Christ see?—He saw what made him weep.—However, too, the "Philanthropist" must have been a very bad man—he saw, in jails, so much evil. To annihilate all this nonsense read the Sermon on the Mount, and consider what it implies.

IN *Essays: Second Series,* by R. W. Emerson (Boston, 1844)

"The Poet"

Also, we use defects and deformities to a sacred purpose, so expressing our sense that the evils of the world are such only to the evil eye.

What does the man mean? If Mr Emerson travelling in Egypt should find the plague-spot come out on him —would he consider that an evil sight or not? And if evil, would his eye be evil because it seemed evil to his eye, or rather, to his sense using the eye for instrument?

But the poet names the thing because he sees it, or comes one step nearer to it than any other.

This is admirable, as many other thoughts of Mr Emerson's are. His gross and astonishing errors & illusions spring from a self-conceit so intensely intellectual and calm that at first one hesitates to call it by its right name. Another species of Mr Emerson's errors, or rather, blindness, proceeds from a defect in the region of the heart.

Hence a great number of such as were professionally expressors of Beauty . . . were punished for that advantage they won, by a dissipation and deterioration.

No, no, no.—Titian—did he deteriorate?—Byron?— did he.—Mr E. is horribly narrow here. He has his Dardanelles for his every Marmora.—But he keeps nobly on, for all that!

IN *Germany* by Madame the Baroness de Staël-Holstein
(New York, 1859)

Bayle has somewhere said, that *atheism does not shelter us
from the fear of eternal suffering.* . . .

If we assume that the existence of God makes eternal suffering possible, *then* it may justly be said that Atheism furnishes no defences against the fear of it.

To Captain Thomas Melville
on the *Bengal*, Hong-Kong

Pittsfield May 25th 1862

My Dear Boy: (or, if that appears disrespectful)
My Dear Captain: Yesterday I received from Gansevoort your long and very entertaining letter to Mamma from Pernambuco. Yes, it was very entertaining. Particularly the account of that interesting young gentleman whom you so uncivilly stigmatise for a jackass, simply because he improves his opportunities in the way of sleeping, eating & other commendable customs. That's the sort of fellow, seems to me, to get along with. For my part I love sleepy fellows, and the more ignorant the better. Damn your wide-awake and knowing chaps. As for sleepiness, it is one of the noblest qualities of humanity. There is something sociable about it, too. Think of those sensible & sociable millions of good fellows all taking a good long friendly snooze together, under the sod—no quarrels, no imaginary troubles, no envies, heart-burnings, & thinking how much better that other chap is off—none of this: but all equally free-&-easy, they sleep away & reel off their nine knots an hour, in perfect amity. If you see your sleepy ignorant jackass-friend again give him my compliments, and say

that however others may think of him, I honor and esteem him. As for your treatment of those young ones, there I entirely commend you. Strap them, I beseech you. You remember what the Bible says:

"Oh ye who teach the children of the nations,
   Holland, France, England, Germany or Spain,
I pray ye *strap* them upon all occasions,
   It mends their morals—never mind the pain."

In another place the Bible says, you know, something about spareing the strap & spoiling the child.—Since I have quoted poetry above, it puts me in mind of my own doggerel. You will be pleased to learn that I have disposed of a lot of it at a great bargain. In fact, a trunk-maker took the whole stock off my hands at ten cents the pound. So, when you buy a new trunk again, just peep at the lining & perhaps you may be rewarded by some glorious stanza staring you in the face & claiming admiration. If you were not such a devil of a ways off, I would send you a trunk, by way of presentation-copy. I cant help thinking what a luckless chap you were that voyage you had a poetaster with you. You remember the romantic moonlight night, when the conceited donkey repeated to you about three cables' length of his verses. But you bore it like a hero. I cant in fact recall so much as a single *wince*. To be sure, you went to bed immediately upon the conclusion of the entertainment; but this much I am sure of, whatever were your sufferings, you never gave them utterance. Tom, my boy, I admire you. I say again, you are a hero.—By the way, I hope in God's name, that rumor which reached your owners (C & P.) a few weeks since —that dreadful rumor is not true. They heard that you had begun to take to——drink? Oh no, but worse—to sonnet-writing. That off Cape Horn instead of being on deck about your business, you devoted your time to writing a sonnet on your mistress' eyebrow, & another upon her "Journal."—"I'll be damned" says Curtis (he was very profane) "if I'll have a sonneteer among my Captains."—"Well, if he has taken to poetry," says Peabody—"God help the ship!"—I have written them contradicting the rumor in your name. What villain & secret enemy of yours set this cursed report afloat, I cant imagine.—Do you want to hear about the war?—The war goes bravely on. McClellan is now within fifteen miles of the rebel capital, Richmond. New Orleans is taken &c &c &c. You will see all no doubt in the papers at your Agents. But when the *end*—the wind-up—the grand pacification is coming, who knows. We beat the rascals in almost every field, & take all their ports &c, but they dont cry "Enough!"—It looks like a long lane, with the turning quite out of sight.—Guert has recently been appointed to the command of a fine new sloop of war. I am rejoiced to hear it. It will do him good in more ways than one. He is brave as a lion, a good seaman, a natural-born officer, & I hope he will yet turn out the hero of a brilliant victory.—I dont write you, My Dear Boy, about family matters, because I know that the girls keep you posted there. But I will just say that of late Lizzie has not been very well, tho' she is now getting better. The children are all well. Macky is studying Latin—"Hic—haec—hoc"—"horum, horum, horum," he goes it every night.—And now, my boy, if you knew how much laziness I overcame in writing you this letter, you would think me, what I am

Always your affectionate brother

Herman

◇◇◇

In preparation for a final removal from the Berkshires to
New York Melville left Arrowhead to go to grass and moved
his family and household goods into the town of Pittsfield.
In November, coming from an errand to the emptied house,
he was thrown from his wagon, and suffered injuries severe
enough to keep him painfully confined for weeks.

◇◇◇

To Samuel Shaw

Pittsfield Dec. 10th 1862

My Dear Sam: I remember that some days after my
mishap, when I was able to give the necessary attention, Lizzie read to me the letter you wrote her on that
occasion.—I can not help telling you how sensible I am
of the kindness you showed, and write you this that
you may have the ocular evidence of my recovery. To
be sure, I still carry my arm (the left one, happily) in
a sling, and the neuralgia gives me a love-pinch in the
cheek now and then. But upon the whole I am now in
a fair way of being completely restored to what I was
before the accident.—This recovery is flattering to my
vanity. I begin to indulge in the pleasing idea that my
life must needs be of some value. Probably I consume
a certain amount of oxygen, which unconsumed might
create some subtle disturbance in Nature. Be that as it
may, I am going to try and stick to the conviction
named above. For I have observed that such an idea,
once well bedded in a man, is a wonderful conservator
of health and almost a prophecy of long life. I once,
like other spoonies, cherished a loose sort of notion that

I did not care to live very long. But I will frankly own
that I have now no serious, no insuperable objections
to a respectable longevity. I dont like the idea of being
left out night after night in a cold church-yard.—In
warm and genial countries, death is much less of a bug-
bear than in our frozen latitudes. A native of Hindostan
takes easily and kindly to his latter end. It is but a
stepping round the corner to him. He knows he will
sleep warm.—Pretty topics these [sketch of a skull and
bones] for a friendly note, you say. (By the way, Death,
in my skull, seems to tip a knowing sort of wink out of
his left eye. What does that mean, I wonder?)

But my page is more than half gone, so I must stop
this trifling. . . .

◇◇◇

A year later the Melvilles moved for good to East 26th
Street, New York City, and in the Spring of 1864 Melville
and his brother Allan visited the Virginia camp where Colonel Henry S. Gansevoort was stationed with his cavalry
regiment. From there Melville brought back the material for
a long poem, "The Scout Toward Aldie," but not without
pain.

◇◇◇

To Colonel Henry Sanford Gansevoort

New York May 10th 1864

My Dear Henry: I embrace the earliest opportunity
afforded by my recovery from an acute attack of neuralgia in the eyes, to thank you for your hospitality at
the camp, and make known the fact that I have not
forgotten you. I enjoyed my visit very much, & would

not have missed it on any account, and can only regret
that you happened to be away when we arrived. But
as when the sun reappears after being hidden; so—&c
&c &c. Your imagination and modesty will supply the
rest. I missed seeing the Dr at Washington, although
I sought him at Willard's. I trust he has got rid of his
temporary disfigurement. When in your tent you introduced him to Gen. Tyler, you should have said:—General, let me make you acquainted with my friend here,
Dont be frightened. This is not his face, but a masque.
A horrible one, I know, but for God's sake dont take it
to be the man. General, that horrible masque, my word
for it, hides a noble and manly countenance &c &c &c
Your wit & invention render further strumming on
this string idle.—How is Captain Brewster? Coke on
Lyttleton, and Strap on the Shoulder. My friendly regards & best wishes to the Captain & say to him that
I hear the neigh of his war-horse in my dreams, likewise that I have a flannel shirt of his in my keeping;
which I hope one day to exhibit as the identical shirt
worn by that renowned soldier shortly after his entrance
into the army.—Edwin Lansing—remember me to him.
Tell him I frequently think of him & his tent & there
is pleasure in the thought. Tell him to tell Dr Wolf
(savage name, but sweet man) that my prayers ascend
for him.

And Gen Tyler, too. Pray, give my respects to him,
& say that I agree with him about "Titan." The worst
thing I can say about it is that it is a little better than
"Mardi" The Terence I highly value; indeed both works,
as memorial of the hospitality of an accomplished General & jolly Christian.

And now, Col. Gansevoort of the 13th N.Y. Cavalry,
conceive me to be standing some paces from you, in

an erect attitude and with manly bearing, giving you the military salute. Farewell. May two small but choice constellations of stars alight on your shoulders. May your sword be a Lesson to the despicable foe & your name in after ages be used by Southern Matrons to frighten their children by. And after death (which God long avert, & bring about after great battles, quickly, in a comfortable bed, with wife & children around) may that same name be transferred to heaven—bestowed upon some new planet or cluster of stars of the first magnitude. Farewell, my hero

& God bless you
Herman Melville

◇◇◇

"With few exceptions, the Pieces in this volume originated in an impulse imparted by the fall of Richmond. They were composed without reference to collective arrangement, but, being brought together in review, naturally fall into the order assumed." Thus Melville introduced and explained his *Battle-Pieces;* elsewhere in the volume he mentioned an editorial decision before publication: ". . . it will hardly occasion surprise that, in looking over the battle-pieces in the foregoing collection, I have been tempted to withdraw or modify some of them, fearful lest in presenting, though but dramatically and by way of a poetic record, the passions and epithets of civil war, I might be contributing to a bitterness which every sensible American must wish at an end. . . . Zeal is not of necessity religion, neither is it always of the the same essence with poetry or patriotism."

◇◇◇

From Battle-Pieces
and Aspects of the War

(1866)

Misgivings, 1860

When ocean-clouds over inland hills
   Sweep storming in late autumn brown,
And horror the sodden valley fills,
   And the spire falls crashing in the town,
I muse upon my country's ills—
The tempest bursting from the waste of Time
On the world's fairest hope linked with man's foulest
   crime.

Nature's dark side is heeded now—
   (Ah! optimist-cheer disheartened flown)—
A child may read the moody brow
   Of yon black mountain lone.
With shouts the torrents down the gorges go,
And storms are formed behind the storm we feel:
The hemlock shakes in the rafter, the oak in the driving
   keel.

A Utilitarian View of the *Monitor's* Fight

Plain be the phrase, yet apt the verse,
   More ponderous than nimble;
For since grimed War here laid aside
His Orient pomp, 'twould ill befit
   Overmuch to ply
   The rhyme's barbaric cymbal.

Hail to victory without the gaud
  Of glory; zeal that needs no fans
Of banners; plain mechanic power
Plied cogently in War now placed—
    Where War belongs—
  Among the trades and artisans.

Yet this was battle, and intense—
  Beyond the strife of fleets heroic;
Deadlier, closer, calm 'mid storm;
No passion; all went on by crank,
    Pivot, and screw,
  And calculations of caloric.

Needless to dwell; the story's known.
  The ringing of those plates on plates
Still ringeth round the world—
The clangor of that blacksmiths' fray.
    The anvil-din
  Resounds this message from the Fates:

War shall yet be, and to the end;
  But war-paint shows the streaks of weather;
War shall yet be, but warriors
Are now but operatives; War's made
    Less grand than Peace,
  And a singe runs through lace and feather.

Commemorative of a Naval Victory

  Sailors there are of gentlest breed,
    Yet strong, like every goodly thing;

The discipline of arms refines,
   And the wave gives tempering.
     The damasked blade its beam can fling;
It lends the last grave grace:
The hawk, the hound, and sworded nobleman
   In Titian's picture for a king,
Are of hunter or warrior race.

In social halls a favored guest
   In years that follow victory won,
How sweet to feel your festal fame
   In woman's glance instinctive thrown:
     Repose is yours—your deed is known,
It musks the amber wine;
It lives, and sheds a light from storied days
   Rich as October sunsets brown,
Which make the barren place to shine.

But seldom the laurel wreath is seen
   Unmixed with pensive pansies dark;
There's a light and a shadow on every man
   Who at last attains his lifted mark—
     Nursing through night the ethereal spark.
Elate he never can be;
He feels that spirits which glad had hailed his worth,
   Sleep in oblivion.—The shark
Glides white through the phosphorous sea.

◇◇◇

At least *Battle-Pieces* did not hinder Melville's appointment
as a customs inspector. Otherwise the book came and went
with few noting or remembering it. A pleasant traveler whom
he met in Italy and rode with for a few days had been appointed Collector of Customs at New York. We don't know
if Henry Smythe "hailed his worth," but he did arrange for
the first regular income that Melville had had since he came

home from sea, and in the not most unpleasant of jobs available—working on the docks, not in the Customs building.

The family did not, however, live happily ever after. No matter how quietly Melville went on writing—nights, Sundays, holidays, vacations—family life was neither normal nor placid. In 1867 carefree Malcolm shot himself—the coroner's jury said it was not deliberate. In 1869 restless Stanwix demanded to be allowed to go to sea—at the same age that his father had signed on the *St. Lawrence*. Bessie, the older daughter, had begun to lock herself in the prison of arthritis. By 1870 their father had decided to take another major risk —he had begun one of his most ambitious and most secret works, a long narrative poem grounded in his trip through Palestine.

◇◇◇

Marginalia

IN *Essays in Criticism* by Matthew Arnold (Boston, 1865)

"Maurice de Guerin"
In him, as in Keats, . . . the temperament, the talent itself, is deeply influenced by their mysterious malady. . . .

So is every one influenced—the robust, the weak— all constitutions—by the very fibre of the flesh, & chalk of the bone. We are what we were made.

"There is more power and beauty," [Maurice de Guerin] writes, "in the well-kept secret of one's self and one's thoughts, than in the display of a whole heaven that one may have inside one. . . . The literary career seems to me unreal, both in its essence and in the rewards which one seeks from it, and therefore fatally marred by a secret absurdity."

This is the finest statement of a truth which every one who thinks in these days must have felt.

"A French Eton"
And such is the fundamental constitution of human affairs,
that the measure of right proves also, in the end, the measure
of power.

Even the truest will say untrue things, and the wisest
say foolish things.

To Maria Gansevoort Melville

New York, May 5, '70

My Dear Mamma:

As you express a wish in your last letter dated the 2nd
inst. to hear from me again before you leave Albany, I
accordingly write this; and that you may be satisfied
that I have not been dilatory about the portrait [by J.O.
Eaton], I will say that I have already had two sittings,
and it is getting on.

We have not heard from Stanwix since receiving his
London letter in February, but are daily in expectation
of one, tho' boy-like he may not think how anxiously we
await it.

The other day I visited out of curiosity the Gansevoort Hotel, corner of "Little Twelfth Street" and West
Street. I bought a paper of tobacco by way of introducing myself: Then I said to the person who served me:
"Can you tell me what this word 'Gansevoort' means? is
it the name of a man? and if so, who was this Gansevoort?" Thereupon a solemn gentleman at a remote table spoke up: "Sir," said he, putting down his newspaper, "this hotel and the street of the same name are
called after a very rich family who in old times owned a
great deal of property hereabouts." The dense ignorance of this solemn gentleman,—his knowing nothing of

the hero of Fort Stanwix, aroused such an indignation in my breast, that disdaining to enlighten his benighted soul, I left the place without further colloquy. Repairing to the philosophic privacy of the District Office, I then moralized upon the instability of human glory and the evanescence of—many other things.

Lizzie and the girls are well, and for some time past have devoted themselves to the shrine of Fashion, engaged in getting up the unaccountable phenomena and wonderful circumferential illusions which in these extraordinary days invest the figure of lovely woman.—I am called away and must close.

My remembrances to Uncle Peter, Aunt Susan, the superb Kate and the benignant Lansing; and believe me

Affectionately Your Son,

Herman

To Abraham Lansing

New York, Aug 5, '75

My Dear Mr Lansing: I have just received your note of yesterday. I thank you for the prospective welcome. But as for meeting me on the wharf—don't mention it. When the Shah of Persia or the Great Khan of Tartary comes to Albany by the night-boat—*him* meet on the wharf and with salvoes of artillery—but not a Custom House Inspector.

I should have mentioned in my note to Kate that I should not appear upon the scene till some time after breakfast—since on Sunday morning my appetite will be clamorous at an hour too early for any rational household to satisfy. As for my plunder or impedimenta, I shall carry nothing but what I take in my hand. . . .

From Clarel

A Poem and Pilgrimage in the Holy Land
(1876)

A Sketch

[On the road to the Dead Sea the travelers have paused]

> For ease upon the ground they sit;
> And Rolfe, with eye still following
> Where Nehemiah slow footed it,
> Asked Clarel: "Know you anything
> Of this man's prior life at all?"
> "Nothing," said Clarel.—"I recall,"
> Said Rolfe, "a mariner like him."
> "A mariner?"—"Yes; one whom grim
> Disaster made as meek as he
> There plodding." Vine here showed the zest
> Of a deep human interest:
> "We crave of you his history."
> And Rolfe began: "Scarce would I tell
> Of what this mariner befell—
> So much is it with cloud o'ercast—
> Were he not now gone home at last
> Into the green land of the dead,
> Where he encamps and peace is shed.
> Hardy he was, sanguine and bold,
> The master of a ship. His mind
> In night-watch frequent he unrolled—
> As seamen sometimes are inclined—

On serious topics, to his mate,
A man to creed austere resigned.
The master ever spurned at fate,
Calvin's or Zeno's. Always still
Man-like he stood by man's free will
And power to effect each thing he would,
Did reason but pronounce it good.
The subaltern held in humble way
That still heaven's over-rulings sway
Will and event.

       "On waters far,
Where map-man never made survey,
Gliding along in easy plight,
The strong one brake the lull of night
Emphatic in his willful war—
But staggered, for there came a jar
With fell arrest to keel and speech:
A hidden rock. The pound—the grind—
Collapsing sails o'er deck declined—
Sleek billows curling in the breach,
And nature with her neutral mind.
A wreck. 'Twas in the former days,
Those waters then obscure; a maze;
The isles were dreaded—every chain;
Better to brave the immense of sea,
And venture for the Spanish Main,
Beating and rowing against the trades,
Than float to valleys 'neath the lee,
Nor far removed, and palmy shades.
So deemed he, strongly erring there.
To boats they take; the weather fair—
Never the sky a cloudlet knew;
A temperate wind unvarying blew
Week after week; yet came despair;
The bread tho' doled, and water stored,

Ran low and lower—ceased. They burn—
They agonize till crime abhorred
Lawful might be. O trade-wind, turn!

"Well may some items sleep unrolled—
Never by the one survivor told.
Him they picked up, where, cuddled down,
They saw the jacketed skeleton,
Lone in the only boat that lived—
His signal frittered to a shred.

" 'Strong need'st thou be,' the rescuers said,
'Who hast such trial sole survived.'
'I *willed* it,' gasped he. And the man,
Renewed ashore, pushed off again.
How bravely sailed the pennoned ship
Bound outward on her sealing trip
Antarctic. Yes; but who returns
Too soon, regaining port by land
Who left it by the bay? What spurns
Were his that so could countermand?
Nor mutineer, nor rock, nor gale
Nor leak had foiled him. No; a whale
Of purpose aiming, stove the bow:
They foundered. To the master now
Owners and neighbors all impute
An inauspiciousness. His wife—
Gentle, but unheroic—she,
Poor thing, at heart knew bitter strife
Between her love and her simplicity:
A Jonah is he?—And men bruit
The story. None will give him place
In a third venture. Came the day
Dire need constrained the man to pace
A night patrolman on the quay
Watching the bales till morning hour
Through fair and foul. Never he smiled;

Call him, and he would come; not sour
In spirit, but meek and reconciled;
Patient he was, he none withstood;
Oft on some secret thing would brood.
He ate what came, though but a crust;
In Calvin's creed he put his trust;
Praised heaven, and said that God was good,
And his calamity but just.
So Silvio Pellico from cell-door
Forth tottering, after dungeoned years,
Crippled and bleached, and dead his peers:
'Grateful, I thank the Emperor.' "

Dirge

[On returning to Jerusalem Clarel finds his betrothed, Ruth,
   prepared for burial]

Stay, Death. Not mine the Christus-wand
Wherewith to charge thee and command:
I plead. Most gently hold the hand
Of her thou leadest far away;
Fear thou to let her naked feet
Tread ashes—but let mosses sweet
Her footing tempt, where'er ye stray.
Shun Orcus; win the moonlit land
Belulled—the silent meadows lone,
Where never any leaf is blown
From lily-stem in Azrael's hand.
There, till her love rejoin her lowly
(Pensive, a shade, but all her own),
On honey feed her, wild and holy;
Or trance her with thy choicest charm.
And if, ere yet the lover's free,

Some added dusk thy rule decree—
That shadow only let it be
Thrown in the moon-glade by the palm.

Epilogue

If Luther's day expand to Darwin's year,
Shall that exclude the hope—foreclose the fear?

Unmoved by all the claims our times avow,
The ancient Sphinx still keeps the porch of shade
And comes Despair, whom not her calm may cow,
And coldly on that adamantine brow
Scrawls undeterred his bitter pasquinade.
But Faith (who from the scrawl indignant turns),
With blood warm oozing from her wounded trust,
Inscribes even on her shards of broken urns
The sign o' the cross—*the spirit above the dust!*

Yea, ape and angel, strife and old debate—
The harps of heaven and dreary gongs of hell;
Science the feud can only aggravate—
No umpire she betwixt the chimes and knell:
The running battle of the star and clod
Shall run for ever—if there be no God.

Degrees we know, unknown in days before;
The light is greater, hence the shadow more;
And tantalized and apprehensive Man
Appealing—Wherefore ripen us to pain?
Seems there the spokesman of dumb Nature's train.

But through such strange illusions have they passed
Who in life's pilgrimage have baffled striven—

Even death may prove unreal at the last,
And stoics be astounded into heaven.

Then keep thy heart, though yet but ill-resigned—
Clarel, thy heart, the issues there but mind;
That like the crocus budding through the snow—
That like a swimmer rising from the deep—
That like a burning secret which doth go
Even from the bosom that would hoard and keep;
Emerge thou mayst from the last whelming sea,
And prove that death but routs life into victory.

To John C. Hoadley

Saturday in Easter Week [31 March] 1877
My Dear Fellow:

I propose buying a hair-shirt and a scourge, and putting them to use for a week or so, as a penalty for my remissness in allowing your most friendly note of the 25 ult. to remain unanswered so long.—And yet I might say something in palliation of my incivility. You are young; but I am verging upon three-score, and at times a certain lassitude steals over one—in fact, a disinclination for doing anything except the indispensable. At such moments the problem of the universe seems a humbug, and epistolary obligations mere moonshine and the—well, nepenthe seems all-in-all.

Your legend from Marco Polo I had never previously met with. How full of significance it is! And beauty too. These legends of the Old Faith are really wonderful both from their multiplicity and their poetry. They far surpass the stories in the Greek mythologies. Dont you think so? See, for example, the life of St. Elizabeth of Hungary.

——"He wins who highest aims":—whose translation [of Virgil] is that? Tell me. Thank you for sending me so beautiful a thing engrossed by your deft & dexterous digits. (The alliteration there was irresis[t]able)

In return for your M.S. favors I send you something I found the other day [a poem, "The Age of the Antonines"]—came across it—in a lot of papers. I remember that the lines were suggested by a passage in Gibbon (Decline & Fall) Have you a copy? Turn to *"Antonine"* &c in index. What the deuce the thing means I dont know; but here it is.

——By the way I have a ship on my District from Girgenti.—Where's that? Why, in Sicily—The ancient Agrigentum. Ships arrive from there in this port, bringing sulphur; but this is the first one I have happened to have officially to do with. I have not succeeded in seeing the captain yet—have only seen the mate—but hear that he has in possession some stones from those magnificent Grecian ruins, and I am going to try to get a fragment, however small, if possible, which I will divide with you.

Best love to Kate & your two Princesses of India.

H Melville

P.S. to the Note—

Just looked over the accompan[y]ing letter which I wrote this morning. It is a queer sort of an absurd scribble, but if it evidences good-fellowship and good feeling, it serves the purpose. You are young (as I said before) but I aint; and at my years, and with my disposition, or rather constitution, one gets to care less and less for everything except downright good feeling. Life is so short, and so ridiculous and irrational (from a certain point of view) that one knows not what to make of it, unless—well, finish the sentence for yourself.

> Thine
> In these inexplicable fleshly bonds
> H.M.

N.B. *I aint crazy.*

◇◇◇

Age—old age—venerability—the "old nutmeg-grater"—had become a standing Melville joke. The "young" brother-in-law Hoadley was actually a year nearer three score than was Melville; and when photograph and rose-petals were sent to Ellen Gifford, his wife's admired and admiring cousin, she was only a few years younger than her "venerable friend."

◇◇◇

To Ellen Marett Gifford

> N.Y. 104 E. 26 St.
> Oct. 5, '85

Dear Mrs. Gifford: It is now quite a time since you first asked me for my photo:—Well, here it is at last, the veritable face (at least, so says the Sun that never lied in his life) of your now venerable friend—venerable in years.——What the deuse makes him look so serious, I wonder. I thought he was of a gay and frolicsome nature, judging from a little rhyme of his about a Kitten, which you once showed me. But is this the same man? Pray, explain the inconsistency, or I shall begin to suspect your venerable friend of being a two-faced old fellow and not to be trusted.

X X X X *That* is to signify an abrupt change in the text.——Bessie returned home from her vacation

Saturday last, and Lizzie would also have come, but
was detained in Boston by an ailment which temporarily keeps her there. But I look for her tomorrow or
next day.

Trusting that you are at present exempt from your
more serious pain, I mean the neuralgia; and begging
you not to exert yourself, out of courtesy, in the unnecessary matter of answering this note, I am always,
in one respect at least, like yourself—

Friendly to the friendly
H. Melville

P.S.
You see the rose-leaves have not yet given out. I shall
always try and have a rose-leaf reserved for you, be
the season what it may.

To Charles James Billson

New York
Dec. 20, '85

Dear Sir: Do not think me indifferent or ungrateful if
your last friendly note and gift remain unacknowledged
till now.—There are natures that after receiving a certain impression as to another, that *other* need therefore hardly ever enter into intricate explanations, happen what may.—This may perhaps be a little obscure
to some, but you will understand.

For the two books I thank you much. It is long since
I have been so interested in a volume as in that of the
"Essays & Phantasies" [by James Thomson]. "Bumble"
—"Indolence"—"The Poet," &c., each is so admirably
honest and original and informed throughout with the
spirit of the noblest natures, that it would have been

wonderful indeed had they hit the popular taste. They would have to be painstakingly diluted for that—diluted with that prudential worldly element, wherewith all Mr Arnold has conciliated the conventionalists, while at the same time showing the absurdity of Bumble.

But for your admirable friend this would have been too much like trimming—if trimming, in fact, it be. The motions of his mind in the best of the Essays are utterly untrammelled and independent, and yet falling naturally into grace and poetry. It is good for me to think of such a mind—to know that such a brave intelligence has been—and may yet be, for aught anyone can *demonstrate* to the contrary.—As to his not achieving "fame"—what of that? He is not the less, but so much the more. And it must have occurred to you, as it has to me, that the further our civilization advances upon its present lines so much the cheaper sort of thing does "fame" become, especially of the literary sort. This species of "fame" a waggish acquaintance says can be manufactured to order, and sometimes is so manufactured thro the agency of a certain house that has a correspondent in every one of the almost innumerable journals that enlighten our millions from the Lakes to the Gulf & from the Atlantic to the Pacific.—But this "vanity of vanities" has been inimitably touched upon by your friend in one of his Essays.—"Satires & Profanities" are, of course, written for another plane than that to which the "Essays" are levelled. But many touches are diverting enough. "The Devil in the Church of England," for instance. But I must close.—

You asked me for my photograph, but I had none to send you. Now that I *have,* I forward it to you, conditional, however, upon your reciprocating with your own, and this, permit me to insist on. . . .

❖❖❖

Ten days later, on the last day of 1885, Melville changed the pattern of his life for the last time. Having resigned his post as Customs Inspector after nineteen years of service, he could devote his days as well as his evenings to his never-ceased need to write. Friendly and family legacies to him and to his wife had relaxed the financial strain and even made it possible to print privately whatever he wished to commit to such controlled circulation. The first of these small volumes was a collection of verses, some dating from the voyage to California in 1860.

❖❖❖

From John Marr
and Other Sailors,
with Some Sea-Pieces

(1888)

John Marr

JOHN MARR, toward the close of the last century born in America of a mother unknown, and from boyhood up to maturity a sailor under divers flags, disabled at last from further maritime life by a crippling wound received at close quarters with pirates of the Keys, eventually betakes himself for a livelihood to less active employment ashore. There, too, he transfers his rambling disposition acquired as a seafarer.

After a variety of removals, at first as a sail-maker from seaport to seaport, then adventurously inland as a rough bench-carpenter, he, finally, in the last-named capacity, settles down about the year 1838 upon what was then a frontier-prairie, sparsely sprinkled with small oak groves and yet fewer log houses of a little colony but recently from one of our elder inland States. Here, putting a period to his rovings, he marries.

Ere long a fever, the bane of new settlements on teeming loam, and whose sallow livery was certain to show itself, after an interval, in the complexions of too many of these people, carries off his young wife and infant child. In one coffin, put together by his own hands, they are committed with meager rites to the earth—another mound, though a small one, in the wide prairie, not far from where the mound builders of a race only conjecturable had left their pottery and bones, one common clay, under a strange terrace serpentine in form.

With an honest stillness in his general mien—swarthy and black-browed, with eyes that could soften or flash, but never harden, yet disclosing at times a melancholy depth—this kinless man had affections which, once placed, not readily could be dislodged or resigned to a substituted object. Being now arrived at middle life, he resolves never to quit the soil that holds the only beings ever connected with him by love in the family tie. His log house he lets to a newcomer, one glad enough to get it, and dwells with the household.

While the acuter sense of his bereavement becomes mollified by time, the void at heart abides. Fain, if possible, would he fill that void by cultivating social relations yet nearer than before with a people whose lot he purposes sharing to the end—relations superadded to that mere work-a-day bond arising from participation in the same outward hardships, making reciprocal helpfulness a matter of course. But here, and nobody to blame, he is obstructed.

More familiarly to consort, men of a practical turn must sympathetically converse, and upon topics of real life. But, whether as to persons or events, one cannot always be talking about the present, much less speculating about the future; one must needs recur to the past, which, with the mass of men, where the past is in any personal way a common inheritance, supplies to most practical natures the basis of sympathetic communion.

But the past of John Marr was not the past of these pioneers. Their hands had rested on the plow-tail, his upon the ship's helm. They knew but their own kind and their own usages; to him had been revealed something of the checkered globe. So limited unavoidably was the mental reach, and by consequence the range of sympathy, in this particular band of domestic emigrants, hereditary tillers of the soil, that the ocean, but a hearsay to their fathers, had now through yet deeper inland removal become to themselves little more than a rumor traditional and vague.

They were a staid people; staid through habituation to monotonous hardship; ascetics by necessity not less than through moral bias; nearly all of them sincerely, however narrowly, religious. They were kindly at need, after their fashion; but to a man wonted—as John Marr in his previous homeless sojournings could not but have been—to the free-and-easy tavern-clubs affording cheap recreation of an evening in certain old and comfortable seaport towns of that time, and yet more familiar with the companionship afloat of the sailors of the same period, something was lacking. That something was geniality, the flower of life springing from some sense of joy in it, more or less. This their lot could not give to these hard-working endurers of the dispiriting malaria—men to whom a holiday never came—and they had too much of uprightness and no art at all or desire to affect what they did not really feel. At a corn-husking, their least grave of gatherings, did the lone-hearted mariner seek to divert his own thoughts from sadness, and in some degree interest theirs, by adverting to aught removed from the crosses and trials of their personal surroundings, naturally enough he would slide into some marine story or picture but would soon recoil upon himself and be silent, finding no encouragement to proceed. Upon one such occasion an elderly man—a blacksmith, and at Sunday gatherings an earnest exhorter—honestly said to him, "Friend, we know nothing of that here."

Such unresponsiveness in one's fellow creatures set apart from factitious life, and by their vocation—in those days little helped by machinery—standing, as it were, next of kin to Nature: this, to John Marr, seemed of a piece with the apathy of Nature herself as envisaged to him here on a prairie where none but the perished mound builders had as yet left a durable mark.

The remnant of Indians thereabout—all but exterminated in their recent and final war with regular white troops, a war waged by the Red Men for their native soil and natural rights—had been coerced into the occupancy of wilds not very far beyond the Mississippi —wilds *then,* but now the seats of municipalities and States. Prior to that, the bisons, once streaming countless in processional herds, or browsing as in an endless battle-line over these vast aboriginal pastures, had retreated, dwindled in number, before the hunters, in main a race distinct from the agricultural pioneers, though generally their advance-guard. Such a double exodus of man and beast left the plain a desert, green or blossoming indeed, but almost as forsaken as the Siberian Obi. Save the prairie-hen, sometimes startled from its lurking-place in the rank grass, and, in their migratory season, pigeons, high overhead on the wing, in dense multitudes eclipsing the day like a passing storm-cloud; save these—there being no wide woods with their underwood—birds were strangely few.

Blank stillness would for hours reign unbroken on this prairie. "It is the bed of a dried-up sea," said the companionless sailor—no geologist—to himself, musing at twilight upon the fixed undulations of that immense alluvial expanse bounded only by the horizon, and missing there the stir that, to alert eyes and ears, animates at all times the apparent solitudes of the deep.

But a scene quite at variance with one's antecedents may yet prove suggestive of them. Hooped round by a level rim, the prairie was to John Marr a reminder of ocean.

With some of his former shipmates, chums on certain cruises, he had contrived, prior to this last and more remote removal, to keep up a little correspondence at odd intervals. But from tidings of anybody or any sort he, in common with the other settlers, was now cut off; quite cut off, except from such news as might be conveyed over the grassy billows by the last-arrived prairie-schooner—the vernacular term, in those parts and times, for the emigrant-wagon arched high over with sail-cloth, and voyaging across the vast champaign. There was no reachable post-office as yet; not even the rude little receptive box with lid and leather hinges, set up at convenient intervals on a stout stake along some solitary green way, affording a perch for birds, and which, later in the unintermitting advance of the frontier, would perhaps decay into a mossy monument, attesting yet another successive overleaped limit of civilized life; a life which in America can today hardly be said to have any western bound but the ocean that washes Asia. Throughout these plains, now in places over-populous with towns over-opulent; sweeping plains elsewhere fenced off in every direction into flourishing farms—pale townsmen and hale farmers alike, in part, the descendants of the first sallow settlers; a region that half a century ago produced little for the sustenance of man but today launching its superabundant wheat-harvest on the world;—of this prairie, now everywhere intersected with wire and rail, hardly can it be said that at the period here written of there was so much as a traceable road. To the long-distance traveler the oak-groves, wide apart, and varying in compass and form; these, with recent settlements, yet more widely separate, offered some landmarks; but otherwise he steered by the sun. In early midsummer, even going but from one log-encampment to the next, a journey it might be of hours or good part of a day, travel was much like navigation. In some more enriched depressions between the long, green, graduated swells, smooth as those of ocean becalmed receiving and subduing to its own tranquillity the voluminous surge raised by some far-off hurricane of days previous, here one would catch the first indication of advancing strangers either in the distance, as a far sail at sea, by the glistening white canvas of the wagon, the wagon itself wading through the rank vegetation and hidden by it, or, failing that, when near to, in the ears of the team, peeking, if not above the tall tiger-lilies, yet above the yet taller grass.

Luxuriant, this wilderness; but, to its denizen, a friend left behind anywhere in the world seemed not alone absent to sight, but an absentee from existence.

Though John Marr's shipmates could not all have departed life, yet as subjects of meditation they were like phantoms of the dead. As the growing sense of his environment threw him more and more upon retrospective musings, these phantoms, next to those of his wife and child, became spiritual companions, losing something of their first indistinctness and putting on at last a dim semblance of mute life; and they were lit by that aureola circling over any object of the affections in the past for reunion with which an imaginative heart passionately yearns.

He invokes these visionary ones—striving, as it were, to get into verbal communion with them, or, under yet stronger illusion, reproaching them for their silence:

> Since as in night's deck-watch ye show,
> Why, lads, so silent here to me,
> Your watchmate of times long ago?
>
> Once, for all the darkling sea,
> You your voices raised how clearly,
> Striking in when tempest sung;
> Hoisting up the storm-sail cheerly,
> *Life is storm—let storm!* you rung.
> Taking things as fated merely,
> Childlike though the world ye spanned;
> Nor holding unto life too dearly,
> Ye who hold your lives in hand—
> Skimmers, who on oceans four
> Petrels were, and larks ashore.
>
> O, not from memory lightly flung,
> Forgot, like strains no more availing,
> The heart to music haughtier strung;

Nay, frequent near me, never staling,
Whose good feeling kept ye young.
Like tides that enter creek or stream,
Ye come, ye visit me, or seem
Swimming out from seas of faces,
Alien myriads memory traces,
To enfold me in a dream!

I yearn as ye. But rafts that strain,
Parted, shall they lock again?
Twined we were, entwined, then riven,
Ever to new embracements driven,
Shifting gulf-weed of the main!
And how if one here shift no more,
Lodged by the flinging surge ashore?

Nor less, as now, in eve's decline,
Your shadowy fellowship is mine.
Ye float around me, form and feature:
Tattooings, ear-rings, love-locks curled;
Barbarians of man's simpler nature,
Unworldly servers of the world.
Yea, present all, and dear to me,
Though shades, or scouring China's sea.

Whither, whither, merchant-sailors,
Whitherward now in roaring gales?
Competing still, ye huntsman-whalers,
In leviathan's wake what boat prevails?
And man-of-war's men, whereaway?
If now no dinned drum beat to quarters
On the wilds of midnight waters—
Foemen looming through the spray;
Do yet your gangway lanterns, streaming,
Vainly strive to pierce below,

When, tilted from the slant plant gleaming,
A brother you see to darkness go?

But, gunmates lashed in shotted canvas,
If where long watch-below ye keep,
Never the shrill *"All hands up hammocks!"*
Breaks the spell that charms your sleep,
And summoning trumps might vainly call,
And booming guns implore—
A beat, a heart-beat musters all,
One heart-beat at heart-core.
It musters. But to clasp, retain;
To see you at the halyards main—
To hear your chorus once again!

Far Off-Shore

Look, the raft, a signal flying,
    Thin—a shred;
None upon the lashed spars lying,
    Quick or dead.

Cries the sea-fowl, hovering over,
    "Crew, the crew?"
And the billow, reckless rover,
    Sweeps anew!

The Berg

A Dream

I saw a ship of martial build
(Her standards set, her brave apparel on)

Directed as by madness mere
Against a stolid iceberg steer,
Nor budge it, though the infatuate ship went down.
The impact made huge ice-cubes fall
Sullen, in tons that crashed the deck;
But that one avalanche was all—
No other movement save the foundering wreck.

Along the spurs of ridges pale,
Not any slenderest shaft and frail,
A prism over glass-green gorges lone,
Toppled; or lace of traceries fine,
Nor pendant drops in grot or mine
Were jarred, when the stunned ship went down.

Nor sole the gulls in cloud that wheeled
Circling one snow-flanked peak afar,
But nearer fowl the floes that skimmed
And crystal beaches, felt no jar.
No thrill transmitted stirred the lock
Of jack-straw needle-ice at base;
Towers undermined by waves—the block
Atilt impending—kept their place.
Seals, dozing sleek on sliddery ledges,
Slipt never, when by loftier edges,
Through very inertia overthrown,
The impetuous ship in bafflement went down.

Hard Berg (methought), so cold, so vast,
With mortal damps self-overcast;
Exhaling still thy dankish breath—
Adrift dissolving, bound for death;
Though lumpish thou, a lumbering one—
A lumbering lubbard loitering slow,
Impingers rue thee and go down,

Sounding thy precipice below,
Nor stir the slimy slug that sprawls
Along thy dead indifference of walls.

To Archibald MacMechan

104 E. 26th St.
Dec. 5, '89

Dear Sir:

I beg you to overlook my delay in acknowledging yours of the 12th ult. It was unavoidable.

Your note gave me pleasure, as how should it not, written in such a spirit.

But you do not know, perhaps, that I have entered my eighth decade. After twenty years nearly, as an out-door Customs House officer, I have latterly come into possession of unobstructed leisure, but only just as, in the course of nature, my vigor sensibly declines. What little of it is left I husband for certain matters as yet incomplete, and which indeed may never be completed.

I appreciate, quite as much as you would have me, your friendly good will and shrink from any appearance to the contrary.

Trusting that you will take all this, and what it implies, in the same spirit that prompts it, I am,

Very truly yours,
Herman Melville

❖❖❖

The "certain matters" were not all verses. Reverting to a form and method that he turned from more than thirty years before, Melville was working on a novel, a distilling, through the long pipes of years and experience, of his "mast-head meditations." It was a synthesis of several actualities, including his own experience on the *United States* in 1843-44 and, closer to the surface, a tragic episode centrally involving his cousin, Guert Gansevoort, while first officer in 1842 on the brig *Somers*. For his last canvas Melville composed a Crucifixion in naval uniform—a great and vital design for the decisions of a lifetime; he set about it in workmanlike manner, buying books, borrowing books, using the public library's reading room. To give detail to his design, he read widely on the British Navy of Nelson's time, and examined all that he could find about the alleged mutiny plot on the *Somers*, all the while expanding and whittling his lines in a process of perpetual dissatisfaction. But he had known when he wrote to MacMechan that *Billy Budd* "may never be completed."

❖❖❖

Billy Budd, Foretopman

What befell him in the year of the Great Mutiny, &c.

Dedicated to

Jack Chase, Englishman

Wherever that great heart may now be,
here on Earth or harbored in Paradise,
Captain of the Main-Top in the year 1843
in the U. S. Frigate *United States*.

Preface

THE YEAR 1797, the year of this narrative, belongs to a period which, as every thinker now feels, involved a crisis for Christendom not exceeded in its undetermined momentousness at the time by any other era whereof there is record. The opening proposition made by the Spirit of that Age,[1] involved the rectification of the Old World's hereditary wrongs. In France to some extent this was bloodily effected. But what then? Straightway the Revolution itself became a wrongdoer, one more oppressive than the Kings. Under Napoleon it enthroned upstart kings, and initiated that prolonged agony of continual war whose final throe was Waterloo. During those years not the wisest could have foreseen that the outcome of all would be what to some thinkers

---

[1] In an earlier version, this continued: "was one hailed by the noblest men of it. Even the dry tinder of a Wordsworth took fire."—*J.L.*

apparently it has since turned out to be, a political advance along nearly the whole line for Europeans.

Now, as elsewhere hinted, it was something caught from the Revolutionary Spirit that at Spithead emboldened the man-of-war's men to rise against real abuses, long-standing ones, and afterwards at the Nore to make inordinate and aggressive demands, successful resistance to which was confirmed only when the ringleaders were hung for an admonitory spectacle to the anchored fleet. Yet in a way analogous to the operation of the Revolution at large the Great Mutiny, though by Englishmen naturally deemed monstrous at the time, doubtless gave the first latent prompting to most important reforms in the British Navy.

Billy Budd, Sailor

An inside narrative

IN THE time before steamships, or then more frequently than now, a stroller along the docks of any considerable sea-port would occasionally have his attention arrested by a group of bronzed mariners, man-of-war's men or merchant-sailors in holiday attire ashore on liberty. In certain instances they would flank, or, like a body-guard, quite surround some superior figure of their own class, moving along with them like Aldebaran among the lesser lights of his constellation. That signal object was the "Handsome Sailor" of the less prosaic time alike of the military and merchant navies. With no perceptible trace of the vainglorious about him, rather with the off-hand unaffectedness of natural regality, he seemed to accept the spontaneous homage of his shipmates. A somewhat remarkable instance recurs to me. In Liverpool, now half a century ago I saw under the shadow of the great dingy street-wall of Prince's Dock (an obstruction long since removed) a common sailor, so intensely black that he must needs have been a native African of the unadulterate blood of Ham. A symmetric figure much above the average height. The two ends of a gay silk handkerchief thrown loose about the neck danced upon the displayed ebony of his chest; in his ears were big hoops of gold, and a Scotch bonnet with a tartan band set off his shapely head.

It was a hot noon in July; and his face, lustrous with perspiration, beamed with barbaric good humor. In jovial sallies right and left, his white teeth flashing into view, he rollicked along, the center of a company of his shipmates. These were made up of such an assortment of tribes and complexions as would have well fitted them to be marched up by Anacharsis Clootz before the bar of the first French Assembly as Representatives of the Human Race. At each spontaneous tribute rendered by the wayfarers to this black pagod of a fellow —the tribute of a pause and stare, and, less frequent an exclamation—the motley retinue showed that they took that sort of pride in the evoker of it which the Assyrian priests doubtless showed for their grand sculptured Bull when the faithful prostrated themselves.

To return. If in some cases a bit of a nautical Murat in setting forth his person ashore, the handsome sailor of the period in question evinced nothing of the dandified Billy-be-Damn, an amusing character all but extinct now, but occasionally to be encountered, and in a form yet more amusing than the original, at the tiller of the boats on the tempestuous Erie Canal or, more likely, vaporing in the groggeries along the tow-path. Invariably a proficient in his perilous calling, he was also more or less of a mighty boxer or wrestler. It was strength and beauty. Tales of his prowess were recited. Ashore he was the champion; afloat the spokesman; on every suitable occasion always foremost. Close-reefing topsails in a gale, there he was, astride the weather yard-arm-end, foot in the Flemish horse as "stirrup," both hands tugging at the "ear-ring" as at a bridle, in very much the attitude of young Alexander curbing the fiery Bucephalus. A superb figure, tossed up as by the horns of Taurus against the thunderous sky, cheerily hallooing to the strenuous file along the spar.

The moral nature was seldom out of keeping with the physical make. Indeed, except as toned by the former, the comeliness and power, always attractive in masculine conjunction, hardly could have drawn the sort of honest homage the Handsome Sailor in some examples received from his less gifted associates.

Such a cynosure, at least in aspect, and something such too in nature, though with important variations made apparent as the story proceeds, was welkin-eyed Billy Budd, or Baby Budd as more familiarly under circumstances hereafter to be given he at last came to be called, aged twenty-one, a foretopman of the British fleet toward the close of the last decade of the eighteenth century. It was not very long prior to the time of the narration that follows that he had entered the King's Service, having been impressed on the Narrow Seas from a homeward-bound English merchantman into a seventy-four outward-bound, *H.M.S. Indomitable;* which ship, as was not unusual in those hurried days, having been obliged to put to sea short of her proper complement of men. Plump upon Billy at first sight in the gangway the boarding officer Lieutenant Ratcliffe pounced, even before the merchantman's crew was formally mustered on the quarter-deck for his deliberate inspection. And him only he elected. For whether it was because the other men when ranged before him showed to ill advantage after Billy, or whether he had some scruples in view of the merchantman being rather short-handed, however it might be, the officer contented himself with his first spontaneous choice. To the surprise of the ship's company, though much to the Lieutenant's satisfaction, Billy made no demur. But, indeed, any demur would have been as idle as the protest of a goldfinch popped into a cage.

Noting this uncomplaining acquiescence, all but cheerful one might say, the shipmates turned a surprised glance of silent reproach at the sailor. The shipmaster was one of those worthy mortals found in every vocation, even the humbler ones—the sort of person whom everybody agrees in calling "a respectable man." And—nor so strange to report as it may appear to be— though a plowman of the troubled waters, life-long contending with the intractable elements, there was nothing this honest soul at heart loved better than simple peace and quiet. For the rest, he was fifty or thereabouts, a little inclined to corpulence, a prepossessing face, unwhiskered, and of an agreeable color—a rather full face, humanely intelligent in expression. On a fair day with a fair wind and all going well, a certain musical chime in his voice seemed to be the veritable unobstructed outcome of the innermost man. He had much prudence, much conscientiousness, and there were occasions when these virtues were the cause of overmuch disquietude in him. On a passage, so long as his craft was in any proximity to land, no sleep for Captain Graveling. He took to heart those serious responsibilities not so heavily borne by some shipmasters.

Now while Billy Budd was down in the forecastle getting his kit together, the *Indomitable*'s lieutenant, burly and bluff, nowise disconcerted by Captain Graveling's omitting to proffer the customary hospitalities on an occasion so unwelcome to him, an omission simply caused by preoccupation of thought, unceremoniously invited himself into the cabin, and also to a flask from the spirit-locker, a receptacle which his experienced eye instantly discovered. In fact he was one of those sea-dogs in whom all the hardship and peril of naval life in the great prolonged wars of his time never impaired the natural instinct for sensuous enjoyment. His duty he always faithfully did; but duty is sometimes a dry obligation, and he was for irrigating its aridity, when-soever possible, with a fertilizing decoction of strong waters. For the cabin's proprietor there was nothing left but to play the part of the enforced host with what-ever grace and alacrity were practicable. As necessary adjuncts to the flask, he silently placed tumbler and water-jug before the irrepressible guest. But excusing himself from partaking just then, he dismally watched the unembarrassed officer deliberately diluting his grog a little, then tossing it off in three swallows, pushing the empty tumbler away, yet not so far as to be beyond easy reach, at the same time settling himself in his seat and smacking his lips with high satisfaction, looking straight at the host.

These proceedings over, the Master broke the silence; and there lurked a rueful reproach in the tone of his voice: "Lieutenant, you are going to take my best man from me, the jewel of 'em."

"Yes, I know," rejoined the other, immediately draw-ing back the tumbler preliminary to a replenishing: "Yes, I know. Sorry."

"Beg pardon, but you don't understand, Lieutenant. See here now. Before I shipped that young fellow, my forecastle was a rat-pit of quarrels. It was black times, I tell you, aboard the *Rights* here. I was worried to that degree my pipe had no comfort for me. But Billy came; and it was like a Catholic priest striking peace in an Irish shindy. Not that he preached to them or said or did anything in particular; but a virtue went out of him, sugaring the sour ones. They took to him like hornets to treacle; all but the buffer of the gang, the big shaggy chap with the fire-red whiskers. He indeed out of envy, perhaps, of the newcomer, and thinking such a 'sweet and pleasant fellow,' as he mockingly designated him to the others, could hardly have the spirit of a game-cock, must needs bestir himself in trying to get up an ugly row with him. Billy forebore with him and reasoned with him in a pleasant way—he is something like myself, lieutenant, to whom aught like a quarrel is hateful —but nothing served. So, in the second dog-watch one day the Red Whiskers in presence of the others, under pretense of showing Billy just whence a sirloin steak was cut—for the fellow had once been a butcher—insultingly gave him a dig under the ribs. Quick as lightning Billy let fly his arm. I dare say he never meant to do quite as much as he did, but anyhow he gave the burly fool a terrible drubbing. It took about half a minute, I should think. And, Lord bless you, the lubber was astonished at the celerity. And will you believe it, Lieutenant, the Red Whiskers now really loves Billy— loves him, or is the biggest hypocrite that ever I heard of. But they all love him. Some of 'em do his washing, darn his old trousers for him; the carpenter is at odd times making a pretty little chest of drawers for him. Anybody will do anything for Billy Budd; and it's the happy family here. But now, Lieutenant, if that young fellow goes—I know how it will be aboard the *Rights*. Not again very soon shall I, coming up from dinner, lean over the capstan smoking a quiet pipe—no, not very soon again, I think. Aye, Lieutenant, you are going to take away the jewel of 'em; you are going to take away my peacemaker!" And with that the good soul had really some ado in checking a rising sob.

"Well," said the officer who had listened with amused interest to all this, and now was waxing merry with his tipple, "well, blessed are the peacemakers, especially the fighting peacemakers! And such are the seventy-four beauties some of which you see poking their noses out of the port-holes of yonder warship lying-to for me," pointing through the cabin window at the *Indomitable*. "But courage! don't look so downhearted, man. Why, I pledge you in advance the royal approbation. Rest assured that His Majesty will be delighted to know that in a time when his hardtack is not sought for by sailors with such avidity as should be; a time also when some shipmasters privily resent the borrowing from them a tar or two for the service; His Majesty, I say, will be delighted to learn that *one* shipmaster at least cheerfully surrenders to the King, the flower of his flock, a sailor who with equal loyalty makes no dissent.—But where's my beauty? Ah," looking through the cabin's open door, "Here he comes; and, by Jove—lugging along his chest—Apollo with his portmanteau!—My man," stepping out to him, "you can't take that big box aboard a warship. The boxes there are mostly shot-boxes. Put your duds in a bag, lad. Boot and saddle for the cavalryman, bag and hammock for the man-of-war's man."

The transfer from chest to bag was made. And, after seeing his man into the cutter and then following him down, the lieutenant pushed off from the *Rights-of-Man*. That was the merchant-ship's name; though by her master and crew abbreviated in sailor fashion into the *Rights*. The hard-headed Dundee owner was a staunch admirer of Thomas Paine, whose book in rejoinder to

Burke's arraignment of the French Revolution had then been published for some time and had gone everywhere. In christening his vessel after the title of Paine's volume the man of Dundee was something like his contemporary shipowner, Stephen Girard of Philadelphia, whose sympathies, alike with his native land and its liberal philosophers, he evinced by naming his ships after Voltaire, Diderot, and so forth.

But now, when the boat swept under the merchantman's stern, and officer and oarsmen were noting—some bitterly and others with a grin—the name emblazoned there; just then it was that the new recruit jumped up from the bow where the coxswain had directed him to sit, and waving his hat to his silent shipmates sorrowfully looking over at him from the taffrail, bade the lads a genial good-by. Then making a salutation as to the ship herself, "And good-by to you too, old *Rights-of-Man!*"

"Down, Sir!" roared the lieutenant, instantly assuming all the rigor of his rank, though with difficulty repressing a smile.

To be sure, Billy's action was a terrible breach of naval decorum. But in that decorum he had never been instructed; in consideration of which the lieutenant would hardly have been so energetic in reproof but for the concluding farewell to the ship. This he rather took as meant to convey a covert sally on the new recruit's part, a sly slur at impressment in general, and that of himself in especial. And yet, more likely, if satire it was in effect, it was hardly so by intention, for Billy, though happily endowed with the gaiety of high health, youth, and a free heart, was yet by no means of a satirical turn. The will to it and the sinister dexterity were alike wanting. To deal in double meaning and insinuations of any sort was quite foreign to his nature.

As to his enforced enlistment, that he seemed to take pretty much as he was wont to take any vicissitude of weather. Like the animals, though no philosopher, he was, without knowing it, practically a fatalist. And, it may be, that he rather liked this adventurous turn in his affairs, which promised an opening into novel scenes and martial excitements.

Aboard the *Indomitable* our merchant-sailor was forthwith rated as an able-seaman and assigned to the starboard watch of the foretop. He was soon at home in the service, not at all disliked for his unpretentious good looks and a sort of genial happy-go-lucky air. No merrier man in his mess: in marked contrast to certain other individuals included like himself among the impressed portion of the ship's company; for these when not actively employed were sometimes, and more particularly in the last dog-watch when the drawing near of twilight induced revery, apt to fall into a saddish mood which in some partook of sullenness. But they were not so young as our Foretopman, and no few of them must have known a hearth of some sort, others may have had wives and children left, too probably, in uncertain circumstances, and hardly any but must have had acknowledged kith and kin, while for Billy, as will shortly be seen, his entire family was practically invested in himself.

●

Though our new-made Foretopman was well received in the top and on the gun-decks, hardly here was he that cynosure he had previously been among those minor ship's companies of the merchant marine, with which companies only had he hitherto consorted.

He was young, and, despite his all but fully developed frame, in aspect looked even younger than he really was, owing to a lingering adolescent expression in the as yet smooth face all but feminine in purity in natural complexion but where, thanks to his seagoing, the lily was quite suppressed and the rose had some ado visibly to flush through the tan.

To one essentially such a novice in the complexities of factious life, the abrupt transition from his former and simpler sphere to the ampler and more knowing world of a great warship—this might well have abashed him had there been any conceit or vanity in his composition. Among her miscellaneous multitude, the *Indomitable* mustered several individuals who however inferior in grade were of no common natural stamp, sailors more signally susceptive of that air which continuous martial discipline and repeated presence in battle can in some degree impart even to the average man. As the Handsome Sailor, Billy Budd's position aboard the seventy-four was something analogous to that of a rustic beauty transplanted from the provinces and brought into competition with the high-born dames of the court. But this change of circumstances he scarce noted. As little did he observe that something about him provoked an ambiguous smile in one or two harder faces among the blue-jackets. Nor less unaware was he of the peculiar favorable effect his person and demeanor had upon the more intelligent gentlemen of the quarter-deck. Nor could this well have been otherwise. Cast in a mold peculiar to the finest physical examples of those Englishmen in whom the Saxon strain would seem not at all to partake of any Norman or other admixture, he showed in face that humane look of reposeful good nature which the Greek sculptor in some instances gave to his heroic strong man, Hercules. But this again was subtly modified by another and pervasive quality. The ear, small and shapely, the arch of the foot, the curve in mouth and nostril, even the indurated hand dyed to the orange-tawny of the toucan's bill, a hand telling alike of the halyards and tar-bucket, but, above all, something in the mobile expression, and every chance attitude and movement, something suggestive of a mother eminently favored by Love and the Graces; all this strangely indicated a lineage in direct contradiction to his lot. The mysteriousness here became less mysterious through a matter of fact elicited when Billy at the capstan was being formally mustered into the service. Asked by the officer, a small brisk little gentleman as it chanced, among other questions, his place of birth, he replied, "Please, Sir, I don't know."

"Don't know where you were born?—Who was your father?"

"God knows, Sir."

Struck by the straightforward simplicity of these replies, the officer next asked "Do you know anything about your beginning?"

"No, Sir. But I have heard that I was found in a pretty silk-lined basket hanging one morning from the knocker of a good man's door in Bristol."

"*Found,* say you? Well," throwing back his head and looking up and down the new recruit, "well, it turns out to have been a pretty good find. Hope they'll find some more like you, my man; the fleet sadly needs them."

Yes, Billy Budd was a foundling, a presumable bye-blow, and, evidently, no ignoble one. Noble descent was as evident in him as in a blood horse.

For the rest, with little or no sharpness of faculty or any trace of the wisdom of the serpent, nor yet quite a dove, he possessed that kind and degree of intelligence going along with the unconventional rectitude of a sound human creature, one to whom not yet has been proffered the questionable apple of knowledge. He was illiterate; he could not read, but he could sing, and like the illiterate nightingale was sometimes the composer of his own song.

Of self-consciousness he seemed to have little or none, or about as much as we may reasonably impute to a dog of St. Bernard's breed.

Habitually living with the elements and knowing little more of the land than as a beach, or, rather, that portion of the terraqueous globe providentially set apart for dance-houses doxies and tapsters, in short what sailors call a "fiddlers' green," his simple nature remained unsophisticated by those moral obliquities which are not in every case incompatible with that manufacturable thing known as respectability. But are sailors, frequenters of "fiddlers' greens," without vices? No; but less often than with landsmen do their vices, so called, partake of crookedness of heart, seeming less to proceed from viciousness than exuberance of vitality after long constraint; frank manifestations in accordance with natural law. By his original constitution aided by the co-operating influences of his lot, Billy in many respects was little more than a sort of upright barbarian, much such perhaps as Adam presumably might have been ere the urbane Serpent wriggled himself into his company.

And here be it submitted that apparently going to corroborate the doctrine of man's fall, a doctrine now popularly ignored, it is observable that where certain virtues pristine and unadulterate peculiarly characterize anybody in the external uniform of civilization, they will upon scrutiny seem not to be derived from custom or convention but rather to be out of keeping with these, as if indeed exceptionally transmitted from a period prior to Cain's city and citified man. The character marked by such qualities has to an unvitiated taste an untampered-with flavor like that of berries, while the man thoroughly civilized, even in a fair specimen of the breed, has to the same moral palate a questionable smack as of a compounded wine. To any stray inheritor of these primitive qualities found, like Caspar Hauser, wandering dazed in any Christian capital of our time, the good-natured poet's famous invocation, near two thousand years ago, of the good rustic out of his latitude in the Rome of the Caesars, still appropriately holds:

> Honest and poor, faithful in word and thought,
> What has thee, Fabian, to the city brought.

Though our Handsome Sailor had as much of masculine beauty as one can expect anywhere to see, nevertheless, like the beautiful woman in one of Hawthorne's minor tales, there was just one thing amiss in him. No visible blemish, indeed, as with the lady; no, but an occasional liability to a vocal defect. Though in the hour of elemental uproar or peril, he was everything that a sailor should be, yet under sudden provocation of strong heart-feeling his voice, otherwise singularly musical, as if expressive of the harmony within, was apt to develop an organic hesitancy, in fact more or less of a stutter or even worse. In this particular Billy was a striking instance that the arch interferer, the envious marplot of Eden still has more or less to do with every human consignment to this planet of earth. In every case, one way or another he is sure to slip in his little card, as much as to remind us—I too have a hand here.

The avowal of such an imperfection in the Handsome Sailor should be evidence not alone that he is not presented as a conventional hero, but also that the story in which he is the main figure is no romance.

•

At the time of Billy Budd's arbitrary enlistment into the *Indomitable* that ship was on her way to join the Mediterranean fleet. No long time elapsed before the junction was effected. As one of that fleet the seventy-four participated in its movements, though at times on account of her superior sailing qualities, in the absence of frigates, dispatched on separate duty as a scout and at times on less temporary service. But with all this the story has little concernment, restricted as it is to the inner life of one particular ship and the career of an individual sailor.

It was the summer of 1797. In the April of that year had occurred the commotion at Spithead followed in May by a second and yet more serious outbreak in the fleet at the Nore. The latter is known, and without exaggeration in the epithet, as the Great Mutiny. It was indeed a demonstration more menacing to England than the contemporary manifestoes and conquering and prose-lyting armies of the French Directory. To the British Empire the Nore Mutiny was what a strike in the fire-brigade would be to London threatened by a general arson. In a crisis when the Kingdom might well have anticipated the famous signal that some years later published along the naval line of battle what it was that upon occasion England expected of Englishmen—*that* was the time when at the mast-heads of the three-deckers and seventy-fours moored in her own roadstead —a fleet the right arm of a Power then all but the sole free conservative one of the Old World, the blue-jackets, to be numbered by thousands, ran up with huzzas the British colors with the union and cross wiped out; by that cancellation transmuting the flag of founded law

and freedom defined into the enemy's red meteor of unbridled and unbounded revolt. Reasonable discontent
growing out of practical grievances in the fleet had been
ignited into irrational combustion as by live cinders
blown across the Channel from France in flames.

The event converted into irony for a time those
spirited strains of Dibdin—as a song-writer no mean
auxiliary to the English Government at the European
conjuncture—strains celebrating, among other things,
the patriotic devotion of the British tar:

> And as for my life, 'tis the King's!

Such an episode in the Island's grand naval story her
naval historians naturally abridge; one of them (James)
candidly acknowledging that fain would he pass it over,
did not "impartiality forbid fastidiousness." And yet his
mention is less a narration than a reference, having to do
hardly at all with details. Nor are these readily to be
found in the libraries. Like some other events in every
age befalling states everywhere including America the
Great Mutiny was of such character that national pride
along with views of policy would fain shade it off into
the historical background. Such events can not be ignored, but there is a considerate way of historically
treating them. If a well-constituted individual refrains
from blazoning aught amiss or calamitous in his family;
a nation in the like circumstance may without reproach
be equally discreet.

Though after parleyings between Government and
the ringleaders, and concessions by the former as to
some glaring abuses, the first uprising—that at Spithead
—with difficulty was put down, or matters for a time
pacified; yet at the Nore the unforeseen renewal of in-
surrection on a yet larger scale, and emphasized in the
conferences that ensued by demands deemed by the

authorities not only inadmissible but aggressively insolent, indicated—if the Red Flag did not sufficiently do
so—what was the spirit animating the men. Final sup-
pression, however, there was; but only made possible
perhaps by the unswerving loyalty of the marine corps
and a voluntary resumption of loyalty among influential
sections of the crews.

To some extent the Nore Mutiny may be regarded as
analogous to the distempering irruption of contagious
fever in a frame constitutionally sound, and which anon
throws it off.

At all events, of these thousands of mutineers were
some of the tars who not so very long afterwards—
whether wholly prompted thereto by patriotism, or pug-
nacious instinct, or by both—helped to win a coronet for
Nelson at the Nile, and the naval crown of crowns for
him at Trafalgar. To the mutineers those battles and
especially Trafalgar were a plenary absoultion; and a
grand one. To all that goes to make up scenic naval display and heroic magnificence in arms, those battles,
especially Trafalgar, stand unmatched in human annals.

Concerning "The greatest sailor since the world began"

In this matter of writing, resolve as one may to keep
to the main road, some bypaths have an enticement not
readily to be withstood. I am going to err into such a
bypath. If the reader will keep me company I shall be
glad. At the least we can promise ourselves that pleasure which is wickedly said to be in sinning, for a literary
sin the divergence will be.

Very likely it is no new remark that the inventions of
our time have at last brought about a change in sea-

warfare in degree corresponding to the revolution in all warfare effected by the original introduction from China into Europe of gunpowder. The first European firearm, a clumsy contrivance, was, as is well known, scouted by no few of the knights as a base implement good enough peradventure for weavers too craven to stand up crossing steel with steel in frank fight. But as ashore knightly valor though shorn of its blazonry did not cease with the knights, neither on the seas, though nowadays in encounters there a certain kind of displayed gallantry be fallen out of date as hardly applicable under changed circumstances, did the nobler qualities of such naval magnates as Don John of Austria, Doria, Van Tromp, Jean Bart, the long line of British admirals, and the American Decaturs of 1812 become obsolete with their wooden walls.

Nevertheless, to anybody who can hold the Present at its worth without being inappreciative of the Past, it may be forgiven if to such an one the solitary old hulk at Portsmouth, Nelson's *Victory*, seems to float there, not alone as the decaying monument of a fame incorruptible, but also as a poetic reproach, softened by its picturesqueness, to the *Monitors* and yet mightier hulls of the European iron-clads. And this not altogether because such craft are unsightly, unavoidably lacking the symmetry and grand lines of the old battleships, but equally for other reasons.

There are some, perhaps, who, while not altogether inaccessible to that poetic reproach just alluded to, may yet on behalf of the New Order, be disposed to parry it; and this to the extent of iconoclasm, if need be. For example, prompted by the sight of the star inserted in the *Victory*'s quarter-deck designating the spot where the Great Sailor fell, these martial utilitarians may suggest considerations implying that Nelson's ornate publication of his person in battle was not only unnecessary, but not military, nay, savored of foolhardiness and vanity. They may add, too, that at Trafalgar it was in effect nothing less than a challenge to death; and death came; and that but for his bravado the victorious admiral might possibly have survived the battle, and so, instead of having his sagacious dying injunctions overruled by his immediate successor in command, he himself when the contest was decided might have brought his shattered fleet to anchor, a proceeding which might have averted the deplorable loss of life by shipwreck in the elemental tempest that followed the martial one.

Well, should we set aside the more disputable point whether for various reasons it was possible to anchor the fleet, then plausibly enough the Benthamites of war may urge the above. But the *might-have-been* is but boggy ground to build on. And certainly in foresight as to the larger issue of an encounter, and anxious preparations for it—buoying the deadly way and mapping it out, as at Copenhagen—few commanders have been so painstakingly circumspect as this same reckless declarer of his person in fight.

Personal prudence, even when dictated by quite other than selfish considerations, surely is no special virtue in a military man; while an excessive love of glory, impassioning a less burning impulse the honest sense of duty, is the first. If the name *Wellington* is not so much of a trumpet to the blood as the simpler name *Nelson,* the reason for this may perhaps be inferred from the above. Alfred in his funeral ode on the victor of Waterloo ventures not to call him the greatest soldier of all time, though in the same ode he invokes Nelson as "the greatest sailor since the world began."

At Trafalgar Nelson on the brink of opening the fight sat down and wrote his last brief will and testament. If under the presentiment of the most magnificent of all victories to be crowned by his own glorious death, a sort of priestly motive led him to dress his person in the jeweled vouchers of his own shining deeds, if thus to have adorned himself for the altar and the sacrifice were indeed vainglory, then affectation and fustian is each more heroic line in the great epics and dramas, since in such lines the poet but embodies in verse those exaltations of sentiment that a nature like Nelson's, the opportunity being given, vitalizes into acts.

•

Yes, the outbreak at the Nore was put down. But not every grievance was redressed. If the contractors, for example, were no longer permitted to ply some practices peculiar to their tribe everywhere, such as providing shoddy cloth, rations not sound, or false in the measure, not the less impressment, for one thing, went on. By custom sanctioned for centuries, and judicially maintained by a Lord Chancellor as late as Mansfield, that mode of manning the fleet, a mode now fallen into a sort of abeyance but never formally renounced, it was not practicable to give up in those years. Its abrogation would have crippled the indispensable fleet, one wholly under canvas, no steam power, its innumerable sails and thousands of cannon, everything in short, worked by muscle alone; a fleet the more insatiate in demand for men, because then multiplying its ships of all grades against contingencies present and to come of the convulsed Continent.

Discontent foreran the Two Mutinies, and more or less it lurkingly survived them. Hence it was not unreasonable to apprehend some return of trouble sporadic or general. One instance of such apprehensions: In the same year with this story, Nelson, then Vice-Admiral

Sir Horatio, being with the fleet off the Spanish coast, was directed by the Admiral in command to shift his pennant from the *Captain* to the *Theseus;* and for this reason: that the latter ship having newly arrived on the station from home where it had taken part in the Great Mutiny, danger was apprehended from the temper of the men; and it was thought that an officer like Nelson was the one, not indeed to terrorize the crew into base subjection, but to win them, by force of his mere presence and heroic personality, back to an allegiance, if not as enthusiastic as his own, yet as true.

So it was that for a time on more than one quarter-deck anxiety did exist. At sea precautionary vigilance was strained against relapse. At short notice an engagement might come on. When it did, the lieutenants assigned to batteries felt it incumbent on them, in some instances, to stand with drawn swords behind the men working the guns.

•

But on board the seventy-four in which Billy now swung his hammock, very little in the manner of the men and nothing obvious in the demeanor of the officers would have suggested to an ordinary observer that the Great Mutiny was a recent event. In their general bearing and conduct the commissioned officers of a warship naturally take their tone from the commander, that is if he has that ascendancy of character that ought to be his.

Captain the Honorable Edward Fairfax Vere, to give his full title, was a bachelor of forty or thereabouts, a sailor of distinction even in a time prolific of renowned seamen. Though allied to the higher nobility his advancement had not been altogether owing to influences connected with that circumstance. He had seen much service, been in various engagements, always acquitting himself as an officer mindful of the welfare of his men but never tolerating an infraction of discipline, thoroughly versed in the science of his profession, and intrepid to the verge of temerity, though never injudiciously so. For his gallantry in the West Indian waters as flag-lieutenant under Rodney in that Admiral's crowning victory over De Grasse, he was made a post-captain.

Ashore in the garb of a civilian scarce any one would have taken him for a sailor, more especially that he never garnished unprofessional talk with nautical terms, and, grave in his bearing, evinced little appreciation of mere humor. It was not out of keeping with these traits that on a passage when nothing demanded his paramount action, he was the most undemonstrative of men. Any landsman observing this gentleman not conspicuous by his stature and wearing no pronounced insignia, emerging from his cabin to the open deck, and noting the silent deference of the officers retiring to leeward, might have taken him for the King's guest, a civilian aboard the King's ship, some highly honorable discreet envoy on his way to an important post. But in fact this unobtrusiveness of demeanor may have proceeded from a certain unaffected modesty of manhood sometimes accompanying a resolute nature, a modesty evinced at all times not calling for pronounced action, and which shown in any rank of life suggests a virtue aristocratic in kind.

As with some others engaged in various departments of the world's more heroic activities, Captain Vere though practical enough upon occasion would at times betray a certain dreaminess of mood. Standing alone on the weather-side of the quarter-deck, one hand holding by the rigging he would absently gaze off at the blank sea. At the presentation to him then of some minor matter interrupting the current of his thoughts he would show more or less irascibility, but instantly he would control it.

In the navy he was popularly known by the appellation "Starry Vere." How such a designation happened to fall upon one who whatever his sturdy qualities was without any brilliant ones was in this wise: a favorite kinsman, Lord Denton, a free-hearted fellow, had been the first to meet and congratulate him upon his return to England from his West Indian cruise; and but the day previous turning over a copy of Andrew Marvell's poems had lighted, not for the first time however, upon the lines entitled "Appleton House," the name of one of the seats of their common ancestor, a hero in the German wars of the seventeenth century, in which poem occur the lines:

> This 'tis to have been from the first
> In a domestic heaven nursed,
> Under the discipline severe
> Of Fairfax and the starry Vere.

And so, upon embracing his cousin fresh from Rodney's victory wherein he had played so gallant a part, brimming over with just family pride in the sailor of their house, he exuberantly exclaimed, "Give ye joy, Ed; give ye joy, my starry Vere!" This got currency, and the novel prefix serving in familiar parlance readily to distinguish the *Indomitable*'s Captain from another Vere his senior, a distant relative, an officer of like rank in the navy, it remained permanently attached to the surname.

•

In view of the part that the commander of the *Indomitable* plays in scenes shortly to follow, it may be well to fill out that sketch of him outlined in the previous chapter. Aside from his qualities as a sea officer Captain Vere was an exceptional character. Unlike no few of England's renowned sailors, long and arduous service with signal devotion to it, had not resulted in absorbing and *salting* the entire man. He had a marked leaning toward everything intellectual. He loved books, never going to sea without a newly replenished library, compact but of the best. The isolated leisure, in some cases so wearisome, falling at intervals to commanders even during a war cruise, never was tedious to Captain Vere. With nothing of that literary taste which less heeds the thing conveyed than the vehicle, his bias was toward those books to which every serious mind of superior order occupying any active post of authority in the world naturally inclines; books treating of actual men and events no matter of what era—history, biography, and unconventional writers, like Montaigne, who, free from cant and convention, honestly, and in the spirit of common sense philosophize upon realities.

In this love of reading he found confirmation of his own more reserved thoughts—confirmation which he had vainly sought in social converse, so that as touching most fundamental topics there had got to be established in him some positive convictions which he forefelt would abide in him essentially unmodified so long as his intelligent part remained unimpaired. In view of the troubled period in which his lot was cast this was well for him. His settled convictions were as a dyke against those invading waters of novel opinion, social, political, and otherwise, which carried away as in a torrent no few minds in those days, minds by nature not inferior to his own. While other members of that aristocracy to which by birth he belonged were incensed at the innovators mainly because their theories were inimical to the privileged classes, Captain Vere disinterestedly opposed them because they seemed to him not alone incapable of embodiment in lasting institutions, but at war with the peace of the world and the true welfare of mankind.

With minds less stored than his and less earnest, some officers of his rank, with whom at times he would necessarily consort, found him lacking in the companionable quality, a dry and bookish gentleman, as they deemed. Upon any chance withdrawal from their company one would be apt to say to another something like this: "Vere is a noble fellow, Starry Vere. 'Spite the gazettes, Sir Horatio is at bottom scarce a better seaman or fighter. But between you and me now don't you think there is a queer streak of the pedantic running through him? Yes, like the King's yarn in a coil of navy-rope?"

Some apparent ground there was for this sort of confidential criticism, since not only did the Captain's discourse never fall into the jocosely familiar, but in illustrating of any point touching the stirring personages and events of the time he would be as apt to cite some historic character or incident of antiquity as that he would cite from the moderns. He seemed unmindful of the circumstance that to his bluff company such remote allusions, however pertinent they might really be, were altogether alien to men whose reading was mainly confined to the journals. But considerateness in such matters is not easy to natures constituted like Captain Vere's. Their honesty prescribes to them directness, sometimes far-reaching like that of a migratory fowl that in its flight never heeds when it crosses a frontier.

•

The lieutenants and other commissioned gentlemen forming Captain Vere's staff it is not necessary here to particularize nor needs it to make any mention of any of the warrant-officers. But among the petty officers was one who having much to do with the story may as well be forthwith introduced. This portrait I essay, but shall never hit it. This was John Claggart, the Master-at-Arms. But that sea-title may to landsmen seem somewhat equivocal. Originally doubtless that petty officer's function was the instruction of the men in the use of arms, sword, or cutlass. But very long ago, owing to the advance in gunnery making hand-to-hand encounters less frequent and giving to nitre and sulphur the preeminence over steel, that function ceased, the master-at-arms of a great warship becoming a sort of chief of police charged among other matters with the duty of preserving order on the populous lower gun-decks.

Claggart was a man of about five-and-thirty, somewhat spare and tall, yet of no ill figure upon the whole. His hand was too small and shapely to have been accustomed to hard toil. The face was a notable one; the features all except the chin cleanly cut as those on a Greek medallion, yet the chin, beardless as Tecumseh's, had something of strange protuberant broadness in its make that recalled the prints of the Reverend Doctor Titus Oates, the historic deponent with the clerical drawl in the time of Charles II and the fraud of the alleged Popish Plot. It served Claggart in his office that his eye could cast a tutoring glance. His brow was of the sort phrenologically associated with more than average intellect; silken jet curls partly clustering over it, making a foil to the pallor below, a pallor tinged with a faint shade of amber akin to the hue of time-tinted marbles of old. This complexion, singularly contrasting with the red or deeply bronzed visages of the sailors, and in part the result of his official seclusion from the sunlight, though it was not exactly displeasing, nevertheless seemed to hint of something defective or abnormal in the constitution and blood. But his general aspect and manner were so suggestive of an education and career incongruous with his naval function that when not actively engaged in it he looked like a man of high quality, social and moral, who for reasons of his own was keeping incognito. Nothing was known of his former life. It might be that he was an Englishman, and yet there lurked a bit of accent in his speech suggesting that possibly he was not such by birth, but through naturalization in early childhood. Among certain grizzled sea-gossips of the gun-decks and forecastle went a rumor perdue that the Master-at-Arms was a *chevalier* who had volunteered into the King's navy by way of compounding for some mysterious swindle whereof he had been arraigned at the King's Bench. The fact that nobody could substantiate this report was, of course, nothing against its secret currency. Such a rumor once started on the gun-decks in reference to almost anyone below the rank of a commissioned officer would, during the period assigned to this narrative, have seemed not altogether wanting in credibility to the tarry old wiseacres of a man-of-war crew. And indeed a man of Claggart's accomplishments, without prior nautical experience entering the navy at mature life, as he did, and necessarily allotted at the start to the lowest grade in it, a man too who never made allusion to his previous life ashore; these were circumstances which in the dearth of exact knowledge as to his true antecedents opened to the invidious a vague field for unfavorable surmise.

But the sailors' dog-watch gossip concerning him derived a vague plausibility from the fact that now for some period the British Navy could so little afford to be squeamish in the matter of keeping up the muster-rolls that not only were press-gangs notoriously abroad both afloat and ashore, but there was little or no secret about another matter, namely that the London police were at liberty to capture any able-bodied suspect, any questionable fellow at large, and summarily ship him to the dock-yard or fleet. Furthermore even among voluntary enlistments there were instances where the motive thereto partook neither of patriotic impulse nor yet of a random desire to experience a bit of sea life and martial adventure. Insolvent debtors of minor grade, together with the promiscuous lame ducks of morality, found in the navy a convenient and secure refuge. Secure, because once enlisted aboard a King's Ship, they were as much in sanctuary as the transgressor of the Middle Ages harboring himself under the shadow of the altar. Such sanctioned irregularities which for obvious reasons the Government would hardly think to parade at the time and which consequently, and as affecting the least influential class of mankind, have all but dropped into oblivion lend color to something for the truth whereof I do not vouch, and hence have some scruple in stating; something I remember having seen in print, though the book I cannot recall; but the same thing was personally communicated to me now more than forty years ago by an old pensioner in a cocked hat with whom I had a most interesting talk on the terrace at Greenwich, a Baltimore Negro, a Trafalgar man. It was to this effect: In the case of a warship short of hands whose speedy sailing was imperative, the deficient quota in lack of any other way of making it good, would be eked out by drafts culled direct from the jails. For reasons previously suggested it would not perhaps be easy at the present day directly to prove or disprove the allegation. But allowed as a verity, how significant would it be of England's straits at the time confronted by those wars which like a flight of harpies rose shrieking from the din and dust of the fallen Bastille. That era appears measurably clear to us who look back at it and but read of it. But to the grandfathers of us gray-beards, the more thoughtful of them, the genius of it presented an aspect like that of Camoëns' Spirit of the Cape, an eclipsing menace mysterious and prodigious. Not America was exempt from apprehension. At the height of Napoleon's unexampled conquests, there were Americans who had fought at Bunker Hill who looked forward to the possibility that the Atlantic might prove no barrier against the ultimate schemes of this French portentous upstart from the revolutionary chaos who seemed in act of fulfilling judgment prefigured in the Apocalypse.

But the less credence was to be given to the gun-deck talk touching Claggart, seeing that no man holding his office in a man-of-war can ever hope to be popular with the crew. Besides, in derogatory comments upon anyone against whom they have a grudge, or for any reason or no reason mislike, sailors are much like landsmen; they are apt to exaggerate or romance it.

About as much was really known to the *Indomitable's* tars of the Master-at-Arms' career before entering the service as an astronomer knows about a comet's travels prior to its first observable appearance in the sky. The verdict of the sea quid-nuncs has been cited only by way of showing what sort of moral impression the man made upon rude uncultivated natures whose conceptions of human wickedness were necessarily of the narrowest, limited to ideas of vulgar rascality—a thief among the swinging hammocks during a night-watch, or the man-brokers and land-sharks of the seaports.

It was no gossip, however, but fact, that though, as before hinted, Claggart upon his entrance into the navy was, as a novice, assigned to the least honorable section of a man-of-war's crew, embracing the drudgery, he did not long remain there. The superior capacity he immediately evinced, his constitutional sobriety, ingratiating deference to superiors, together with a peculiar ferreting genius manifested on a singular occasion, all this capped by a certain austere patriotism abruptly advanced him to the position of master-at-arms.

Of this maritime chief of police the ship's-corporals, so called, were the immediate subordinates, and compliant ones; and this, as is to be noted in some business departments ashore, almost to a degree inconsistent with entire moral volition. His place put various converging wires of underground influence under the Chief's control, capable when astutely worked through his understrappers of operating to the mysterious discomfort, if nothing worse, of any of the sea-commonalty.

•

Life in the foretop well agreed with Billy Budd. There, when not actually engaged on the yards yet higher aloft, the topmen, who as such had been picked out for youth and activity, constituted an aerial club lounging at ease against the smaller stunsails rolled up into cushions, spinning yarns like the lazy gods, and frequently amused with what was going on in the busy world of the decks below. No wonder then that a young fellow of Billy's disposition was well content in such society. Giving no cause of offense to anybody, he was always alert at a call. So in the merchant service it had been with him. But now such a punctiliousness in duty was shown that his topmates would sometimes goodnaturedly laugh at him for it. This heightened alacrity had its cause; namely, the impression made upon him by the first formal gangway-punishment he had ever witnessed, which befell the day following his impressment. It had been incurred by a little fellow, young, a novice, an after-guardsman absent from his assigned post when the ship was being put about; a dereliction resulting in a rather serious hitch to that maneuver, one demanding instantaneous promptitude in letting go and making fast. When Billy saw the culprit's naked back under the scourge gridironed with red welts, and worse, when he marked the dire expression on the liberated man's face as with his woolen shirt flung over him by the executioner he rushed forward from the spot to bury himself in the crowd, Billy was horrified. He resolved that never through remissness would he make himself liable to such a visitation or do or omit aught that might merit even verbal reproof. What then was his surprise and concern when ultimately he found himself getting into petty trouble occasionally about such matters as the stowage of his bag or something amiss in his hammock, matters under the police oversight of the ship's-corporals of the lower decks, and which brought down on him a vague threat from one of them.

So heedful in all things as he was, how could this be? He could not understand it, and it more than vexed him. When he spoke to his young topmates about it they were either lightly incredulous, or found something comical in his unconcealed anxiety. "Is it your bag, Billy?" said one. "Well, sew yourself up in it, bully boy, and then you'll be sure to know if anybody meddles with it."

Now there was a veteran aboard who because his years began to disqualify him for more active work had been recently assigned duty as mainmast-man in his watch, looking to the gear belayed at the rail roundabout that great spar near the deck. At off-times the Foretopman had picked up some acquaintance with him, and now in his trouble it occurred to him that he might be the sort of person to go to for wise counsel. He was an old Dansker long anglicized in the service, of few words, many wrinkles, and some honorable scars. His wizened face, time-tinted and weather-stained to the complexion of an antique parchment, was here and there peppered blue by the chance explosion of a gun-cartridge in action. He was an *Agamemnon* man; some two years prior to the time of this story having served under Nelson, when but Sir Horatio, in that ship immortal in naval memory, and which dismantled and in part broken up to her bare ribs is seen a grand skeleton in Haydon's etching. As one of a boarding-party from the *Agamemnon* he had received a cut slantwise along one temple and cheek, leaving a long pale scar like a streak of dawn's light falling athwart the dark visage. It was on account of that scar and the affair in which it was known that he had received it, as well as from his blue-peppered complexion that the Dansker went among the *Indomitable*'s crew by the name of "Board-her-in-the-smoke."

Now the first time that his small weazel-eyes happened to light on Billy Budd, a certain grim internal merriment set all his ancient wrinkles into antic play. Was it that his eccentric unsentimental old sapience primitive in its kind saw or thought it saw something which in contrast with the warship's environment looked oddly incongruous in the handsome sailor? But after slyly studying him at intervals, the old Merlin's equivocal merriment was modified; for now when the twain would meet, it would start in his face a quizzing sort of look, but it would be but momentary and sometimes replaced by an expression of speculative query as to what might eventually befall a nature like that, dropped into a world not without some man-traps and against whose subtleties simple courage lacking experience and address and without any touch of defensive ugliness is of little avail; and where such innocence as man is capable of does yet in a moral emergency not always sharpen the faculties or enlighten the will.

However it was, the Dansker in his ascetic way rather took to Billy. Nor was this only because of a certain philosophic interest in such a character. There was another cause. While the old man's eccentricities, sometimes bordering on the ursine, repelled the juniors, Billy, undeterred thereby, revering him as a salt hero, would make advances, never passing the old *Agamemnon* man without a salutation marked by that respect which is seldom lost on the aged however crabbed at times or whatever their station in life. There was a vein of dry humor, or what not, in the mast-man; and, whether in freak of patriarchal irony touching Billy's youth and athletic frame, or for some other and more recondite reason, from the first in addressing him he always substituted Baby for Billy, the Dansker in fact being the originator of the name by which the Foretopman eventually became known aboard ship.

Well then, in his mysterious little difficulty going in quest of the wrinkled one, Billy found him off duty in a dog-watch ruminating by himself seated on a shot-box of the upper gun-deck, now and then surveying with a somewhat cynical regard certain of the more swaggering promenaders there. Billy recounted his trouble, again wondering how it all happened. The salt seer attentively listened, accompanying the Foretopman's recital with queer twitchings of his wrinkles and problematical little sparkles of his small ferret eyes. Making an end of his story, the Foretopman asked, "And now, Dansker, do tell me what you think of it."

The old man, shoving up the front of his tarpaulin and deliberately rubbing the long slant scar at the point where it entered the thin hair, laconically said, "Baby Budd, *Jemmy Legs*" (meaning the Master-at-Arms) "is down on you."

"*Jemmy Legs!*" ejaculated Billy, his welkin eyes expanding; "what for? Why he calls me 'the sweet and pleasant young fellow,' they tell me."

"Does he so?" grinned the grizzled one; then said, "Ay, Baby lad, a sweet voice has Jemmy Legs."

"No, not always. But to me he has. I seldom pass him but there comes a pleasant word."

"And that's because he's down upon you, Baby Budd."

Such reiteration, along with the manner of it, incomprehensible to a novice, disturbed Billy almost as much as the mystery for which he had sought explanation. Something less unpleasingly oracular he tried to extract; but the old sea-Chiron, thinking perhaps that for the nonce he had sufficiently instructed his young Achilles, pursed his lips, gathered his wrinkles together and would commit himself to nothing further.

Years, and those experiences which befall certain shrewder men subordinated life-long to the will of superiors, all this had developed in the Dansker the pithy guarded cynicism that was his leading characteristic.

•

The next day an incident served to confirm Billy Budd in his incredulity as to the Dansker's strange summing up of the case submitted.

The ship at noon going large before the wind was rolling on her course, and he, below at dinner and engaged in some sportful talk with the members of his mess, chanced in a sudden lurch to spill the entire contents of his soup-pan upon the new-scrubbed deck. Claggart, the Master-at-Arms, official rattan in hand, happened to be passing along the battery in a bay of which the mess was lodged, and the greasy liquid streamed just across his path. Stepping over it, he was proceeding on his way without comment, since the matter was nothing to take notice of under the circumstances, when he happened to observe who it was that had done the spilling. His countenance changed. Pausing, he was about to ejaculate something hasty at the sailor, but checked himself, and pointing down to the streaming soup, playfully tapped him from behind with his rattan, saying in a low musical voice peculiar to him at times, "Handsomely done, my lad! And handsome is as handsome did it too!" and with that passed on. Not noted by Billy as not coming within his view was the involuntary smile, or rather grimace, that accompanied Claggart's equivocal words. Aridly it drew down the thin corners of his shapely mouth. But everybody taking his remark as meant for humorous, and at which therefore as coming from a superior they were bound to laugh "with counterfeited glee," acted accordingly; and Billy, tickled, it may be, by the allusion to his being the handsome sailor, merrily joined in; then addressing his messmates exclaimed, "There now, who says that Jemmy Legs is down on me!"

"And who said he was, Beauty?" demanded one Donald with some surprise. Whereat the Foretopman looked a little foolish, recalling that it was only one person, Board-her-in-the-smoke, who had suggested what to him was the smoky idea that this Master-at-Arms was in any peculiar way hostile to him. Meantime that functionary resuming his path must have momentarily worn some expression less guarded than that of the bitter smile and, usurping the face from the heart, some distorting expression perhaps, for a drummer-boy, heedlessly frolicking along from the opposite direction, and chancing to come into light collision with his person was strangely disconcerted by his aspect. Nor was the impression lessened when the official, impulsively giving him a sharp cut with the rattan, vehemently exclaimed, "Look where you go!"

•

What was the matter with the Master-at-Arms? And, be the matter what it might, how could it have direct relation to Billy Budd with whom prior to the affair of the spilled soup he had never come into any special contact official or otherwise? What indeed could the trouble have to do with one so little inclined to give offense as the merchant-ship's *peacemaker,* even him who in Claggart's own phrase was "the sweet and pleasant young fellow"? Yes, why should "Jemmy Legs," to borrow the Dansker's expression, be *down* on the Handsome Sailor? But at heart and not for nothing, as the late chance encounter may indicate to the discerning, down on him, secretly down on him, he assuredly was.

Now to invent something touching the more private career of Claggart, something involving Billy Budd, of which something the latter should be wholly ignorant, some romantic incident implying that Claggart's knowledge of the young blue-jacket began at some period anterior to catching sight of him on board the seventy-four—all this, not so difficult to do, might avail in a way more or less interesting to account for whatever enigma may appear to lurk in the case. But in fact there was nothing of the sort. And yet the cause, necessarily to be assumed as the sole one assignable, is in its very realism as much charged with that prime element of Radcliffian romance, *the mysterious,* as any that the ingenuity of the author of *The Mysteries of Udolpho* could devise. For what can more partake of the mysterious than an antipathy spontaneous and profound such as is evoked in certain exceptional mortals by the mere aspect of some other mortal, however harmless he may be? if not called forth by this very harmlessness itself.

Now there can exist no irritating juxtaposition of dissimilar personalities comparable to that which is possible aboard a great warship fully manned and at sea. There, every day among all ranks almost every man comes into more or less of contact with almost every other man. Wholly there to avoid even the sight of an aggravating object one must needs give it Jonah's toss or jump overboard himself. Imagine how all this might eventually operate on some peculiar human creature the direct reverse of a saint?

But for the adequate comprehending of Claggart by a normal nature these hints are insufficient. To pass from a normal nature to him one must cross "the deadly space between." And this is best done by indirection.

Long ago an honest scholar, my senior, said to me in reference to one who like himself is now no more, a man so unimpeachably respectable that against him nothing was ever openly said though among the few something was whispered, "Yes, X—— is a nut not to be cracked by the tap of a lady's fan. You are aware that I am the adherent of no organized religion, much less of any philosophy built into a system. Well, for all that, I think that to try and get into X——, enter his labyrinth and get out again, without a clue derived from some source other than what is known as *knowledge of the world*—that were hardly possible, at least for me."

"Why," said I, "X——, however singular a study to some, is yet human, and knowledge of the world assuredly implies the knowledge of human nature, and in most of its varieties."

"Yes, but a superficial knowledge of it, serving ordinary purposes. But for anything deeper, I am not certain whether to know the world and to know human nature be not two distinct branches of knowledge, which while they may coexist in the same heart, yet either may exist with little or nothing of the other. Nay, in an average man of the world, his constant rubbing with it blunts that fine spiritual insight indispensable to the understanding of the essential in certain exceptional characters, whether evil ones or good. In a matter of some importance I have seen a girl wind an old lawyer about her little finger. Nor was it the dotage of senile love. Nothing of the sort. But he knew law better than he knew the girl's heart. Coke and Blackstone hardly shed so much light into obscure spiritual places as the Hebrew prophets. And who were they? Mostly recluses."

At the time my inexperience was such that I did not quite see the drift of all this. It may be that I see it now. And, indeed, if that lexicon which is based on Holy Writ were any longer popular, one might with less difficulty define and denominate certain phenomenal men. As it is, one must turn to some authority not liable to the charge of being tinctured with the Biblical element.

In a list of definitions included in the authentic translation of Plato, a list attributed to him, occurs this: "Natural Depravity: a depravity according to nature." A definition which though savoring of Calvinism, by no means involves Calvin's dogma as to total mankind. Evidently its intent makes it applicable but to individuals. Not many are the examples of this depravity which the gallows and jail supply. At any rate for notable instances, since these have no vulgar alloy of the brute in them, but invariably are dominated by intellectuality, one must go elsewhere. Civilization, especially if of the austerer sort, is auspicious to it. It folds itself in the mantle of respectability. It has its certain negative virtues serving as silent auxiliaries. It never allows wine to get within its guard. It is not going too far to say that it is without vices or small sins. There is a phenomenal pride in it that excludes them from anything mercenary or avaricious. In short the depravity here meant partakes nothing of the sordid or sensual. It is serious, but free from acerbity. Though no flatterer of mankind it never speaks ill of it.

But the thing which in eminent instances signalizes so exceptional a nature is this: though the man's even temper and discreet bearing would seem to intimate a mind peculiarly subject to the law of reason, not the less in his heart he would seem to riot in complete exemption from that law, having apparently little to do with reason further than to employ it as an ambidexter implement for effecting the irrational. That is to say: toward the accomplishment of an aim which in wantonness of malignity would seem to partake of the insane, he will direct a cool judgment sagacious and sound.

These men are true madmen, and of the most dangerous sort, for their lunacy is not continuous but occasional, evoked by some special object; it is probably secretive, which is as much as to say it is self-contained, so that when, moreover, most active, it is to the average mind not distinguishable from sanity, and for the reason above suggested: that whatever its aims may be, and the aim is never declared, the method and the outward proceeding is always perfectly rational.

Now something such an one was Claggart, in whom was the mania of an evil nature, not engendered by vicious training or corrupting books or licentious living, but born with him and innate; in short "a depravity according to nature."

Lawyers, Experts, Clergy: An Episode

By the way, can it be the phenomenon, disowned or at least concealed, that in some criminal cases puzzles the courts? For this cause have our juries at times not only to endure the prolonged contentions of lawyers with their fees, but also the yet more perplexing strife of the medical experts with theirs? But why leave it to them? Why not subpoena as well the clerical proficients? Their vocation bringing them into peculiar contact with so many human beings, and sometimes in their least guarded hour, in interviews very much more confidential than those of physician and patient—this would seem to qualify them to know something about those intricacies involved in the question of moral responsibility; whether in a given case, say, the crime proceeded from mania in the brain or rabies of the heart. As to any differences among themselves these clerical proficients might develop on the stand, these could hardly be greater than the direct contradictions exchanged between the remunerated medical experts.

Dark sayings are these, some will say. But why? Is it because they somewhat savor of Holy Writ in its phrase "mysteries of iniquity"? If they do, such savor was far enough from being intended, for little will it commend these pages to many a reader of today.

The point of the present story turning on the hidden nature of the master-at-arms has necessitated this chapter. With an added hint or two in connection with the incident at the mess, the resumed narrative must be left to vindicate as it may, its own credibility.

"Pale ire, envy, and despair"

That Claggart's figure was not amiss, and his face, save the chin, well moulded, has already been said. Of these favorable points he seemed not insensible, for he was not only neat but careful in his dress. But the form of Billy Budd was heroic; and if his face was without the intellectual look of the pallid Claggart's, not the less was it lit, like his, from within, though from a different source. The bonfire in his heart made luminous the rose-tan in his cheek.

In view of the marked contrast between the persons of the twain, it is more than probable that when the Master-at-Arms in the scene last given applied to the sailor the proverb "Handsome is as handsome does," he there let escape an ironic inkling, not caught by the young sailors who heard it, as to what it was that had first moved him against Billy, namely, his significant personal beauty.

Now envy and antipathy, passions irreconcilable in reason, nevertheless in fact may spring conjoined like Chang and Eng in one birth. Is envy then such a monster? Well, though many an arraigned mortal has in hopes of mitigated penalty pleaded guilty to horrible actions, did ever anybody seriously confess to envy? Something there is in it universally felt to be more shameful than even felonious crime. And not only does everybody disown it but the better sort are inclined to incredulity when it is in earnest imputed to an intelligent man. But since its lodgment is in the heart not the brain, no degree of intellect supplies a guarantee against it. But Claggart's was no vulgar form of the passion. Nor, as directed toward Billy Budd, did it partake of that streak of apprehensive jealousy that marred Saul's visage perturbedly brooding on the comely young David. Claggart's envy struck deeper. If askance he eyed the good looks, cheery health and frank enjoyment of young life in Billy Budd, it was because these went along with a nature that, as Claggart magnetically felt, had in its simplicity never willed malice or experienced the reactionary bite of that serpent. To him, the spirit lodged within Billy, and looking out from his welkin eyes as from windows, that ineffability it was which made the dimple in his dyed cheek, suppled his joints, and dancing in his yellow curls made him pre-eminently the Handsome Sailor. One person excepted, the Master-at-Arms was perhaps the only man in the ship intellectually capable of adequately appreciating the moral phenomenon presented in Billy Budd. And the insight but intensified his passion, which, assuming various secret forms within him, at times assumed that of cynic disdain—disdain of innocence. To be nothing more than innocent! Yet in an aesthetic way he saw the charm of it, the courageous free-and-easy temper of it, and fain would have shared it, but he despaired of it.

With no power to annul the elemental evil in him, though readily enough he could hide it; apprehending the good, but powerless to be it; a nature like Claggart's, surcharged with energy as such natures almost invariably are, what recourse is left to it but to recoil upon itself and like the scorpion for which the Creator alone is responsible, act out to the end the part allotted it?

•

Passion, and passion in its profoundest, is not a thing demanding a palatial stage whereon to play its part. Down among the groundlings, among the beggars and rakers of the garbage, profound passion is enacted. And the circumstances that provoke it, however trivial or mean, are no measure of its power. In the present instance the stage is a scrubbed gun-deck, and one of the external provocations a man-of-war's man's spilled soup.

Now when the Master-at-Arms noticed whence came that greasy fluid streaming before his feet, he must have taken it—to some extent willfully perhaps—not for the mere accident it assuredly was, but for the sly escape of a spontaneous feeling on Billy's part more or less answering to the antipathy on his own. In effect a foolish demonstration, he must have thought, and very harmless, like the futile kick of a heifer, which yet were the heifer a shod stallion would not be so harmless. Even so was it that into the gall of Claggart's envy he infused the vitriol of his contempt. But the incident confirmed to him certain tell-tale reports purveyed to his ear by Squeak, one of his more cunning corporals, a grizzled little man, so nicknamed by the sailors on account of his squeaky voice, and sharp visage ferreting about the dark corners of the lower decks after interlopers, satirically suggesting to them the idea of a rat in a cellar.

From his Chief's employing him as an implicit tool in laying little traps for the worriment of the Foretopman—for it was from the Master-at-Arms that the petty persecutions heretofore adverted to had proceeded—the corporal, having naturally enough concluded that his master could have no love for the sailor, made it his business, faithful understrapper that he was, to foment the ill blood by perverting to his Chief certain innocent frolics of the good-natured Foretopman, besides inventing for his mouth sundry contumelious epithets he claimed to have overheard him let fall. The Master-at-Arms never suspected the veracity of these reports, more especially as to the epithets, for he well knew how secretly unpopular may become a master-at-arms, at least a master-at-arms of those days, zealous in his function, and how the blue-jackets shoot at him in private their raillery and wit; the nickname by which he goes among them (Jemmy Legs) implying under the form of merriment their cherished disrespect and dislike. But in view of the greediness of hate for patrolmen it hardly needed a purveyor to feed Claggart's passion. An uncommon prudence is habitual with the subtler depravity, for it has everything to hide. And in case of an injury but suspected, its secretiveness voluntarily cuts it off from enlightenment or disillusion; and, not unreluctantly, action is taken upon surmise as upon certainty. And the retaliation is apt to be in monstrous disproportion to the supposed offense; for when in anybody was revenge in its exactions aught else but an inordinate usurer?

But how with Claggart's conscience? For though consciences are unlike as foreheads, every intelligence, not excluding the Scriptural devils who "believe and tremble," has one. But Claggart's conscience being but the lawyer to his will, made ogres of trifles, probably arguing that the motive imputed to Billy in spilling the soup just when he did, together with the epithets alleged— these, if nothing more, made a strong case against him, nay, justified animosity into a sort of retributive righteousness. The Pharisee is the Guy Fawkes prowling in the hid chambers underlying the Claggarts. And they can really form no conception of an unreciprocated malice. Probably, the Master-at-Arms' clandestine persecutions of Billy were started to try the temper of the man; but they had not developed any quality in him that enmity could make official use of or even pervert into plausible self-justification; so that the occurrence at the

mess, petty if it were, was a welcome one to that peculiar conscience assigned to be the private mentor of
Claggart; and for the rest, not improbably it put him
upon new experiments.

•

Not many days after the last incident narrated something befell Billy Budd that more graveled him than
aught that had previously occurred.

It was a warm night for the latitude; and the Foretopman, whose watch at the time was properly below,
was dozing on the uppermost deck whither he had ascended from his hot hammock, one of hundreds suspended so closely wedged together over a lower gun-
deck that there was little or no swing to them. He lay
as in the shadow of a hillside stretched under the lee
of the *booms,* a piled ridge of spare spars amidships
between foremast and mainmast and among which the
ship's largest boat, the launch, was stowed. Alongside
of three other slumberers from below, he lay near that
end of the booms which approaches from the foremast;
his station aloft on duty as a foretopman being just over
the deck-station of the forecastlemen, entitling him according to usage to make himself more or less at home
in that neighborhood.

Presently he was stirred into semi-consciousness by
somebody, who must have previously sounded the sleep
of the others, touching his shoulder, and then as the
Foretopman raised his head, breathing into his ear in
a quick whisper, "Slip into the lee fore-chains, Billy;
there is something in the wind. Don't speak. Quick, I
will meet you there"; and disappeared.

Now Billy, like sundry other essentially good-natured
ones, had some of the weaknesses inseparable from essential good-nature, and among these was a reluctance,

almost an incapacity, of plumply saying "no" to an abrupt proposition not obviously absurd on the face of it, or obviously unfriendly, nor iniquitous. And being of warm blood he had not the phlegm tacitly to negative any proposition by an unresponsive inaction. Like his sense of fear, his apprehension as to aught outside of the honest and natural was seldom very quick. Besides, upon the present occasion, the drowse from his sleep still hung upon him.

However it was, he mechanically rose, and, sleepily wondering what could be in the wind, betook himself to the designated place, a narrow platform, one of six, outside of the high bulwarks and screened by the great dead-eyes and multiple columned lanyards of the shrouds and back-stays, and, in a great warship of that time, of dimensions commensurate to the hull's magnitude; a tarry balcony, in short, overhanging the sea, and so secluded that one mariner of the *Indomitable*, a nonconformist old tar of a serious turn, made it even in daytime his private oratory.

In this retired nook the stranger soon joined Billy Budd. There was no moon as yet; a haze obscured the starlight. He could not distinctly see the stranger's face. Yet from something in the outline and carriage, Billy took him to be, and correctly, one of the afterguard.

"Hist! Billy," said the man in the same quick cautionary whisper as before, "You were impressed, weren't you? Well, so was I"; and he paused, as to mark the effect. But Billy not knowing exactly what to make of this said nothing. Then the other: "We are not the only impressed ones, Billy. There's a gang of us. Couldn't you—help—at a pinch?"

"What do you mean?" demanded Billy here thoroughly shaking off his drowse.

"Hist, hist!" the hurried whisper now growing husky,

"see here"; and the man held up two small objects faintly twinkling in the night light; "see, they are yours, Billy, if you'll only—"

But Billy broke in, and in his resentful eagerness to deliver himself his vocal infirmity somewhat intruded, "D-D-Damme, I don't know what you are d-d-driving at, or what you mean, but you had better g-g-go where you belong!" For the moment the fellow, as confounded, did not stir; and Billy, springing to his feet, said, "If you d-don't start I'll t-t-toss you back over the r-rail!" There was no mistaking this and the mysterious emissary decamped, disappearing in the direction of the mainmast in the shadow of the booms.

"Hallo, what's the matter?" here came growling from a forecastleman awakened from his deck-doze by Billy's raised voice. And as the Foretopman reappeared and was recognized by him; "Ah, Beauty, is it you? Well, something must have been the matter for you st-st-stuttered."

"Oh," rejoined Billy, now mastering the impediment, "I found an afterguardsman in our part of the ship here and I bid him be off where he belongs."

"And is that all you did about it, Foretopman?" gruffly demanded another, an irascible old fellow of brick-colored visage and hair, and who was known to his associate forecastlemen as Red Pepper; "Such sneaks I should like to marry to the gunner's daughter!" by that expression meaning that he would like to subject them to disciplinary castigation over a gun.

However, Billy's rendering of the matter satisfactorily accounted to these inquirers for the brief commotion, since of all the sections of a ship's company the forecastlemen, veterans for the most part and bigoted in their sea-prejudices, are the most jealous in resenting territorial encroachments, especially on the part of any of the afterguard, of whom they have but a sorry opinion, chiefly landsmen, never going aloft except to reef or furl the mainsail, and in no wise competent to handle a marlin-spike or turn in a dead-eye, say.

•

This incident sorely puzzled Billy Budd. It was an entirely new experience, the first time in his life that he had ever been personally approached in underhand intriguing fashion. Prior to this encounter he had known nothing of the afterguardsman, the two men being stationed wide apart, one forward and aloft during his watch, the other on deck and aft.

What could it mean? And could they really be guineas, those two glittering objects the interloper had held up to his (Billy's) eyes? Where could the fellow get guineas? Why even spare buttons are not so plentiful at sea. The more he turned the matter over, the more he was nonplused, and made uneasy and discomforted. In his disgustful recoil from an overture which though he but ill comprehended he instinctively knew must involve evil of some sort, Billy Budd was like a young horse fresh from the pasture suddenly inhaling a vile whiff from some chemical factory and by repeated snortings trying to get it out of his nostrils and lungs. This frame of mind barred all desire of holding further parley with the fellow, even were it but for the purpose of gaining some enlightenment as to his design in approaching him. And yet he was not without natural curiosity to see how such a visitor in the dark would look in broad day.

He espied him the following afternoon in his first dog-watch below, one of the smokers on that forward part of the upper gun-deck allotted to the pipe. He recognized him by his general cut and build, more than by his round freckled face and glassy eyes of pale blue, veiled with lashes all but white.

And yet Billy was a bit uncertain whether indeed it were he—yonder chap about his own age, chatting and laughing in free-hearted way, leaning against a gun; a genial young fellow enough to look at, and something of a rattle-brain, to all appearance. Rather chubby too for a sailor, even an afterguardsman. In short, the last man in the world, one would think, to be overburdened with thoughts, especially those perilous thoughts that must needs belong to a conspirator in any serious project, or even to the underling of such a conspirator.

Although Billy was not aware of it, the fellow, with a sidelong watchful glance had perceived Billy first, and then noting that Billy was looking at him, thereupon nodded a familiar sort of friendly recognition as to an old acquaintance, without interrupting the talk he was engaged in with the group of smokers. A day or two afterward, chancing in the evening promenade on a gun-deck to pass Billy, he offered a flying word of good-fellowship as it were, which by its unexpectedness and equivocalness under the circumstances so embarrassed Billy that he knew not how to respond to it, and let it go unnoticed.

Billy was now left more at a loss than before. The ineffectual speculations into which he was led were so disturbingly alien to him that he did his best to smother them. It never entered his mind that here was a matter which, from its extreme questionableness, it was his duty as a loyal blue-jacket to report in the proper quarter. And, probably, had such a step been suggested to him, he would have been deterred from taking it by the thought, one of novice-magnanimity, that it would savor overmuch of the dirty work of a tell-tale. He kept the thing to himself. Yet upon one occasion, he could not forbear a little disburdening himself to the old Dansker, tempted thereto perhaps by the influence of a balmy night when the ship lay becalmed; the twain, silent for the most part, sitting together on deck, their heads propped against the bulwarks. But it was only a partial and anonymous account that Billy gave, the unfounded scruples above referred to preventing full disclosure to anybody. Upon hearing Billy's version, the sage Dansker seemed to divine more than he was told; and after a little meditation during which his wrinkles were pursed as into a point, quite effacing for the time that quizzing expression his face sometimes wore, "Didn't I say so, Baby Budd?"

"Say what?" demanded Billy.

"Why, Jemmy Legs is *down* on you."

"And what," rejoined Billy in amazement, "has Jemmy Legs to do with that cracked afterguardsman?"

"Ho, it was an afterguardsman, then. A cat's-paw, a cat's-paw!" And with that exclamation, which, whether it had reference to a light puff of air just then coming over the calm sea, or subtler relation to the afterguardsman, there is no telling, the old Merlin gave a twisting wrench with his black teeth at his plug of tobacco, vouchsafing no reply to Billy's impetuous question, though now repeated, for it was his wont to relapse into grim silence when interrogated in skeptical sort as to any of his sententious oracles, not always very clear ones, rather partaking of that obscurity which invests most Delphic deliverances from any quarter.

Long experience had very likely brought this old man to that bitter prudence which never interferes in aught and never gives advice.

•

Yes, despite the Dansker's pithy insistence as to the Master-at-Arms being at the bottom of these strange experiences of Billy on board the *Indomitable,* the young sailor was ready to ascribe them to almost anybody but the man who, to use Billy's own expression, "always had a pleasant word for him." This is to be wondered at. Yet not so much to be wondered at. In certain matters, some sailors even in mature life remain unsophisticated enough. But a young seafarer of the disposition of our athletic Foretopman is much of a child-man. And yet a child's utter innocence is but its blank ignorance, and the innocence more or less wanes as intelligence waxes. But in Billy Budd intelligence, such as it was, had advanced, while yet his simple-mindedness remained for the most part unaffected. Experience is a teacher indeed; yet did Billy's years make his experience small. Besides, he had none of that intuitive knowledge of the bad which in natures not good or incompletely so foreruns experience, and therefore may pertain, as in some instances it too clearly does pertain, even to youth.

And what could Billy know of man except of man as a mere sailor? And the old-fashioned sailor, the veritable man-before-the-mast, the sailor from boyhood up, he, though indeed of the same species as a landsman, is in some respects singularly distinct from him. The sailor is frankness, the landsman is finesse. Life is not a game with the sailor, demanding the long head; no intricate game of chess where few moves are made in straightforwardness, and ends are attained by indirection; an oblique, tedious, barren game hardly worth that poor candle burnt out in playing it.

Yes, as a class, sailors are in character a juvenile

race. Even their deviations are marked by juvenility. And this more especially holding true with the sailors of Billy's time. Then, too, certain things which apply to all sailors do more pointedly operate here and there upon the junior one. Every sailor, too, is accustomed to obey orders without debating them; his life afloat is externally ruled for him; he is not brought into that promiscuous commerce with mankind where unobstructed free agency on equal terms—equal superficially, at least—soon teaches one that unless upon occasion he exercises a distrust keen in proportion to the fairness of the appearance, some foul turn may be served him. A ruled undemonstrative distrustfulness is so habitual, not with businessmen so much as with men who know their kind in less shallow relations than business, namely, certain men-of-the-world, that they come at last to employ it all but unconsciously; and some of them would very likely feel real surprise at being charged with it as one of their general characteristics.

•

But after the little matter at the mess Billy Budd no more found himself in strange trouble at times about his hammock or his clothes-bag or what not. While, as to that smile that occasionally sunned him, and the pleasant passing word, these were, if not more frequent, yet if anything more pronounced than before.

But for all that, there were certain other demonstrations now. When Claggart's unobserved glance happened to light on belted Billy rolling along the upper gun-deck in the leisure of the second dog-watch, exchanging passing broadsides of fun with other young promenaders in the crowd, that glance would follow the cheerful sea-Hyperion with a settled meditative and melancholy expression, his eyes strangely suffused with

incipient feverish tears. Then would Claggart look like
the man of sorrows. Yes, and sometimes the melancholy
expression would have in it a touch of soft yearning,
as if Claggart could even have loved Billy but for fate
and ban. But this was an evanescence, and quickly
repented of, as it were, by an immitigable look, pinching and shriveling the visage into the momentary semblance of a wrinkled walnut. But sometimes catching
sight in advance of the Foretopman coming in his direction, he would, upon their nearing, step aside a little
to let him pass, dwelling upon Billy for the moment
with the glittering dental satire of a Guise. But upon
any abrupt unforeseen encounter a red light would
flash forth from his eye like a spark from an anvil in a
dusk smithy. That quick fierce light was a strange one,
darted from orbs which in repose were of a color
nearest approaching a deeper violet, the softest of
shades.

Though some of these caprices of the pit could not
but be observed by their object, yet were they beyond
the construing of such a nature. And the thews of Billy
were hardly compatible with that sort of sensitive spiritual organization which in some cases instinctively
conveys to ignorant innocence an admonition of the
proximity of the malign. He thought the Master-at-Arms
acted in a manner rather queer at times. That was all.
But the occasional frank air and pleasant word went
for what they purported to be, the young sailor never
having heard as yet of the "too fair-spoken man."

Had the Foretopman been conscious of having done
or said anything to provoke the ill will of the official,
it would have been different with him, and his sight
might have been purged if not sharpened. As it was,
innocence was his blinder.

So was it with him in yet another matter. Two minor

officers—the Armorer, and Captain of the Hold, with whom he had never exchanged a word, his position on the ship not bringing him into contact with them— these men now for the first began to cast upon Billy when they chanced to encounter him that peculiar glance which evidences that the man from whom it comes has been some way tampered with and to the prejudice of him upon whom the glance lights. Never did it occur to Billy as a thing to be noted or a thing suspicious, though he well knew the fact, that the Armorer and Captain of the Hold, with the ship's yeo-man, apothecary, and others of that grade, were by naval usage messmates of the Master-at-Arms, men with ears convenient to his confidential tongue.[1]

But the general popularity that our Handsome Sail-or's manly forwardness upon occasion and irresistible good nature indicating no mental superiority tending to excite an invidious feeling—this good will on the part of most of his shipmates made him the less to concern himself about such mute aspects toward him as those whereto allusion has just been made as far as he could not so fathom as to infer their whole import.

As to the afterguardsman, though Billy for reasons already given necessarily saw little of him, yet when the two did happen to meet, invariably came the fellow's offhand cheerful recognition, sometimes accompanied by a passing pleasant word or two. Whatever that equivocal young person's original design may really have been, or the design of which he might have been the deputy, certain it was from his manner upon these occasions that he had wholly dropped it.

It was as if his precocity of crookedness (and every

[1] A conclusion to this paragraph has been canceled: "and, moreover—which he did not know—that in this exclusive mess the Master-at-Arms was the ascendant man."—*J.L.*

vulgar villain is precocious) had for once deceived
him, and the man he had sought to entrap as a simpleton had, through his very simplicity, ignorantly
baffled him.

But shrewd ones may opine that it was hardly possible for Billy to refrain from going up to the afterguardsman and bluntly demanding to know his purpose
in the initial interview, so abruptly closed in the fore-
chains. Shrewd ones may also think it but natural in
Billy to set about sounding some of the other impressed
men of the ship in order to discover what basis, if
any, there was for the emissary's obscure suggestions
as to plotting disaffection aboard. Yes, shrewd ones may
so think. But something more, or rather something else,
than mere shrewdness is perhaps needful for the due
understanding of such a character as Billy Budd's.

As to Claggart, the monomania in the man—if that
indeed it were—as involuntarily disclosed by starts in
the manifestations detailed, yet in general covered over
by his self-contained and rational demeanor; this like
a subterranean fire was eating its way deeper and
deeper in him. Something decisive must come of it.

•

After the mysterious interview in the fore-chains, the
one so abruptly ended there by Billy, nothing especially
germane to the story occurred until the events now
about to be narrated.

Elsewhere it has been said that in the lack of frigates (of course better sailers than line-of-battle ships)
in the English squadron up the Straits at that period,
the *Indomitable* was occasionally employed not only as
an available substitute for a scout but at times on detached service of more important kind. This was not
alone because of her sailing qualities, not common in

a ship of her rate, but quite as much, probably, that the character of her commander, it was thought, specially adapted him for any duty where under unforeseen difficulties a prompt initiative might have to be taken in some matter demanding knowledge and ability in addition to those qualities implied in good seamanship. It was on an expedition of the latter sort, a somewhat distant one, and when the *Indomitable* was almost at her furthest remove from the fleet that in the latter part of an afternoon-watch she unexpectedly came in sight of a ship of the enemy. It proved to be frigate. The latter, perceiving through the glass that the weight of men and metal would be heavily against her, invoking her light heels crowded sail to get away. After a chase urged almost against hope and lasting until about the middle of the first dog-watch, she signally succeeded in effecting her escape.

Not long after the pursuit had been given up, and ere the excitement incident thereto had altogether waned away, the Master-at-Arms ascending from his cavernous sphere made his appearance cap in hand by the mainmast, respectfully awaiting the notice of Captain Vere then solitary walking the weather-side of the quarter-deck, doubtless somewhat chafed at the failure of the pursuit. The spot where Claggart stood was the place allotted to men of lesser grades seeking some more particular interview either with the officer-of-the-deck or the Captain himself. But from the latter it was not often that a sailor or petty-officer of those days would seek a hearing; only some exceptional cause, would, according to established custom, have warranted that.

Presently, just as the commander absorbed in his reflections was on the point of turning aft in his promenade, he became sensible of Claggart's presence, and saw the doffed cap held in deferential expectancy. Here be it said that Captain Vere's personal knowledge of this petty-officer had only begun at the time of the ship's last sailing from home, Claggart then for the first, in transfer from a ship detained for repairs, supplying on board the *Indomitable* the place of a previous master-at-arms disabled and ashore.

No sooner did the commander observe who it was that now deferentially stood awaiting his notice than a peculiar expression came over him. It was not unlike that which uncontrollably will flit across the countenance of one at unawares encountering a person who though known to him indeed has hardly been long enough known for thorough knowledge, but something in whose aspect nevertheless now for the first provokes a vaguely repellent distaste. But coming to a stand and resuming much of his wonted official manner, save that a sort of impatience lurked in the intonation of the opening word, he said, "Well? what is it, Master-at-Arms?"

With the air of a subordinate grieved at the necessity of being a messenger of ill tidings, and while conscientiously determined to be frank, yet equally resolved upon shunning overstatement, Claggart at this invitation or rather summons to disburden spoke up. What he said, conveyed in the language of no uneducated man, was to the effect following if not altogether in these words, namely, that during the chase and preparations for the possible encounter he had seen enough to convince him that at least one sailor aboard was a dangerous character in a ship mustering some who not only had taken a guilty part in the late serious troubles, but others also who, like the man in question, had entered His Majesty's service under another form than enlistment.

At this point Captain Vere with some impatience, interrupted him: "Be direct, man; say impressed men."

Claggart made a gesture of subservience and proceeded.

Quite lately he (Claggart) had begun to suspect that on the gun-decks some sort of movement prompted by the sailor in question was covertly going on, but he had not thought himself warranted in reporting the suspicion so long as it remained indistinct. But from what he had that afternoon observed in the man referred to, the suspicion of something clandestine going on had advanced to a point less removed from certainty. He deeply felt, he added, the serious responsibility assumed in making a report involving such possible consequences to the individual mainly concerned, besides tending to augment those natural anxieties which every naval commander must feel in view of extraordinary outbreaks so recent as those which, he sorrowfully said it, it needed not to name.

Now at the first broaching of the matter Captain Vere, taken by surprise, could not wholly dissemble his disquietude. But as Claggart went on, the former's aspect changed into restiveness under something in the witness's manner in giving his testimony. However, he refrained from interrupting him. And Claggart, continuing, concluded with this:

"God forbid, your honor, that the *Indomitable*'s should be the experience of the—"

"Never mind that!" here peremptorily broke in the superior, his face altering with anger, instinctively divining the ship that the other was about to name, one in which the Nore Mutiny had assumed a singularly tragical character that for a time jeopardized the life of its commander. Under the circumstances he was indignant at the purposed allusion. When the commissioned officers themselves were on all occasions very heedful how they referred to the recent events, for a petty-officer unnecessarily to allude to them in the presence of his Captain, this struck him as a most immodest presumption. Besides, to his quick sense of self-respect, it even looked under the circumstances something like an attempt to alarm him. Nor at first was he without some surprise that one who so far as he had hitherto come under his notice had shown considerable tact in his function should in this particular evince such lack of it.

But these thoughts and kindred dubious ones flitting across his mind were suddenly replaced by an intuitional surmise which though as yet obscure in form served practically to affect his reception of the ill tidings. Certain it is, that long versed in everything pertaining to the complicated gun-deck life, which like every other form of life has its secret mines and dubious side, the side popularly disclaimed, Captain Vere did not permit himself to be unduly disturbed by the general tenor of his subordinate's report.

Furthermore, if in view of recent events prompt action should be taken at the first palpable sign of recurring insubordination, for all that, not judicious would it be, he thought, to keep the idea of lingering disaffection alive by undue forwardness in crediting an informer, even if his own subordinate and charged among other things with police surveillance of the crew. This feeling would not perhaps have so prevailed with him were it not that upon a prior occasion the patriotic zeal officially evinced by Claggart had somewhat irritated him as appearing rather superserviceable and strained. Furthermore, something even in the official's self-possessed and somewhat ostentatious manner in making his specifications strangely reminded him of a bandsman, a perjured witness in a capital case before a court-martial ashore of which when a lieutenant he (Captain Vere) had been a member.

Now the peremptory check given to Claggart in the matter of the arrested allusion was quickly followed up by this: "You say that there is at least one dangerous man aboard. Name him."

"William Budd. A foretopman, your honor—"

"William Budd," repeated Captain Vere with unfeigned astonishment, "and mean you the man that Lieutenant Ratcliffe took from the merchantman not very long ago—the young fellow who seems to be so popular with the men—Billy, the Handsome Sailor, as they call him?"

"The same, your honor; but for all his youth and good looks, a deep one. Not for nothing does he insinuate himself into the good will of his shipmates, since at the least all hands will at a pinch say a good word for him at all hazards. Did Lieutenant Ratcliffe happen to tell your honor of that adroit fling of Budd's jumping up in the cutter's bow under the merchantman's stern when he was being taken off? It is even masked by that sort of good-humored air that at heart he resents his impressment. You have but noted his fair cheek. A mantrap may be under the ruddy-tipped clover."

Now the Handsome Sailor as a signal figure among the crew had naturally enough attracted the Captain's attention from the first. Though in general not very demonstrative to his officers, he had congratulated Lieutenant Ratcliffe upon his good fortune in lighting on such a fine specimen of the genus Homo who in the nude might have posed for a statue of young Adam before the Fall.

As to Billy's adieu to the ship *Rights-of-Man,* which the boarding lieutenant had indeed reported to him, but in a deferential way, more as a good story than

aught else, Captain Vere, though mistakenly understanding it as a satiric sally, had but thought so much
the better of the impressed man for it, as a military
sailor admiring the spirit that could take an arbitrary
enlistment so merrily and sensibly. The Foretopman's
conduct, too, so far as it had fallen under the Captain's
notice, had confirmed the first happy augury, while the
new recruit's qualities as a *sailor-man* seemed to be such
that he had thought of recommending him to the ex-
ecutive officer for promotion to a place that would
more frequently bring him under his own observation,
namely, the captaincy of the mizzen-top, replacing there
in the starboard watch a man not so young whom partly
for that reason he deemed less fitted for the post. Be it
parenthesized here that since the mizzen-top-men having not to handle such breadths of heavy canvas as the
lower sails on the main-mast and fore-mast, a young
man if of the right stuff not only seems best adapted to
duty there, but in fact is generally selected for the captaincy of that top, and the company under him are light
hands and often but striplings. In sum, Captain Vere
had from the beginning deemed Billy Budd to be what
in the naval parlance of the time was called a "King's
bargain," that is to say, for His Britannic Majesty's navy
a capital investment at small outlay or none at all.

After a brief pause during which the reminiscences
above mentioned passed vividly through his mind and
he weighed the import of Claggart's last suggestion,
conveyed in the phrase, "man-trap under the clover,"
and the more he weighed it the less reliance he felt in
the informer's good faith. Suddenly he turned upon him
and in a low voice: "Do you come to me, Master-at-
Arms, with so foggy a tale? As to Budd, cite me an act
or spoken word of his confirmatory of what you in general charge against him. Stay," drawing nearer to him,

"heed what you speak. Just now and in a case like this, there is a yard-arm-end for the false-witness."

"Ah, your honor!" sighed Claggart mildly shaking his shapely head as in sad deprecation of such unmerited severity of tone. Then, bridling—erecting himself as in virtuous self-assertion, he circumstantially alleged certain words and acts, which collectively, if credited, led to presumptions mortally inculpating Budd. And for some of these averments, he added, substantiating proof was not far.

With gray eyes impatient and distrustful essaying to fathom to the bottom Claggart's calm violet ones, Captain Vere again heard him out; then for the moment stood ruminating. The mood he evinced, Claggart— himself for the time liberated from the other's scrutiny —steadily regarded with a look difficult to render—a look curious of the operation of his tactics, a look such as might have been that of the spokesman of the envious children of Jacob deceptively imposing upon the troubled patriarch the blood-dyed coat of young Joseph.

Though something exceptional in the moral quality of Captain Vere made him, in earnest encounter with a fellow-man, a veritable touch-stone of that man's essential nature, yet now as to Claggart and what was really going on in him his feeling partook less of intuitional conviction than of strong suspicion clogged by strange dubieties. The perplexity he evinced proceeded less from aught touching the man informed against— as Claggart doubtless opined—than from considerations how best to act in regard to the informer. At first indeed he was naturally for summoning that substantiation of his allegations which Claggart said was at hand. But such a proceeding would result in the matter at once getting abroad, which in the present stage of it, he thought, might undesirably affect the ship's company. If Claggart was a false witness—that closed the affair. And therefore before trying the accusation, he would first practically test the accuser; and he thought this could be done in a quiet undemonstrative way.

The measure he determined upon involved a shifting of the scene, a transfer to a place less exposed to observation than the broad quarter-deck. For although the few gun-room officers there at the time had, in due observance of naval etiquette, withdrawn to leeward the moment Captain Vere had begun his promenade on the deck's weather-side; and though during the colloquy with Claggart they of course ventured not to diminish the distance; and though throughout the interview Captain Vere's voice was far from high, and Claggart's silvery and low; and the wind in the cordage and the wash of the sea helped the more to put them beyond earshot; nevertheless, the interview's continuance already had attracted observation from some topmen aloft and other sailors in the waist or further forward.

Having determined upon his measures, Captain Vere forthwith took action. Abruptly turning to Claggart, he asked, "Master-at-Arms, is it now Budd's watch aloft?"

"No, your honor." Whereupon, "Mr. Wilkes!" summoning the nearest midshipman, "tell Albert to come to me." Albert was the Captain's hammock-boy, a sort of sea-valet in whose discretion and fidelity his master had much confidence. The lad appeared. "You know Budd the Foretopman?"

"I do, Sir."

"Go find him. It is his watch off. Manage to tell him out of earshot that he is wanted aft. Contrive it that he speaks to nobody. Keep him in talk yourself. And not till you get well aft here, not till then let him know that the place where he is wanted is my cabin. You understand. Go.—Master-at-Arms, show yourself on the decks below, and when you think it time for Albert to be coming with his man, stand by quietly to follow the sailor in."

●

Now when the Foretopman found himself in the cabin, closeted there, as it were, with the Captain and Claggart, he was surprised enough. But it was a surprise unaccompanied by apprehension or distrust. To an immature nature essentially honest and humane, fore-warning intimations of subtler danger from one's kind come tardily if at all. The only thing that took shape in the young sailor's mind was this: Yes, the Captain, I have always thought, looks kindly upon me. Wonder if he's going to make me his coxswain. I should like that. And maybe now he is going to ask the Master-at-Arms about me.

"Shut the door there, sentry," said the commander; "stand without, and let nobody come in.—Now, Master-at-Arms, tell this man to his face what you told of him to me"; and stood prepared to scrutinize the mutually confronting visages.

With the measured step and calm collected air of an asylum-physician approaching in the public hall some patient beginning to show indications of a coming par-oxysm, Claggart deliberately advanced within short range of Billy, and mesmerically looking him in the eye, briefly recapitulated the accusation.

Not at first did Billy take it in. When he did the rose-tan of his cheek looked struck as by white leprosy. He stood like one impaled and gagged. Meanwhile the accuser's eyes, removing not as yet from the blue dilated ones, underwent a phenomenal change, their wonted rich violet color blurring into a muddy purple, those lights of human intelligence losing human expression, gelidly protruding like the alien eyes of certain uncatalogued creatures of the deep. The first mesmeric glance was one of serpent fascination; the last was as the hungry lurch of the torpedo-fish.

"Speak, man!" said Captain Vere to the transfixed one, struck by his aspect even more than by Claggart's, "Speak! defend yourself." Which appeal caused but a strange dumb gesturing and gurgling in Billy; amazement at such an accusation so suddenly sprung on inexperienced nonage—this, and, it may be, horror of the accuser, serving to bring out his lurking defect and in this instance for the time intensifying it into a convulsed tongue-tie; while the intent head and entire form straining forward in an agony of ineffectual eagerness to obey the injunction to speak and defend himself gave an expression to the face like that of a condemned Vestal priestess in the moment of being buried alive, and in the first struggle against suffocation.

Though at the time Captain Vere was quite ignorant of Billy's liability to vocal impediment, he now immediately divined it, since vividly Billy's aspect recalled to him that of a bright young schoolmate of his whom he had once seen struck by much the same startling impotence in the act of eagerly rising in the class to be foremost in response to a testing question put to it by the master. Going close up to the young sailor, and laying a soothing hand on his shoulder, he said: "There is no hurry, my boy. Take your time, take your time." Contrary to the effect intended, these words, so fatherly in tone, doubtless touching Billy's heart to the quick, prompted yet more violent efforts at utterance—efforts soon ending for the time in confirming the paralysis, and bringing to his face an expression which was as a crucifixion to behold. The next instant, quick as the flame from a discharged cannon at night, his right arm shot out, and Claggart dropped to the deck. Whether intentionally or but owing to the young athlete's superior height, the blow had taken effect full upon the forehead, so shapely and intellectual-looking a feature in the Master-at-Arms; so that the body fell over lengthwise, like a heavy plank tilted from erectness. A gasp or two, and he lay motionless.

"Fated boy," breathed Captain Vere in tone so low as to be almost a whisper, "what have you done! But here, help me."

The twain raised the felled one from the loins up into a sitting position. The spare form flexibly acquiesced, but inertly. It was like handling a dead snake. They lowered it back. Regaining erectness Captain Vere with one hand covering his face stood to all appearance as impassive as the object at his feet. Was he absorbed in taking in all the bearings of the event and what was best not only now at once to be done, but also in the sequel? Slowly he uncovered his face; and the effect was as if the moon emerging from eclipse should reappear with quite another aspect than that which had gone into hiding. The father in him, manifested towards Billy thus far in the scene, was replaced by the military disciplinarian. In his official tone he bade the Foretopman retire to a stateroom aft (pointing it out) and there remain till thence summoned. This order Billy in silence mechanically obeyed. Then going to the cabin door where it opened on the quarter-deck, Captain Vere said to the sentry without, "Tell somebody to send Albert here." When the lad appeared his master so contrived it that he should not catch sight of the prone one. "Albert," he said to him, "tell the Surgeon I wish to see him. You need not come back till called."

When the Surgeon entered—a self-poised character

of that grave sense and experience that hardly anything could take him aback—Captain Vere advanced to meet him, thus unconsciously intercepting his view of Claggart, and interrupting the other's wonted ceremonious salutation, said, "Nay, tell me how it is with yonder man," directing his attention to the prostrate one.

The Surgeon looked, and for all his self-command, somewhat started at the abrupt revelation. On Claggart's always pallid complexion, thick black blood was now oozing from nostril and ear. To the gazer's professional eye it was unmistakably no living man that he saw.

"Is it so then?" said Captain Vere intently watching him. "I thought it. But verify it." Whereupon the customary tests confirmed the Surgeon's first glance, who now looking up in unfeigned concern cast a look of intense inquisitiveness upon his superior. But Captain Vere, with one hand to his brow, was standing motionless. Suddenly, catching the Surgeon's arm convulsively, he exclaimed, pointing down to the body, "It is the divine judgment on Ananias! Look!"

Disturbed by the excited manner he had never before observed in the *Indomitable*'s Captain, and as yet wholly ignorant of the affair, the prudent Surgeon nevertheless held his peace, only again looking an earnest interrogatory as to what it was that had resulted in such a tragedy.

But Captain Vere was now again motionless standing absorbed in thought. But again starting, he vehemently exclaimed, "Struck dead by an angel of God! Yet the angel must hang!"

At these passionate interjections, mere incoherences to the listener as yet unapprised of the antecedent events, the Surgeon was profoundly discomposed. But now, as recollecting himself, Captain Vere in less harsh tone briefly related the circumstances leading up to the event.

"But come; we must dispatch," he added. "Help me to remove him" (meaning the body) "to yonder compartment," designating one opposite that where the Foretopman remained immured. Anew disturbed by a request that as implying a desire for secrecy seemed unaccountably strange to him, there was nothing for the subordinate to do but comply.

"Go now," said Captain Vere with something of his wonted manner. "Go now. I shall presently call a drumhead court. Tell the lieutenants what has happened, and tell Mr. Mordant," meaning the Captain of Marines, "and charge them to keep the matter to themselves."

As the Surgeon withdrew he could not help thinking how more than futile the utmost discretion sometimes proves in this human sphere, subject as it is to unforeseeable fatalities; the prudent method adopted by Captain Vere to obviate publicity and trouble having resulted in an event that necessitated the former, and, under existing circumstances in the navy, indefinitely magnified the latter.

•

Full of disquietude and misgiving the Surgeon left the cabin. Was Captain Vere suddenly affected in his mind, or was it but a transient excitement, brought about by so strange and extraordinary a happening? As to the drumhead court, it struck the Surgeon as impolitic, if nothing more. The thing to do, he thought, was to place Billy Budd in confinement, and in a way dictated by usage, and postpone further action in so extraordinary a case, to such time as they should rejoin the squadron,

and then refer it to the Admiral. He recalled the unwonted agitation of Captain Vere and his excited exclamations so at variance with his normal manner. Was
he unhinged? But assuming that he is, it is not so susceptible of proof. What then could he do? No more trying situation is conceivable than that of an officer subordinate under a Captain whom he suspects to be, not
mad indeed, but yet not quite unaffected in his intellect. To argue his order to him would be insolence. To
resist him would be mutiny.

In obedience to Captain Vere he communicated what
had happened to the Lieutenants and Captain of Marines, saying nothing as to the Captain's state. They
fully shared his own surprise and concern. Like him
they seemed to think that such a matter should be referred to the Admiral.

●

Who in the rainbow can draw the line where the violet
tint ends and the orange tint begins? Distinctly we see
the difference of the colors, but where exactly does the
one first blendingly enter into the other? So with sanity
and insanity. In pronounced cases there is no question
about them. But in some supposed cases, in various
degrees supposedly less pronounced, to draw the exact
line of demarcation few will undertake, though for a
fee some professional experts will. There is nothing
namable but that some men will undertake to do it
for pay.

Whether Captain Vere, as the Surgeon professionally
and primarily surmised, was really the sudden victim of
any degree of aberration, one must determine for himself by such light as this narrative may afford.

That the unhappy event which has been narrated
could not have happened at a worse juncture was but

too true. For it was close on the heel of the suppressed insurrections, an aftertime very critical to naval authority, demanding from every English sea-commander two qualities not readily interfusable—prudence and rigor. Moreover there was something crucial in the case.

In the jugglery of circumstances preceding and attending the event on board the *Indomitable* and in the light of that martial code whereby it was formally to be judged, innocence and guilt—personified in Claggart and Budd—in effect changed places.

In a legal view the apparent victim of the tragedy was he who had sought to victimize a man blameless; and the indisputable deed of the latter, navally regarded, constituted the most heinous of military crimes. Yet more. The essential right and wrong involved in the matter, the clearer that might be, so much the worse for the responsibility of a loyal sea-commander, inasmuch as he was not authorized to determine the matter on that primitive basis.[1]

Small wonder then that the *Indomitable*'s Captain, though in general a man of rapid decision, felt that circumspectness not less than promptitude was necessary. Until he could decide upon his course, and in each detail, and not only so, but until the concluding measure was upon the point of being enacted, he deemed it advisable, in view of all the circumstances, to guard as much as possible against publicity. Here he may or may not have erred. Certain it is however that subsequently in the confidential talk of more than one or two gunrooms and cabins he was not a little criticized by some officers, a fact imputed by his friends, and vehemently by his cousin Jack Denton, to professional jealousy of

[1] This paragraph originally ended: "not seldom an impracticable abstraction even in civil life and under the most liberal form of it."—*J.L.*

"Starry Vere." Some imaginative ground for invidious comment there was. The maintenance of secrecy in the matter, the confining all knowledge of it for a time to the place where the homicide occurred, the quarter-deck cabin—in these particulars lurked some resemblance to the policy adopted in those tragedies of the palace which have occurred more than once in the capital founded by Peter the Barbarian.

The case indeed was such that fain would the *Indomitable's* Captain have deferred taking any action whatever respecting it, further than to keep the Fore-topman a close prisoner till the ship rejoined the squadron and then submitting the matter to the judgment of his Admiral.

But a true military officer is in one particular like a true monk. Not with more of self-abnegation will the latter keep his vows of monastic obedience than the former his vows of allegiance to martial duty.

Feeling that unless quick action were taken on it, the deed of the Foretopman, so soon as it should be known on the gun-decks, would tend to awaken any slumbering embers of the Nore among the crew, a sense of the urgency of the case overruled in Captain Vere every other consideration. But though a conscientious disciplinarian he was no lover of authority for mere authority's sake. Very far was he from embracing opportunities for monopolizing to himself the perils of moral responsibility—none at least that could properly be referred to an official superior or shared with him by his official equals or even subordinates. So thinking, he was glad it would not be at variance with usage to turn the matter over to a summary court of his own officers, reserving to himself as the one on whom the ultimate accountability would rest, the right of maintaining a supervision of it, or formally or informally interposing at need. Accordingly a drumhead court was summarily convened, he electing the individuals composing it, the First Lieutenant, the Captain of Marines, and the Sailing Master.

In associating an officer of marines with the sealieutenants in a case having to do with a sailor the Commander perhaps deviated from general custom. He was prompted thereto by the circumstance that he took that soldier to be a judicious person, thoughtful, and not altogether incapable of grappling with a difficult case unprecedented in his prior experience. Yet even as to him he was not without some latent misgiving, for withal he was an extremely good-natured man, an enjoyer of his dinner, a sound sleeper, and inclined to obesity. A man who though he would always maintain his manhood in battle might not prove altogether reliable in a moral dilemma involving aught of the tragic. As to the First Lieutenant and the Sailing Master Captain Vere could not but be aware that, though honest natures, of approved gallantry upon occasion, their intelligence was mostly confined to the matter of active seamanship and the fighting demands of their profession. The court was held in the same cabin where the unfortunate affair had taken place. This cabin, the commander's, embraced the entire area under the poopdeck. Aft, and on either side was a small stateroom, the one room temporarily a jail and the other a dead-house, and a yet smaller compartment leaving a space between, expanding forward into a goodly oblong of length coinciding with the ship's beam. A skylight of moderate dimension was overhead and at each end of the oblong space were two sashed port-hole windows easily convertible back into embrasures for short carronades.

All being quickly in readiness, Billy Budd was arraigned. Captain Vere necessarily appearing as the sole witness in the case, and as such temporarily sinking his rank, though singularly maintaining it in a matter apparently trivial; namely, that he testified from the ship's weather-side with that object having caused the court to sit on the lee-side. Concisely he narrated all that had led up to the catastrophe, omitting nothing in Claggart's accusation and deposing as to the manner in which the prisoner had received it. At this testimony the three officers glanced with no little surprise at Billy Budd, the last man they would have suspected either of the mutinous design alleged by Claggart or the undeniable deed he himself had done. The First Lieutenant taking judicial primacy and turning toward the prisoner, said, "Captain Vere has spoken. Is it or is it not as Captain Vere says?" In response came syllables not so much impeded in the utterance as might have been anticipated. They were these: "Captain Vere tells the truth. It is just as Captain Vere says, but it is not as the Master-at-Arms said. I have eaten the King's bread and I am true to the King."

"I believe you, my man," said the witness, his voice indicating a suppressed emotion not otherwise betrayed.

"God will bless you for that, Your Honor!" not without stammering said Billy, and all but broke down. But immediately was recalled to self-control by another question, to which with the same emotional difficulty of utterance he said, "No, there was no malice between us. I never bore malice against the Master-at-Arms. I am sorry that he is dead. I did not mean to kill him. Could I have used my tongue I would not have struck him. But he foully lied to my face and in presence of my Captain, and I had to say something, and I could only say it with a blow, God help me!"

In the impulsive above board manner of the frank one the court saw confirmed all that was implied in words that just previously had perplexed them, coming as they did from the testifier to the tragedy and promptly following Billy's impassioned disclaimer of mutinous intent—Captain Vere's words, "I believe you, my man."

Next it was asked of him whether he knew of or suspected aught savoring of incipient trouble (meaning mutiny, though the explicit term was avoided) going on in any section of the ship's company.

The reply lingered. This was naturally imputed by the court to the same vocal embarrassment which had retarded or obstructed previous answers. But in main it was otherwise here; the question immediately recalling to Billy's mind the interview with the afterguardsman in the fore-chains. But an innate repugnance to playing a part at all approaching that of an informer against one's own shipmates—the same erring sense of uninstructed honor which had stood in the way of his reporting the matter at the time, though as a loyal man-of-war-man it was incumbent on him and failure so to do, if charged against him and proven, would have subjected him to the heaviest of penalties; this, with the blind feeling now his, that nothing really was being hatched, prevailed with him. When the answer came it was a negative.

"One question more," said the officer of marines, now first speaking and with a troubled earnestness. "You tell us that what the Master-at-Arms said against you was a lie. Now why should he have so lied, so maliciously lied, since you declare there was no malice between you?"

At that question unintentionally touching on a spiritual sphere wholly obscure to Billy's thoughts, he was nonplused, evincing a confusion indeed that some observers, such as can readily be imagined, would have construed into involuntary evidence of hidden guilt. Nevertheless he strove some way to answer, but all at once relinquished the vain endeavor, at the same time turning an appealing glance toward Captain Vere as deeming him his best helper and friend. Captain Vere, who had been seated for a time, rose to his feet, addressing the interrogator. "The question you put to him comes naturally enough. But how can he rightly answer it? or anybody else? unless indeed it be he who lies within there," designating the compartment where lay the corpse. "But the prone one there will not rise to our summons. In effect though, as it seems to me, the point you make is hardly material. Quite aside from any conceivable motive actuating the Master-at-Arms, and irrespective of the provocation to the blow, a martial court must needs in the present case confine its attention to the blow's consequence, which consequence justly is to be deemed not otherwise than as the striker's deed."

This utterance, the full significance of which it was not at all likely that Billy took in, nevertheless caused him to turn a wistful interrogative look toward the speaker, a look in its dumb expressiveness not unlike that which a dog of generous breed might turn upon his master, seeking in his face some elucidation of a previous gesture ambiguous to the canine intelligence. Nor was the same utterance without marked effect upon the three officers, more especially the soldier. Couched in it seemed to them a meaning unanticipated, involving a prejudgment on the speaker's part. It served to augment a mental disturbance previously evident enough.

The soldier once more spoke; in a tone of suggestive dubiety addressing at once his associates and Captain

Vere: "Nobody is present—none of the ship's company, I mean, who might shed lateral light, if any is to be had, upon what remains mysterious in this matter."

"That is thoughtfully put," said Captain Vere; "I see your drift. Aye, there is a mystery; but to use a Scriptural phrase, it is 'a mystery of iniquity,' a matter for psychologic theologians to discuss. But what has a military court to do with it? Not to add that for us any possible investigation of it is cut off by the lasting tongue-tie of—him—in yonder," again designating the mortuary stateroom. "The prisoner's deed—with that alone we have to do."

To this, and particularly the closing reiteration, the marine soldier, knowing not how aptly to reply, sadly abstained from saying aught. The First Lieutenant, who at the outset had not unnaturally assumed primacy in the court, now overrulingly instructed by a glance from Captain Vere, a glance more effective than words, resumed that primacy. Turning to the prisoner, "Budd," he said, and scarce in equable tones, "Budd, if you have aught further to say for yourself, say it now."

Upon this the young sailor turned another quick glance toward Captain Vere; then, as taking a hint from that aspect, a hint confirming his own instinct that silence was now best, replied to the Lieutenant, "I have said all, Sir."

The marine—the same who had been the sentinel without the cabin-door at the time that the Foretopman followed by the Master-at-Arms, entered it—he, standing by the sailor throughout these judicial proceedings, was now directed to take him back to the after compartment originally assigned to the prisoner and his custodian. As the twain disappeared from view, the three officers, as partially liberated from some inward constraint associated with Billy's mere presence, simultaneously stirred in their seats. They exchanged looks of troubled indecision, yet feeling that decide they must and without long delay. For Captain Vere, he for the time stood—unconsciously with his back toward them, apparently in one of his absent fits, gazing out from a sashed port-hole to windward upon the monotonous blank of the twilight sea. But the court's silence continuing, broken only at moments by brief consultations in low earnest tones, this seemed to assure him and encourage him. Turning, he to-and-fro paced the cabin athwart; in the returning ascent to windward, climbing the slant deck in the ship's lee roll; without knowing it symbolizing thus in his action a mind resolute to surmount difficulties even if against primitive instincts strong as the wind and the sea. Presently he came to a stand before the three. After scanning their faces he stood less as mustering his thoughts for expression, than as one inly deliberating how best to put them to well-meaning men not intellectually mature, men with whom it was necessary to demonstrate certain principles that were axioms to himself. Similar impatience as to talking is perhaps one reason that deters some minds from addressing any popular assemblies.

When speak he did, something both in the substance of what he said and his manner of saying it showed the influence of unshared studies modifying and tempering the practical training of an active career. This, along with his phraseology, now and then was suggestive of the grounds whereon rested that imputation of a certain pedantry socially alleged against him by certain naval men of wholly practical cast, captains who nevertheless would frankly concede that His Majesty's navy mustered no more efficient officer of their grade than "Starry Vere."

What he said was to this effect: "Hitherto I have

been but the witness, little more; and I should hardly
think now to take another tone, that of your coadjutor,
for the time, did I not perceive in you—at the crisis
too—a troubled hesitancy, proceeding, I doubt not from
the clash of military duty with moral scruple—scruple
vitalized by compassion. For the compassion, how can
I otherwise than share it? But, mindful of paramount
obligations I strive against scruples that may tend to
enervate decision. Not, gentlemen, that I hide from myself that the case is an exceptional one. Speculatively
regarded, it well might be referred to a jury of casuists.
But for us here, acting not as casuists or moralists, it is
a case practical, and under martial law practically to
be dealt with.

"But your scruples: do they move as in a dusk? Challenge them. Make them advance and declare themselves. Come now: do they import something like this:
If, mindless of palliating circumstances, we are bound
to regard the death of the Master-at-Arms as the prisoner's deed, then does that deed constitute a capital
crime whereof the penalty is a mortal one. But in natural justice is nothing but the prisoner's overt act to
be considered? How can we adjudge to summary and
shameful death a fellow-creature innocent before God,
and whom we feel to be so?—Does that state it aright?
You sign sad assent. Well, I too feel that, the full force
of that. It is Nature. But do these buttons that we wear
attest that our allegiance is to Nature? No, to the King.
Though the ocean, which is inviolate Nature primeval,
though this be the element where we move and have
our being as sailors, yet as the King's officers lies our
duty in a sphere correspondingly natural? So little is
that true, that in receiving our commissions we in the
most important regards ceased to be natural free agents.
When war is declared, are we the commissioned fight-

ers previously consulted? We fight at command. If our judgments approve the war, that is but coincidence. So in other particulars. So now. For suppose condemnation to follow these present proceedings. Would it be so much we ourselves that would condemn as it would be martial law operating through us? For that law and the rigor of it, we are not responsible. Our vowed responsibility is in this: That however pitilessly that law may operate in any instance, we nevertheless adhere to it and administer it.

"But the exceptional in the matter moves the hearts within you. Even so too is mine moved. But let not warm hearts betray heads that should be cool. Ashore in a criminal case will an upright judge allow himself off the bench to be waylaid by some tender kinswoman of the accused seeking to touch him with her tearful plea? Well the heart, sometimes the feminine in man, here is as that piteous woman, and hard though it be, she must here be ruled out."

He paused, earnestly studying them for a moment; then resumed.

"But something in your aspect seems to urge that it is not solely the heart that moves in you, but also the conscience, the private conscience. But tell me whether or not, occupying the position we do, private conscience should not yield to that imperial one formulated in the code under which alone we officially proceed?"

Here the three men moved in their seats, less convinced than agitated by the course of an argument troubling but the more the spontaneous conflict within.

Perceiving which, the speaker paused for a moment; then abruptly changing his tone, went on.

"To steady us a bit, let us recur to the facts.—In wartime at sea a man-of-war's-man strikes his superior in grade, and the blow kills. Apart from its effect the blow itself is, according to the Articles of War, a capital crime. Furthermore—"

"Aye, Sir," emotionally broke in the officer of marines, "in one sense it was. But surely Budd purposed neither mutiny nor homicide."

"Surely not, my good man. And before a court less arbitrary and more merciful than a martial one that plea would largely extenuate. At the Last Assizes it shall acquit. But how here? We proceed under the law of the Mutiny Act. In feature no child can resemble his father more than that Act resembles in spirit the thing from which it derives—War. In His Majesty's service— in this ship indeed—there are Englishmen forced to fight for the King against their will. Against their conscience, for aught we know. Though as their fellow-creatures some of us may appreciate their position, yet as navy officers, what reck we of it? Still less recks the enemy. Our impressed men he would fain cut down in the same swath with our volunteers. As regards the enemy's naval conscripts, some of whom may even share our own abhorrence of the regicidal French Directory, it is the same on our side. War looks but to the front-age, the appearance. And the Mutiny Act, War's child, takes after the father. Budd's intent or non-intent is nothing to the purpose.

"But while, put to it by those anxieties in you which I cannot but respect, I only repeat myself—while thus strangely we prolong proceedings that should be summary—the enemy may be sighted and an engagement result. We must do; and one of two things must we do —condemn or let go."

"Can we not convict and yet mitigate the penalty?" asked the junior Lieutenant, here speaking, and falter-ingly, for the first.

"Lieutenant, were that clearly lawful for us under

the circumstances consider the consequence of such clemency. The people" (meaning the ship's company) "have native sense; most of them are familiar with our naval usage and tradition; and how would they take it? Even could you explain to them—which our official position forbids—they, long moulded by arbitrary discipline, have not that kind of intelligent responsiveness that might qualify them to comprehend and discriminate. No, to the people the Foretopman's deed, however it be worded in the announcement, will be plain homicide committed in a flagrant act of mutiny. What penalty for that should follow, they know. But it does not follow. *Why?* They will ruminate. You know what sailors are. Will they not revert to the recent outbreak at the Nore? Aye. They know the well-founded alarm— the panic it struck throughout England. Your clement sentence they would account pusillanimous. They would think that we flinch, that we are afraid of them—afraid of practicing a lawful rigor singularly demanded at this juncture, lest it should provoke new troubles. What shame to us such a conjecture on their part, and how deadly to discipline. You see then, whither, prompted by duty and the law, I steadfastly drive. But I beseech you, my friends, do not take me amiss. I feel as you do for this unfortunate boy. But did he know our hearts, I take him to be of that generous nature that he would feel even for us on whom in this military necessity so heavy a compulsion is laid."

With that, crossing the deck he resumed his place by the sashed port-hole, tacitly leaving the three to come to a decision. On the cabin's opposite side the troubled court sat silent. Loyal lieges, plain and practical, though at bottom they dissented from some points Captain Vere had put to them, they were without the faculty, hardly had the inclination to gainsay one whom they felt to be an earnest man, one too not less their superior in mind than in naval rank. But it is not improbable that even such of his words as were not without influence over them less came home to them than his closing appeal to their instinct as sea-officers in the forethought he threw out as to the practical consequences to discipline, considering the unconfirmed tone of the fleet at the time, should a man-of-war's-man's violent killing at sea of a superior in grade be allowed to pass for aught else than a capital crime, so demanding prompt infliction of the penalty.

Not unlikely they were brought to something more or less akin to that harassed frame of mind which in the year 1842 actuated the commander of the United States brig-of-war *Somers* to resolve, under the so-called Articles of War, Articles modeled upon the English Mutiny Act, to resolve upon the execution at sea of a midshipman and two petty-officers as mutineers designing the seizure of the brig. Which resolution was carried out though in a time of peace and within not many days' sail of home, an act vindicated by a naval court of inquiry subsequently convened ashore. History, and here cited without comment. True, the circumstances on board the *Somers* were different from those on board the *Indomitable*. But the urgency felt, well-warranted or otherwise, was much the same.

Says a writer whom few know, "Forty years after a battle it is easy for a noncombatant to reason about how it ought to have been fought. It is another thing personally and under fire to direct the fighting while involved in the obscuring smoke of it. Much so with respect to other emergencies involving considerations both practical and moral, and when it is imperative promptly to act. The greater the fog the more it imperils the steamer, and speed is put on though at the hazard of running somebody down. Little ween the snug card-players in the cabin of the responsibilities of the sleepless man on the bridge."

In brief, Billy Budd was formally convicted and sentenced to be hung at the yard-arm in the early morning-watch, it being now night. Otherwise, as is customary in such cases, the sentence would forthwith have been carried out. In war-time, on the field or in the fleet, a mortal punishment decreed by a drumhead court—on the field sometimes decreed by but a nod from the General—follows without delay on the heel of conviction, without appeal.

●

It was Captain Vere himself who of his own motion communicated the finding of the court to the prisoner; for that purpose going to the compartment where he was in custody and bidding the marine there to withdraw for the time.

Beyond the communication of the sentence, what took place at this interview was never known. But in view of the character of the twain briefly closeted in that state-room, each radically sharing in the rarer qualities of our nature—so rare indeed as to be all but incredible to average minds however much cultivated—some conjectures may be ventured.

It would have been in consonance with the spirit of Captain Vere should he on this occasion have concealed nothing from the condemned one—should he indeed have frankly disclosed to him the part he himself had played in bringing about the decision, at the same time revealing his actuating motives. On Billy's side it is not improbable that such a confession would have been received in much the same spirit that prompted it. Not without a sort of joy indeed he might have appreciated the brave opinion of him implied in his Captain making such a confidant of him. Nor, as to the sentence itself, could he have been insensible that it was imparted to him as to one not afraid to die. Even more may have been. Captain Vere in end may have developed the passion sometimes latent under an exterior stoical or indifferent. He was old enough to have been Billy's father. The austere devotee of military duty letting himself melt back into what remains primeval in our formalized humanity may in end have caught Billy to his heart even as Abraham may have caught young Isaac on the brink of resolutely offering him up in obedience to the exacting behest. But there is no telling the sacrament, seldom, if in any case, revealed to the gadding world wherever under circumstances at all akin to those here attempted to be set forth two of great Nature's nobler order embrace. There is privacy at the time, inviolable to the survivor, and holy oblivion, the sequel to each diviner magnanimity, providentially covers all at last.

The first to encounter Captain Vere in act of leaving the compartment was the senior Lieutenant. The face he beheld, for the moment one expressive of the agony of the strong, was to that officer, though a man of fifty, a startling revelation. That the condemned one suffered less than he who mainly had effected the condemnation was apparently indicated by the former's exclamation in the scene soon perforce to be touched upon.

•

Of a series of incidents within a brief term rapidly following each other, the adequate narration may take up a term less brief, especially if explanation or comment here and there seem requisite to the better understanding of such incidents. Between the entrance into the cabin of him who never left it alive, and him who when he did leave it left it as one condemned to die; between this and the closeted interview just given less than an hour and a half had elapsed. It was an interval long enough however to awaken speculations among no few of the ship's company as to what it was that could be detaining in the cabin the Master-at-Arms and the sailor; for a rumor that both of them had been seen to enter it and neither of them had been seen to emerge, this rumor had got abroad upon the gun-decks and in the tops; the people of a great warship being in one respect like villagers, taking microscopic note of every outward movement or non-movement going on. When therefore in weather not at all tempestuous all hands were called in the second dog-watch, a summons under such circumstances not usual in those hours, the crew were not wholly unprepared for some announcement extraordinary, one having connection too with the continued absence of the two men from their wonted haunts.

There was a moderate sea at the time; and the moon, newly risen and near to being at its full, silvered the white spar-deck wherever not blotted by the clear-cut shadows horizontally thrown of fixtures and moving men. On either side the quarter-deck the marine guard under arms was drawn up; and Captain Vere standing in his place surrounded by all the ward-room officers, addressed his men. In so doing his manner showed neither more nor less than that properly pertaining to his supreme position aboard his own ship. In clear terms and concise he told them what had taken place in the cabin; that the Master-at-Arms was dead; that he who had killed him had been already tried by a summary court and condemned to death; and that the execution would take place in the early morning watch. The word *mutiny* was not named in what he said. He refrained too from making the occasion an opportunity for any preachment as to the maintenance of discipline, thinking perhaps that under existing circumstances in the navy the consequence of violating discipline should be made to speak for itself.

Their Captain's announcement was listened to by the throng of standing sailors in a dumbness like that of a seated congregation of believers in hell listening to the clergyman's announcement of his Calvinistic text.

At the close, however, a confused murmur went up. It began to wax. All but instantly, then, at a sign, it was pierced and suppressed by shrill whistles of the Boatswain and his mates piping down one watch. The order was given to about ship.

To be prepared for burial Claggart's body was delivered to certain petty-officers of his mess. And here, not to clog the sequel with lateral matters, it may be added that at a suitable hour the Master-at-Arms was committed to the sea with every funeral honor properly belonging to his naval grade.

In this proceeding as in every public one growing out of the tragedy strict adherence to usage was observed. Nor in any point could it have been at all deviated from, either with respect to Claggart or Billy Budd, without begetting undesirable speculations in the ship's company, sailors, and more particularly men-of-war's-men, being of all men the greatest sticklers for usage.

For similar cause all communication between Captain Vere and the condemned one ended with the closeted interview already given, the latter being now surrendered to the ordinary routine preliminary to the end. This transfer under guard from the Captain's quarters was effected without unusual precautions—at least no visible ones. If possible not to let the men so much as surmise that their officers anticipate aught amiss from them is the tacit rule in a military ship. And the more that some sort of trouble should really be apprehended the more do the officers keep that apprehension to themselves; though not the less unostentatious vigilance may be augmented.

In the present instance the sentry placed over the prisoner had strict orders to let no one have communication with him but the Chaplain. And certain unobtrusive measures were taken absolutely to insure this point.

•

In a seventy-four of the old order the deck known as the upper gun-deck was the one covered over by the spar-deck, which last, though not without its armament, was for the most part exposed to the weather. In general it was at all hours free from hammocks; those of the crew swinging on the lower gun-deck, and berth-deck, the latter being not only a dormitory but also the place for the stowing of the sailors' bags, and on both sides lined with the large chests or movable pantries of the many messes of the men.

On the starboard side of the *Indomitable*'s upper gun-deck, behold Billy Budd under sentry lying prone in irons in one of the bays formed by the regular spacing of the guns comprising the batteries on either side. All these pieces were of the heavier caliber of that period. Mounted on lumbering wooden carriages they were hampered with cumbersome harness of breeching and strong side-tackles for running them out. Guns and carriages, together with the long rammers and shorter lintstocks lodged in loops overhead—all these, as customary, were painted black; and the heavy hempen breechings tarred to the same tint wore the like livery of the undertakers. In contrast with the funereal tone of these surroundings the prone sailor's exterior apparel, white jumper and white duck trousers, each more or less soiled, dimly glimmered in the obscure light of the bay like a patch of discolored snow in early April lingering at some upland cave's black mouth. In effect he is already in his shroud or the garments that shall serve him in lieu of one. Over him but scarce illuminating him, two battle-lanterns swing from two massive beams of the deck above. Fed with the oil supplied by the war-contractors (whose gains, honest or otherwise, are in every land an anticipated portion of the harvest of death), with flickering splashes of dirty yellow light they pollute the pale moonshine all but ineffectually struggling in obstructed flecks through the open ports from which the tompioned cannon protrude. Other lanterns at intervals serve but to bring out somewhat the obscurer bays which like small confessionals or side-chapels in a cathedral branch from the long dim-vistaed broad aisle between the two batteries of that covered tier.

Such was the deck where now lay the Handsome Sailor. Through the rose-tan of his complexion, no pallor could have shown. It would have taken days of sequestration from the winds and the sun to have brought about the effacement of that. But the skeleton in the cheek-bone at the point of its angle was just beginning delicately to be defined under the warm-tinted skin. In fervid hearts self-contained some brief experiences devour our human tissue as secret fire in a ship's hold consumes cotton in the bale.

But now lying between the two guns, as nipped in the vise of fate, Billy's agony, mainly proceeding from a generous young heart's virgin experience of the diabolical incarnate and effective in some men—the tension of that agony was over now. It survived not the something healing in the closeted interview with Captain Vere. Without movement, he lay as in a trance. That adolescent expression previously noted as his, taking on something akin to the look of a slumbering child in the cradle when the warm hearth-glow of the still chamber at night plays on the dimples that at whiles mysteriously form in the cheek, silently coming and going there. For now and then in the gyved one's trance a serene happy light born of some wandering reminiscence or dream would diffuse itself over his face, and then wane away only anew to return.

The Chaplain coming to see him and finding him thus, and perceiving no sign that he was conscious of his presence, attentively regarded him for a space, then slipping aside, withdrew for the time, peradventure feeling that even he, the minister of Christ though receiving his stipend from Mars, had no consolation to proffer which could result in a peace transcending that which he beheld. But in the small hours he came again. And the prisoner now awake to his surroundings noticed his approach and civilly, all but cheerfully, welcomed him. But it was to little purpose that in the interview following the good man sought to bring Billy Budd to some godly understanding that he must die, and at dawn. True, Billy himself freely referred to his death as a thing close at hand; but it was something in the way that children will refer to death in general, who yet among their other sports will play a funeral with hearse and mourners.

Not that like children Billy was incapable of conceiving what death really is. No, but he was wholly without irrational fear of it, a fear more prevalent in highly civilized communities than those so-called barbarous ones which in all respects stand nearer to unadulterate Nature. And, as elsewhere said, a barbarian Billy radically was; as much so, for all the costume, as his country-men the British captives, living trophies, made to march in the Roman triumph of Germanicus. Quite as much so as those later barbarians, young men probably, and picked specimens among the earlier British converts to Christianity, at least nominally such, and taken to Rome (as today converts from lesser isles of the sea may be taken to London), of whom the Pope of that time, admiring the strangeness of their personal beauty so unlike the Italian stamp, their clear ruddy complexion and curled flaxen locks, exclaimed, "Angles" (meaning "*English*," the modern derivative), "Angles do you call them? And is it because they look so like angels?" Had it been later in time one would think that the Pope had in mind Fra Angelico's seraphs some of whom, plucking apples in gardens of the Hesperides, have the faint rosebud complexion of the more beautiful English girls.

If in vain the good Chaplain sought to impress the young barbarian with ideas of death akin to those conveyed in the skull, dial, and cross-bones on old tombstones, equally futile to all appearance were his efforts to bring home to him the thought of salvation and a Saviour. Billy listened, but less out of awe or reverence perhaps than from a certain natural politeness; doubtless at bottom regarding all that in much the same way that most mariners of his class take any discourse abstract or out of the common tone of the work-a-day world. And this sailor way of taking clerical discourse is not wholly unlike the way in which the pioneer of Christianity full of transcendent miracles was received long ago on tropic isles by any superior *savage*, so called —a Tahitian say of Captain Cook's time or shortly after that time. Out of natural courtesy he received but did not appropriate. It was like a gift placed in the palm of an outstretched hand upon which the fingers do not close.

But the *Indomitable*'s Chaplain was a discreet man possessing the good sense of a good heart. So he insisted not in his vocation here. At the instance of Captain Vere, a lieutenant had apprised him of pretty much everything as to Billy; and since he felt that innocence was even a better thing than religion wherewith to go to Judgment, he reluctantly withdrew; but in his emotion not without first performing an act strange enough in an Englishman, and under the circumstances yet more so in any regular priest. Stooping over, he kissed on the fair cheek his fellow-man, a felon in martial law, one who though on the confines of death he felt he could never convert to a dogma; nor for all that did he fear for his future.

Marvel not that having been made acquainted with the young sailor's essential innocence (an irruption of heretic thought hard to suppress) the worthy man lifted not a finger to avert the doom of such a martyr to martial discipline. So to do would not only have been as idle as invoking the desert but would also have been an audacious transgression of the bounds of his function, one as exactly prescribed to him by military law as that of the boatswain or any other naval officer. Bluntly put, a chaplain is the minister of the Prince of Peace serving in the host of the God of War—Mars. As such, he is as incongruous as that musket of Blücher would be on the altar at Christmas. Why then is he there? Because he indirectly subserves the purpose attested by the cannon; because too he lends the sanction of the religion of the meek to that which practically is the abrogation of everything but brute Force.

The night, so luminous on the spar-deck but otherwise on the cavernous ones below, levels so like the tiered galleries in a coalmine—the luminous night passed away. But, like the prophet in the chariot disappearing in heaven and dropping his mantle to Elisha, the withdrawing night transferred its pale robe to the breaking day. A meek shy light appeared in the east, where stretched a diaphanous fleece of white furrowed vapor. That light slowly waxed. Suddenly eight bells was struck aft, responded to by one louder metallic stroke from forward. It was four o'clock in the morning. Instantly the silver whistles were heard summoning all hands to witness punishment. Up through the great hatchways rimmed with racks of heavy shot, the watch below came pouring, overspreading with the watch already on deck the space between the mainmast and foremast including that occupied by the capacious launch and the black booms tiered on either side of it, boat and booms making a summit of observation for the powderboys and younger tars. A different group comprising one watch of topmen leaned over the rail of that sea-balcony, no small one in a seventy-four, looking down on the crowd below. Man or boy none spake but in whisper, and few spake at all. Captain Vere —as before, the central figure among the assembled commissioned officers—stood nigh the break of the poop-deck facing forward. Just below him on the quarter-deck the marines in full equipment were drawn up much as at the scene of the promulgated sentence.

At sea in the old time, the execution by halter of a military sailor was generally from the fore-yard. In the present instance, for special reasons, the main-yard was assigned. Under an arm of that weather- or lee-yard the prisoner was presently brought up, the Chaplain attending him. It was noted at the time and remarked upon afterward that in this final scene the good man evinced little or nothing of the perfunctory. Brief speech indeed he had with the condemned one, but the genuine Gospel was less on his tongue than in his aspect and manner toward him. The final preparations personal to the latter being speedily brought to an end by two boatswain's-mates, the consummation impended. Billy stood facing aft. At the penultimate moment, his words, his only ones, words wholly unobstructed in the utterance were these—"God bless Captain Vere!" Syllables so unanticipated coming from one with the ignominious hemp about his neck—a conventional felon's benediction directed aft toward the quarters of honor; syllables too delivered in the clear melody of a singing-bird on the point of launching from the twig, had a phenomenal effect, not unenhanced by the rare personal beauty of the young sailor spiritualized now through late experiences so poignantly profound.

Without volition as it were, as if indeed the ship's populace were but the vehicles of some vocal current electric, with one voice from alow and aloft, came a resonant sympathetic echo—"God bless Captain Vere!" And yet at that instant Billy alone must have been in their hearts, even as he was in their eyes.

At the pronounced words and the spontaneous echo that voluminously rebounded them, Captain Vere, either through stoic self-control or a sort of momentary paralysis induced by emotional shock, stood erectly rigid as a musket in the ship-armorer's rack.

The hull deliberately recovering from the periodic roll to leeward was just regaining an even keel, when the last signal, a preconcerted dumb one, was given. At the same moment it chanced that the vapory fleece hanging low in the east, was shot through with a soft glory as of the fleece of the Lamb of God seen in mystical vision and simultaneously therewith, watched by the wedged mass of upturned faces, Billy ascended; and, ascending, took the full rose of the dawn.

In the pinioned figure, arrived at the yard-end, to the wonder of all no motion was apparent save that created by the ship's motion, in moderate weather so majestic in a great ship ponderously cannoned.

A Digression

When some days afterward in reference to the singularity just mentioned, the Purser, a rather ruddy rotund person more accurate as an accountant than profound as a philosopher, said at mess to the Surgeon, "What testimony to the force lodged in will-power," the latter, saturnine, spare and tall, one in whom a discreet causticity went along with a manner less genial than polite, replied, "Your pardon, Mr. Purser. In a hanging scientifically conducted—and under special orders I myself directed how Budd's was to be effected—any movement following the completed suspension and originating in the body suspended, such movement indicates mechanical spasm in the muscular system. Hence the absence of that is no more attributable to will-power, as you call it, than to horse-power—begging your pardon."

"But this muscular spasm you speak of, is not that in a degree more or less invariable in these cases?"

"Assuredly so, Mr. Purser."

"How then, my good Sir, do you account for its absence in this instance?"

"Mr. Purser, it is clear that your sense of the singularity in this matter equals not mine. You account for it by what you call will-power, a term not yet included in the lexicon of science. For me I do not, with my present knowledge, pretend to account for it at all. Even should one assume the hypothesis that at the first touch of the halyards the action of Budd's heart, intensified by extraordinary emotion at its climax, abruptly stopped —much like a watch when in carelessly winding it up you strain at the finish, thus snapping the chain—even under that hypothesis how account for the phenomenon that followed?"

"You admit then that the absence of spasmodic movement was phenomenal."

"It was phenomenal, Mr. Purser, in the sense that it was an appearance the cause of which is not immediately to be assigned."

"But tell me, my dear Sir," pertinaciously continued the other, "was the man's death effected by the halter, or was it a species of euthanasia?"

"*Euthanasia*, Mr. Purser, is something like your *will-power;* I doubt its authenticity as a scientific term— begging your pardon again. It is at once imaginative and metaphysical,—in short, Greek. But," abruptly changing his tone, "there is a case in the sick-bay which I do not care to leave to my assistants. Beg your pardon, but excuse me." And rising from the mess he formally withdrew.

•

The silence at the moment of execution and for a moment or two continuing thereafter, a silence but emphasized by the regular wash of the sea against the hull or the flutter of a sail, caused by the helmsman's eyes being tempted astray, this emphasized silence was gradually disturbed by a sound not easily to be verbally rendered. Whoever has heard the freshet-wave of a torrent suddenly swelled by pouring showers in tropical mountains, showers not shared by the plain; whoever has heard the first muffled murmur of its sloping advance through precipitous woods, may form some conception of the sound now heard. The seeming remoteness of its source was because of its murmurous indistinctness, since it came from close by, even from the men massed on the ship's open deck. Being inarticulate, it was dubious in significance further that it seemed to indicate some capricious revulsion of thought or feeling such as mobs ashore are liable to, in the present instance possibly implying a sullen revocation on the men's part of their involuntary echoing of Billy's benediction. But ere the murmur had time to wax into clamor it was met by a strategic command, the more telling that it came with abrupt unexpectedness.

"Pipe down the starboard watch, Boatswain, and see that they go."

Shrill as the shriek of the sea-hawk the whistles of the Boatswain and his Mates pierced that ominous low sound, dissipating it; and yielding to the mechanism of discipline the throng was thinned by one half. For the remainder most of them were set to temporary employments connected with trimming the yards and so forth, business readily to be got up to serve occasion by any officer-of-the-deck.

Now each proceeding that follows a mortal sentence pronounced at sea by a drumhead court is characterized by promptitude not perceptibly merging into hurry, though bordering that. The hammock, the one which had been Billy's bed when alive, having already been ballasted with shot and otherwise prepared to serve for his canvas coffin, the last office of the sea-undertakers, the Sailmaker's Mates, was now speedily completed. When everything was in readiness a second call for all hands, made necessary by the strategic movement before mentioned, was sounded and now to witness burial.

The details of this closing formality it needs not to give. But when the tilted plank let slide its freight into the sea, a second strange human murmur was heard, blended now with another inarticulate sound proceeding from certain larger sea-fowl whose attention having been attracted by the peculiar commotion in the water resulting from the heavy sloped dive of the shotted hammock into the sea, flew screaming to the spot. So near the hull did they come, that the stridor or bony creak of their gaunt double-jointed pinions was audible. As the ship under light airs passed on, leaving the burial-spot astern, they still kept circling it low down with the moving shadow of their outstretched wings and the croaked requiem of their cries.

Upon sailors as superstitious as those of the age preceding ours, men-of-war's-men too who had just beheld the prodigy of repose in the form suspended in air, and now foundering in the deeps; to such mariners the action of the sea-fowl though dictated by mere animal greed for prey, was big with no prosaic significance. An uncertain movement began among them, in which some encroachment was made. It was tolerated but for a moment. For suddenly the drum-beat to quarters, which familiar sound happening at least twice every day, had upon the present occasion some signal peremptoriness in it. True martial discipline long continued superinduces in average man a sort of impulse of docility whose operation at the official sound of command much resembles in its promptitude the effect of an instinct.

The drum-beat dissolved the multitude, distributing most of them along the batteries of the two covered gun-decks. There, as wont, the guns' crews stood by their respective cannon erect and silent. In due course the First Officer, sword under arm and standing in his place on the quarter-deck, formally received the successive reports of the sworded Lieutenants commanding the sections of batteries below; the last of which reports being made the summed report he delivered with the customary salute to the commander. All this occupied time, which, in the present case, was the object of beating to quarters at an hour prior to the customary one. That such variance from usage was authorized by an officer like Captain Vere, a martinet as some deemed him, was evidence of the necessity for unusual action implied in what he deemed to be temporarily the mood of his men. "With mankind," he would say "forms, measured forms, are everything; and that is the import couched in the story of Orpheus with his lyre spell-binding the wild denizens of the wood." And this he once applied to the disruption of forms going on across the Channel and the consequences thereof.

At this unwonted muster at quarters, all proceeded as at the regular hour. The band on the quarter-deck played a sacred air. After which the Chaplain went through with the customary morning service. That done, the drum beat the retreat, and toned by music and religious rites subserving the discipline and purpose of War, the men in their wonted orderly manner dispersed to the places allotted them when not at the guns.

And now it was full day. The fleece of low-hanging vapor had vanished, licked up by the sun that late had so glorified it. And the circumambient air in the clearness of its serenity was like smooth white marble in the polished block not yet removed from the marble-dealer's yard.

•

The symmetry of form attainable in pure fiction cannot so readily be achieved in a narration essentially having less to do with fable than with fact. Truth uncompromisingly told will always have its ragged edges; hence the conclusion of such a narration is apt to be less finished than an architectural finial.

How it fared with the Handsome Sailor during the year of the great mutiny has been faithfully given. But though properly the story ends with his life something in way of sequel will not be amiss. Three brief chapters will suffice.

In the general rechristening under the Directory of the craft originally forming the navy of the French monarchy, the *St. Louis* line-of-battle ship was named the *Athéiste*. Such a name, like some other substituted ones in the Revolutionary fleet, while proclaiming the infidel audacity of the ruling power was yet, though not so intended to be, the aptest name, if one consider it, ever given to a warship; far more so indeed than the *Devastation,* the *Erebus* (the *Hell*) and similar names bestowed upon fighting-ships.

On the return passage to the English fleet from the detached cruise during which occurred the events already recorded, the *Indomitable* fell in with the *Athéiste*. An engagement ensued; during which Captain Vere in the act of putting his ship alongside the enemy with a view of throwing his boarders across her bulwarks, was hit by a musket-ball from a port-hole of the enemy's main cabin. More than disabled he dropped to the deck and was carried below to the same cock-pit where some of his men already lay. The senior Lieutenant took command. Under him the enemy was finally captured and though much crippled was by rare good fortune sucessfully taken into Gibraltar, an English port not very distant from the scene of the fight. There, Captain Vere with the rest of the wounded was put ashore. He lingered for some days, but the end came. Unhappily he was cut off too early for the Nile and Trafalgar.

The spirit that spite its philosophic austerity may yet have indulged in the most secret of all passions, ambition, never attained to the fullness of fame.

Not long before death, while lying under the influence of that magical drug which soothing the physical frame mysteriously operates on the subtler element in man, he was heard to murmur words inexplicable to his attendant—"Billy Budd, Billy Budd." That these were not the accents of remorse would seem clear from what the attendant said to the *Indomitable*'s senior officer of marines, who as the most reluctant to condemn of the members of the drumhead court too well knew, though here he kept the knowledge to himself, who Billy Budd was.

●

Some few weeks after the execution, among other matters under the head of "News from the Mediterranean," there appeared in a naval chronicle of the time, an authorized weekly publication, an account of the affair. It was doubtless for the most part written in good faith, though the medium, partly rumor, through which the facts must have reached the writer, served to deflect and in part falsify them. The account was as follows:

On the tenth of the last month a deplorable occurrence took place on board H.M.S. *Indomitable*. John Claggart, the ship's Master-at-Arms, discovering that some sort of plot was incipient among an inferior section of the ship's company, and that the ringleader was one William Budd; he, Claggart, in the act of arraigning the man before the Captain, was vindictively stabbed to the heart by the suddenly drawn sheath-knife of Budd.

The deed and the implement employed sufficiently suggest that though mustered into the service under an English name, the assassin was no Englishman, but one of those aliens adopting English cognomens, whom the present extraordinary necessities of the Service have caused to be admitted into it in considerable numbers.

The enormity of the crime and the extreme depravity of the criminal, appear the greater in view of the character of the victim, a middle-aged man respectable and discreet, belonging to that minor official grade, the petty-officers, upon whom, as none know better than the commissioned gentlemen, the efficiency of His Majesty's navy so largely depends. His function was a responsible one, at once onerous and thankless, and his fidelity in it the greater because of his strong patriotic impulse. In this instance as in so many other instances in these days, the character of this unfortunate man signally refutes, if refutation were needed, that peevish saying attributed to the late Dr. Johnson, that patriotism is the last refuge of a scoundrel.

The criminal paid the penalty of his crime. The promptitude of the punishment has proved salutary. Nothing amiss is now apprehended aboard H.M.S. *Indomitable*.

The above appearing in a publication now long ago superannuated and forgotten is all that hitherto has stood in human record to attest what manner of men respectively were John Claggart and Billy Budd.[1]

•

Everything is for a term remarkable in navies. Any tangible object associated with some striking incident of the service is converted into a monument. The spar from which the Foretopman was suspended was for

---

[1] Another concluding paragraph was canceled by the author: "Here ends a story not unwarranted by what sometimes happens in this incomprehensible world of ours—Innocence and infamy, spiritual depravity and fair repute."—*J.L.*

some few years kept trace of by the blue-jackets. Then knowledge followed it from ship to dock-yard and again from dock-yard to ship, still pursuing it even when at last reduced to a mere dock-yard boom. To them a chip of it was as a piece of the Cross. Ignorant though they were of the secret facts of the tragedy, and not thinking but that the penalty was somehow unavoidably inflicted from the naval point of view, for all that, they instinctively felt that Billy was a sort of man as incapable of mutiny as of willful murder. They recalled the fresh young image of the Handsome Sailor, that face never deformed by a sneer or subtler vile freak of the heart within. This impression of him was doubtless deepened by the fact that he was gone, and in a measure mysteriously gone. On the gun-decks of the *Indomitable* the general estimate of his nature and its unconscious simplicity eventually found rude utterance from another foretopman, one of his own watch, gifted as some sailors are with an artless poetic temperament. The tarry hands made some lines which, after circulating among the shipboard crew for a while, finally got rudely printed at Portsmouth as a ballad. The title given to it was the sailor's.

Billy in the Darbies

Good of the Chaplain to enter Lone Bay
And down on his marrow-bones here and pray
For the likes just o' me, Billy Budd.—But look:
Through the port comes the moonshine astray!
It tips the guard's cutlass and silvers this nook;
But 'twill die in the dawning of Billy's last day.
A jewel-block they'll make of me tomorrow,
Pendant pearl from the yard-arm-end

Like the ear-drop I gave to Bristol Molly—
O, 'tis me, not the sentence they'll suspend.
Aye, aye, all is up; and I must up too,
Early in the morning, aloft from alow.
On an empty stomach, now, never it would do.
They'll give me a nibble—bit o' biscuit ere I go.
Sure, a messmate will reach me the last parting cup;
But, turning heads away from the hoist and the belay,
Heaven knows who will have the running of me up!
No pipe to those halyards—but aren't it all sham?
A blur's in my eyes; it is dreaming that I am.
A hatchet to my hauser? all adrift to go?
The drum roll to grog, and Billy never know?
But Donald he has promised to stand by the plank;
So I'll shake a friendly hand ere I sink.
But—no! It is dead then I'll be, come to think.—
I remember Taff the Welshman when he sank.
And his cheek it was like the budding pink.
But me they'll lash me in hammock, drop me deep.
Fathoms down, fathoms down, how I'll dream fast
    asleep.
I feel it stealing now, Sentry, are you there?
Just ease these darbies at the wrist,
And roll me over fair.
I am sleepy, and the oozy weeds about me twist.

April 19th 1891

◇◇◇

The leisurely process of *Billy Budd*'s composition went
on through Melville's last months, even after he gave the
manuscript its terminal date; his own approaching end may
have accelerated the revisions but not with sufficient speed
to finish his book before his life, weakened by erysipelas,
ended a half hour after midnight on the morning of September 28, 1891. Glued on the inside of the writing box on

which *Billy Budd* and the last poems were composed was found a tiny clipping—Melville's own motto—"Keep true to the dreams of thy youth."

❖❖❖

Last Verses

Camoens

1

Restless, restless, craving rest,
Forever must I fan this fire,
Forever in flame on flame aspire?
Yea, for the God demands thy best.
The world with endless beauty teems,
And thought evokes new worlds of dreams:
Then hunt the flying herds of themes.
And fan, yet fan thy fervid fire
Until the crucible ore shall show
That fire can purge, as well as glow.
In ordered ardor nobly strong,
Flame to the height of ancient song.

2

Camoens in the Hospital

What now avails the pageant verse,
Trophies and arms with music borne?
Base is the world; and some rehearse
How noblest meet ignoble scorn.

Vain now thy ardor, vain thy fire,
Delirium mere, unsound desire:
Fate's knife hath ripped the chorded lyre.
Exhausted by the exacting lay,
Thou dost but fall a surer prey
To wile and guile ill understood;
While they who work them, fair in face,
Still keep their strength in prudent place,
And claim they worthier run life's race,
Serving high God with useful good.

Suggested by the Ruins of a Mountain-Temple in Arcadia, One Built by the Architect of the Parthenon

Like stranded ice when freshets die
These shattered marbles tumbled lie:
    They trouble me.

What solace?—Old in inexhaustion,
Interred alive from storms of fortune,
    The quarries be!

The New Rosicrucians

To us, disciples of the Order
    Whose rose-vine twines the Cross,
Who have drained the rose's chalice
    Never heeding gain or loss;
For all the preacher's din
There is no mortal sin—
    No, none to us but Malice!

Exempt from that, in blest recline
    We let life's billows toss;
If sorrow come, anew we twine
    The Rose-Vine round the Cross.

Art

In placid hours well-pleased we dream
Of many a brave, unbodied scheme.
But form to lend, pulsed life create,
What unlike things must meet and mate:
A flame to melt—a wind to freeze;
Sad patience—joyous energies;
Humility—yet pride and scorn;
Instinct and study; love and hate;
Audacity—reverence. These must mate,
And fuse with Jacob's mystic heart,
To wrestle with the angel—Art.

Notes on Manuscripts
and Textual Sources

The text of *Typee* is based on that of the first English edition (for the loan of which I am indebted to the generosity of Mr. Thomas Gomez); since the American edition not only provided the publishers with an opportunity to omit passages but also allowed the author to alter phrasing, some of his corrections have been incorporated here. Beyond this, the only changes that seemed advisable were to make the rendering of Marquesan words and names slightly more consistent than Murray's proofreaders demanded, though no effort has been made to bring the author's renderings into line with what Stevenson would have found more acceptable. The extracts from *Mardi, Moby Dick, The Piazza Tales, Israel Potter, The Confidence-Man,* and *Battle-Pieces* have been based on the first American editions of these works. Melville left tables of printing errors in *Clarel* and *John Marr,* and these have been consulted in editing the extracts from these works. The text of "Hawthorne and His Mosses" is transcribed from the amanuensis copy, corrected by the author, in the Duyckinck Collection, New York Public Library. The stenographic report of the "South Seas" lecture appeared in the *Baltimore American and Commercial Daily Advertiser* of 9 February 1859 (courteously furnished me by the Enoch Pratt Free Library, Baltimore). The manuscripts of the "Early Verse" and "Last Verses" are in the Melville Collection, Houghton Library, Harvard University, as is the manuscript of *Billy Budd.* This important manuscript has been transcribed many times, each time revealing a little more of its fullness; I hope that the present transcript continues that tradition. F. Barron Freeman's edition of *Billy Budd* (Cambridge: Harvard University Press, 1948) presents a minute study of the manuscript and of the background of its composition.

The manuscripts of all journals drawn upon for this edition are in the Melville Collection at Harvard. The complete text of the 1849 journal is available as *Journal of a Visit to London and the Continent,* edited by Eleanor Melville Metcalf (Cambridge: Harvard University Press, 1948). The text of the 1856–57 journal is available as *Journal up the Straits,* edited by Raymond Weaver (The Colophon, 1935). A new transcript of this journal has been prepared for publication by Howard C. Horsford [Princeton University Press, 1955]; Mr. Horsford has been generous in his aid to the *Portable*'s extracts. The brief journal kept during the 1860 voyage is printed here in its entirety.

Melville's letters are scattered. All those to Evert Duyckinck used here are in the Duyckinck Collection, New York Public Library, which also includes Elizabeth Melville's copy of the "memoranda" sent to Allan Melville on 22 May 1860. The Gansevoort-Lansing Collection at the New York Public Library contains the letter to H. S. Gansevoort, a background for which appeared in *Twice a Year,* 1948, p. 259–72; and those to Maria Melville (as transcribed by J. C. Hoadley), to Abraham Lansing, and to J. C. Hoadley. The Melville Collection at Harvard University contains the 13 August 1852 letter to Nathaniel Hawthorne (this, with the accompanying memorandum, was edited by Samuel E. Morison in *The New England Quarterly,* April 1929), and the letters to Elizabeth Melville, Thomas Melville, and Samuel Shaw. In the collection of H. Bradley Martin, Jr., New York, N. Y., are the letters to Sophia Hawthorne, Charles James Billson, and Richard Bentley (the complete sequence of the letters to Bentley was edited by John J. Birss for *The New Colophon,* July 1948). The letter to Gansevoort Melville, 29 May 1846, is in the archive of the Misses Morewood, Pittsfield, Mass.; those to John Murray, 2 September 1846, 25 March 1848, are in the archive of Sir John Murray V, London, and were obtained through the courtesy of Harvard University; that to Lemuel Shaw, 6 October 1849, is in the Shaw Papers, Massachusetts Historical Society, Boston. The present location of the letter to N. P. Willis, 14 December 1849, is unknown; this portion was transcribed by Willis for *The Home*

Journal, 12 January 1850. Those to R. H. Dana are in the Dana Papers, Massachusetts Historical Society (the letters to Dana were edited by Harrison Hayford for *ELH, A Journal of English Literary History,* XI, 1944, p. 76–83). Those to Nathaniel Hawthorne, 16(?) April 1851, 1(?) June 1851, are given as transcribed by Julian Hawthorne for *Nathaniel Hawthorne and His Wife* (Boston, 1885); the first of these three letters is corrected with alternative readings in G. P. Lathrop's earlier transcript in *A Study of Hawthorne* (1876); the third letter has been corrected from Julian Hawthorne's manuscript transcription. The letter to Sarah Morewood is in the collection of Dr. Henry A. Murray, Topsfield, Mass. That to Nathaniel Hawthorne, 17(?) November 1851, is given as transcribed by Rose Hawthorne Lathrop for *Memories of Hawthorne* (Boston, 1897). The letter to Nathaniel Hawthorne, 17 July 1852, is in the collection of Norman Holmes Pearson, New Haven, Conn.; that to E. M. Gifford, in the Baldwin Papers, Yale University Library; that to Archibald MacMechan, in the archive of Mrs. C. R. E. Willets, Halifax, Nova Scotia.

The annotations in books from Melville's library are quoted from volumes now in the Melville Collection at Harvard. "Melville's Reading" was catalogued by Merton M. Sealts, Jr., *Harvard Library Bulletin,* II, p. 2–3; III, p. 1–3; IV, p. 1.

A Bibliographic Note

Besides the editions of Melville's writing already mentioned, some modern editions of his work should be recommended to the reader. The Hendricks House project (now under the roof of Farrar Straus) to issue reliable annotated editions of the complete works has encountered natural difficulties, but among the volumes already published are Howard Vincent's edition of the *Poems* and Henry Murray's edition of *Pierre,* and the most needed of the promised volumes are those of *Clarel* and the collection of Melville's miscellaneous prose. To be especially suggested among the many editions of *Moby Dick* available are the Rinehart edition conforming to the 1851 text, introduced by Newton Arvin; the Modern Library College Edition introduced by Leon Howard; and the Oxford edition, annotated by Willard Thorp. The severally published journals have been noted; an edition of the letters is still lacking. *Family Correspondence of Herman Melville,* edited by Victor Hugo Paltsits, contains most of the materials related to Melville in the Gansevoort-Lansing Collection, New York Public Library.

The earliest formal biography of Melville, Raymond Weaver's *Herman Melville: Mariner and Mystic* (New York: Doran, 1921), was followed by John Freeman's *Herman Melville* (1926); Lewis Mumford's more critical work, *Herman Melville* (New York: Harcourt Brace, 1929); and Charles Anderson's *Melville in the South Seas* (New York: Columbia University Press, 1939). Subsequent analytical studies are Willard Thorp's *Herman Melville: Representative Selections* (New York: American Book Company, 1938) with an extensive but selected bibliography; William Ellery Sedgwick's *Herman Melville: The Tragedy of Mind* (Cambridge: Harvard University Press, 1944); Charles Olson's *Call Me Ishmael* (New York: Reynal & Hitchcock, 1947); Richard Chase's *Herman Melville: A Critical Study* (New York: Macmillan, 1949), Howard Vincent's *The Trying-Out of Moby Dick* (Boston: Houghton Mifflin, 1949), Newton Arvin's *Herman Melville* (New York: Holt, 1950), and William Gilman's *Melville's Early Life and Redburn* (New York: New York University Press, 1951). *American Renaissance* by F. O. Matthiessen (New York: Oxford University Press, 1941) contains a valuable study of Melville's work. The best of the works combining biography and analysis is by Leon Howard: *Herman Melville* (Berkeley: University of California Press, 1951). This editor's *Melville Log* (New York: Harcourt, Brace, 1951) is a reconstruction in documents of his life.

Important additions to Melville studies since the publication of this Portable are: Eleanor Metcalf, *Herman Melville: Cycle and Epicycle* (Harvard University Press, 1952); Merrell R. Davis, *Melville's "Mardi": A Chartless Voyage* (Yale University Press, 1952); Merton L. Sealts, Jr., *Melville as Lecturer* (Harvard University Press, 1957). 402